D1251458

COME HITHER

BOOKS BY

WALTER DE LA MARE

In Prose

HENRY BROCKEN

THE RETURN

THE RIDDLE AND OTHER TALES

MEMOIRS OF A MIDGET

THE CONNOISSEUR AND OTHER STORIES

THE THREE MULLA-MULGARS

BROOMSTICKS AND OTHER TALES

CROSSINGS (*A Play for Children*)

RUPERT BROOKE AND THE INTELLECTUAL IMAGINATION (*A Lecture*)

TOLD AGAIN

With Thomas Quayle

READINGS (*Selections*)

In Verse

THE LISTENERS AND OTHER POEMS

MOTLEY AND OTHER POEMS

FLORA

POEMS: 1901–1918

THE VEIL AND OTHER POEMS

SONGS OF CHILDHOOD

PEACOCK PIE

A CHILD'S DAY

DING DONG BELL

COME HITHER! (*An Anthology with Notes*)

COME
HITHER
A
COLLECTION
OF RHYMES
AND POEMS
FOR THE
YOUNG OF
ALL AGES
MADE BY
WALTER DE LA MARE
AND EMBELLISHED
BY
ALEC BUCKELS
NEW YORK
ALFRED A. KNOPF

First published December 1923
New and revised edition November 1928
Second printing June 1931
Third printing October 1936
Fourth printing February 1941

MANUFACTURED IN THE UNITED STATES
OF AMERICA

TO
LAURA COLTMAN
IN LOVE AND
GRATITUDE

CONTENTS

COME HITHER

THE STORY OF THIS BOOK

In my rovings and ramblings as a boy I had often skirted the old stone house in the hollow. But my first clear remembrance of it is of a hot summer's day. I had climbed to the crest of a hill till then unknown to me, and stood there, hot and breathless in the bright slippery grass, looking down on its grey walls and chimneys as if out of a dream. And as if out of a dream already familiar to me.

My real intention in setting out from home that morning had been to get to a place called East Dene. My mother had often spoken to me of East Dene—of its trees and waters and green pastures, and the rare birds and flowers to be found there. Ages ago, she had told me, an ancestor of our family had dwelt in this place. But she smiled a little strangely when I asked her to take me there. "All in good time, my dear," she whispered into my ear, "all in very good time! Just follow your small nose." What kind of time, I wondered, was *very good time.* And *follow my nose*—how far? Such reflections indeed only made me the more anxious to be gone.

Early that morning, then, I had started out when the dew was still sparkling, and the night mists had but just lifted. But my young legs soon tired of the steep, boulder-strown hills, the chalky ravines, and burning sun, and having, as I say, come into view of the house in the valley, I went no further. Instead, I sat down on the hot turf—the sweet smell of thyme in the air, a few harebells nodding around me—and stared, down and down.

After that first visit, scarcely a week passed but that I found myself on this hill again. The remembrance of the house stayed in my mind; would keep returning to me, like a bird to its nest. Sometimes even in the middle of the night I would wake up and lie unable to sleep again for thinking of it—seeing it in my head; solemn, secret, strange.

There is a little flickering lizard called the Chameleon which, they say, changes its colour according to the place where it happens to be. So with this house. It was never the same for two hours together. I have seen it gathered close up in its hollow in the livid and coppery gloom of storm; crouched like a hare in winter under a mask of snow; dark and silent beneath the changing sparkle of the stars; and like a palace out of an Arabian tale in the milky radiance of the moon. THRAE was the name inscribed on its gateway, but in letters so faint and faded as to be almost illegible.

In a sense I was, I suppose, a trespasser in this Thrae; until at least I became acquainted with Miss Taroone, the lady who lived in it. For I made pretty free with her valley, paddled and fished in its stream, and now and then helped myself to a windfall in her green bird-haunted orchards, where grew a particularly sharp and bright-rinded apple of which I have never heard the name. As custom gave me confidence, I ventured nearer and nearer to the house and would sometimes take a rest squatting on a manger in the big empty barn, looking out into the sunshine. The wings of the flies shone like glass in its shafts of light, and the robins whistled under its timber roof so shrill as almost to deafen one's ears.

Few strangers passed that way. Now and then I saw in the distance what might have been a beggar. To judge from his bundle he must have done pretty well at the house. Once, as I turned out of a little wood of birches, I met a dreadful-faced man in the lane who lifted up his hand at sight of me, and with white glaring eyes, uttered a horrible imprecation. He was chewing some fruit stolen out of the orchard, and at the very sight of him I ran like Wat himself.

Once, too, as my head looked over the hill-crest, there stood an old carriage and a drowsy horse drawn up beside the porch—with its slender wooden pillars and a kind of tray above, on which rambled winter jasmine, tufts of self-sown weeds and Traveller's Joy. I edged near enough to see there was a crown emblazoned on the panel of the carriage door. Nobody sat inside, and the coachman asleep on the box made me feel more solitary and inquisitive than ever.

Yet in its time the old house must have seen plenty of company. Friends of later years have spoken to me of it. Indeed, not far distant from Thrae as the crow flies, there was a crossing of high roads, so that any traveller from elsewhere not in haste could turn aside and examine the place if he cared for its looks and was in need of a night's lodging. Yet I do not think many such travellers—if they were men merely of the Town—can have *chosen* to lift that knocker or to set ringing that bell. To any one already lost and benighted its looks must have been forbidding.

Well, as I say, again and again, my lessons done, morning or evening would find me either on the grass slopes above Thrae, or actually in its valley. If I was tired, I would watch from a good distance off its small dark windows in their stone embrasures, and up above them the round greenish tower or turret over which a winged weather-vane twirled with the wind. I might watch: but the only person that I ever actually observed at the windows was an old maid with flaps to her cap, who would sometimes shake a duster out into the air as if for a signal to someone up in the hills.

Apart from her, I had occasionally seen Miss Taroone herself in the overgrown garden, with her immense shears, or with her trencher of bread-crumbs and other provender, feeding the birds. And I once stole near enough under a hedge to watch this sight. They hopped and pecked in a multitude beneath her hands, tits and robins, starlings and blackbirds, and other much wilder and rarer birds, as if they had no need here for wings, or were under an enchantment more powerful than that of mere crumbs of bread. The meal done, the platter empty, Miss Taroone would clap her hands, and off they would fly with a skirring of wings, with shrill cries and snatches of song to their haunts.

She seemed to mind no weather; standing bare-headed in heavy rain or scorching sunlight. And I confess the sight of her never failed to alarm me. But I made up my mind always to keep my wits about me and my eyes open; and never to be *caught* trespassing.

Then one day, as I slid down from the roof of the barn from amid the branches of a chestnut tree, green with its spiky balls of fruit, I found Miss Taroone standing there in the entry, looking out on me as if out of a frame, or like a stone figure in the niche of a church. She made no stir herself, but her eyes did. Clear cold eyes of the colour of pebbly water, in which I seemed to be of no more importance than a boat floating on the sea. I could neither speak nor run away. I could only gawk at her, my pockets bulging with the unripe chestnuts I had pilfered, and a handsome slit in one leg of my breeches.

She asked me what I did there; my name; why I was not at school; where I lived; and did I eat the chestnuts? It appeared she had more often seen me—I suppose from her windows—than I had seen her. She made no movement, never even smiled while I stammered out answers to her questions, but merely kept her eyes steadily fixed on me, while her own lips just opened enough to let the words out of her mouth. She listened to me with a severe face, and said, "Well, if you are happy to be here with the rest, so much the better."

It was a relief when she turned away, bidding me follow her—and a foolish figure I must have cut as I clattered after her across the cobbled yard under the old red-brick arch and so through the porch and into the house.

When I was sat down in one of the shaded rooms within the house, she summoned the tall gaunt old maid with the cap-flaps I had seen at the windows, and bade her bring me some fruit and a dish of cream. Miss Taroone watched me while I ate it. And uncommonly good it was, though I would rather have been enjoying it alone. From the way she looked at me it might have been supposed it was a bird or a small animal that was sitting up at her table. The last spoonful finished, she asked me yet more questions and appeared to be not displeased with my rambling answers, for she invited me to come again and watched me take up my cap and retire.

This was the first time I was ever in Miss Taroone's house—within its solid walls I mean; and what a multitude of rooms, with their coffers and presses and cabinets, containing I knew not what treasures and wonders! But Thrae was not Miss Taroone's only house, for more than once she spoke of another—named SURE VINE, as if of a family mansion and estate, very ancient and magnificent. When, thinking of my mother, I myself ventured a question about East Dene, her green-grey eyes oddly settled on mine a moment, but she made no answer. I noticed this particularly.

Soon I was almost as free and familiar in Miss Taroone's old house as in my own father's. Yet I cannot say that she was ever anything else than curt with me in her manner. It was a long time before I became accustomed to the still, secret way she had of looking at me. I liked best being in her company when she appeared, as was usually so, not to be aware that she was not alone. She had again asked me my name "for a sign" as she said, "to know you by"; though she always afterwards addressed me as Simon. Certainly in those days I was "simple" enough.

My next friend was the woman whom I had seen shaking her duster out of the upper windows. She, I discovered, was called Linnet Sara Queek or Quek or Cuec or Cueque, I don't know how to spell it. She was an exceedingly curious woman and looked as if she had never been any different, though, of course, she must once have been young and have grown up. She was bony, awkward, and angular, and when you spoke to her, she turned on you with a look that was at the same time vacant and piercing. At first she greeted me sourly, but soon became friendlier, and would allow me to sit in her huge kitchen with her parrot, her sleek tabby cat, and perhaps a dainty or two out of her larder.

She was continually muttering—though I could never quite catch what she said; never idle; and though slow and awkward in her movements, she did a vast deal of work. With small short-sighted eyes fixed on her mortar she would stand pounding and pounding; or stewing and seething things in pots—strange-looking roots and fruit and fungi. Her pantry was crammed with pans, jars, bottles, and phials, all labelled in her queer handwriting. An extraordinary place—especially when the sunbeams of evening struck into it from a high window in its white-washed wall.

Linnet she might be called, but her voice was no bird's, unless the crow's; and you would have guessed at once, at sight of her standing in front of the vast open hearth, stooping a little, her long gaunt arms beside her, that her other name was Sara. But she could tell curious and rambling stories (as true as she could make them); and many of them were about the old days in Thrae, older days in Sure Vine, and about Miss Taroone, in whose service she had been since she was a small child.

She told me, too, some specially good tales—as good as Grimm—about some villages she knew of called the Ten Laps; and gave me a custard when I asked for more. I once mentioned East Dene to her, too, and she said there was a short cut to it (though it seemed to me a long way about) through the quarry, by the pits, and that way round. "And then you come to a Wall," she said, staring at me. "And you climb over."

"Did *you?*" said I, laughing; and at that she was huffed.

Boy though I was, it occurred to me that in this immense house there must be a great deal more work than Sara could manage unaided. Something gave me the fancy that other hands must lend their help; but if any maids actually came in to Thrae from East Dene, or from elsewhere, they must have come and gone very late, or early. It seemed bad manners to be too curious. On the other hand, I rarely saw much of the back parts of the house.

I have sometimes wondered if Thrae had not once in fact lain within the borders of East Dene, and that being so, if Miss Taroone, like myself, was unaware of it. It may have been merely pride that closed her lips, for one day, she showed me, with a curious smile, how Thrae's architect, centuries before, had planned its site. She herself led me from room to room; and she talked as she had never talked before.

Its southernmost window looked on a valley, beyond which on clear still days was visible the sea, and perhaps a brig or a schooner on its surface—placid blue as turquoise. Sheer against its easternmost window the sun mounted to his summer solstice from in between a cleft of the hills—like a large topaz between the forks of a catapult. On one side of this cleft valley was a windmill, its sails lanking up into the sky, and sometimes spinning in the wind with an audible clatter. Who owned the mill and what he ground I never heard.

Northwards, through a round bull's-eye window you could see, past a maze of coppices and hills, and in the distance, the cock of a cathedral spire. And to the west stood a wood of yew, its pool partially greened over, grey with willows, and the haunt of rare birds. On the one side of this pool spread exceedingly calm meadows; and on the other, in a hollow, the graveyard lay. The stones and bones in it were all apparently of Miss Taroone's kinsfolk. At least Linnet Sara told me so. Nor was she mournful about it. She seemed to have nobody to care for but her mistress; working for love, whatever her wages might be.

It is an odd thing to say, but though I usually tried to avoid meeting Miss Taroone, and was a little afraid of her, there was a most curious happiness at times in being in her company. She never once asked me about my character, never warned me of anything, never said "You must"; and yet I knew well that if in stupidity or carelessness I did anything in her house which she did not approve of, my punishment would come.

She once told me, "Simon, you have, I see, the beginnings of a bad feverish cold. It is because you were stupid enough yesterday to stand with the sweat on your face talking to me in a draught. It will probably be severe." And so it was.

She never said anything affectionate; she never lost her temper. I never saw her show any pity or meanness or revenge. "Well, Simon," she would say, "Good morning"; or "Good evening" (as the case might be);

"you are always welcome. Have a good look about you. Don't waste your time here. Even when all is said, you will not see too much of me and mine. But don't believe *everything* you may hear in the kitchen. Linnet Sara is a good servant, but still a groper."

Not the least notion of what she meant occurred to me. But I peacocked about for a while as if she had paid me a compliment. An evening or two afterwards, and soon after sunset, I found her sitting in her westward window. Perhaps because rain was coming, the crouching headstones under the hill looked to be furlongs nearer. "Sleeping, waking; waking, sleeping, Simon"; she said, "sing while you can." Like a little owl I fixed sober eyes on the yew-wood, but again I hadn't any inkling of what she meant.

She would sit patiently listening to me as long as I cared to unbosom myself to her. Her calm, severe, and yet, I think, beautiful face is clear in my memory. It resembles a little the figure in Albrecht Dürer's picture of a woman sitting beneath the wall of a house, with a hound crouched beside her, an inclined ladder, the rainbowed sea in the distance, and a bat—a tablet of magic numbers and a pent-housed bell over her head.

Sometimes I would be questioned at home about my solitary wanderings, but I never mentioned Miss Taroone's name, and spoke of her house a little deceitfully, since I did not confess how much I loved being in it.

One evening—and it was already growing late—Miss Taroone, after steadily gazing into my eyes for a few moments, asked me if I liked pictures. I professed that I did, though I had never spent much time in looking at the queer portraits and charts and mementoes that hung thick and closely on her own walls. "Well," she replied, "if you like pictures I must first tell you about Nahum."

I could not at first make head or tail of Mr. Nahum. Even now I am uncertain whether he was Miss Taroone's brother or her nephew or a cousin many times removed; or whether perhaps she was really and truly Mrs. Taroone and he her only son; or she still Miss Taroone and he an adopted one. I am not sure even whether or not she had much love for him, though she appeared to speak of him with pride. What I do know is that Miss Taroone had nurtured him from his cradle and had taught him all the knowledge that was not already his by right of birth.

Before he was come even to be my own age, she told me, Nahum Taroone had loved "exploring." As a boy he had ranged over the countryside for miles around. I never dared ask her if he had sat on Linnet Sara's "Wall"! He had scrawled plans and charts and maps, marking on them all his wanderings. And not only the roads, paths, chaces, and tracks, the springs and streams, but the rare-birds' nesting-places and the rarer wild flowers, the eatable or poisonous fruits, trees, animal lairs, withies for whips, clay for modelling, elder shoots for pitch pipes, pebbles for his catapult, flint arrows, and everything of that kind. He was a night-boy too; could guide himself by the stars, was a walking almanac of the moon; and could decoy owls and nightjars, and find any fox's or badger's earth he was after, even in a dense mist.

I came to know Mr. Nahum pretty well—so far at any rate as one can know anybody from hearsay—before Miss Taroone referred to the pictures again. And I became curious about him, and hoped to see this strange traveller, and frequently hung around Thrae in mere chance of that.

Strangely enough, by the looks on her face and the tones of her voice, Miss Taroone was inclined to mock a little at Mr. Nahum because of his restlessness. She didn't seem to approve of his leaving her so much—though she herself had come from Sure Vine. Her keys would jangle at her chatelaine as if they said, "Ours secrets enough." And she would stand listening, and mute, as if in expectation of voices or a footfall. Then as secretly as I could, I would get away.

All old memories resemble a dream. And so too do these of Miss Taroone and Thrae. When I was most busy and happy and engrossed in it, it seemed to be a house which might at any moment vanish before your eyes, showing itself to be but the outer shell or hiding place of an abode still more enchanting.

This sounds nonsensical. But if you have ever sat and watched a Transformation Scene in a pantomime, did you suppose, just before the harlequin slapped with his wand on what looked like a plain brick-and-mortar wall, that it would instantly after dissolve into a radiant coloured scene of trees and fountains and hidden beings—growing lovelier in their own showing as the splendour spread and their haunts were revealed? Well, so at times I used to feel in *Thrae*.

At last, one late evening in early summer, beckoning me with her finger, Miss Taroone lit a candle in an old brass stick and bade me follow her down a long narrow corridor and up a steep winding stone staircase. "You have heard, Simon, of Mr. Nahum's round room; now you shall see it."

On the wider step at the top, before a squat oak door, she stayed, lifted her candle, and looked at me. "You will remember," she said, "that what I am about to admit you into is Mr. Nahum's room; not mine. You may look at the pictures, you may examine anything that interests you, you may compose yourself to the view. But replace what you look at, have a care in your handling, do nothing out of *idle* curiosity, and come away when you are tired. Remember that Mr. Nahum may be returning at any hour. He would be pleased to find you here. But hasten away out of his room the very instant you feel you have no right, lot or pleasure to be in it. Hasten away, I mean, so that you may return to it with a better mind and courage."

She laid two fingers on my shoulder, cast another look into my face under her candle, turned the key in the lock, gently thrust me beyond the door, shut it: and left me to my own devices.

What first I noticed, being for awhile a little alarmed at this strange proceeding, was the evening light that poured in on the room from the encircling windows. Below, by walking some little distance from room to room, corridor to corridor, you could get (as I have said) a single narrow view out north, south, east or west. Here, you could stand in the middle, and turning slowly like a top on your heels, could watch float by one after the other, hill and windmill, ocean, distant city, dark yew-wood.

The crooning of doves was audible on the roof, swallows were coursing in the placid and rosy air, the whole world seemed to be turning softly out of the day's sunshine, stretching long dark shadows across hill and valley as if in delight to be on the verge of rest and slumber again, now that the heats of full summer were so near.

But I believe my first *thought* was— What a boiling hot and glaring place to sit in in the middle of the morning. And then I noticed that heavy curtains hung on either side each rounded window, for shade, concealment and solitude. As soon, however, as my eyes were accustomed to the dazzle, I spent little time upon the great view, but immediately peered about me at what was in this curious chamber.

Never have I seen in any room—and this was none so large—such a hugger-mugger of strange objects—odd-shaped coloured shells, fragments of quartz, thunderbolts and fossils; skins of brilliant birds; outlandish shoes; heads, faces, masks of stone, wood, glass, wax, and metal; pots, images, glass shapes, and what not; lanterns and bells; bits of harness and ornament and weapons. There were, besides, two or three ships of different rigs in glass cases, and one in a green bottle; peculiar tools, little machines; silent clocks, instruments of music, skulls and bones of beasts, frowsy bunches of linen or silk queerly marked, and a mummied cat (I think). And partly concealed, as I twisted my head, there, dangling in an alcove, I caught sight of a full-length skeleton, one hollow eye-hole concealed by a curtain looped to the floor from the ceiling.

I just cast my glance round on all these objects without of course seeing them one by one. The air was clear as water in the evening light, a little dust had fallen; all was in order, though at that first hasty glance there seemed none. Last, but not least, there was row on row of painted pictures. Wherever there was space on the walls free of books, this round tower room was hung with them as close as their frames and nails allowed. There I stood, hearing faintly the birds, conscious of the pouring sunlight, the only live creature amidst this departed traveller's treasures and possessions.

I was so much taken aback by it all, so mystified by Miss Taroone's ways, so cold at sight of the harmless bones above me, and felt so suddenly out of my familiars, that without a moment's hesitation I turned about, flung open the door and went helter skelter clattering down the stairs—out of the glare into the gloom.

There was no sign of Miss Taroone as I crossed through the house and sneaked off hastily through the garden. And not until the barn had shut me out from the lower windows behind me did I look back at the upper ones of Mr. Nahum's tower. Until that moment I did not know how frightened I had been. Yet why, or at what, I cannot even now decide.

But I soon overcame this folly. Miss Taroone made no inquiry how I had fared on this first visit to Mr. Nahum's fortress. As I have said, she seldom asked questions—except with her eyes, expressions, and hands. But some time afterwards, and after two or three spells of exploration, I myself began to talk to her of the strange things up there.

"I have looked at a good many, Miss Taroone. But the pictures! Some of them are of places I *believe* I know. I wish I could be a traveller and see what the others are of. Did Mr. Nahum paint them all himself?"

Miss Taroone was sitting bolt upright in a high-backed chair, her eyes and face very intent, as always happened when Mr. Nahum's name was mentioned.

"I know very little about them, Simon. When Nahum was younger he used to make pictures of Thrae, and of the woods and valleys hereabouts. There are boxfulls put away. Others are pictures brought back from foreign parts, but many of them, as I believe," she turned her face and looked into a shadowy corner of the room, "are pictures of nothing on earth. He has his two worlds. Take your time. Some day you too, I dare say, will go off on your travels. Remember that, like Nahum, you are as old as the hills which neither spend nor waste time, but dwell in it for ages, as if it were light or sunshine. Some day perhaps Nahum will shake himself free of Thrae altogether. I don't *know*, myself, Simon. This house is enough for me, and what I remember of Sure Vine, compared with which Thrae is but the smallest of bubbles in a large glass."

I do not profess to have understood one half of what

Miss Taroone meant in these remarks. It was in English and yet in a hidden tongue.

But by this time I had grown to be bolder in her company, and pounced on this:—"What, please Miss Taroone, do you mean by the 'two worlds'? Or shall I ask downstairs?" I added the latter question because now and then in the past Miss Taroone had bidden me go down to Linnet Sara for my answers. She now appeared at first not to have heard it.

"Now I must say to you, Simon," she replied at last, folding her hands on her knee, "wherever you may be in that body of yours, you feel you look out of it, do you not?"

I nodded. "Yes, Miss Taroone."

"Now think, then, of Mr. Nahum's round room; where is that?"

"Up there," said I, pointing up a rambling finger.

"Ah!" cried Miss Taroone, "so it may be. But even if to-morrow you are thousands of miles distant from here on the other side of this great Ball, or in its bowels, or flying free—you will still carry a picture of it, will you not? And that will be within you?"

"Yes, in my mind, Miss Taroone?" I answered rather sheepishly.

"In your mind," she echoed me, but not as if she were particularly pleased at the fact. "Well, many of the pictures I take it in Mr. Nahum's round tower are of *that* world. His MIND. I have never examined them. My duties are elsewhere. Your duty is to keep your senses, heart and courage and to go where you are called. And in black strange places you will at times lose yourself and find yourself, Simon. Now Mr. Nahum is calling. Don't think of me too much. I have great faith in him. Sit up there with him then. Share your eyes with his pictures. And having seen them, compare them if you will. Say, This is this, and that is that. And make of all that he has exactly what use you can."

With this counsel in my head I once more groped my way up the corkscrew stone staircase, and once more passed on from picture to picture; in my engrossment actually knocking my head against the dangling foot-bones of Mr. Nahum's treasured and now unalarming skeleton.

The pictures were of all kinds and sizes—in water colour, in chalks, and in oil. Some I liked for their vivid colours and deep shadows, and some I did not like at all. Nor could I always be sure even what they were intended to represent. Many of them completely perplexed me. A few of them seemed to me to be absurd; some made me stupidly ashamed; and one or two of them terrified me. But I went on examining them when I felt inclined, and a week or so after, as I was lifting out one of them into the sunshine, by chance it twisted on its cord and disclosed its wooden back.

And there, pasted on to it, was a scrap of yellowing paper with the letters BLAKE, followed by a number—CXLVII, in Roman figures. As with this one, so with the others. Each had its name and a number.

And even as I stood pondering what this might mean, my eyes rested on a lower shelf of one of Mr. Nahum's cases of books—book-cases which I have forgotten to say stood all round the lower part of the room. I had already discovered that many of these books were the writings of travellers in every part of the globe. One whole book-case consisted of what Mr. Nahum appeared to call Kitchen Work. But the one on a lower shelf which had now taken my attention was new to me—an enormous, thick, home-made-looking volume covered in a greenish shagreen or shark-skin.

Scrawled in ungainly capitals on the strip of vellum pasted to the back of this book was its title: THE-

OTHERWORLDE. Would you believe it?—at first I was stupid enough to suppose this title was one word, a word in a strange tongue, which I pronounced to myself as best I could, THEEOTHAWORLDIE—saying the TH as in *thimble*. And that is what, merely for old sake's sake, I have continued to call the book in my mind to this day!

I glanced out of the window. The upper boughs of the yew-wood and the stones this side of it among the bright green grasses were impurpled by the reflected sunlight. Nothing there but motionless shadows. I stood looking vacantly out for a moment or two; then stooped and lugged out the ponderous fusty old volume on to the floor and raised its clumsy cover.

To my surprise and pleasure, I found, that attached within was the drawing of a boy of about my own age, but dressed like a traveller, whose face faintly resembled a portrait I had noticed on the walls downstairs, though this child had wings painted to his shoulders and there was a half circle of stars around his head. Beneath this portrait in the book, in small letters, was scrawled in a faded handwriting, NAHUM TARUNE. This, then, was Mr. Nahum when he was a boy. It pleased me to find that he was no better a speller than myself. He had not even got his own name right! I liked his face. He looked out from under his stars at me, full in the eyes.

Next—after I had searched his looks and clothes and what he carried pretty closely—I turned over a few of the stiff leaves and found more of his writing with a big VII scrawled on the top. On page one of this book you will find the writing. I should have been a stupider boy even than I was if I had not at once turned over the pictures till I came to that with VII on the label on the back of it. This picture was of a Maze outlined in gaudy colours which faded towards the middle—a sort of oasis in which grew a tree. Fabulous looking animals and creatures with wings sprawled around its margins. After repeated attempts I found to my disappointment that your only way out of the oasis and the maze was, after long groping, by the way you went in. Underneath it was written "*This is the key*." And above it in green letters stood this:—Behold upon the mountains the feet of him that bringeth good tidings, that publisheth peace!

It was unfortunate that so little more of daylight was now left dying in the sky that evening; for as yet I had not the confidence to kindle the wax candles that stood in their brass sticks in the round tower. It was high time for me to be getting home. In my haste to be off I nearly collided with Miss Taroone, who happened to be standing in the dusklight looking out from under her porch. Too much excited even to beg her pardon, I blurted out: "Miss Taroone, I have found out what the pictures are of. It's a Book. *Theeothaworldie.* Mr. Nahum's portrait's in it, but they've put wings to him; and it's all in his writing—rhymes."

She looked down at me, though I could not quite see her face.

"Then, good-night to you, Simon; and happy dreams," she said, in her unfriendly voice.

"I like the round room better and better," I replied as heartily as I could. "That picture of Mr. Nahum—and there are lots more, I think—is a *little* bit like an uncle of mine who died in Russia; my Uncle John."

"John's as good a name, I suppose, as any other, Simon," said Miss Taroone. She stood looking out on the dusky country scene. "There's a heavy dew tonight, and the owls are busy."

They were indeed. Their screechings sounded on all sides of me as I ran off homewards, chanting over to myself the words that had somehow stuck in my memory.

Well, at last I began to read in Mr. Nahum's book—I won't say page by page, but as the fancy took me. It consisted chiefly of rhymes and poems, and some of them had pictured capitals and were decorated in clear bright colours like the pages of the old books illuminated by monks centuries ago. Apart from the poems were here and there pieces of prose. These, I found, always had some bearing on the poems, and, like them, many of them were queerly spelt. Occasionally Mr. Nahum had jotted down his own thoughts in the margin. But the pictures were my first concern.

Sometimes I went off to them from the book in order to find the particular one I wanted. And sometimes the other way round: I would have a good long stare at a picture, then single out the proper rhyme in the book. Often, either in one way or the other, I failed. For there were far fewer pictures than there were pages in the book, and for scores of pages I found no picture at all. It seemed Mr. Nahum had made paintings only of those he liked best.

The book itself, I found, was the first of three, the other two being similar to itself but much thicker and heavier. Into these I dipped occasionally, but found that the rhymes in them interested me less or were less easily understandable. Even some of those in the first book were a little beyond my wits at the time. But experience seems to be like the shining of a bright lantern. It suddenly makes clear in the mind what was already there perhaps, but dim. And often though I immediately liked what I read, long years were to go by before I really understood it, made it my own. There would come a moment, something would happen; and I would say to myself:—"Oh, that, then, is what *that* meant!"

Before going any further I must confess that I was exceedingly slow over Mr. Nahum's writings. Even over Volume I. When first I opened its pages I had had a poor liking for poetry because of a sort of contempt for it. "Poetry!" I would scoff to myself, and would shut up the covers of any such book with a kind of yawn inside me. Some of it had come my way in lesson books. This I could gabble off like a parrot, and with as much understanding; and I had just begun to grind out a little Latin verse for my father.

But I had never troubled to think about it; to share my Self with it; to examine it in order to see whether or not it was true; or to ask why it was written in this one way and in no other way. But apart from this, there were many old rhymes in Mr. Nahum's book—nursery things—which I had known since I knew anything. And I still have an old childish love for rhymes and jingles like them.

But what about the others? I began to ponder. After being so many hours alone in Mr. Nahum's room, among his secret belongings, I almost felt his presence there. When your mind is sunk in study, it is as if you were in a dream. But you cannot tell where, or in whose company, you may wake out of a dream. I remember one sultry afternoon being started out of my wits by a sudden clap of thunder. I looked up, to find the whole room black, zizzag, and strange, and for a moment I fancied Mr. Nahum was actually there behind me; and not a friendly Mr. Nahum.

That is mere fancy; though in other ways he became so real to me at last that I would do things as if he had asked me to do them. For this reason, I think, I persevered with his book, swallowing some of the poems as if they were physic, simply because he had written them there. But the more I read, the more I came to enjoy them for their own sakes. Not all of them, of course. But I did see this, that like a carpenter who makes a table, a man who has written a poem has written it like that *on purpose*.

With this thought in my head I tried one day to alter the words of one or two of the simple and easy poems; or to put the words in a different order. And I found by so doing that you not only altered the sound of the poem, but that even the slightest alteration in the sound a little changed the sense. Either you lost something of the tune and runningness; or the words did not clash right; or you blurred the picture the words gave you; or some half-hidden meaning vanished away. I don't mean that every poem is perfect; but only that when I changed them it was almost always very much for the worse. I was very slow in all this; but, still, I went on. No. III, I remember, was the old nursery jingle, "Old King Cole":—

> Old King Cole was a merry old soul,
> And a merry old soul was he;
> He called for his pipe,
> And he called for his bowl,
> And he called for his fiddlers three. . . .

Now, suppose, instead of these four lines of the rhyme you put:—

> Old King Cole was a jolly old man,
> The jolliest old man alive;
> He called for his cup, and he called for a pipe
> And he called for his fiddlers five.

By so doing you have actually added two extra fiddlers; and yet somehow you have taken away some of the old three's music. Or you may put: —

"Cole the First was now a monarch advanced in

age, and of a convivial temperament. On any festive occasion he would bid his retainers bring him his goblet and smoking materials, and would command his musicians to entertain him on their violins: which they did."

Well, all the *facts* are there and many more words, but scarcely a trace of *my* old King Cole, and not a single tweedle-eedle of the fiddling. Would anyone trouble to learn that by heart?

Now underneath this rhyme Mr. Nahum had written a sort of historical account of King Cole, a good deal of it in German and other languages. All I could make out of it was this: if ever a King Cole inhabited the world, he probably had another name; that he lived too far back in history for anyone to make sure when he had lived or that he had lived at all; and that his "pipe" and "bowl" probably stand for objects much more mysterious and far less common.

Having the rhyme quite free to myself, I didn't mind reading this; but if ever I have to give up either, I shall keep the rhyme.

Having discovered, then, that every poem must have been written as it was written, on purpose, I took a little more pains with those I cared for least. In some even then I could not piece out the meaning; in others I could not easily catch the beat and rhythm and tune. But I learned to read them very slowly, so as fully and quietly to fill up the time allowed for each line and to listen to its music, and to see and hear all that the words were saying.

Then, too, what Miss Taroone had said came back to my mind. Even when Mr. Nahum's poems were about real things and places and people, they were still only of places and people the words made for me in my *mind*. I must, that is, myself imagine all they told. And I found that the mention in a poem even of quite common and familiar things—such as a star, or a buttercup, or a beetle—did not bring into the mind quite the same kind of images of them as the things and creatures themselves do in the naked eye.

Now the day is over,
Night is drawing nigh;
Shadows of the evening
Steal across the sky. . . .

This was one of the earliest poems in Mr. Nahum's book. I had often, of course, seen the shadows of evening—every grass-blade or pebble casts its own; but these words not only called them vividly into my mind, but set shadows there (shadows across the sky) that I had never really seen at all—with my own eyes I mean. I discovered afterwards, also, that shadows are only the absence of light, though light is needed to make them visible. Just the same, again, with the sailors in the same poem:

Guard the sailors tossing
On the deep blue sea. . . .

They are plain and common words, but their *order* here is the poem's only, and the effect they had on me, and still have, is different from the effect of any other words on the same subject. Though, too, like Mr. Nahum, I have now seen something of the world (have been seasick and nearly drowned) I have never forgotten those imaginary sailors, or that imaginary sea; can still hear the waves lapping against that (unmentioned) ship's thin wooden walls, as if I myself were sleeping there, down below.

So what I then read has remained a clear and single remembrance, as if I myself had seen it in a world made different, or in a kind of vision or dream. And I think Mr. Nahum had chosen such poems in Volume I. as carried away the imagination like that; either into the past, or into another mind, or into the all-but-forgotten; at times as if into another world. And this kind has been my choice in this book.

Not that his picture to a particular poem was always the picture I should have made of it. Take for example another nursery jingle in his book:

> "How many miles to Babylon?"
> "Three score and ten."
> "Can I get there by candle-light?"
> "Ay, and back again."

Mr. Nahum's corresponding picture was not of Babylon or of a candle, or of a traveller at all, but of a stone tomb. On its thick upper slab he had drawn-in an old earthen lamp, with a serpent for handle—its wick alight, and shining up on a small owl perched in the lower branches of the thick tree above.

That is one of the pleasures of reading—you may make any picture out of the words you can and will; and a poem may have as many different meanings as there are different minds.

There I would sit, then, and Mr. Nahum's book made of "one little room an everywhere." And though I was naturally rather stupid and dense, I did in time realize that "rare poems ask rare friends," and that even the simplest ones may have secrets which will need a pretty close searching out.

Of course I could not copy out all of the poems even in THEEOTHAWORLDIE, Volume I., and I took very few from Volumes II. and III. I chose what I liked best —those that, when I read them, never failed to carry me away, as if on a Magic Carpet, or in Seven League

Boots, into a region of their own. When the nightingale sings, other birds, it is said, will sit and listen to him: and I remember very well hearing a nightingale so singing on a spray in a dewy hedge, and there were many small birds perched mute and quiet near. The cock crows at midnight; and for miles around his kinsmen answer. The fowler whistles his decoy for the wild duck to come. So certain rhymes and poems affected my mind when I was young, and continue to do so now that I am old.

To these (and the few bits of prose) which I chose from Mr. Nahum, I added others afterwards, and they are in this book too. All of them are in English; a few from over the ocean: but how very few they all are by comparison with the multitudes even of their own kind. And there are the whole world's languages besides! Even of my own favourites not all have found a place. There was not room enough. I have left out others also that may be found easily elsewhere. I am afraid, too, there may be many mistakes in my copying, though I have tried to be careful.

Miss Taroone knew that I was making use of Mr. Nahum's book; though she never questioned me about it. I came and went in her house at last like a rabbit in a warren, a mouse in a mousery. The hours I spent in those far-gone days in Mr. Nahum's round room! At times I wearied of it, and hated his books, and even wished I had never so much as set eyes on Thrae at all.

But after such sour moments, a gossip and an apple with Linnet Sara in her kitchen, or a scamper home, or a bathe under the hazels in the stream whose source, I believe, is in the hills beyond East Dene, would set me to rights again. For sheer joy of return I could scarcely breathe for a while after remounting the stone staircase, re-entering Mr. Nahum's room, and closing the door behind me.

From above his broad scrawled pages I would lift my eyes to his windows and stare as if out of one dream into another. How strange from across the sky was the gentle scented breeze blowing in on my cheek, softly stirring the dried kingfisher skin that hung from its beam; how near understanding then the tongues of the wild birds; how close the painted scene—as though I were but a picture too, and this my frame.

But there came a day that was to remove me out of the neighbourhood of Miss Taroone's Thrae into a different kind of living altogether. I was to be sent to school. After a hot debate with myself, and why I scarcely know, I asked my father's permission to spend the night at Miss Taroone's. He gave me a steady look and said, Yes.

I found Miss Taroone seated on the steps of her porch, and now that I look back at her then, she curiously reminds me—though she was ages older— of a picture you will find in the second stanza of poem No. 233 in this book. Standing before her—it was already getting towards dark—I said I was come to bid her goodbye; and might I spend the night in Mr. Nahum's round room. She raised her eyes on me, luminous and mysterious as the sky itself, even though in the dusk.

"You may *say* goodbye, Simon," she replied; "but unless I myself am much mistaken in you, your feet will not carry you out of all thought of me; and some day they will return to me whether you will or not."

Inside I was already in a flutter at thought of the hours to come, and I was accustomed to her strange speeches, though this struck on my mind more coldly than usual. I made a little jerk forwards; "I must thank you, please Miss Taroone, for having been so kind to me," I gulped in an awkward voice. "And I hope," I added, as she made no answer, "I hope I haven't been much of a bother —coming like this, I mean?"

"None, Simon"; was her sole reply. The hand that I had begun to hold out, went back into my pocket, and feeling extremely uncomfortable I half turned away.

"Why, who knows?—" said the solemn voice, "Mr. Nahum may at this very moment be riding home. Have a candle alight."

"Thank you, Miss Taroone. Thank you very much indeed."

With that I turned about and hastened across the darkening garden into the house. My candle stick and matches stood ready on the old oak bench at the foot of the tower. I lit up, and began to climb the cold steps. My heart in my mouth, I hesitated at the hob-nailed door; but managed at last to turn the key in the lock.

With two taller candles kindled, and its curtains drawn over the western window, I at once began to copy out the few last things I wanted for mine in Volume I. But there were two minds in me as midnight drew on, almost two selves, the one busy with pen and ink, the other stealthily listening to every faintest sound in my eyrie, a swift glance now and then up at the darkened glass only setting me more sharply to work. I had never before sat in so enormous a silence; the scratching of my pen its only tongue.

Steadily burned my candles; no sound of hoofs, no owl-cry, no knocking disturbed my peace; the nightingales had long since journeyed South. What I had hoped for, expected, dreaded in this long vigil, I cannot recall; all that I remember of it is that I began to shiver a little at last, partly because my young nerves were on the stretch, and partly because the small hours grew chill. In the very middle of the night there came to my ear what seemed a distant talking or gabbling. It may have been fancy; it may have been Linnet Sara. What certainly was fancy is the notion that, as I started up out of an instant's drowse, a stooping shape had swiftly withdrawn itself from me. But this was merely the shadow of a dream.

I returned at last from the heavy sleep I had fallen into, my forehead resting on the backs of my hands, and they flat on the huge open volume, my whole body stiff with cold, and the first clear grey of daybreak in the East. And suddenly as my awakened eyes stared dully about them in that thin light—the old windows, the strange outlandish objects, the clustering pictures, the countless books, my own ugly writing on my paper—an indescribable despair and anxiety—almost terror even—seized upon me at the rushing thought of my own *ignorance;* of how little I knew, of how unimportant I was. And, again and again, my ignorance. Then I thought of Miss Taroone, of Mr. Nahum, of the life before me, and everything yet to do. And a sullen misery swept up in me at these reflections. And once more I wished from the bottom of my heart that I had never come to this house.

But gradually the light broadened. And with it, confidence began to return. The things around me that had seemed strange and hostile became familiar again. I stood up and stretched myself and, I think, muttered a prayer.

To this day I see the marvellous countryside of that morning with its hills and low thick mists and woodlands stretched like a painted scene beneath the windows—and that finger of light from the risen Sun presently piercing across the dark air, and as if by a miracle causing birds and water to awake and sing and shine.

With a kind of grief that was yet rapture in my mind, I stood looking out over the cold lichen-crusted shingled roof of Thrae–– towards the East and towards those far horizons. Yet again the apprehension (that was almost a hope) drew over me that at any moment wall and chimney-shaft might thin softly away, and the Transformation

Scene begin. I was but just awake: and so too was the world itself, and ever is. And somewhere—Wall or no Wall—was my mother's East Dene. . . .

In a while I crept softly downstairs, let myself out, and ran off into the morning. Having climbed the hill from which I had first stared down upon Thrae, I stopped for a moment to recover my breath, and looked back. I looked back.

The gilding sun-rays beat low upon the house in the valley. All was still, wondrous, calm. For a moment my heart misgave me at this farewell. The next, in sheer excitement—the cold sweet air, the height, the morning, a few keen beckoning stars—I broke into a kind of Indian war-dance in the thin dewy grass, and then, with a last wave of my hand, like Mr. Nahum himself, I set off at a sharp walk on the journey that has not yet come to an end.

MORNING AND MAY

1

THIS IS THE KEY

THIS is the Key of the Kingdom
In that Kingdom is a city;
In that city is a town; [1]
In that town there is a street;
In that street there winds a lane;
In that lane there is a yard;
In that yard there is a house;
In that house there waits a room;
In that room an empty bed;
And on that bed a basket—
A Basket of Sweet Flowers:
Of Flowers, of Flowers;
A Basket of Sweet Flowers.

Flowers in a Basket;
Basket on the bed;
Bed in the chamber;
Chamber in the house;
House in the weedy yard;
Yard in the winding lane;
Lane in the broad street;
Street in the high town;
Town in the city;
City in the Kingdom—
This is the Key of the Kingdom.
Of the Kingdom this is the Key.

2

A NEW YEAR CAROL

HERE we bring new water
from the well so clear,

[1] That heart of it, within *walls*

For to worship God with,
this happy New Year.
Sing levy dew, sing levy dew,
the water and the wine;
The seven bright gold wires
and the bugles that do shine.

Sing reign of Fair Maid,
with gold upon her toe,—
Open you the West Door,
and turn the Old Year go.

Sing reign of Fair Maid
with gold upon her chin,—
Open you the East Door,
and let the New Year in.
Sing levy dew, sing levy dew,
the water and the wine;
The seven bright gold wires
and the bugles they do shine.

3 HEY! NOW THE DAY DAWNS

"Hay, nou the day dauis;	Hey! now the day dawns;
The jolie Cok crauis;	The jolly Cock crows;
Nou shroudis the shauis,	Thick-leaved the green shaws,
Throu Natur anone.	Through Nature anon.
The thissell-cok cryis	The thistle-cock cries
On louers wha lyis,	On lovers who lies,
Nou skaillis the skyis;	All cloudless the skies;
The nicht is neir gone.	The night is near gone.
"The feildis ouerflouis	The fields overflow
With gowans that grouis,	With daisies a-blow,
Quhair lilies lyk lou is,	And lilies like fire shine,
Als rid as the rone.	And red is the rowan.
The turtill that true is,	The wood-dove that true is
With nots that reneuis,	Her crooling reneweth,
Hir pairtie perseuis;	And her sweet mate pur-
The nicht is neir gone.	sueth;
	The night is near gone.

"Nou Hairtis with Hyndis,	Now Harts with their Hinds
Conforme to thair kyndis,	Conform to their kinds,
Hie tursis thair tyndis,	They vaunt their branched
On grund whair they grone.	antlers,
Nou Hurchonis, with Hairis,	They bell and they groan.
Ay passis in pairis;	Now Urchins[1] and Hares
Quhilk deuly declaris	Keep a-passing in pairs;
The nicht is neir gone . . ."	Which duly declares
	The night is near gone. . . .

ALEXANDER MONTGOMERIE

4

THE SLUGGARD

'TIS the voice of a sluggard; I heard him complain—
"You have waked me too soon; I must slumber again;"
As the door on its hinges, so he on his bed,
Turns his sides, and his shoulders, and his heavy head.
"A little more sleep, and a little more slumber"—
Thus he wastes half his days, and his hours without number;
And when he gets up, he sits folding his hands,
Or walks about saunt'ring, or trifling he stands.

I passed by his garden, and saw the wild brier
The thorn and the thistle grow broader and higher;
The clothes that hang on him are turning to rags;
And his money still wastes till he starves or he begs.

I made him a visit, still hoping to find
That he took better care for improving his mind;
He told me his dreams, talked of eating and drinking,
But he scarce reads his Bible, and never loves thinking.

Said I then to my heart: "Here's a lesson for me;
That man's but a picture of what I might be;
But thanks to my friends for their care in my breeding,
Who taught me betimes to love working and reading."

ISAAC WATTS

[1] Hedgehogs

5 HARK, HARK, THE LARK

HEARKE, hearke, the Larke at Heaven's gate sings,
And Phoebus 'gins arise,
His Steeds to water at those Springs
On chaliced Flowres that lyes:
And winking Mary-buds begin
To ope their Golden eyes:
With every thing that pretty is,
My Lady sweet, arise:
Arise, arise!

WILLIAM SHAKESPEARE

6 THE LARK NOW LEAVES HIS WATERY NEST

THE lark now leaves his watery nest,
And climbing shakes his dewy wings;
He takes your window for the East,
And to implore your light, he sings:
Awake, awake! the morn will never rise
Till she can dress her beauty at your eyes.

The merchant bows unto the seaman's star,
The ploughman from the sun his season takes;
But still the lover wonders what they are
Who look for day before his mistress wakes:
Awake, awake! break through your veils of lawn;
Then draw your curtains, and begin the dawn!

SIR WILLIAM DAVENANT

7 EARLY MORN

WHEN I did wake this morn from sleep,
It seemed I heard birds in a dream;
Then I arose to take the air—
The lovely air that made birds scream;
Just as a green hill launched the ship
Of gold, to take its first clear dip.

And it began its journey then,
As I came forth to take the air;
The timid Stars had vanished quite,
The Moon was dying with a stare;
Horses, and kine, and sheep were seen
As still as pictures, in fields green.

It seemed as though I had surprised
And trespassed in a golden world
That should have passed while men still slept!
The joyful birds, the ship of gold,
The horses, kine and sheep did seem
As they would vanish for a dream.

WILLIAM H. DAVIES

8 GOOD-MORROW

PACK, clouds, away, and welcome day!
With night we banish sorrow.
Sweet air, blow soft, mount, lark, aloft
To give my Love good morrow.
Wings from the wind to please her mind,
Notes from the lark I'll borrow:
Bird, prune thy wing, nightingale, sing,
To give my Love good morrow!
To give my Love good morrow
Notes from them all I'll borrow.

Wake from thy nest, robin redbreast!
Sing, birds, in every furrow,
And from each bill let music shrill
Give my fair Love good morrow!
Blackbird and thrush in every bush,
Stare,[1] linnet, and cock-sparrow,
You pretty elves, amongst yourselves
Sing my fair Love good morrow!
To give my Love good morrow
Sing, birds, in every furrow!

THOMAS HEYWOOD

[1] Starling

9 THE QUESTION

I DREAMED that, as I wandered by the way,
Bare Winter suddenly was changed to Spring,
And gentle odours led my steps astray,
Mixed with a sound of waters murmuring
Along a shelving bank of turf, which lay
Under a copse, and hardly dared to fling
Its green arms round the bosom of the stream,
But kissed it and then fled, as thou mightest in dream.

There grew pied wind-flowers and violets,
Daisies, those pearled Arcturi of the earth,
The constellated flower that never sets;
Faint oxlips; tender blue-bells, at whose birth
The sod scarce heaved; and that tall flower that wets—
Like a child, half in tenderness and mirth—
Its mother's face with Heaven's collected tears,
When the low wind, its playmate's voice, it hears.

And in the warm hedge grew lush eglantine,
Green cowbind and the moonlight-coloured may
And cherry-blossoms, and white cups, whose wine
Was the bright dew, yet drained not by the day;
And wild roses, and ivy serpentine
With its dark buds and leaves, wandering astray;
And flowers azure, black, and streaked with gold,
Fairer than any wakened eyes behold.

And nearer to the river's trembling edge
There grew broad flag-flowers, purple prankt with white
And starry river-buds among the sedge,
And floating water-lilies, broad and bright,
Which lit the oak that overhung the hedge
With moonlight beams of their own watery light;
And bulrushes, and reeds of such deep green
As soothed the dazzled eye with sober sheen.

Methought that of these visionary flowers

I made a nosegay, bound in such a way
That the same hues, which in their natural bowers
Were mingled or opposed, the like array
Kept these imprisoned children of the Hours
Within my hand,—and then, elate and gay,
I hastened to the spot whence I had come,
That I might there present it!—Oh! to whom?

PERCY BYSSHE SHELLEY

10 THE FRESH AIR

THE fresh air moves like water round a boat.
The white clouds wander. Let us wander too.
The whining, wavering plover flap and float.
That crow is flying after that cuckoo.
Look! Look! . . . They're gone. What are the great trees calling?
Just come a little farther, by that edge
Of green, to where the stormy ploughland, falling
Wave upon wave, is lapping to the hedge.
Oh, what a lovely bank! Give me your hand.
Lie down and press your heart against the ground.
Let us both listen till we understand,
Each through the other, every natural sound . . .
I can't hear anything to-day, can you,
But, far and near: "Cuckoo! Cuckoo! Cuckoo!"?

HAROLD MONRO

11 WEATHERS

THIS is the weather the cuckoo likes,
And so do I;
When showers betumble the chestnut spikes,
And nestlings fly:
And the little brown nightingale bills his best,
And they sit outside at "The Travellers' Rest,"
And maids come forth sprig-muslin drest,
And citizens dream of the south and west,
And so do I.

This is the weather the shepherd shuns,
And so do I;
When beeches drip in browns and duns,
And thresh, and ply;
And hill-hid tides throb, throe on throe,
And meadow rivulets overflow,
And drops on gate-bars hang in a row,
And rooks in families homeward go,
And so do I.

THOMAS HARDY

12 GREEN RAIN

INTO the scented woods we'll go,
And see the blackthorn swim in snow.
High above, in the budding leaves,
A brooding dove awakes and grieves;
The glades with mingled music stir,
And wildly laughs the woodpecker.
When blackthorn petals pearl the breeze,
There are the twisted hawthorne trees
Thick-set with buds, as clear and pale
As golden water or green hail—
As if a storm of rain had stood
Enchanted in the thorny wood,
And, hearing fairy voices call,
Hung poised, forgetting how to fall.

MARY WEBB

13 SONG ON MAY MORNING

Now the bright morning Star, Dayes harbinger,
Comes dancing from the East, and leads with her
The Flowry *May,* who from her green lap throws
The yellow Cowslip and the pale Primrose.
Hail, bounteous *May*, that dost inspire
Mirth and youth and young desire,

Woods and Groves, are of thy dressing,
Hill and Dale doth boast thy blessing.
Thus we salute thee with our early Song,
And welcome thee, and wish thee long.

John Milton

14 SISTER, AWAKE!

Sister, awake! close not your eyes.
The day her light discloses,
And the bright morning doth arise
Out of her bed of roses.

See the clear sun, the world's bright eye,
In at our window peeping:
Lo, how he blusheth to espy
Us idle wenches sleeping!

Therefore awake! make haste, I say,
And let us, without staying,
All in our gowns of green so gay
Into the park a-maying.

15 HERE WE COME A-PIPING

Here we come a-piping,
In Springtime and in May;
Green fruit a-ripening,
And Winter fled away.
The Queen she sits upon the strand,
Fair as lily, white as wand;
Seven billows on the sea,
Horses riding fast and free,
And bells beyond the sand.

16 AS WE DANCE ROUND

As we dance round a-ring-a-ring,
A maiden goes a-maying;

And here a flower, and there a flower,
Through mead and meadow straying:
O gentle one, why dost thou weep?—
Silver to spend with; gold to keep;
Till spin the green round World asleep,
And Heaven its dews be staying.

17 OLD MAY SONG

ALL in this pleasant evening, together come are we,
For the summer springs so fresh, green, and gay;
We tell you of a blossoming and buds on every tree,
Drawing near unto the merry month of May.

Rise up, the master of this house, put on your charm of gold,
For the summer springs so fresh, green, and gay;
Be not in pride offended with your name we make so bold,
Drawing near unto the merry month of May.

Rise up, the mistress of this house, with gold along your breast;
For the summer springs so fresh, green, and gay;
And if your body be asleep, we hope your soul's at rest,
Drawing near unto the merry month of May.

Rise up, the children of this house, all in your rich attire,
For the summer springs so fresh, green, and gay;
And every hair upon your heads shines like the silver wire:
Drawing near unto the merry month of May.

God bless this house and arbour, your riches and your store,
For the summer springs so fresh, green, and gay;
We hope the Lord will prosper you, both now and evermore,
Drawing near unto the merry month of May.

And now comes we must leave you, in peace and plenty here,
For the summer springs so fresh, green, and gay;
We shall not sing you May again until another year,
To draw you these cold winters away.

18 SONG OF THE MAYERS

REMEMBER us poor Mayers all,
  And thus do we begin,
To lead our lives in righteousness,
  Or else we die in sin.

We have been rambling all the night,
  And almost all the day,
And now returning back again,
  We have brought you a bunch of May.

A bunch of May we have brought you,
  And at your door it stands,
It is but a sprout, but it's well budded out
  By the work of our Lord's hands.

The hedges and trees they are so green,
  As green as any leek,
Our Heavenly Father, He watered them
  With his heavenly dew so sweet.

The heavenly gates are open wide,
  Our paths are beaten plain,
And if a man be not too far gone,
  He may return again.

The life of man is but a span,
  It flourishes like a flower;
We are here to-day, and gone to-morrow,
  And are dead in an hour.

The moon shines bright, and the stars give a light,
  A little before it is day,
God bless you all, both great and small,
  And send you a joyful May.

19 AND AS FOR ME

. . . AND as for me, thogh that I can but lyte, [1]
On bokės for to rede I me delyte,

[1] Know but little

And to hem yeve [1] I feyth and ful credènce,
And in myn herte have hem in reverence
So hertėly, that there is gamė noon
That fro my bokės maketh me to goon,
But hit be seldom on the holyday,
Save, certeynly, whan that the month of May
Is comen, and that I here the foulės [2] singe
And that the flourės ginnen for to springe,—
Farewel my boke, and my devocioun!

Now have I than swich [3] a condicioun,
That, of alle the flourės in the mede,
Than love I most these flourės whyte and rede,
Swiche as men callen daysies in our toun.
To hem have I so greet affeccioun,
As I seyde erst, whan comen is the May,
That in my bed ther daweth me no day,
That I nam up, and walking in the mede,
To seen this flour agein the sonnė sprede,
When hit uprysith erly by the morwe; [4]
That blisful sightė softneth all my sorwė [5]

And whan that hit is eve, I rennė blyve, [6]
As soon as evere the sonnė ginneth weste,
To seen this flour, how it wol go to reste,
For fere of nyght, so hateth she derknesse! . . .

GEOFFREY CHAUCER

20

THE SPRING

WHAT bird so sings, yet so does wail?
O, 'tis the ravished nightingale!
"Jug, jug, jug, jug, tereu," she cries,
And still her woes at midnight rise.
Brave prick-song! who is't now we hear?
None but the lark so shrill and clear;
Now at heaven's gates she claps her wings,
The morn not waking till she sings.
Hark, hark, with what a pretty throat
Poor robin-redbreast tunes his note;

[1] Give [2] Birds [3] Such [4] The first thing in the morning [5] Sorrow
[6] Run quickly, hasten away

Hark, how the jolly cuckoos sing
Cuckoo—to welcome in the spring!
Cuckoo—to welcome in the spring!

JOHN LYLY

21 SPRING, THE SWEET SPRING

SPRING, the sweet Spring, is the year's pleasant king·
Then blooms each thing, then maids dance in a ring,
Cold doth not sting, the pretty birds do sing:
Cuckoo, jug, jug, pu we, to witta woo!

The Palm and May make country houses gay,
Lambs frisk and play, the shepherds pipe all day,
And we hear aye birds tune this merry lay:
Cuckoo, jug, jug, pu we, to witta woo!

The fields breathe sweet, the daisies kiss our feet,
Young lovers meet, old wives a-sunning sit,
In every street these tunes our ears do greet:
Cuckoo, jug, jug, pu we, to witta woo!
Spring, the sweet Spring!

THOMAS NASH

22 A MAY DAY

. . . AND now all nature seemed in love;
The lusty sap began to move;
New juice did stir the embracing vines,
And birds had drawn their valentines.
The jealous trout that now did lie,
Rose at a well-dissembled fly:
There stood my friend with patient skill,
Attending of his trembling quill.[1]
Already were the eaves possessed
With the swift pilgrim's daubèd nest:
The groves already did rejoice
In Philomel's triumphing voice.
The showers were short, the weather mild,
The morning fresh, the evening smiled.

[1] Float

Joan takes her neat-rubbed pail and now
She trips to milk the sand-red cow;
Where, for some sturdy football swain,
Joan strokes [1] a sillabub or twain.
The field and gardens were beset
With tulip, crocus, violet;
And now, though late, the modest rose
Did more than half a blush disclose.
Thus all looked gay, all full of cheer,
To welcome the new-liveried year.

Sir Henry Wotton

23

EASTER

I got me flowers to straw thy way,
I got me boughs off many a tree:
But thou wast up by break of day,
And brought'st thy sweets along with thee.

The Sun arising in the East,
Though he give light, and the East perfume,[2]
If they should offer to contest
With thy arising, they presume.

Can there be any day but this,
Though many sunnes to shine endeavour?
We count three hundred, but we misse:
There is but one, and that one ever.

George Herbert

24

PLEASURE IT IS

Pleasure it is
To hear, iwis,[3]
The birdes sing.
The deer in the dale,
The sheep in the vale,

[1] Milks straight into the bowl [2] Refresh; make sweet [3] Truly, in sooth

The corn springing;
God's purveyance
For sustenance
It is for man.
Then we always
To Him give praise,
And thank Him than,
And thank Him than.

WILLIAM CORNISH

MOTHER, HOME AND SWEETHEART

25 I SING OF A MAIDEN

I sing of a maiden
That is makeless, [1]
King of all kings
To her son she ches. [2]

He came all so still
Where his mother was,
As dew in April
That falleth on the grass.

He came all so still
To his mother's bower,
As dew in April
That falleth on the flower.

He came all so still
Where his mother lay,
As dew in April
That falleth on the spray.

Mother and maiden
Was never none but she;
Well may such a lady
God's mother be.

26 LULLABY

UPON my lap my sovereign sits
And sucks upon my breast;
Meantime his love maintains my life
And gives my sense her rest.

Sing lullaby, my little boy,
Sing lullaby, mine only joy!

When thou hast taken thy repast,
Repose, my babe, on me;

[1] Mateless and matchless [2] Chose

So may thy mother and thy nurse
Thy cradle also be.
Sing lullaby, my little boy,
Sing lullaby, mine only joy!

I grieve that duty doth not work
All that my wishing would,
Because I would not be to thee
But in the best I should.
Sing lullaby, my little boy,
Sing lullaby, mine only joy!

Yet as I am, and as I may,
I must and will be thine,
Though all too little for thy self
Vouchsafing to be mine.
Sing lullaby, my little boy,
Sing lullaby, mine only joy!

RICHARD ROWLANDS

27 THE LITTLE BLACK BOY

My mother bore me in the southern wild,
And I am black, but O! my soul is white;
White as an angel is the English child,
But I am black, as if bereaved of light.

My mother taught me underneath a tree,
And, sitting down before the heat of day,
She took me on her lap and kissèd me,
And, pointing to the east, began to say:

"Look on the rising sun; there God does live,
And gives his light, and gives his heat away;
And flowers and trees and beasts and men receive
Comfort in morning, joy in the noonday.

"And we are put on earth a little space,
That we mày learn to bear the beams of love;

And these black bodies and this sunburnt face
Is but a cloud, and like a shady grove.

"For when our souls have learned the heat to bear,
The cloud will vanish; we shall hear his voice,
Saying: 'Come out from the grove, my love and care,
And round my golden tent like lambs rejoice.'"

Thus did my mother say, and kissèd me;
And thus I say to little English boy.
When I from black and he from white cloud free,
And round the tent of God like lambs we joy,

I'll shade him from the heat, till he can bear
To lean in joy upon our Father's knee;
And then I'll stand and stroke his silver hair,
And be like him, and he will then love me.

WILLIAM BLAKE

28 THE ECHOING GREEN

THE Sun does arise,
And make happy the skies;
The merry bells ring
To welcome the Spring;
The skylark and thrush,
The birds of the bush,
Sing louder around
To the bells' cheerful sound,
While our sports shall be seen
On the Echoing Green.

Old John, with white hair,
Does laugh away care,
Sitting under the oak,
Among the old folk,
They laugh at our play,
And soon they all say:
"Such, such were the joys

When we all, girls and boys,
In our youth time were seen
On the Echoing Green."

Till the little ones, weary,
No more can be merry;
The sun does descend,
And our sports have an end.
Round the laps of their mothers
Many sisters and brothers,
Like birds in their nest,
Are ready for rest,
And sport no more seen
On the darkening Green.

WILLIAM BLAKE

29 IF I HAD BUT TWO LITTLE WINGS

IF I had but two little wings
And were a little feathery bird,
To you I'd fly, my dear!
But thoughts like these are idle things,
And I stay here.

But in my sleep to you I fly:
I'm always with you in my sleep!
The world is all one's own.
But then one wakes, and where am I?
All, all alone.

Sleep stays not, though a monarch bids:
So I love to wake ere break of day:
For though my sleep be gone,
Yet while 'tis dark, one shuts one's lids,
And still dreams on.

SAMUEL TAYLOR COLERIDGE

30 I REMEMBER

I REMEMBER, I remember,
The house where I was born,
The little window where the sun
Came peeping in at morn;
He never came a wink too soon,
Nor brought too long a day;
But now, I often wish the night
Had borne my breath away.

I remember, I remember,
The roses, red and white,
The violets, and the lily-cups!—
Those flowers made of light!
The lilacs where the robin built,
And where my brother set
The laburnum on his birth-day,—
The tree is living yet!

I remember, I remember,
Where I used to swing,
And thought the air must rush as fresh
To swallows on the wing;
My spirit flew in feathers then,
That is so heavy now,
And summer pools could hardly cool
The fever on my brow!

I remember, I remember,
The fir trees dark and high;
I used to think their slender tops
Were close against the sky:
It was a childish ignorance,
But now 'tis little joy
To know I'm farther off from Heaven
Than when I was a boy.

THOMAS HOOD

31 MIDNIGHT ON THE GREAT WESTERN

In the third-class seat sat the journeying boy,
And the roof-lamp's oily flame
Played down on his listless form and face,
Bewrapt past knowing to what he was going,
Or whence he came.

In the band of his hat the journeying boy
Had a ticket stuck; and a string
Around his neck bore the key of his box,
That twinkled gleams of the lamp's sad beams
Like a living thing.

What past can be yours, O journeying boy
Towards a world unknown,
Who calmly, as if incurious quite
On all at stake, can undertake
This plunge alone?

Knows your soul a sphere, O journeying boy,
Our rude realms far above,
Whence with spacious vision you mark and mete
This region of sin that you find you in,
But are not of?

Thomas Hardy

32 THE RUNAWAY

Once when the sun of the year was beginning to fall
We stopped by a mountain pasture to say, "Whose colt?"
A little Morgan had one forefoot on the wall,
The other curled at his heart. He dipped his head
And snorted to us; and then he had to bolt.
We heard the muffled thunder when he fled
And we saw him or thought we saw him dim and grey
Like a shadow against the curtain of falling flakes.
We said, "The little fellow's afraid of the snow.
He isn't winter broken." "It isn't play

With the little fellow at all. He's running away.
I doubt if even his mother could tell him, 'Sakes,
It's only weather.' He'd think she didn't know.
Where is his mother? He can't be out alone."
And now he comes again with a clatter of stone
And mounts the wall again with whited eyes
And all his tail that isn't hair up straight.
He shudders his coat as if to throw off flies.
Whoever it is that leaves him out so late
When everything else has gone to stall and bin
Ought to be told to go and bring him in.

ROBERT FROST

33 ON EASTNOR KNOLL

SILENT are the woods, and the dim green boughs are
Hushed in the twilight; yonder, in the path through
The apple orchard, is a tired plough-boy
Calling the cows home.

A bright white star blinks, the pale moon rounds, but
Still the red, lurid wreckage of the sunset
Smoulders in smoky fire, and burns on
The misty hill-tops.

Ghostly it grows, and darker, the burning
Fades into smoke, and now the gusty oaks are
A silent army of phantoms thronging
A land of shadows.

JOHN MASEFIELD

34 "HOME NO MORE HOME TO ME"

HOME no more home to me, whither must I wander?
Hunger my driver, I go where I must.
Cold blows the winter wind over hill and heather;
Thick drives the rain, and my roof is in the dust.
Loved of wise men was the shade of my roof-tree.

The true word of welcome was spoken in the door—
Dear days of old, with the faces in the firelight,
Kind folks of old, you come again no more.

Home was home then, my dear, full of kindly faces,
Home was home then, my dear, happy for the child,
Fire and the windows bright glittered on the moorland;
Song, tuneful song, built a palace in the wild.
Now, when day dawns on the brow of the moorland,
Lone stands the house, and the chimney-stone is cold.
Lone let it stand, now the friends are all departed,
The kind hearts, the true hearts, that loved the place of old.

Spring shall come, come again, calling up the moor-fowl,
Spring shall bring the sun and rain, bring the bees and flowers;
Red shall the heather bloom over hill and valley,
Soft flow the stream through the even-flowing hours;
Fair the day shine as it shone on my childhood—
Fair shine the day on the house with open door;
Birds come and cry there and twitter in the chimney—
But I go for ever and come again no more.

ROBERT LOUIS STEVENSON

35

DALYAUNCE

Mundus. Welcome, fayre chylde, what is thy name?

Infans. I wote not, syr, withouten blame.
But ofte tyme my moder in her game
Callèd me dalyaunce.

Mundus. Dalyaunce, my swetė chylde,
It is a name that is ryght wylde,
For whan thou waxest olde.
It is a name of no substaunce
But, my fayre chylde, what woldest thou have?

Infans. Syr of some comforte I you crave—
Mete and clothe my lyfe to save:
And I your true servaunt shall be.

Mundus. Fayre chylde, I graunte thee thyne askynge.
I wyll thee fynde [1] whyle thou art yinge [2]
So thou wylte be obedyent to my byddynge.
These garments gaye I gyve to thee.
And also I gyve to thee a name,
And clepe [3] thee Wanton, in every game;
Tyll XIII yere be come and gone,
And than come agayne to me.

[*Infans is now called Wanton.*]

Wanton. Gramercy, Worlde, for myne araye,
For now I purpose me to playe.

Mundus. Fare well, fayre chylde, and have good daye.
All rychelesnesse [4] is kynde [5] for thee.

[*Mundus goes out leaving Wanton alone.*]

Wanton. Aha, Wanton is my name!
I can many a quaynte game.
Lo, my toppe I dryve in same,
Se, it torneth rounde!
I can with my scorge-stycke
My felowe upon the heed hytte,
And wyghtly [6] from hym make a skyppe;
And blere [7] on hym my tonge.
If brother or syster do me chyde
I wyll scratche and also byte.
I can crye, and also kyke,
And mocke them all berewe.
If fader or mother wyll me smyte,
I wyll wrynge [8] with my lyppe;
And lyghtly from hym make a skyppe;
And call my dame shrewe.
Aha, a newe game have I founde:

[1] Keep [2] Young [3] Call [4] Heedlessness [5] Natural
[6] Nimbly [7] Stick out [8] Squiggle

Se this gynne[1] it renneth rounde;
And here another have I founde,
And yet mo[2] can I fynde.
I can mowe[3] on a man;
And make a lesynge[4] well I can,
And mayntayne it ryght well than.
This connynge[5] came me of kynde.
Ye, syrs,[6] I can well gelde a snayle;
And catche a cowe by the tayle;
This is a fayre connynge!
I can daunce, and also skyppe;
I can playe at the chery pytte;
And I can wystell you a fytte,[7]
Syres, in a whylowe ryne.[8]
Ye, syrs, and every daye
Whan I to scole shall take the waye
Some good mannes gardyn I wyll assaye,
Perys[9] and plommes to plucke.
I can spye a sparowes nest.
I wyll not go to scole but whan me lest,
For there begynneth a sory fest[10]
Whan the mayster sholde lyfte my docke.[11]
But, syrs, whan I was seven yere of age,
I was sent to the Worlde to take wage.
And this seven yere I have ben his page
And kept his commaundement . . .

36 CHRISTMAS AT SEA

THE sheets were frozen hard, and they cut the naked hand;
The decks were like a slide, where a seaman scarce could stand;
The wind was a nor'wester, blowing squally off the sea;
And cliffs and spouting breakers were the only things a-lee.

They heard the surf a-roaring before the break of day;

[1] Toy or trap [2] More [3] Make grimaces
[4] Falsehood [5] Learning [6] Yea, sirs [7] Air, tune, stave
[8] Willow rind [9] Pears [10] Feast [11] Gown or coat-tail

But 'twas only with the peep of light we saw how ill we lay.
We tumbled every hand on deck instanter, with a shout,
And we gave her the maintops'l, and stood by to go about.

All day we tacked and tacked between the South Head and
the North;
All day we hauled the frozen sheets, and got no further forth;
All day as cold as charity, in bitter pain and dread,
For very life and nature we tacked from head to head.

We gave the South a wider berth, for there the tide-race
roared;
But every tack we made we brought the North Head close
aboard:
So's we saw the cliffs and houses, and the breakers running
high,
And the coastguard in his garden, with his glass against
his eye.

The frost was on the village roofs as white as ocean foam;
The good red fires were burning bright in every 'longshore
home;
The windows sparkled clear, and the chimneys volleyed out;
And I vow we sniffed the victuals as the vessel went about.

The bells upon the church were rung with a mighty jovial
cheer
For it's just that I should tell you how (of all days in the
year)
This day of our adversity was blessèd Christmas morn,
And the house above the coastguard's was the house where
I was born.

O well I saw the pleasant room, the pleasant faces there,
My mother's silver spectacles, my father's silver hair;
And well I saw the firelight, like a flight of homely elves,
Go dancing round the china-plates that stand upon the
shelves.

And well I knew the talk they had, the talk that was of me,
Of the shadow on the household and the son that went to sea;
And O the wicked fool I seemed, in every kind of way,
To be here and hauling frozen ropes on blessèd Christmas Day.

They lit the high sea-light, and the dark began to fall.
"All hands to loose topgallant sails," I heard the captain call,
"By the Lord, she'll never stand it," our first mate, Jackson, cried.
. . ."It's the one way or the other, Mr. Jackson," he replied.

She staggered to her bearings, but the sails were new and good.
And the ship smelt up to windward just as though she understood.
As the winter's day was ending, in the entry of the night,
We cleared the weary headland, and passed below the light.

And they heaved a mighty breath, every soul on board but me,
As they saw her nose again pointing handsome out to sea;
But all that I could think of, in the darkness and the cold,
Was just that I was leaving home and my folks were growing old.

ROBERT LOUIS STEVENSON

TWILIGHT

THE twilight is sad and cloudy,
The wind blows wild and free,
And like the wings of sea-birds
Flash the white caps of the sea.

But in the fisherman's cottage
There shines a ruddier light,
And a little face at the window
Peers out into the night.

Close, close it is pressed to the window,
As if those childish eyes
Were looking into the darkness,
To see some form arise.

And a woman's waving shadow
Is passing to and fro,
Now rising to the ceiling,
Now bowing and bending low.

What tale do the roaring ocean,
And the night-wind, bleak and wild,
As they beat at the crazy casement,
Tell to that little child?

And why do the roaring ocean,
And the night-wind, wild and bleak,
As they beat at the heart of the mother,
Drive the colour from her cheek?

HENRY WADSWORTH LONGFELLOW

38 "HOW'S MY BOY?"

"Ho, sailor of the sea!
How's my boy—my boy?"
"What's your boy's name, good wife,
And in what good ship sailed he?"
"My boy John—
He that went to sea—
What care I for the ship, sailor?
My boy's my boy to me.

"You come back from sea
And not know my John!
I might as well have asked some landsman
Yonder down in the town.
There's not an ass in all the parish
But he knows my John.

"How's my boy—my boy?
And unless you let me know,

I'll swear you are no sailor,
Blue jacket or no,
Brass button or no, sailor,
Anchor and crown or no!
Sure his ship was the Jolly Briton."—
"Speak low, woman, speak low!"

"And why should I speak low, sailor,
About my own boy John?
If I was loud as I am proud
I'd sing him o'er the town!
Why should I speak low, sailor?"
"That good ship went down."

"How's my boy—my boy?
What care I for the ship, sailor,
I never was aboard her.
Be she afloat, or be she aground,
Sinking or swimming, I'll be bound,
Her owners can afford her!
I say, how's my John?"
"Every man on board went down,
Every man aboard her."

"How's my boy—my boy?
What care I for the men, sailor?
I'm not their mother—
How's my boy—my boy?
Tell me of him and no other!
How's my boy—my boy?"

SYDNEY DOBELL

39 CAM' YE BY?

CAM' ye by the salmon fishers?
Cam' ye by the roperee?
Saw ye a sailor laddie
Waiting on the coast for me?

I ken fahr[1] I'm gyain,[2]
I ken fahs[3] gyain wi' me;
I ha'e a lad o' my ain,
Ye daurna tack 'im fae[4] me.

Stockings of blue silk,
Shoes of patent leather,
Kid to tie them up,
And gold rings on his finger.

Oh for six o'clock!
Oh for seven I weary!
Oh for eight o'clock!
And then I'll see my dearie.

40 MY BOY TAMMY

"WHAR hae ye been a' day, my boy Tammy?
Whar hae ye been a' day, my boy Tammy?"
"I've been by burn and flow'ry brae,
Meadow green and mountain grey,
Courtin' o' this young thing just come frae her Mammy."

"And whar gat ye that young thing, my boy Tammy?"
"I gat her down in yonder howe,[5]
Smiling on a broomy knowe,[6]
Herding ae wee Lamb and Ewe for her poor Mammy."

"What said ye to the bonny bairn, my boy Tammy?"
" 'I hae a house, it cost me dear,
I've walth o' plenishen and gear,[7]
Yese get it a', war't ten times mair, gin[8] ye will leave your Mammy.'

"The smile gaed aff her bonny face—'I mauna leave my Mammy!
She's gi'en me meat, she's gi'en me claes,[9]
She's been my comfort a' my days,

[1] Where [2] Going [3] Who's [4] From [5] Dale or hollow
[6] Knoll or hillock [7] Goods and chattels [8] If [9] Clothes

My father's death brought mony waes—I canna leave my Mammy.' "

" 'We'll tak her hame and mak her fain, my ain kind-hearted Lammy,
We'll gie her meat, we'll gi'e her claes,
We'll be her comfort a' her days':
The wee thing gi'es her hand, and says, 'There, gang and ask my Mammy.' "

"Has she been to kirk wi' thee, my boy Tammy?"
"She has been to kirk wi' me,
And the tear was in her ee,
But Oh! she's but a young thing just come frae her Mammy."

HECTOR MACNEILL

41 ROSY APPLE, LEMON, OR PEAR

ROSY apple, lemon or pear,
Bunch of roses she shall wear;
Gold and silver by her side,
I know who will be the bride.
Take her by her lily-white hand,
Lead her to the altar;
Give her kisses,—one, two, three,—
Mother's runaway daughter.

42 IN PRAISE OF ISABEL PENNELL

BY Saint Mary, my lady,
Your mammy and your daddy
Brought forth a goodly baby!

My maiden Isabell,—
Reflaring [1] rosabell,
The flagrant camamell,

The ruddy rosary,
The sovereign rosemary,
The pretty strawberry,

[1] Sweet-smelling

The columbine, the nepte,[1]
The ieloffer[2] well set,
The proper violet,

Ennewèd, your colour
Is like the daisy flower
After the April shower!

Star of the morrow gray,
The blossom on the spray,
The freshest flower of May;

Maidenly demure,
Of womanhood the lure,
Wherefore I make you sure:

It were an heavenly health,
It were an endless wealth,
A life for God himself,

To hear this nightingale,
Among the birdės smale,
Warbling in the vale:—

Dug, dug,
Iug, iug,
Good year and good luck,
With chuk, chuk, chuk, chuk!

John Skelton

43

MY SWEET SWEETING

She is so proper and so pure,
Full stedfast, stabill and demure,
There is none such, ye may be sure,
As my swete swetyng.

[1] Cat-mint [2] Gillyflower

In all thys world, as thynketh me,
Is none so plesaunt to my e'e,
That I am glad soo ofte to see,
As my swete swetyng.

When I behold my swetyng swete,
Her face, her hands, her minion fete,
They seme to me there is none so mete,
As my swete swetyng.

Above all other prayse must I,
And love my pretty pygsnye,
For none I fynd so womanly
As my swete swetyng.

44 SWEET STAY-AT-HOME

Sweet Stay-at-Home, sweet Well-content,
Thou knowest of no strange continent:
Thou hast not felt thy bosom keep
A gentle motion with the deep;
Thou hast not sailed in Indian seas,
Where scent comes forth in every breeze.
Thou hast not seen the rich grape grow
For miles, as far as eyes can go;
Thou hast not seen a summer's night
When maids could sew by a worm's light;
Nor the North Sea in spring send out
Bright hues that like birds flit about
In solid cages of white ice—
Sweet Stay-at-Home, sweet Love-one-place.
Thou hast not seen black fingers pick
White cotton when the bloom is thick,
Nor heard black throats in harmony;
Nor hast thou sat on stones that lie
Flat on the earth, that once did rise
To hide proud kings from common eyes.
Thou hast not seen plains full of bloom
Where green things had such little room

They pleased the eye like fairer flowers—
Sweet Stay-at-Home, all these long hours.
Sweet Well-content, sweet Love-one-place,
Sweet, simple maid, bless thy dear face;
For thou hast made more homely stuff
Nurture thy gentle self enough;
I love thee for a heart that's kind—
Not for the knowledge in thy mind.

WILLIAM H. DAVIES

45

WAITING

RICH in the waning light she sat
While the fierce rain on the window spat.
The yellow lamp-glow lit her face,
Shadows cloaked the narrow place
She sat adream in. Then she'd look
Idly upon an idle book;
Anon would rise and musing peer
Out at the misty street and drear;
Or with her loosened dark hair play,
Hiding her fingers' snow away;
And, singing softly, would sing on
When the desire of song had gone.
"O lingering day!" her bosom sighed,
"O laggard Time!" each motion cried.
Last she took the lamp and stood
Rich in its flood,
And looked and looked again at what
Her longing fingers' zeal had wrought;
And turning then did nothing say,
Hiding her thoughts away.

JOHN FREEMAN

46

THE SICK CHILD

Child. O MOTHER, lay your hand on my brow!
O mother, mother, where am I now?

Why is the room so gaunt and great?
Why am I lying awake so late?

Mother. Fear not at all: the night is still.
Nothing is here that means you ill—
Nothing but lamps the whole town through,
And never a child awake but you.

Child. Mother, mother, speak low in my ear,
Some of the things are so great and near,
Some are so small and far away,
I have a fear that I cannot say.
What have I done, and what do I fear,
And why are you crying, mother dear?

Mother. Out in the city, sounds begin.
Thank the kind God, the carts come in!
An hour or two more, and God is so kind,
The day shall be blue in the window blind,
Then shall my child go sweetly asleep,
And dream of the birds and the hills of sheep.

ROBERT LOUIS STEVENSON

47

STILLNESS

WHEN the words rustle no more,
  And the last work's done,
When the bolt lies deep in the door,
  And Fire, our Sun,
Falls on the dark-laned meadows of the floor;

When from the clock's last chime to the next chime
  Silence beats his drum,
And Space with gaunt grey eyes and her brother Time
  Wheeling and whispering come,
She with the mould of form and he with the loom of rhyme:

Then twittering out in the night my thought-birds flee,
  I am emptied of all my dreams:

I only hear Earth turning, only see
Ether's long bankless streams,
And only know I should drown if you laid not your hand on me.

JAMES ELROY FLECKER

48 LINES ON RECEIVING HIS MOTHER'S PICTURE

O THAT those lips had language! Life has passed
With me but roughly since I heard thee last.
Those lips are thine—thy own sweet smiles I see,
The same that oft in childhood solaced me;
Voice only fails, else how distinct they say,
"Grieve not, my child—chase all thy fears away!" . . .
My Mother! when I learnt that thou wast dead,
Say, wast thou conscious of the tears I shed?
Hovered thy spirit o'er thy sorrowing son,
Wretch even then, life's journey just begun?
Perhaps thou gav'st me, though unseen, a kiss,
Perhaps a tear, if souls can weep in bliss—
Ah, that maternal smile! it answers—Yes.
I heard the bell tolled on thy burial day,
I saw the hearse that bore thee slow away,
And, turning from my nursery window, drew
A long, long sigh, and wept a last adieu!
But was it such?—It was. Where thou art gone
Adieus and farewells are a sound unknown.
May I but meet thee on that peaceful shore,
The parting word shall pass my lips no more!
Thy maidens, grieved themselves at my concern,
Oft gave me promise of thy quick return.
What ardently I wished, I long believed,
And, disappointed still, was still deceived,
By expectation every day beguiled,
Dupe of *to-morrow* even from a child.
Thus many a sad to-morrow came and went,
Till, all my stock of infant sorrow spent,
I learnt at last submission to my lot.

But, though I less deplored thee, ne'er forgot.
Where once we dwelt our name is heard no more,
Children not thine have trod my nursery floor;
And where the gardener Robin, day by day,
Drew me to school along the public way,
Delighted with my bauble coach, and wrapped
In scarlet mantle warm, and velvet-capped,
'Tis now become a history little known,
That once we called the pastoral house our own.
Short-lived possession! but the record fair
That memory keeps, of all thy kindness there,
Still outlives many a storm, that has effaced
A thousand other themes less deeply traced.
Thy nightly visits to my chamber made,
That thou mightst know me safe and warmly laid;
Thy morning bounties ere I left my home,
The biscuit, or confectionary plum;
The fragrant waters on my cheek bestowed
By thy own hand, till fresh they shone and glowed;
All this, and more endearing still than all,
Thy constant flow of love, that knew no fall. . . .

William Cowper

49 THE CHIMNEY SWEEPER

When my mother died I was very young,
And my father sold me while yet my tongue
Could scarcely cry " 'weep! 'weep! 'weep! 'weep!"
So your chimneys I sweep, and in soot I sleep.

There's little Tom Dacre, who cried when his head,
That curled like a lamb's back, was shaved: so I said
"Hush, Tom! never mind it, for when your head's bare
You know that the soot cannot spoil your white hair."

And so he was quiet, and that very night,
As Tom was a-sleeping, he had such a sight!
That thousands of sweepers, Dick, Joe, Ned, and Jack,
Were all of them locked up in coffins of black.

And by came an Angel who had a bright key,
And he opened the coffins and set them all free;
Then down a green plain leaping, laughing, they run,
And wash in a river, and shine in the Sun.

Then naked and white, all their bags left behind,
They rise upon clouds and sport in the wind;
And the Angel told Tom, if he'd be a good boy,
He'd have God for his father, and never want joy.

And so Tom awoke; and we rose in the dark,
And got with our bags and our brushes to work.
Tho' the morning was cold, Tom was happy and warm;
So if all do their duty they need not fear harm.

WILLIAM BLAKE

50 BONNIE GEORGE CAMPBELL

HIE upon Hielands,
and laigh upon Tay,
Bonnie George Campbell
rode out on a day.

Saddled and briddled
and booted rade he;
Toom [1] hame cam' the saddle,
but never cam' he.

Down cam' his auld mither,
greetin' [2] fu' sair,
And down cam' his bonny wife,
wringin' her hair:—

"My meadow lies green,
and my corn is unshorn,
My barn is to build
and my babe is unborn."

[1] Empty [2] Weeping

Saddled and briddled
and booted rade he;
Toom hame cam' the saddle
but never cam' he.

51 THE ORPHAN'S SONG

I HAD a little bird,
I took it from the nest;
I prest it, and blest it,
And nurst it in my breast.

I set it on the ground,
I danced round and round,
And sang about it so cheerly,
With "Hey my little bird, and ho my little bird,
And ho but I love thee dearly!"

I make a little feast
Of food soft and sweet,
I hold it in my breast,
And coax it to eat;

I pit, and I pat,
I call it this and that,
And sing about it so cheerly,
With "Hey my little bird, and ho my little bird,
And ho but I love thee dearly!"

I may kiss, I may sing,
But I can't make it feed,
It taketh no heed
Of any pleasant thing.

I scolded and I socked,
But it minded not a whit,
Its little mouth was locked,
And I could not open it.

Tho' with pit, and with pat,
And with this, and with that,
I sang about it so cheerly,
With "Hey my little bird, and ho my little bird,
And ho but I love thee dearly!"

But when the day was done,
And the room was at rest,
And I sat all alone
With my birdie in my breast,

And the light had fled,
And not a sound was heard,
Then my little bird
Lifted up its head,

And the little mouth
Loosened its sullen pride,
And it opened, it opened,
With a yearning strong and wide.

Swifter than I speak
I brought it food once more,
But the poor little beak
Was locked as before.

I sat down again,
And not a creature stirred;
I laid the little bird
Again where it had laid;

And again when nothing stirred,
And not a word I said,
Then my little bird
Lifted up its head,

And the little beak
Loosed its stubborn pride,
And it opened, it opened,
With a yearning strong and wide.

It lay in my breast,
It uttered no cry,
'Twas famished, 'twas famished,
And I couldn't tell why.

I couldn't tell why,
But I saw that it would die,
For all that I kept dancing round and round,
And singing about it so cheerly,
With "Hey my little bird, and ho my little bird,
And ho but I love thee dearly!"

I never look sad,
I hear what people say,
I laugh when they are gay
And they think I am glad.

My tears never start,
I never say a word,
But I think that my heart
Is like that little bird.

Every day I read,
And I sing, and I play,
But thro' the long day
It taketh no heed.

It taketh no heed
Of any pleasant thing,
I know it doth not read,
I know it doth not sing.

With my mouth I read,
With my hands I play,
My shut heart is shut,
Coax it how you may.

You may coax it how you may
While the day is broad and bright,
But in the dead night
When the guests are gone away,

And no more the music sweet
Up the house doth pass,
Nor the dancing feet
Shake the nursery glass;

And I've heard my aunt
Along the corridor,
And my uncle gaunt
Lock his chamber door;

And upon the stair
All is hushed and still,
And the last wheel
Is silent in the square;

And the nurses snore,
And the dim sheets rise and fall,
And the lamplight's on the wall,
And the mouse is on the floor;

And the curtains of my bed
Are like a heavy cloud,
And the clock ticks loud,
And sounds are in my head;

And little Lizzie sleeps
Softly at my side,
It opens, it opens,
With a yearning strong and wide!

It yearns in my breast,
It utters no cry,
'Tis famished, 'tis famished,
And I feel that I shall die,
I feel that I shall die,
And none will know why.

Tho' the pleasant life is dancing round and round,
And singing about me so cheerly,

With "Hey my little bird, and ho my little bird,
And ho but I love thee dearly!"

SYDNEY DOBELL

52 THE FIRST GRIEF

"OH! call my brother back to me,
  I cannot play alone;
The summer comes with flower and bee—
  Where is my brother gone?

"The butterfly is glancing bright
  Across the sunbeam's track;
I care not now to chase its flight—
  Oh! call my brother back.

"The flowers run wild—the flowers we sowed
  Around our garden tree;
Our vine is drooping with its load—
  Oh! call him back to me."

"He would not hear my voice, fair child!
  He may not come to thee;
The face that once like spring-time smiled
  On earth no more thou'lt see.

"A rose's brief, bright life of joy,
  Such unto him was given;
Go—thou must play alone, my boy—
  Thy brother is in heaven!"

"And has he left the birds and flowers,
  And must I call in vain;
And through the long, long summer hours,
  Will he not come again?

"And bv the brook, and in the glade,
  Are all our wanderings o'er?

Oh! while my brother with me played,
Would I had loved him more!"

FELICIA HEMANS

53 THE POPLAR FIELD

THE poplars are felled; farewell to the shade
And the whispering sound of the cool colonnade;
The winds play no more and sing in the leaves,
Nor Ouse on his bosom their image receives.

Twelve years have elapsed since I first took a view
Of my favourite field, and the bank where they grew;
And now in the grass below they are laid,
And the tree is my seat that once lent me a shade.

The blackbird has fled to another retreat
Where the hazels afford him a screen from the heat,
And the scene where his melody charmed me before
Resounds with his sweet-flowing ditty no more.

My fugitive years are all hasting away,
And I must ere long lie as lowly as they
With a turf on my breast, and a stone at my head,
Ere another such grove shall arise in its stead.

'Tis a sight to engage me, if anything can,
To muse on the perishing pleasures of man;
Though his life be a dream, his enjoyments, I see,
Have a being less durable even than he.

WILLIAM COWPER

54 FAREWELL

NOT soon shall I forget—a sheet
Of golden water, cold and sweet,
The young moon with her head in veils
Of silver, and the nightingales.

A wain of hay came up the lane—
O fields I shall not walk again,
And trees I shall not see, so still
Against a sky of daffodil!

Fields where my happy heart had rest,
And where my heart was heaviest,
I shall remember them at peace
Drenched in moon-silver like a fleece.

The golden water sweet and cold,
The moon of silver and of gold,
The dew upon the gray grass-spears,
I shall remember them with tears.

KATHARINE TYNAN

55 "YE BANKS AND BRAES O' BONNIE DOON"

YE banks and braes o' boonie Doon,
  How can ye bloom sae fair?
How can ye chant, ye little birds,
  And I sae fu' o' care?

Thou'll break my heart, thou bonnie bird
  That sings upon the bough;
Thou minds me o' the happy days
  When my fause Luve was true.

Thou'll break my heart, thou bonnie bird
  That sings beside thy mate;
For sae I sat, and nae I sang,
  And wist na o' my fate.

Aft hae I roved by bonnie Doon
  To see the woodbine twine,
And ilka [1] bird sang o' its love;
  And sae did I o' mine.

[1] Every

Wi' lightsome heart I pu'd a rose,
Frae aff its thorny tree;
And my fause luver staw [1] the rose,
But left the thorn wi' me.

ROBERT BURNS

56 TO A RIVER IN THE SOUTH

CALL me no more, O gentle stream,
To wander through thy sunny dream,
No more to lean at twilight cool
Above thy weir and glimmering pool.

Surely I know thy hoary dawns,
The silver crisp on all thy lawns,
The softly swirling undersong
That rocks thy reeds the winter long.

Surely I know the joys that ring
Through the green deeps of leafy spring;
I know the elfin cups and domes
That are their small and secret homes.

Yet is the light for ever lost
That daily once thy meadows crossed,
The voice no more by thee is heard
That matched the song of stream and bird.

Call me no more!—thy waters roll
Here, in the world that is my soul,
And here, though Earth be drowned in night,
Old love shall dwell with old delight.

HENRY NEWBOLT

57 THE DESERTED HOUSE

THERE'S no smoke in the chimney,
And the rain beats on the floor;

[1] Stole

There's no glass in the window,
  There's no wood in the door;
The heather grows behind the house,
  And the sand lies before.

No hand hath trained the ivy,
  The walls are gray and bare;
The boats upon the sea sail by,
  Nor ever tarry there.
No beast of the field comes nigh,
  Nor any bird of the air.

MARY COLERIDGE

58 AN OLD WOMAN OF THE ROADS

O, to have a little house!
  To own the hearth and stool and all!
The heaped-up sods upon the fire,
  The pile of turf against the wall!

To have a clock with weights and chains
  And pendulum swinging up and down!
A dresser filled with shining delph,
  Speckled and white and blue and brown!

I could be busy all the day
  Clearing and sweeping hearth and floor,
And fixing on their shelf again
  My white and blue and speckled store!

I could be quiet there at night
  Beside the fire and by myself,
Sure of a bed, and loth to leave
  The ticking clock and the shining delph!

Och! but I'm weary of mist and dark,
  And roads where there's never a house or bush,
And tired I am of bog and road
  And the crying wind and the lonesome hush!

And I am praying to God on high,
And I am praying Him night and day,
For a little house—a house of my own—
Out of the wind's and the rain's way.

PADRAIC COLUM

59 A DESERTED HOME

HERE where the fields lie lonely and untended,
Once stood the old house grey among the trees,
Once to the hills rolled the waves of the cornland—
Long waves and golden, softer than the sea's.

Long, long ago has the ploughshare rusted,
Long has the barn stood roofless and forlorn;
But oh! far away are some who still remember
The songs of the young girls binding up the corn.

Here where the windows shone across the darkness,
Here where the stars once watched above the fold,
Still watch the stars, but the sheepfold is empty;
Falls now the rain where the hearth glowed of old.

Here where the leagues of melancholy lough-sedge
Moan in the wind round the grey forsaken shore,
Once waved the corn in the mid-month of autumn,
Once sped the dance when the corn was on the floor.

SIDNEY ROYSE LYSAGHT

60 UNDER THE WOODS

WHEN these old woods were young
The thrushes' ancestors
As sweetly sung
In the old years.

There was no garden here,
Apples nor mistletoe;

No children dear
Ran to and fro.

New then was this thatched cot,
But the keeper was old,
And he had not
Much lead or gold.

Most silent beech and yew:
As he went round about
The woods to view
Seldom he shot.

But now that he is gone
Out of most memories,
Still lingers on,
A stoat of his,

But one, shrivelled and green,
And with no scent at all,
And barely seen
On this shed wall.

EDWARD THOMAS

61 "BLOWS THE WIND TO-DAY"

Blows the wind to-day, and the sun and the rain are flying,
  Blows the wind on the moors to-day and now,
Where about the graves of the martyrs the whaups are crying,
  My heart remembers how!

Grey recumbent tombs of the dead in desert places,
  Standing stones on the vacant wine-red moor,
Hills of sheep, and the howes of the silent vanished races,
  And winds, austere and pure:

Be it granted me to behold you again in dying,
  Hills of home! and to hear again the call;
Hear about the graves of the martyrs the peewees crying,
  And hear no more at all.

ROBERT LOUIS STEVENSON

THE TWA BROTHERS

THERE were twa brethren in the north,
They went [1] to the school thegither;
The one unto the other said,
"Will you try a warsle [2] afore?"

They warsled up, they warsled down,
Till Sir John fell to the ground,
And there was a knife in Sir Willie's pouch,
Gied him a deadlie wound.

"O brither dear, take me on your back,
Carry me to yon burn clear,
And wash the blood from off my wound,
And it will bleed nae mair."

He took him up upon his back,
Carried him to yon burn clear,
And washed the blood from off his wound,
And aye it bled the mair.

"O brither dear, take me on your back,
Carry me to yon kirk-yard,
And dig a grave baith wide and deep,
And lay my body there."

He's taen him up upon his back,
Carried him to yon kirk-yard,
And dug a grave baith deep and wide,
And laid his body there.

"But what will I say to my father dear,
Gin [3] he chance to say, Willie, whar's John?"
"Oh say that he's to England gone,
To buy him a cask of wine."

"And what will I say to my mother dear,
Gin she chance to say, Willie, whar's John?"

[1] Had been [2] Wrestle [3] If

"Oh say that he's to England gone,
To buy her a new silk gown."

"And what will I say to my sister dear,
Gin she chance to say, Willie, whar's John?"
"Oh say that he's to England gone,
To buy her a wedding ring."

"But what will I say to her you lo'e dear,
Gin she cry, Why tarries my John?"
"Oh tell her I lie in Kirk-land fair,
And home shall never come."

63 THE DEAD KNIGHT

The cleanly rush of the mountain air,
And the mumbling, grumbling humble-bees,
Are the only things that wander there,
The pitiful bones are laid at ease,
The grass has grown in his tangled hair,
And a rambling bramble binds his knees.

To shrieve his soul from the pangs of hell,
The only requiem-bells that rang
Were the hare-bell and the heather-bell.
Hushed he is with the holy spell
In the gentle hymn the wind sang,
And he lies quiet, and sleeps well.

He is bleached and blanched with the summer sun;
The misty rain and the cold dew
Have altered him from the kingly one
(That his lady loved, and his men knew)
And dwindled him to a skeleton.

The vetches have twined about his bones,
The straggling ivy twists and creeps
In his eye-sockets; the nettle keeps
Vigil about him while he sleeps.

Over his body the wind moans
With a dreary tune throughout the day,
In a chorus wistful, eerie, thin
As the gull's cry—as the cry in the bay,
The mournful word the seas say
When tides are wandering out or in.

JOHN MASEFIELD

64

SHEATH AND KNIFE

ONE king's daughter said to anither,
Brume blumes bonnie and grows sae fair,
"We'll gae ride like sister and brither,"
And we'll neer gae down to the brume nae mair.

"We'll ride doun into yonder valley,
Brume blumes bonnie and grows sae fair,
Whare the greene greene trees are budding sae gaily.
And we'll neer gae down to the brume nae mair.

"Wi' hawke and hounde we will hunt sae rarely,
Brume blumes bonnie and grows sae fair,
And we'll come back in the morning early."
And we'll neer gae down to the brume nae mair.

They rade on like sister and brither,
Brume blumes bonnie and grows sae fair,
And they hunted and hawket in the valley thegither.
And we'll neer gae down to the brume nae mair.

"Now, lady, hauld my horse and my hawk,
Brume blumes bonnie and grows sae fair,
For I maun na [1] ride, and I daur na [2] walk,
And we'll neer gae down to the brume nae mair.

"But set me doun be the rute o' this tree,
Brume blumes bonnie and grows sae fair,

[1] Must not [2] Dare not

For there ha'e I dreamt that my bed sall be."
And we'll neer gae down to the brume nae mair.

The ae king's daughter did lift doun the ither,
Brume blumes bonnie and grows sae fair,
She was licht in her armis like ony fether.
And we'll neer gae down to the brume nae mair.

Bonnie Lady Ann sat doun be the tree,
Brume blumes bonnie and grows sae fair,
And a wide grave was houkit [1] whare nane suld be.
And we'll neer gae down to the brume nae mair.

The hawk had nae lure, and the horse had nae master,
Brume blumes bonnie and grows sae fair,
And the faithless hounds thro' the woods ran faster.
And we'll neer gae down to the brume nae mair.

The one king's daughter has ridden awa',
Brume blumes bonnie and grows sae fair,
But bonnie Lady Ann lay in the deed-thraw.[2]
And we'll neer gae down to the brume nae mair.

65 I HAVE A YOUNG SISTER

I HAVE a yong suster fer beyondyn the se; Many be the drowryis that che sente me.	I HAVE a young sister Far beyond the sea; Many are the keepsakes That she's sent me.
Che sente me the cherye, withoutyn ony ston, And so che dede (the) dowe, withoutyn ony bon.	She sent me a cherry— It hadn't any stone; And so she did a wood dove Withouten any bone.
Sche sente me the brere, withoutyn ony rynde, Sche bad me love my lem- man	She sent me a briar Withouten any rind; She bade me love my sweet- heart

[1] Dug, delved [2] Her death-throes

withoute longyng.

Withouten longing in my
mind.

How shuld ony cherye
be withoute ston?
And how shuld ony dowe
ben withoute bon?

How should any cherry
Be withouten stone?
And how should any wood
dove
Be withouten bone?

How shuld any brere
ben withoute rynde?
How shuld I love my lemman
withoute longyng?

How should any briar,
Be withouten rind?
And how love a sweetheart
Withouten longing in my
mind?

Quan the cherye was a flour,
than hadde it non ston;
Quan the dowe was an ey,
than hadde it non bon.

When the cherry was a flower
Then it had no stone;
When the wood-dove was an
egg
Then it had no bone.

Quan the brere was onbred,
than hadde it non rynde;
Quan the mayden hayt that
che lovit,
che is withoute longyng.

When the briar was unbred
Then it had no rind;
And when a maid hath that
she loves,
She longs not in her mind.

66 ANNABEL LEE

It was many and many a year ago,
In a kingdom by the sea,
That a maiden there lived whom you may know
By the name of Annabel Lee;
And this maiden she lived with no other thought
Than to love and be loved by me.

I was a child and she was a child,
In this kingdom by the sea;

But we loved with a love that was more than love—
I and my Annabel Lee;
With a love that the winged seraphs of heaven
Coveted her and me.

And this was the reason that, long ago
In this kingdom by the sea,
A wind blew out of a cloud, chilling
My beautiful Annabel Lee;
So that her highborn kinsman came
And bore her away from me,
To shut her up in a sepulchre
In this kingdom by the sea.

The angels, not half so happy in heaven,
Went envying her and me—
Yes!—that was the reason (as all men know,
In this kingdom by the sea)
That the wind came out of the cloud by night,
Chilling and killing my Annabel Lee.

But our love it was stronger by far than the love
Of those who were older than we,
Of many far wiser than we;
And neither the angels in heaven above
Nor the demons down under the sea
Can ever dissever my soul from the soul
Of the beautiful Annabel Lee.

For the moon never beams without bringing me dreams
Of the beautiful Annabel Lee;
And the stars never rise but I feel the bright eyes
Of the beautiful Annabel Lee;
And so, all the night-tide, I lie down by the side
Of my darling—my darling—my life and my bride,
In the sepulchre by the sea,
In her tomb by the sounding sea.

EDGAR ALLAN POE

67 THE SHELL

AND then I pressed the shell
  Close to my ear
And listened well,
And straightway like a bell
  Came low and clear
The slow, sad murmur of far distant seas,
Whipped by an icy breeze
  Upon a shore
Windswept and desolate.
  It was a sunless strand that never bore
The footprint of a man,
  Nor felt the weight
Since time began
Of any human quality or stir
Save what the dreary winds and waves incur.
And in the hush of waters was the sound
Of pebbles rolling round,
For ever rolling with a hollow sound.
And bubbling sea-weeds as the waters go
Swish to and fro
Their long, cold tentacles of slimy grey.
There was no day,
Nor ever came a night
Setting the stars alight
To wonder at the moon:
Was twilight only and the frightened croon,
Smitten to whimpers, of the dreary wind
And waves that journeyed blind—
And then I loosed my ear—oh, it was sweet
To hear a cart go jolting down the street!

JAMES STEPHENS

FEASTS: FAIRS: BEGGARS: GIPSIES

LONDON BRIDGE is broken down,
Dance o'er my Lady Lee,
London Bridge is broken down,
With a gay lady.

How shall we build it up again?
Dance o'er my Lady Lee,
How shall we build it up again?
With a gay lady.

Silver and gold will be stole away,
Dance o'er my Lady Lee,
Silver and gold will be stole away,
With a gay lady.

Build it up with iron and steel,
Dance o'er my Lady Lee,
Build it up with iron and steel,
With a gay lady.

Iron and steel will bend and bow,
Dance o'er my Lady Lee,
Iron and steel will bend and bow,
With a gay lady.

Build it up with wood and clay,
Dance o'er my Lady Lee,
Build it up with wood and clay,
With a gay lady.

Wood and clay will wash away,
Dance o'er my Lady Lee,
Wood and clay will wash away,
With a gay lady.

Build it up with stone so strong,
Dance o'er my Lady Lee,
Huzza! 'twill last for ages long,
With a gay lady.

69 HOLY THURSDAY

'TWAS on a Holy Thursday, their innocent faces clean,
Came children walking two and two, in red and blue and green,
Grey-headed beadles walked before, with wands as white as snow,
Till into the high dome of Paul's they like Thames' waters flow.

O what a multitude they seemed, these flowers of London town!
Seated in companies they sit with radiance all their own.
The hum of multitudes was there, but multitudes of lambs,
Thousands of little boys and girls raising their innocent hands.

Now, like a mighty wind they raise to Heaven the voice of song,
Or like harmonious thunderings the seats of Heaven among.
Beneath them sit the agèd men, wise guardians of the poor;
Then cherish pity, lest you drive an angel from your door.

WILLIAM BLAKE

70 THE MAYORS

THIS city and this country has brought forth many mayors,
To sit in state and give forth laws out of their old oak chairs,
With face as brown as any nut with drinking of strong ale;
Good English hospitality, O then it did not fail!
With scarlet gowns and broad gold lace would make a yeoman sweat,
With stockings rolled above their knees and shoes as black as jet,
With eating beef and drinking beer, O they were stout and hale!
Good English hospitality, O then it did not fail!

Thus sitting at the table wide, the Mayor and Aldermen
Were fit to give law to the city; each ate as much as ten:
The hungry poor entered the hall to eat good beef and
ale—
Good English hospitality, O then it did not fail!

WILLIAM BLAKE

71 THE FINE OLD ENGLISH GENTLEMAN

I'LL sing you a good old song,
Made by a good old pate,
Of a fine old English gentleman
Who had an old estate,
And who kept up his old mansion
At a bountiful old rate;
With a good old porter to relieve
The old poor at his gate,
Like a fine old English gentleman
All of the olden time.

His hall so old was hung around
With pikes and guns and bows,
And swords, and good old bucklers,
That had stood some tough old blows;
'Twas there *his worship* held his state
In doublet and trunk hose,
And quaffed his cup of good old sack,
To warm his good old nose,
Like a fine old English gentleman
All of the olden time.

When winter's cold brought frost and snow,
He opened house to all;
And though threescore and ten his years,
He featly led the ball;
Nor was the houseless wanderer
E'er driven from his hall;
For while he feasted all the great,

He ne'er forgot the small;
Like a fine old English gentleman
All of the olden time.

But time, though old, is strong in flight,
And years rolled swiftly by;
And Autumn's falling leaves proclaimed
This good old man must die!
He laid him down right tranquilly,
Gave up life's latest sigh;
And mournful stillness reigned around,
And tears bedewed each eye,
For this fine old English gentleman
All of the olden time.

Now surely this is better far
Than all the new parade
Of theatres and fancy balls,
"At home" and masquerade:
And much more economical,
For all his bills were paid.
Then leave your new vagaries quite,
An take up the old trade
Of a fine old English gentleman,
All of the olden time.

72 BRING US IN GOOD ALE

Bring us in good ale, and bring us in good ale;
For our blessed Lady sake bring us in good ale!

BRING us in no browne bred, for that is made of brane,[1]
Nor bring us in no white bred, for therein is no gane,
But bring us in good ale!

Bring us in no befe, or there is many bones,
But bring us in good ale, for that goth downe at ones,
And bring us in good ale!

[1] Bran

Bring us in no bacon, for that is passing fat,
But bring us in good ale, and gife us enought of that;
And bring us in good ale!

Bring us in no mutton, for that is often lene,
Nor bring us in no tripes, for they be seldom clene,
But bring us in good ale!

Bring us in no egges, for there are many schelles,
But bring us in good ale, and gife us nothing elles;
And bring us in good ale!

Bring us in no butter, for therein are many hores, [1]
Nor bring us in no pigges flesch, for that will make us bores,
But bring us in good ale!

Bring us in no podinges, for therein is all Godes good,[2]
Nor bring us in no venesen, for that is not for our blod;
But bring us in good ale!

Bring us in no capons flesch, for that is ofte dere,
Nor bring us in no dokes [3] flesch, for they slober in the mere,
But bring us in good ale!

73 THE VISION OF MAC CONGLINNE

A VISION that appeared to me,
An apparition wonderful
I tell to all:
There was a coracle all of lard
Within a Port of New-Milk Lake
Upon the world's smooth sea.

We went into that man-of-war,
'Twas warrior-like to take the road

[1] Hairs [2] Yeast [3] Duck's

O'er ocean's heaving waves.
Our oar-strokes then we pulled
Across the level of the main,
Throwing the sea's harvest up
Like honey, the sea-soil.

The fort we reached was beautiful,
With works of custards thick,
Beyond the lake.
Fresh butter was the bridge in front,
The rubble dyke was fair white wheat,
Bacon the palisade.

Stately, pleasantly it sat,
A compact house and strong.
Then I went in:
The door of it was hung beef,
The threshold was dry bread,
Cheese-curds the walls. . . .

Behind it was a well of wine,
Beer and bragget in streams,
Each full pool to the taste.
Malt in smooth wavy sea
Over a lard-spring's brink
Flowed through the floor. . . .

A row of fragrant apple-trees,
An orchard in its pink-tipped bloom,
Between it and the hill.
A forest tall of real leeks,
Of onions and of carrots, stood
Behind the house.

Within, a household generous,
A welcome of red, firm-fed men,
Around the fire:
Seven bead-strings and necklets seven
Of cheeses and of bits of tripe
Round each man's neck.

The Chief in cloak of beefy fat
Beside his noble wife and fair
I then beheld.
Below the lofty cauldron's spit
Then the Dispenser I beheld,
His fleshfork on his back.

74 STOOL BALL

. . . Now milkmaids' pails are deckt with flowers,
And men begin to drink in bowers,
The mackarels come up in shoals,
To fill the mouths of hungry souls;
Sweet sillabubs, and lip-loved tansey,
For William is prepared by Nancy.
Much time is wasted now away,
At pigeon-holes, and nine-pin play,
Whilst hob-nail Dick, and simp'ring Frances,
Trip it away in country dances;
At stool-ball and at barley-break,
Wherewith they harmless pastime make. . . .

75 MILKING PAILS

MARY's gone a-milking,
A rea, a ria, a roses,
Mary's gone a-milking,
Gentle sweet mother o' mine.

Take your pails and go after her,
A rea, a ria, a roses,
Take your pails and go after her,
Gentle sweet daughter o' mine?

Buy me a pair of new milking pails,
A rea, a ria, a roses,
Buy me a pair of new milking pails,
Gentle sweet mother o' mine.

Where's the money to come from,
A rea, a ria, a roses,
Where's the money to come from,
Gentle sweet daughter o' mine?

Sell my father's feather bed,
A rea, a ria, a roses,
Sell my father's feather bed,
Gentle sweet mother o' mine.

What's your father to sleep on,
A rea, a ria, a roses,
What's your father to sleep on,
Gentle sweet daughter o' mine?

Put him in the truckle bed,
A rea, a ria, a roses,
Put him in the truckle bed,
Gentle sweet mother o' mine.

What are the children to sleep on,
A rea, a ria, a roses,
What are the children to sleep on,
Gentle sweet daughter o' mine?

Put them in the pig-sty,
A rea, a ria, a roses,
Put them in the pig-sty,
Gentle sweet mother o' mine.

What are the pigs to lie in,
A rea, a ria, a roses,
What are the pigs to lie in,
Gentle sweet daughter o' mine?

Put them in the washing-tubs,
A rea, a ria, a roses,
Put them in the washing-tubs,
Gentle sweet mother o' mine.

What am I to wash in,
A rea, a ria, a roses,
What am I to wash in,
Gentle sweet daughter o' mine?

Wash in the thimble,
A rea, a ria, a roses,
Wash in the thimble,
Gentle sweet mother o' mine.

Thimble won't hold your father's shirt,
A rea, a ria, a roses,
Thimble won't hold your father's shirt,
Gentle sweet daughter o' mine.

Wash in the river,
A rea, a ria, a roses,
Wash in the river,
Gentle sweet mother o' mine.

Suppose the clothes should blow away,
A rea, a ria, a roses,
Suppose the clothes should blow away,
Gentle sweet daughter o' mine?

Set a man to watch them,
A rea, a ria, a roses,
Set a man to watch them,
Gentle sweet mother o' mine.

Suppose the man should go to sleep,
A rea, a ria, a roses,
Suppose the man should go to sleep,
Gentle sweet daughter o' mine?

Take a boat and go after them,
A rea, a ria, a roses,
Take a boat and go after them,
Gentle sweet mother o' mine.

Suppose the boat should be upset,
A rea, a ria, a roses,
Suppose the boat should be upset,
Gentle sweet daughter o' mine?

Then that would be an end of you,
A rea, a ria, a roses,
Then that would be an end of you,
Gentle sweet mother o' mine.

76 THE PEDLAR'S SONG

LAWNE as white as driven Snow,
Cypresse blacke as ere was Crow,
Cloves as sweete as Damaske Roses,
Maskes for faces, and for noses,
Bugle-bracelet, Necke-lace Amber,
Perfume for a Ladies Chamber:
Golden Quoifes, and Stomachers
For my Lads, to give their deers:
Pins, and peaking-stickes of steele:
What Maids lacke from head to heele:
Come buy of me, come: come buy, come buy,
Buy Lads, or else your Lasses cry: Come buy.

WILLIAM SHAKESPEARE

77 FINE KNACKS FOR LADIES

FINE knacks for ladies! cheap, choice, brave, and new,
Good pennyworths—but money cannot move:
I keep a fair but for the Fair to view—
A beggar may be liberal of love.
Though all my wares be trash, the heart is true,
The heart is true.

Great gifts are guiles and look for gifts again;
My trifles come as treasures from my mind:
It is a priceless jewel to be plain;

Sometimes in shell the orient'st pearls we find:—
Of others take a sheaf, of me a grain!
Of me a grain! . . .

78 OH! DEAR!

Oh! dear! what can the matter be?
Dear! dear! what can the matter be?
Oh! dear! what can the matter be?
Johnny's so long at the fair.

He promised he'd buy me a fairing should please me,
And then for a kiss, oh! he vowed he would tease me,
He promised he'd bring me a bunch of blue ribbons
To tie up my bonny brown hair.

And it's oh! dear! what can the matter be?
Dear! dear! what can the matter be?
Oh! dear! what can the matter be?
Johnny's so long at the fair.

He promised he'd bring me a basket of posies,
A garland of lilies, a garland of roses,
A little straw hat, to set off the blue ribbons
That tie up my bonny brown hair.

And it's oh! dear! what can the matter be?
Dear! dear! what can the matter be?
Oh! dear! what can the matter be?
Johnny's so long at the fair.

79 SLEDBURN FAIR

I'd oft heard tell of this Sledburn fair,
And fain I would gan thither,
'Twere in the prime of summer-time,
In fine and pleasant weather;

My Dad and Mam they did agree
  That Nell and I should gae
See for to view this Sledburn fair,
  And ride on Dobbin, oh . . .

So Nell gat on and I gat on,
  And we both rode off together,
  And everybody we did meet
  Enquired how far 'twas thither?
Until we came to t'other field end,
  'Twas about steeple high,
"See yonder, Nell, see yonder, Nell,
  There's Sledburn town," cried I.

And when we reached this famous town
  We enquirèd for an alehouse,
We lookèd up and saw a sign
  As high as any gallows;
We called for Harry, the ostler,
  To give our horse some hay,
For we had come to Sledburn Fair
  And meant to stop all day.

The landlord then himself came out
  And led us up an entry;
He took us in the finest room
  As if we'd been quite gentry.
And puddings and sauce they did so smell,
  Pies and roast beef so rare,
"Oh, Zooks!" says Nell, "we've acted well
  In coming to Sledburn Fair."

80 WIDDECOMBE FAIR

"Tom Pearse, Tom Pearse, lend me your gray mare,"
  All along, down along, out along, lee.
"For I want for to go to Widdecombe Fair,
  Wi' Bill Brewer, Jan Stewer, Peter Gurney, Peter Davy.
    Dan'l Whiddon, Harry Hawk,

Old Uncle Tom Cobley and all."
Old Uncle Tom Cobley and all.

"And when shall I see again my gray mare?"
All along, down along, out along, lee.
"By Friday soon, or Saturday noon,
Wi' Bill Brewer, Jan Stewer, Peter Gurney, Peter Davy.
Dan'l Whiddon, Harry Hawk,
Old Uncle Tom Cobley and all."
Old Uncle Tom Cobley and all.

Then Friday came and Saturday noon,
All along, down along, out along, lee.
But Tom Pearse's old mare hath not trotted home,
Wi' Bill Brewer, Jan Stewer, Peter Gurney, Peter Davy,
Dan'l Whiddon, Harry Hawk,
Old Uncle Tom Cobley and all.
Old Uncle Tom Cobley and all.

So Tom Pearse he got up to the top o' the hill,
All along, down along, out along, lee.
And he seed his old mare down a-making her will,
Wi' Bill Brewer, Jan Stewer, Peter Gurney, Peter Davy.
Dan'l Whiddon, Harry Hawk,
Old Uncle Tom Cobley and all.
Old Uncle Tom Cobley and all.

So Tom Pearse's old mare her took sick and her died,
All along, down along, out along, lee.
And Tom he sat down on a stone, and he cried
Wi' Bill Brewer, Jan Stewer, Peter Gurney, Peter Davy.
Dan'l Whiddon, Harry Hawk,
Old Uncle Tom Cobley and all.
Old Uncle Tom Cobley and all.

But this isn't the end o' this shocking affair,
All along, down along, out along, lee.
Nor, though they be dead, of the horrid career
Of Bill Brewer, Jan Stewer, Peter Gurney, Peter Davy,

Dan'l Whiddon, Harry Hawk,
Old Uncle Tom Cobley and all.
Old Uncle Tom Cobley and all.

When the wind whistles cold on the moor of a night,
All along, down along, out along, lee.
Tom Pearse's old mare doth appear, gashly white,
Wi' Bill Brewer, Jan Stewer, Peter Gurney, Peter Davy,
Dan'l Whiddon, Harry Hawk,
Old Uncle Tom Cobley and all.
Old Uncle Tom Cobley and all.

And all the long night he heard skirling and groans,
All along, down along, out along, lee.
From Tom Pearse's old mare in her rattling bones,
And from Bill Brewer, Jan Stewer, Peter Gurney, Peter
Davy, Dan'l Whiddon, Harry Hawk,
Old Uncle Tom Cobley and all.
Old Uncle Tom Cobley and all.

81 GIPSIES

THE snow falls deep; the forest lies alone;
The boy goes hasty for his load of brakes,[1]
Then thinks upon the fire and hurries back;
The gipsy knocks his hands and tucks them up,
And seeks his squalid camp, half hid in snow,
Beneath the oak which breaks away the wind,
And bushes close in snow-like hovel warm;
There tainted mutton wastes upon the coals,
And the half-wasted dog squats close and rubs,
Then feels the heat too strong, and goes aloof;
He watches well, but none a bit can spare,
And vainly waits the morsel thrown away.
'Tis thus they live—a picture to the place,
A quiet, pilfering, unprotected race.

JOHN CLARE

[1] Bracken

82 THE IDLERS

THE gipsies lit their fires by the chalk-pit gate anew,
And the hobbled horses supped in the further dusk and dew;
The gnats flocked round the smoke like idlers as they were
And through the goss and bushes the owls began to churr.

An ell above the woods the last of sunset glowed
With a dusky gold that filled the pond beside the road;
The cricketers had done, the leas all silent lay,
And the carrier's clattering wheels went past and died away.

The gipsies lolled and gossiped, and ate their stolen swedes,
Made merry with mouth-organs, worked toys with piths of
reeds:
The old wives puffed their pipes, nigh as black as their hair,
And not one of them all seemed to know the name of care.

EDMUND BLUNDEN

83 THE WRAGGLE TAGGLE GIPSIES

THERE were three gipsies a-come to my door,
And down-stairs ran this a-lady, O!
One sang high, and another sang low,
And the other sang, Bonny, bonny Biscay, O!

Then she pulled off her silk-finished gown
And put on hose of leather, O!
The ragged, ragged rags about our door—
She's gone with the wraggle taggle gipsies, O!

It was late last night, when my lord came home,
Enquiring for his a-lady, O!
The servants said, on every hand:
"She's gone with the wraggle taggle gipsies, O!"

"O saddle to me my milk-white steed,
Go and fetch me my pony, O!

That I may ride and seek my bride,
Who is gone with the wraggle taggle gipsies, O!"

O he rode high and he rode low,
He rode through woods and copses too,
Until he came to an open field,
And there he espied his a-lady, O!

"What makes you leave your house and land?
What makes you leave your money, O?
What makes you leave your new-wedded lord;
To go with the wraggle taggle gipsies, O!"

"What care I for my house and my land?
What care I for my money, O?
What care I for my new-wedded lord?
I'm off with the wraggle taggle gipsies, O!"

"Last night you slept on a goose-feather bed,
With the sheet turned down so bravely, O!
And to-night you'll sleep in a cold open field,
Along with the wraggle taggle gipsies, O!"

"What care I for a goose-feather bed,
With the sheet turned down so bravely, O?
For to-night I shall sleep in a cold open field,
Along with the wraggle taggle gipsies, O!"

84 WHERE DO THE GIPSIES COME FROM?

WHERE do the gipsies come from?
The gipsies come from Egypt.
The fiery sun begot them,
  Their dam was the desert dry.
She lay there stripped and basking,
And gave them suck for the asking,
And an Emperor's bone to play with,
  Whenever she heard them cry.

What did the gipsies do there?
They built a tomb for Pharoah,
They built a tomb for Pharoah,
  So tall it touched the sky.
They buried him deep inside it,
Then let what would betide it,
They saddled their lean-ribbed ponies
  And left him there to die.

What do the gipsies do now?
They follow the Sun, their father,
They follow the Sun, their father,
  They know not whither nor why.
Whatever they find they take it,
And if it's a law they break it.
So never you talk to a gipsy,
  Or look in a gipsy's eye.

H. H. Bashford

85 BEGGARS

What noise of viols is so sweet
  As when our merry clappers ring?
What mirth doth want when beggars meet?
  A beggar's life is for a king.
Eat, drink, and play, sleep when we list,
Go where we will—so stocks be missed.
  Bright shines the sun; play, beggars, play!
  Here's scraps enough to serve to-day.

The world is ours, and ours alone;
  For we alone have world at will.
We purchase not—all is our own;
  Both fields and street we beggars fill.
  Bright shines the sun; play, beggars, play!
  Here's scraps enough to serve to-day.

Francis Davidson

86 "WEEP, WEEP, YE WOODMEN!"

Weep, weep, ye woodmen! wail;

Your hands with sorrow wring!
Your master Robin Hood lies dead,
Therefore sigh as you sing.

Here lie his primer and his beads,
His bent bow and his arrows keen,
His good sword and his holy cross:
Now cast on flowers fresh and green.

And, as they fall, shed tears and say
Well, well-a-day! well, well-a-day!
Thus cast ye flowers fresh, and sing,
And on to Wakefield take your way.

ANTHONY MUNDAY

87 MY HANDSOME GILDEROY

GILDEROY was a bonnie boy,
Had roses tull [1] his shoone,
His stockings were of silken soy,
Wi' garters hanging doune:
It was, I weene, a comelie sight,
To see sae trim a boy;
He was my joy and heart's delight,
My handsome Gilderoy.

Oh! sike twe [2] charming een he had,
A breath as sweet as rose;
He never ware a Highland plaid,
But costly silken clothes.
He gained the luve of ladies gay,
Nane eir tull him was coy,
Ah! wae is mee! I mourn the day,
For my dear Gilderoy.

My Gilderoy and I were born
Baith in one toun together;
We scant [3] were seven years beforn

[1] To [2] Such two [3] Scarce

We gan to luve each other;
Our daddies and our mammies thay
Were fill'd wi' mickle joy,
To think upon the bridal day
'Twixt me and Gilderoy.

For Gilderoy, that luve of mine,
Gude waith! I freely bought
A wedding sark of Holland fine
Wi' silken flowers wrought:
And he gied me a wedding ring,
Which I received with joy,
Nae lad nor lassies eir could sing
Like me and Gilderoy.

Wi' mickle joy we spent our prime,
Till we were baith sixteen,
And aft we past the langsome time
Among the leaves sae green:
Aft on the banks we'd sit us thair,
And sweetly kiss and toy;
Wi' garlands gay wad deck my hair
My handsome Gilderoy.

Oh! that he still had been content
Wi' me to lead his life;
But, ah! his manfu' heart was bent
To stir in feats of strife.
And he in many a venturous deed
His courage bauld wad try;
And now this gars [1] mine heart to bleed
For my dear Gilderoy.

And when of me his leave he tuik,
The tears they wet mine ee;
I gave tull him a parting luik,
"My benison gang wi' thee!
God speed thee weil, mine ain dear heart,

[1] Makes

For gane is all my joy;
My heart is rent, sith we maun part,
My handsome Gilderoy!"

My Gilderoy, baith far and near,
Was feared in ev'ry toun,
And bauldly bare away the gear
Of many a lawland loun:
Nane eir durst meet him man to man,
He was sae brave a boy;
At length wi' numbers he was tane,
My winsome Gilderoy.

Wae worth the loun that made the laws,
To hang a man for gear,
To 'reave of life for ox or ass,
For sheep, or horse, or mare:
Had not their laws been made sae strick,
I neir had lost my joy;
Wi' sorrow neir had wat my cheek
For my dear Gilderoy.

Giff[1] Gilderoy had done amisse,
He mought hae banisht been,
Ah, what fair cruelty is this,
To hang sike handsome men!
To hang the flower o' Scottish land,
Sae sweet and fair a boy;
Nae lady had so white a hand
As thee, my Gilderoy.

Of Gilderoy sae fraid they were,
They bound him mickle strong,
Tull Edenburrow they led him thair,
And on a gallows hung:
They hung him high aboon the rest,
He was so trim a boy:
Thair dyed the youth whom I lued best,
My handsome Gilderoy.

[1] If

Thus having yielded up his breath,
  I bare his corpse away;
Wi' tears, that trickled for his death,
  I washt his comely clay;
And siker [1] in a grave sae deep
  I laid the dear-lued boy,
And now for evir maun I weep
  My winsome Gilderoy.

[1] Safely

BEASTS OF THE FIELD: FOWLS OF THE AIR

88 BINGO

THE miller's mill-dog lay at the mill-door,
And his name was Little Bingo.
B with an I, I with an N, N with a G, G with an O,
And his name was Little Bingo.

The miller he bought a cask of ale,
And he called it right good Stingo.
S with a T, T with an I, I with an N, N with a G, G with
an O,
And he called it right good Stingo.

The miller he went to town one day,
And he bought a wedding Ring-o!
R with an I, I with an N, N with a G, G with an O,
And he bought a wedding Ring-o!

89 THE IRISH HARPER AND HIS DOG

ON the green banks of Shannon, when Sheelah was nigh,
No blithe Irish lad was so happy as I;
No harp like my own could so cheerily play,
And wherever I went was my poor dog Tray.

When at last I was forced from my Sheelah to part,
She said—while the sorrow was big at her heart—
"Oh! remember your Sheelah, when far, far away,
And be kind, my dear Pat, to our poor dog Tray."

Poor dog! he was faithful and kind, to be sure,
And he constantly loved me, although I was poor;
When the sour-looking folks sent me heartless away,
I had always a friend in my poor dog Tray.

When the road was so dark, and the night was so cold,
And Pat and his dog were grown weary and old,
How snugly we slept in my old coat of grey,
And he licked me for kindness—my poor dog Tray.

Though my wallet was scant, I remembered his case,
Nor refused my last crust to his pitiful face;
But he died at my feet on a cold winter day,
And I played a lament for my poor dog Tray.

Where now shall I go, poor, forsaken, and blind?
Can I find one to guide me, so faithful and kind?
To my sweet native village, so far, far away,
I can never return with my poor dog Tray.

THOMAS CAMPBELL

90 POOR OLD HORSE

MY clothing was once of the linsey woolsey fine,
My tail it grew at length, my coat did likewise shine;
But now I'm growing old; my beauty does decay,
My master frowns upon me; one day I heard him say,
Poor old horse: poor old horse.

Once I was kept in the stable snug and warm,
To keep my tender limbs from any cold or harm;
But now, in open fields, I am forced for to go,
In all sorts of weather, let it be hail, rain, freeze, or snow.
Poor old horse: poor old horse.

Once I was fed on the very best corn and hay
That ever grew in yon fields, or in yon meadows gay;
But now there's no such doing can I find at all,
I'm glad to pick the green sprouts that grow behind yon wall.
Poor old horse: poor old horse.

"You are old, you are cold, you are deaf, dull, dumb and slow,
You are not fit for anything, or in my team to draw.
You have eaten all my hay, you have spoiled all my straw,
So hang him, whip, stick him, to the huntsman let him go."
Poor old horse: poor old horse.

My hide unto the tanners then I would freely give,
My body to the hound dogs, I would rather die than live,

Likewise my poor old bones that have carried you many a mile,
Over hedges, ditches, brooks, bridges, likewise gates and stiles.
Poor old horse: poor old horse.

91 AY ME, ALAS, HEIGH HO!

Ay me, alas, heigh ho, heigh ho!
Thus doth Messalina go
Up and down the house a-crying,
For her monkey lies a-dying.
Death, thou art too cruel
To bereave her of her jewel,
Or to make a seizure
Of her only treasure.
If her monkey die,
She will sit and cry,
Fie fie fie fie fie!

92 THE FLY

ONCE musing as I sat,
And candle burning by,
When all were hushed, I might discern
A simple, sely fly;
That flew before mine eyes,
With free rejoicing heart,
And here and there with wings did play,
As void of pain and smart.
Sometime by me she sat
When she had played her fill;
And ever when she rested had
About she fluttered still.
When I perceived her well
Rejoicing in her place,
"O happy fly!" (quoth I), and eke
O worm in happy case!
Which of us two is best?
I that have reason? No:
But thou that reason art without,

And therefore void of woe.
I live, and so dost thou:
But I live all in pain,
And subject am to one, alas!
That makes my grief her gain.
Thou livest, but feel'st no grief;
No love doth thee torment.
A happy thing for me it were
(If God were so content)
That thou with pen were placèd here,
And I sat in thy place:
Then I should joy as thou dost now,
And thou should'st wail thy case.

BARNABE GOOGE

93

BÊTE HUMAINE

RIDING through Ruwu swamp, about sunrise,
I saw the world awake; and as the ray
Touched the tall grasses where they sleeping lay,
Lo, the bright air alive with dragonflies:
With brittle wings aquiver, and great eyes
Piloting crimson bodies, slender and gay.
I aimed at one, and struck it, and it lay
Broken and lifeless, with fast-fading dyes . . .

Then my soul sickened with a sudden pain
And horror, at my own careless cruelty,
That in an idle moment I had slain
A creature whose sweet life it is to fly:
Like beasts that prey with tooth and claw . . .
Nay, they
Must slay to live, but what excuse had I?

FRANCIS BRETT YOUNG

94

THE LAMB

LITTLE Lamb, who made thee?
Dost thou know who made thee?

Gave thee life, and bid thee feed,
By the stream, and o'er the mead;
Gave thee clothing of delight,
Softest clothing, woolly, bright;
Gave thee such a tender voice,
Making all the vales rejoice?
Little Lamb, who made thee?
Dost thou know who made thee?

Little Lamb, I'll tell thee,
Little Lamb, I'll tell thee:
He is callèd by thy name,
For he calls Himself a Lamb.
He is meek, and He is mild;
He became a little child.
I a child, and thou a lamb,
We are callèd by His name.
Little Lamb, God bless thee!
Little Lamb, God bless thee!

WILLIAM BLAKE

95 THE SALE OF THE PET LAMB

OH! poverty is a weary thing, 'tis full of grief and pain;
It boweth down the heart of man, and dulls his cunning brain;
It maketh even the little child with heavy sighs complain. . . .

A thousand flocks were on the hills, a thousand flocks and more,
Feeding in sunshine pleasantly; they were the rich man's store:
There was the while one little lamb beside a cottage door;

A little lamb that rested with the children 'neath the tree,
That ate, meek creature, from their hands, and nestled to their knee;
That had a place within their hearts, one of the family.

But want, even as an armèd man, came down upon their shed,
The father laboured all day long that his children might be fed,

And, one by one, their household things were sold to buy them
bread.

That father, with a downcast eye, upon his threshold stood,
Gaunt poverty each pleasant thought had in his heart subdued.
"What is the creature's life to us?" said he: " 'twill buy us
food.

"Ay, though the children weep all day, and with down-drooping
head
Each does his small task mournfully, the hungry must be fed;
And that which has a price to bring must go to buy us bread."

It went. Oh! parting has a pang the hardest heart to wring,
But the tender soul of a little child with fervent love doth cling,
With love that hath no feignings false, unto each gentle thing.

Therefore most sorrowful it was those children small to see,
Most sorrowful to hear them plead for the lamb so piteously:
"Oh! mother dear, it loveth us; and what beside have we?"

"Let's take him to the broad green hill!" in his impotent despair
Said one strong boy: "let's take him off, the hills are wide and
fair;
I know a little hiding-place, and we will keep him there."

Oh vain! They took the little lamb, and straightway tied him
down,
With a strong cord they tied him fast; and o'er the common
brown,
And o'er the hot and flinty roads, they took him to the town.

The little children through that day, and throughout all the
morrow,
From every thing about the house a mournful thought did
borrow;
The very bread they had to eat was food unto their sorrow.

Oh! poverty is a weary thing, 'tis full of grief and pain;
It keepeth down the soul of man, as with an iron chain;
It maketh even the little child with heavy sighs complain.

Mary Howitt

96 A CHILD'S PET

WHEN I sailed out of Baltimore
With twice a thousand head of sheep,
They would not eat, they would not drink,
But bleated o'er the deep.

Inside the pens we crawled each day,
To sort the living from the dead;
And when we reached the Mersey's mouth,
Had lost five hundred head.

Yet every night and day one sheep,
That had no fear of man or sea,
Stuck through the bars its pleading face,
And it was stroked by me.

And to the sheep-men standing near,
"You see," I said, "this one tame sheep:
It seems a child has lost her pet,
And cried herself to sleep."

So every time we passed it by,
Sailing to England's slaughter-house,
Eight ragged sheep-men—tramps and thieves—
Would stroke that sheep's black nose.

WILLIAM H. DAVIES

97 THE SNARE

I HEAR a sudden cry of pain!
There is a rabbit in a snare:
Now I hear the cry again,
But I cannot tell from where.

But I cannot tell from where
He is calling out for aid;
Crying on the frightened air,
Making everything afraid.

Making everything afraid,
Wrinkling up his little face,
As he cries again for aid;
And I cannot find the place!

And I cannot find the place
Where his paw is in the snare:
Little one! Oh, little one!
I am searching everywhere.

James Stephens

98 THE MONK AND HIS PET CAT

I and my white Pangur
Have each his special art:
His mind is set on hunting mice,
Mine is upon my special craft.

I love to rest—better than any fame!—
With close study at my little book;
White Pangur does not envy me:
He loves his childish play.

When in our house we two are all alone—
A tale without tedium!
We have—sport never-ending!
Something to exercise our wit.

At times by feats of derring-do
A mouse sticks in his net,
While into my net there drops
A difficult problem of hard meaning.

He points his full shining eye
Against the fence of the wall:
I point my clear though feeble eye
Against the keenness of science.

He rejoices with quick leaps
When in his sharp claw sticks a mouse:

I too rejoice when I have grasped
A problem difficult and dearly loved.

Though we are thus at all times,
Neither hinders the other,
Each of us pleased with his own art
Amuses himself alone.

He is a master of the work
Which every day he does:
While I am at my own work
To bring difficulty to clearness.

99

THE TYGER

TYGER! Tyger! burning bright
In the forests of the night,
What immortal hand or eye
Could frame thy fearful symmetry?

In what distant deeps or skies
Burnt the fire of thine eyes?
On what wings dare he aspire?
What the hand dare seize the fire?

And what shoulder, and what art,
Could twist the sinews of thy heart?
And when they heart began to beat,
What dread hand? and what dread feet?

What the hammer? what the chain?
In what furnace was thy brain?
What the anvil? what dread grasp
Dare its deadly terrors clasp?

When the stars threw down their spears,
And watered heaven with their tears,
Did he smile his work to see?
Did he who made the Lamb make thee?

Tyger! Tyger! burning bright
In the forests of the night,
What immortal hand or eye,
Dare frame thy fearful symmetry?

WILLIAM BLAKE

100 THE NYMPH COMPLAINING FOR THE DEATH OF HER FAWN

THE wanton Troopers riding by
Have shot my Fawn, and it will dye.
Ungentle men! they cannot thrive
Who killed thee. Thou ne'er didst alive
Them any Harm: alas! nor cou'd
Thy Death yet do them any Good . . .
For it was full of sport, and light
Of foot and heart, and did invite
Me to its game; it seemed to bless
Itself in me; how could I less
Than love it? O, I cannot be
Unkind to a beast that loveth me . . .
With sweetest Milk, and Sugar, first
I it at mine own Fingers nurst;
And as it grew, so every Day
It waxed more white and sweet than they.
It had so sweet a Breath! And oft
I blushed to see its Foot more soft,
And white (shall I say than my Hand?)
Nay, any Ladie's of the Land.
It is a wond'rous Thing how fleet
'Twas on those little Silver Feet;
With what a pretty skipping Grace,
It oft would challenge me the Race;
And when't had left me far away,
'Twould stay, and run again, and stay;
For it was nimbler much than Hindes,
And trot as if on the Four Winds.
I have a Garden of my own,
But so with Roses over-grown,

And Lillies, that you would it guess
To be a little Wilderness;
And all the Spring Time of the Year
It only lovèd to be there.
Among the Beds of Lillies I
Have sought it oft, where it should lye;
Yet could not, till it self would rise,
Find it, although before mine Eyes:
For, in the flaxen Lillies' Shade,
It like a Bank of Lillies laid.
Upon the Roses it would feed,
Until its Lips ev'n seemed to bleed;
And then to me 'twould boldly trip,
And print those Roses on my Lip.
But all its chief Delight was still
On Roses thus itself to fill,
And its pure Virgin Limbs to fold
It whitest sheets of Lillies cold:
Had it lived long, it would have been
Lillies without, Roses within. . . .

ANDREW MARVELL

101 OF ALL THE BIRDS

OF all the birds that I do know,
  Philip my sparrow hath no peer;
For sit she high, or sit she low,
  Be she far off, or be she near,
There is no bird so fair, so fine,
Nor yet so fresh as this of mine;
For when she once hath felt a fit,
Philip will cry still: *Yet, yet, yet.*

Come in a morning merrily
  When Philip hath been lately fed;
Or in an evening soberly
  When Philip list to go to bed;
It is a heaven to hear my Phipp,
How she can chirp with merry lip,

For when she once hath felt a fit,
Philip will cry still: *Yet, yet, yet.*

She never wanders far abroad,
  But is at home when I do call.
If I command she lays on load [1]
  With lips, with teeth, with tongue and all.
She chants, she chirps, she makes such cheer,
That I believe she hath no peer.
For when she once hath felt the fit,
Philip will cry still: *Yet, yet, yet.*

And yet besides all this good sport
  My Philip can both sing and dance,
With new found toys of sundry sort
  My Philip can both prick and prance.
And if you say but: Fend cut,[2] Phipp!
Lord, how the peat [3] will turn and skip!
For when she once hath felt the fit,
Philip will cry still: *Yet, yet, yet.*

And to tell truth he were to blame—
  Having so fine a bird as she,
To make him all this goodly game
  Without suspect or jealousy—
He were a churl and knew no good,
Would see her faint for lack of food,
For when she once hath felt the fit,
Philip will cry still: *Yet, yet, yet.*

102 THE DEAD SPARROW

TELL me not of joy; there's none,
Now my little Sparrow's gone:
    He, just as you,
    Would try and woo,
He would chirp and flatter me;
He would hang the wing awhile—

[1] Lustily [2] *Cave!* [3] Pretty dear

Till at length he saw me smile
Lord, how sullen he would be!

He would catch a crumb, and then
Sporting, let it go agen;
He from my lip
Would moisture sip;
He would from my trencher feed;
Then would hop, and then would run,
And cry *Philip* when he'd done.
O! whose heart can choose but bleed?

O how eager would he fight,
And ne'er hurt, though he did bite.
No morn did pass,
But on my glass
He would sit, and mark and do
What I did—now ruffle all
His feathers o'er, now let 'em fall;
And then straightway sleek them too.

Whence will Cupid get his darts
Feathered now to pierce our hearts?
A wound he may
Not, Love, convey,
Now this faithful bird is gone;
O let mournful turtles join
With loving red-breasts, and combine
To sing dirges o'er his stone!

WILLIAM CARTWRIGHT

103 ON A LITTLE BIRD

HERE lies a little bird.
Once all day long
In Martha's house was heard
His rippling song.

Tread lightly where he lies
Beneath this stone
With nerveless wings, closed eyes,
And sweet voice gone.

MARTIN ARMSTRONG

104 ADLESTROP

YES. I remember Adlestrop—
The name, because one afternoon
Of heat the express-train drew up there
Unwontedly. It was late June.

The steam hissed. Someone cleared his throat.
No one left and no one came
On the bare platform. What I saw
Was Adlestrop—only the name

And willows, willow-herb, and grass,
And meadowsweet, and haycocks dry,
No whit less still and lonely fair
Than the high cloudlets in the sky.

And for that minute a blackbird sang
Close by, and round him, mistier,
Farther and farther, all the birds
Of Oxfordshire and Gloucestershire.

EDWARD THOMAS

105 THE REVERIE OF POOR SUSAN

AT the corner of Wood Street, when daylight appears,
Hangs a Thrush that sings loud, it has sung for three years.
Poor Susan has passed by the spot, and has heard
In the silence of morning the song of the bird.

'Tis a note of enchantment; what ails her? She sees
A mountain ascending, a vision of trees;
Bright volumes of vapour through Lothbury glide,
And a river flows on through the vale of Cheapside.

Green pastures she views in the midst of the dale
Down which she so often has tripped with her pail;
And a single small cottage, a nest like a dove's,
The one only dwelling on earth that she loves

She looks, and her heart is in heaven: but they fade,
The mist and the river, the hill and the shade;
The stream will not flow, and the hill will not rise,
And the colours have all passed away from her eyes!

William Wordsworth

106 THE THRUSH'S SONG

Dear, dear, dear,
Is the rocky glen.
Far away, far away, far away
The haunts of men.

Here shall we dwell in love
With the lark and the dove,
Cuckoo and cornrail;
Feast on the banded snail,
Worm and gilded fly;
Drink of the crystal rill
Winding adown the hill,
Never to dry.

With glee, with glee, with glee,
Cheer up, cheer up, cheer up, here
Nothing to harm us, then sing merrily,
Sing to the loved ones whose nest is near—
Qui, qui, qui, kweeu quip,
Tiurru, tiurru, chipiwi,
Too-tee, too-tee, chiu choo,
Chirri, chirri, chooee,
Quiu, qui, qui.

W. Macgillivray

107 SWEET SUFFOLK OWL

SWEET Suffolk Owl, so trimly dight
With feathers, like a lady bright,
Thou sing'st alone, sitting by night,
Te whit! Te whoo! Te whit! To whit!

Thy note that forth so freely rolls
With shrill command the mouse controls;
And sings a dirge for dying souls—
Te whit! Te whoo! Te whit! To whit!

THOMAS VAUTOR

108 WHO? WHO?

"WHO—Who—the bride will be?"
"The owl she the bride shall be."
The owl quoth,
Again to them both,
"I am sure a grim ladye;
Not I the bride can be,
I not the bride can be!"

109 WHEN CATS RUN HOME

WHEN cats run home and light is come,
And dew is cold upon the ground,
And the far-off stream is dumb,
And the whirring sail goes round,
And the whirring sail goes round;
Alone and warming his five wits,
The white owl in the belfry sits.

When merry milkmaids click the latch,
And rarely smells the new-mown hay,
And the cock hath sung beneath the thatch
Twice or thrice his roundelay,
Twice or thrice his roundelay;

Alone and warming his five wits,
The white owl in the belfry sits.

ALFRED, LORD TENNYSON

110

ONCE

ONCE I was a monarch's daughter,
And sat on a lady's knee;
But am now a nightly rover,
Banished to the ivy tree.

Crying hoo, hoo, hoo, hoo, hoo, hoo,
Hoo, hoo, hoo, my feet are cold.
Pity me, for here you see me
Persecuted, poor, and old.

111

THE WATER-OUSEL

WHERE on the wrinkled stream the willows lean,
And fling a very ecstacy of green
Down the dim crystal; and the chestnut tree
Admires her large-leaved shadow, swift and free,
A water-ousel came, with such a flight
As archangels might envy. Soft and bright
Upon a water-kissing bough she lit,
And washed and preened her silver breast, though it
Was dazzling fair before. Then twittering
She sang, and made obeisance to the Spring.
And in the wavering amber at her feet
Her silent shadow, with obedience meet,
Made her quick, imitative curtsies, too.
Maybe she dreamed a nest, so safe and dear,
Where the keen spray leaps whitely to the weir;
And smooth, warm eggs that hold a mystery;
And stirrings of life and twitterings, that she
Is passionately glad of; and a breast
As silver-white as hers, which without rest
Or languor, borne by spread wings swift and strong,

Shall fly upon her service all day long.
She hears a presage in the ancient thunder
Of the silken fall, and her small soul in wonder
Makes preparation as she deems most right,
Repurifying what before was white
Against the day when, like a beautiful dream,
Two little ousels shall fly with her down stream,
And even the poor, dumb shadow-bird shall flit
With two small shadows following after it.

MARY WEBB

112

L'OISEAU BLEU

THE lake lay blue below the hill.
O'er it, as I looked, there flew
Across the waters, cold and still,
A bird whose wings were palest blue.

The sky above was blue at last,
The sky beneath me blue in blue.
A moment, ere the bird had passed,
It caught his image as he flew.

MARY COLERIDGE

113

I HAD A DOVE

I HAD a dove and the sweet dove died;
And I have thought it died of grieving:
O what could it grieve for? Its feet were tied,
With a silken thread of my own hand's weaving;
Sweet little red feet! why should you die—
Why should you leave me, sweet bird! Why?
You lived alone in the forest-tree,
Why, pretty thing! would you not live with me?
I kissed you oft and gave you white peas;
Why not live sweetly, as in the green trees?

JOHN KEATS

114 PHILOMEL

As it fell upon a day
In the merry month of May,
Sitting in a pleasant shade
Which a grove of myrtles made,
Beasts did leap and birds did sing,
Trees did grow and plants did spring;
Everything did banish moan
Save the Nightingale alone:
She, poor bird, as all forlorn
Leaned her breast up-till a thorn,
And there sung the doleful'st ditty.
That to hear it was great pity.

Fie, fie, fie! now would she cry;
Tereu, tereu! by and by;
That to hear her so complain
Scarce I could from tears refrain;
For her griefs so lively shown
Made me think upon mine own.
Ah! thought I, thou mourn'st in vain,
None takes pity on thy pain:
Senseless trees they cannot hear thee,
Ruthless beasts they will not cheer thee:
King Pandion he is dead,
All thy friends are lapped in lead;
All thy fellow birds do sing
Careless of thy sorrowing:
Even so, poor bird, like thee,
None alive will pity me.

RICHARD BARNFIELD

115 A SPARROW-HAWK

A SPARHAWK proud did hold in wicked jail
Music's sweet chorister, the Nightingale;
To whom with sighs she said: "O set me free,
And in my song I'll praise no bird but thee."

The Hawk replied: "I will not lose my diet
To let a thousand such enjoy their quiet."

116 THE EAGLE

He clasps the crag with crooked hands;
Close to the sun in lonely lands,
Ringed with the azure world, he stands.

The wrinkled sea beneath him crawls;
He watches from his mountain walls,
And like a thunderbolt he falls.

Alfred, Lord Tennyson

117 THE TWA CORBIES

As I was walking all alane,
I heard twa corbies making a mane,
And tane unto the tither say:—
"Where sall we gang and dine to-day?"

"—In behint yon auld fail dyke,[1]
I wat there lies a new-slain Knight;
And naebody kens that he lies there
But his hawk, his hound, and lady fair.

"His hound is to the hunting gane,
His hawk to fetch the wild-fowl hame,
His lady's ta'en another mate,
So we may mak our dinner sweet.

"Ye'll sit on his white hause-bane,
And I'll pick out his bonnie blue een.
Wi' ae lock o' his gowden hair
We'll theek[2] our nest when it grows bare.

"Mony a one for him maks mane,
But nane sall ken where he is gane.
O'er his white banes, where they are bare,
The wind sall blaw for evermair."

[1] Green-walled ditch [2] Thatch mend

118 IN THE WILDERNESS

CHRIST of His gentleness
Thirsting and hungering
Walked in the wilderness;
Soft words of grace He spoke
Unto lost desert-folk
That listened wondering.
He heard the bitterns call
From ruined palace-wall,
Answered them brotherly.
He held communion
With the she-pelican
Of lonely piety.
Basilisk, cockatrice,
Flocked to His homilies,
With mail of dread device,
With monstrous barbèd stings,
With eager dragon-eyes;
Great rats on leather wings
And poor blind broken things,
Foul in their miseries.
And ever with Him went,
Of all His wanderings
Comrade, with ragged coat,
Gaunt ribs—poor innocent—
Bleeding foot, burning throat,
The guileless old scape-goat;
For forty nights and days
Followed in Jesus' ways,
Sure guard behind Him kept,
Tears like a lover wept.

ROBERT GRAVES

119 STUPIDITY STREET

I SAW with open eyes
Singing birds sweet
Sold in the shops
For the people to eat,

Sold in the shops of
Stupidity Street.

I saw in vision
The worm in the wheat,
And in the shops nothing
For people to eat;
Nothing for sale in
Stupidity Street.

RALPH HODGSON

120

COME WARY ONE

"'COME wary one, come slender feet,
Come pretty bird and sing to me,
I have a cage of wizard wood
With perch of ebony;
Come pretty bird, there's dainty food,
There's cherry, plum, and strawberry,
In my red cage, my wizard cage,
The cage I made for thee.'

"The bird flew down, the bird flew in,
The cherries they were dried and dead,
She tied him with a silken skein
To a perch of molten lead;
And first most dire he did complain,
And next he sulky sad did fall,
Chained to his perch, his burning perch,
He would not sing at all.

"There came an elf, a silent elf,
A silver wand hung by his side,
And when that wand lay on the door,
The door did open wide.
The pretty bird with beak he tore
That silken skein, then out flew he,
From that red cage, that greedy cage,
That cage of wizardry."

RUTH MANNING-SANDERS

121 UPON THE LARK AND THE FOWLER

THOU simple Bird what mak'st thou here to play?
Look, there's the Fowler, prethee come away.
Dost not behold the Net? Look there 'tis spread,
Venture a little further thou art dead.

Is there not room enough in all the Field
For thee to play in, but thou needs must yield
To the deceitful glitt'ring of a Glass,
Placed betwixt Nets to bring thy death to pass?

Bird, if thou art so much for dazling light,
Look, there's the Sun above thee, dart upright.
Thy nature is to soar up to the Sky,
Why wilt thou come down to the nets, and dye?

Take no heed to the Fowler's tempting Call;
This whistle he enchanteth Birds withal.
Or if thou seest a live Bird in his net,
Believe she's there 'cause thence she cannot get.
Look how he tempteth thee with his Decoy,
That he may rob thee of thy Life, thy Joy:
Come, prethee Bird, I prethee come away,
Why should this net thee take, when 'scape thou may?

Hadst thou not Wings, or were thy feathers pulled,
Or wast thou blind or fast asleep wer't lulled:
The case would somewhat alter, but for thee,
Thy eyes are ope, and thou hast Wings to flee.

Remember that thy Song is in thy Rise,
Not in thy Fall, Earth's not thy Paradise.
Keep up aloft then, let thy circuits be
Above, where Birds from Fowlers nets are free. . . .

JOHN BUNYAN

122 THE BIRDS

He. WHERE thou dwellest, in what Grove,
Tell me Fair One, tell me Love;
Where thou thy charming nest dost build,
O thou pride of every field!

She. Yonder stands a lonely tree,
There I live and mourn for thee;
Morning drinks my silent tear,
And evening winds my sorrow bear.

He. O thou summer's harmony,
I have lived and mourned for thee;
Each day I mourn along the wood,
And night hath heard my sorrows loud.

She. Dost thou truly long for me?
And am I thus sweet to thee?
Sorrow now is at an end,
O my Lover and my Friend!

He. Come, on wings of joy we'll fly
To where my bower hangs on high;
Come, and make thy calm retreat
Among green leaves and blossoms sweet.

WILLIAM BLAKE

123 TWO PEWITS

UNDER the after-sunset sky
Two pewits sport and cry,
More white than is the moon on high
Riding the dark surge silently;
More black than earth. Their cry
Is the one sound under the sky.
They alone move, now low, now high,
And merrily they cry
To the mischievous Spring sky,
Plunging earthward, tossing high,
Over the ghost who wonders why
So merrily they cry and fly,
Nor choose 'twixt earth and sky,
While the moon's quarter silently
Rides, and earth rests as silently.

EDWARD THOMAS

TO A WATERFOWL

WHITHER, midst falling dew,
While glow the heavens with the last steps of day.
Far, through their rosy depths, dost thou pursue
Thy solitary way?

Vainly the fowler's eye
Might mark thy distant flight to do thee wrong,
As, darkly painted on the crimson sky,
Thy figure floats along.

Seek'st thou the plashy brink
Of weedy lake, or marge of river wide,
Or where the rocking billows rise and sink
On the chafed ocean-side?

There is a Power whose care
Teaches thy way along that pathless coast,—
The desert and illimitable air,—
Lone wandering, but not lost.

All day thy wings have fanned
At that far height, the cold thin atmosphere,
Yet stoop not, weary, to the welcome land,
Though the dark night is near.

And soon that toil shall end;
Soon shall thou find a summer home, and rest,
And scream among thy fellows; reeds shall bend,
Soon, o'er thy sheltered nest.

Thou'rt gone: the abyss of heaven
Hath swallowed up thy form; yet, on my heart
Deeply hath sunk the lesson thou hast given,
And shall not soon depart.

He who, from zone to zone,
Guides through the boundless sky thy certain flight,
In the long way that I must tread alone,
Will lead my steps aright.

WILLIAM CULLEN BRYANT

125 MIDNIGHT

. . . MIDNIGHT was come, when every vital thing
With sweet sound sleep their weary limbs did rest,
The beasts were still, the little birds that sing
Now sweetly slept, beside their mother's breast,
The old and all were shrouded in their nest:
  The waters calm, the cruel seas did cease,
  The woods, and fields, and all things held their peace.

The golden stars were whirled amid their race,
And on the earth did laugh with twinkling light,
When each thing, nestled in his resting place,
Forgat day's pain with pleasure of the night:
The hare had not the greedy hounds in sight,
  The fearful deer of death stood not in doubt,
  The partridge dreamed not of the falcon's foot.

The ugly bear now minded not the stake,
Nor how the cruel mastives do him tear;
The stag lay still unrousèd from the brake;
The foamy boar feared not the hunter's spear:
All things were still, in desert, bush, and brere:[1]
  With quiet heart, now from their travails ceased,
  Soundly they slept in midst of all their rest.

THOMAS SACKVILLE, LORD BUCKHURST

[1]Briar : wildwood

ELPHIN, OUPH AND FAY

126 COME UNTO THESE YELLOW SANDS

(*Ariel singing*) COME unto these yellow sands,
And then take hands:
Curtsied when you have, and kist,
The wilde waves whist:
Foote it featly heere, and there,
And sweete Sprights the burthen beare.
Harke, harke, *bowgh wawgh*:
The watch-dogges barke, *bowgh wawgh*.
Hark, hark, I heare,
The straine of strutting Chanticlere
Cry *Cockadidle-dowe*.

WILLIAM SHAKESPEARE

127 THE ELVES' DANCE

ROUND about, round about
In a fair ring-a,
Thus we dance, thus we dance
And thus we sing-a,
Trip and go, to and fro
Over this green-a,
All about, in and out,
For our brave Queen-a.

128 BY THE MOON

"BY the moone we sport and play,
With the night begins our day:
As we daunce the deaw doth fall,
Trip it little urchins all:
Lightly as the little Bee,
Two by two, and three by three:
And about go we, and about go wee.

"I do come about the coppes,
Leaping upon flowers toppes:

Then I get upon a flie,
Shee carries me above the skie:
And trip and goe.

"When a deawe drop falleth downe,
And doth light upon my crowne,
Then I shake my head and skip,
And about I trip.
Two by two, and three by three:
And about go we, and about go wee."

THOMAS RAVENSCROFT

129 FOR A MOCKING VOICE

WHO calls? Who calls? Who?
Did you call? Did you?—
I call! I call! I!
Follow where I fly.—
Where? O where? O where?
On Earth or in the Air?—
Where you come, I'm gone!
Where you fly, I've flown!—
Stay! ah, stay! ah, stay,
Pretty Elf, and play!
Tell me where you are—
Ha, ha, ha, ha, ha!

ELEANOR FARJEON

130 WHERE THE BEE SUCKS

WHERE the Bee sucks, there suck I,
In a Cowslip's bell I lie,
There I cowch when Owles do crie;
On the Batt's back I doe flie
After Sommer merrily.
Merrily, merrily, shall I live now
Under the blossom that hangs on the Bow.

WILLIAM SHAKESPEARE

131 ECHO

How see you Echo? When she calls I see
Her pale face looking down through some great tree,
Whose world of green is like a moving sea,
That shells re-echo.
I see her with a white face like a mask,
That vanishes to come again; damask
Her cheek, but deeply pale,
Her eyes are green,
With a silver sheen,
And she mocks the thing you ask.
"O Echo!" (hear the children calling) "are you there?" . . .
"Where?" . . .

When the wind blows over the hill,
She hides with a vagrant will,
And call you may loud, and call you may long,
She lays finger on lip when the winds are strong,
And for all your pains she is still.
But when young plants spring, and the chiff-chaffs sing,
And the scarlet capped woodpecker flies through the vale,
She is out all day,
Through the fragrant May,
To babble and tattle her Yea and Nay.
"O Echo!" (still the children call) "Where are you? where?" . . .
"Air . . ."

VISCOUNTESS GREY

132 THE SPLENDOUR FALLS

THE splendour falls on castle walls
  And snowy summits old in story:
The long light shakes across the lakes,
  And the wild cataract leaps in glory.
Blow, bugle, blow, set the wild echoes flying,
Blow, bugle; answer, echoes, dying, dying, dying.

O hark, O hear! how thin and clear,
And thinner, clearer, farther going!
O sweet and far from cliff and scar
The horns of Elfland faintly blowing!
Blow, let us hear the purple glens replying:
Blow, bugle; answer, echoes, dying, dying, dying.

O love, they die in yon rich sky,
They faint on hill or field or river:
Our echoes roll from soul to soul,
And grow for ever and for ever
Blow, bugle, blow, set the wild echoes flying,
And answer, echoes, answer, dying, dying, dying.

ALFRED, LORD TENNYSON

133

THE FAIRIES

UP the airy mountain,
Down the rushy glen,
We daren't go a-hunting
For fear of little men;
Wee folk, good folk,
Trooping all together;
Green jacket, red cap,
And white owl's feather!

Down along the rocky shore
Some make their home,
They live on crispy pancakes
Of yellow tide-foam;
Some in the reeds
Of the black mountain-lake,
With frogs for their watch-dogs,
All night awake.

High on the hill-top
The old King sits;
He is now so old and gray
He's nigh lost his wits.

With a bridge of white mist
  Columbkill he crosses,
On his stately journeys
  Fom Slieveleague to Rosses;
Or going up with music
  On cold starry nights,
To sup with the Queen
  Of the gay Northern Lights.

They stole little Bridget
  For seven years long;
When she came down again
  Her friends were all gone.
They took her lightly back,
  Between the night and morrow,

They thought that she was fast asleep,
  But she was dead with sorrow.
They have kept her ever since
  Deep within the lake,
On a bed of flag-leaves,
  Watching till she wake.

By the craggy hill-side,
  Through the mosses bare,
They have planted thorn-trees
  For pleasure here and there.
Is any man so daring
  As to dig one up in spite,
He shall find the thornies set
  In his bed at night.

Up the airy mountain,
  Down the rushy glen,
We daren't go a-hunting
  For fear of little men;
Wee folk, good folk,
  Trooping all together;
Green jacket, red cap,
  And white owl's feather!

WILLIAM ALLINGHAM

NYMPH, nymph, what are your beads?

Green glass, goblin. Why do you stare at them?

Give them me.

No.

Give them me. Give them me.

No.

Then I will howl all night in the reeds,
Lie in the mud and howl for them.

Goblin, why do you love them so?

They are better than stars or water,
Better than voices of winds that sing,
Better than any man's fair daughter,
Your green glass beads on a silver ring.

Hush, I stole them out of the moon.

Give me your beads, I want them.

No.

I will howl in a deep lagoon
For your green glass beads, I love them so.
Give them me. Give them.

No.

HAROLD MONRO

135

THE FAIRY THORN

"GET up, our Anna dear, from the weary spinning wheel;
For your father's on the hill, and your mother is asleep:
Come up above the crags, and we'll dance a highland reel
Around the fairy thorn on the steep."

At Anna Grace's door 'twas thus the maidens cried,
Three merry maidens fair in kirtles of the green;

And Anna laid the rock [1] and the weary wheel aside,
The fairest of the four, I ween.

They're glancing through the glimmer of the quiet eve,
Away in milky wavings of neck and ankle bare;
The heavy-sliding stream in its sleep song they leave,
And the crags in the ghostly air.

And linking hand and hand, and singing as they go,
The maids along the hill-side have ta'en their fearless way,
Till they come to where the rowan trees in lonely beauty grow
Beside the Fairy Hawthorn grey.

The hawthorn stands between the ashes tall and slim,
Like matron with her twin grand-daughters at her knee;
The rowan berries cluster o'er her low head grey and dim
In ruddy kisses sweet to see.

The merry maidens four have ranged them in a row,
Between each lovely couple a stately rowan stem,
And away in mazes wavy, like skimming birds they go,
Oh, never carolled bird like them!

But solemn is the silence of the silvery haze
That drinks away their voices in echoless repose,
And dreamily the evening has stilled the haunted braes,
And dreamier the gloaming grows.

And sinking one by one, like lark-notes from the sky
When the falcon's shadow saileth across the open shaw,
Are hushed the maiden's voices, as cowering down they lie
In the flutter of their sudden awe.

For, from the air above, and the grassy ground beneath,
And from the mountain-ashes and the old Whitethorn between,
A power of faint enchantment doth through their beings breathe,
And they sink down together on the green.

[1] Distaff

They sink together silent, and stealing side to side,
  They fling their lovely arms o'er their drooping necks so fair.
Then vainly strive again their naked arms to hide,
    For their shrinking necks again are bare.

Thus clasped and prostrate all, with their heads together bowed,
  Soft o'er their bosom's beating—the only human sound—
They hear the silky footsteps of the silent fairy crowd,
    Like a river in the air, gliding round.

Nor scream can any raise, nor prayer can any say,
  But wild, wild, the terror of the speechless three—
For they feel fair Anna Grace drawn silently away,
    By whom they dare not look to see.

They fell their tresses twine with her parting locks of gold,
  And the curls elastic falling, as her head withdraws;
They fell her sliding arms from their trancèd arms unfold,
    But they dare not look to see the cause:

For heavy on their senses the faint enchantment lies
  Through all that night of anguish and perilous amaze;
And neither fear nor wonder can ope their quivering eyes
    Or their limbs from the cold ground raise,

Till out of Night the Earth has rolled her dewy side,
  With every haunted mountain and streamy vale below;
When, as the mist dissolves in the yellow morning-tide,
    The maidens' trance dissolveth so.

Then fly the ghastly three as swiftly as they may,
  And tell their tale of sorrow to anxious friends in vain—
They pined away and died within the year and day,
    And ne'er was Anna Grace seen again.

SAMUEL FERGUSON

136 THOMAS RYMER

TRUE Thomas lay oer yond grassy bank,
  And he beheld a ladie gay,

A ladie that was brisk and bold,
  Come riding oer the fernie brae.

Her skirt was of the grass-green silk,
  Her mantel of the velvet fine,
At ilka tett of her horse's mane
  Hung fifty silver bells and nine.

True Thomas he took off his hat,
  And bowed him low down till his knee:
"All hail, thou mighty Queen of Heaven!
  For your peer on earth I never did see."

"O no, O no, True Thomas," she says,
  "That name does not belong to me;
I am but the queen of fair Elfland,
  And I'm come here for to visit thee. . . .

"But ye maun go wi me now, Thomas,
  True Thomas, ye maun go wi me,
For ye maun serve me seven years,
  Thro weel or wae as may chance to be.

"Then harp and carp, Thomas," she said,
  "Then harp and carp, alang wi me;
But it will be seven years and a day
  Till ye win back to yere ain countrie."

She turned about her milk-white steed,
  And took True Thomas up behind,
And aye wheneer her bridle rang,
  The steed flew swifter than the wind.

For forty days and forty nights
  He wade thro red blude to the knee,
And he saw neither sun nor moon,
  But heard the roaring of the sea.

O they rade on, and further on,
  Until they came to a garden green:
"Light down, light down, ye laddie free,
  Some of that fruit let me pull to thee."

"O no, O no, True Thomas," she says,
"That fruit maun not be touched by thee,
For a' the plagues that are in hell
Light on the fruit of this countrie.

"But I have a loaf here in my lap,
Likewise a bottle of claret wine,
And now ere we go farther on,
We'll rest a while, and ye may dine."

When he had eaten and drunk his fill:—
"Lay down your head upon my knee,"
The lady sayd, "ere we climb yon hill
And I will show you fairlies three.

"O see not ye yon narrow road,
So thick beset wi thorns and briers?
That is the path of righteousness,
Tho after it but few enquires.

"And see not ye that braid braid road,
That lies across yon lillie leven?
That is the path of wickedness,
Tho some call it the road to heaven.

"And see not ye that bonny road,
Which winds about the fernie brae?
That is the road to fair Elfland,
Where you and I this night maun gae.

"But Thomas, ye maun hold your tongue,
Whatever you may hear or see,
For gin ae word you should chance to speak,
You will neer get back to your ain countrie."

He has gotten a coat of the even cloth,
And a pair of shoes of velvet green,
And till seven years were past and gone
True Thomas on earth was never seen.

137 LA BELLE DAME SANS MERCI

O, WHAT can ail thee, knight at arms,
Alone and palely loitering;
The sedge has withered from the lake,
And no birds sing.

O, what can ail thee, knight at arms,
So haggard and so woe-begone?
The squirrel's granary is full,
And the harvest's done.

I see a lilly on thy brow
With anguish moist and fever-dew,
And on thy cheeks a fading rose
Fast withereth too.

I met a lady in the meads,
Full beautiful—a faery's child,
Her hair was long, her foot was light,
And her eyes were wild.

I made a garland for her head,
And bracelets too, and fragrant zone,
She looked at me as she did love,
And made sweet moan.

I set her on my pacing steed
And nothing else saw all day long;
For sideways would she lean, and sing
A faery's song.

She found me roots of relish sweet,
And honey wild and manna dew;
And sure in language strange she said—
I love thee true.

She took me to her elfin grot,
And there she gazed and sighed full sore:
And there I shut her wild wild eyes
With kisses four.

And there she lullèd me asleep,
  And there I dreamed, ah woe betide,
The latest dream I ever dreamed
  On the cold hill side.

I saw pale kings and princes too,
  Pale warriors, death-pale were they all:
They cry'd—"La belle Dame sans Merci
  Hath thee in thrall!"

I saw their starved lips in the gloam
  With horrid warning gapèd wide,
And I awoke, and found me here
  On the cold hill side.

And this is why I sojourn here
  Alone and palely loitering,
Though the sedge is withered from the lake,
  And no birds sing.

JOHN KEATS

138 SABRINA

"SABRINA fair
  Listen where thou art sitting
Under the glassie, cool, translucent wave,
  In twisted braids of Lillies knitting
The loose train of thy amber-dropping hair,
  Listen for dear honour's sake,
  Goddess of the silver lake,
      Listen and save! . . .

"By all the *Nymphs* that nightly dance
Upon thy streams with wily[1] glance,
Rise, rise, and heave thy rosie head
From thy coral-pav'n bed,
And bridle in thy headlong wave,
Till thou our summons answered have.
      Listen and save!"

[1] Wile-full, beguiling

"By the rushy-fringèd bank
Where grows the Willow and the Osier dank,
My sliding Chariot stayes,
Thick set with Agat, and the azurn sheen
Of Turkis blew, and Emrauld green
That in the channell strayes,
Whilst from off the waters fleet
Thus I set my printless feet
O're the Cowslips Velvet head,
That bends not as I tread,
Gentle swain at thy request
I am here."

JOHN MILTON

139 NOW THE HUNGRY LION ROARS

"Now the hungry Lyon rores,
And the Wolfe behowls the Moone:
Whilst the heavy ploughman snores,
All with weary taske fordone.
Now the wasted brands doe glow,
Whil'st the scritch-owle scritching loud,
Puts the wretch that lies in woe
In remembrance of a shrowd.
Now it is the time of night
That the graves, all gaping wide,
Every one lets forth his spright,
In the Church-way paths to glide.
And we Fairies, that do runne
By the triple *Hecate's* teame,
From the presence of the Sunne,
Following darknesse like a dreame,
Now are frollicke; not a Mouse
Shall disturbe this hallowed house.
I am sent with broome before,
To sweep the dust behinde the doore."

"Through the house give glimmering light,
By the dead and drowsie fier;

Everie Elfe and Fairie spright
Hop as light as bird from brier! . . ."

WILLIAM SHAKESPEARE

140 THE FAIRIES FEAST

". . . *Awn.* Who feasts tonight?

Some Elves. Prince Olbin is troth-plight
To Rosalind, daughter of the Faery Queen.

Other Elves. She's a mannikin changeling; her name shows it.

Other Elves. We have heard tell; that she as dream is fair.

Awn. I've heard old Paigle say, fays gave for her
To humans, in the cradle, Moonsheen bright.

Other Elves. And Eglantine should wedded be this night,
To Ivytwine, in the laughing full moon.

Moth. I was there and saw it: on hoar roots,
All gnarled and knotty, of an antique oak, . . .
Crowned, some with plighted frets of violets
sweet;
Other, with flower-cups many-hewed, had dight
Their locks of gold; the gentle faeries sate:
All in their watchet cloaks: were dainty mats
Spread under them, of dwarve-wives rushen work:
And primroses were strewed before their feet.
They at banquet sate, from dim of after-noon. . .
(*Enter more elves running.*)

Howt. Whence come ye foothot?

One of the new-come Elves. O Awn, O Howt!
Not past a league from hence, lies close-cropped
plot,
Where purple milkworts blow, which conies haunt,
haunt,

Amidst the windy heath. We saw gnomes dance
dance
There; that not bigger been than harvest mice.
Some of their heads were deckt, as seemed to us,
With moonbeams bright: and those to-night hold
feast:
Though in them there none utterance is of speech.

Be those our mother's cousins, dainty of grace:
But seld now, in a moonlight, are they seen.
They live not longer than do humble been.

Elves. We saw of living herb, intressed with moss,
Their small wrought cabins open on the grass.

Awn. Other, in gossamer bowers, wonne underclod.

Elves. And each gnome held in hand a looking glass;
Wherein he keeked, and kissed oft the Moons
face.

Awn. Are they a faery offspring, without sex,
Of the stars' rays.

Elves. They'd wings on their flit feet;
That seemed, in their oft shining, glancing drops
Of rain, which beat on bosom of the grass:
Wherein be some congealed as adamant.

We stooped to gaze (a neighbour tussock hid
us,)
On sight so fair: their beauty being such,
That seemed us it all living thought did pass.
Yet were we spied! for looked down full upon us,
Disclosing then murk skies, Moons clear still face.
In that they shrunk back, and clapped tó their
doors. . . .

CHARLES M. DOUGHTY

SUMMER: GREENWOOD: SOLITUDE

141 THE HUNT IS UP

THE hunt is up, the hunt is up,
  And it is well nigh day;
And Harry our King is gone hunting
  To bring his deer to bay.

The east is bright with morning light,
  And darkness it is fled;
And the merry horn wakes up the morn
  To leave his idle bed.

Behold the skies with golden dyes
  Are glowing all around;
The grass is green, and so are the treen
  All laughing at the sound.

The horses snort to be at sport,
  The dogs are running free,
The woods rejoice at the merry noise
  Of *Hey tantara tee ree!*

The sun is glad to see us clad
  All in our lusty green,
And smiles in the sky as he riseth high
  To see and to be seen.

Awake all men, I say again,
  Be merry as you may;
For Harry our King is gone hunting,
  To bring his deer to bay.

142 THE CHEERFUL HORN

THE cheerful arn he blaws in the marn,
  And we'll a-'untin' goo;
The cheerful arn he blaws in the marn,
  And we'll a-'huntin' goo,
  And we'll a-'huntin' goo,
  And we'll a-'untin' goo . . .

Var all my vancy dwells upon Nancy,
And I'll zing Tally ho!
Var all my vancy dwells upon Nancy,
And I'll zing Tally ho!

The vox jumps awer the 'edge zo 'igh,
An' the 'ouns all atter un goo;
Var all my vancy dwells upon Nancy,
And I'll zing Tally ho!

Then never despoise the soldjer lod,
Thof 'is ztaition be boot low;
Var all my vancy dwells upon Nancy,
And I'll zing Tally ho!

Then push about the coop, my bwoys,
An' we will wumwards goo,
Var all my vancy dwells upon Nancy,
And I'll zing Tally ho!

If you áx me the zénze of this zóng vur to téll,
Or the reäzon vur to zhow;
Woy, I doän't exacaly knoo,
Woy, I doän't exacaly knoo:
Var all my vancy dwells upon Nancy,
And I'll zing Tally ho!
Var all my vancy dwells upon Nancy,
And I'll zing Tally ho!

143 JOHN PEEL

D'YE ken John Peel with his coat so gray?
D'ye ken John Peel at the break of the day?
D'ye ken John Peel when he's far, far away,
With his hounds and his horn in the morning?
'Twas the sound of his horn called me from my bed,
And the cry of his hounds has me oft-times led,
For Peel's *View-hollo* would waken the dead,
Or a fox from his lair in the morning.

D'ye ken that bitch whose tongue is death?
D'ye ken her sons of peerless faith?
D'ye ken that a fox with his last breath
Cursed them all as he died in the morning?

Yes, I ken John Peel and Ruby too
Ranter and Royal and Bellman as true;
From the drag to the chase, from the chase to a view,
From a view to the death in the morning.

And I've followed John Peel both often and far
O'er the rasper-fence and the gate and the bar,
From Low Denton Holme up to Scratchmere Scar,
When we vied for the brush in the morning.

Then here's to John Peel with my heart and soul,
Come fill—fill to him another strong bowl:
And we'll follow John Peel through fair and through foul,
While we're waked by his horn in the morning.
'Twas the sound of his horn called me from my bed,
And the cry of his hounds has me oft-times led,
For Peel's *View-hollo* would waken the dead
Or a fox from his lair in the morning.

JOHN WOODCOCK GRAVES

144

THE SCHOOLBOY

I LOVE to rise in a summer morn
When the birds sing on every tree;
The distant huntsman winds his horn,
And the skylark sings with me.
O! what sweet company.

But to go to school in a summer morn,
O! it drives all joy away;
Under a cruel eye outworn,
The little ones spend the day
In sighing and dismay.

Ah! then at times I drooping sit,
And spend many an anxious hour,
Nor in my book can I take delight,
Nor sit in learning's bower,
Worn thro' with the dreary shower.

How can the bird that is born for joy
Sit in a cage and sing?
How can a child, when fears annoy,
But droop his tender wing,
And forget his youthful spring?

O! father and mother, if buds are nipped,
And blossoms blown away,
And if the tender plants are stripped
Of their joy in the springing day,
By sorrow and care's dismay,

How shall the summer arise in joy,
Or the summer fruits appear?
Or how shall we gather what griefs destroy,
Or bless the mellowing year,
When the blasts of winter appear?

WILLIAM BLAKE

145

A BOY'S SONG

WHERE the pools are bright and deep,
Where the grey trout lies asleep,
Up the river and over the lea,
That's the way for Billy and me.

Where the blackbird sings the latest,
Where the hawthorn blooms the sweetest,
Where the nestlings chirp and flee,
That's the way for Billy and me.

Where the mowers mow the cleanest,
Where the hay lies thick and greenest,

There to track the homeward bee,
That's the way for Billy and me.

Where the hazel bank is steepest,
Where the shadow falls the deepest,
Where the clustering nuts fall free,
That's the way for Billy and me.

Why the boys should drive away
Little sweet maidens from their play,
Or love to banter and fight so well,
That's the thing I never could tell.

But this I know, I love to play
Through the meadow, among the hay;
Up the water and over the lea,
That's the way for Billy and me.

JAMES HOGG

146 MARKET DAY

WHO'LL walk the fields with us to town,
In an old coat and a faded gown?
We take our roots and country sweets,
Where high walls shade the steep old streets,
And golden bells and silver chimes
Ring up and down the sleepy times.
The morning mountains smoke like fires;
The sun spreads out his shining wires;
The mower in the half-mown lezza
Sips his tea and takes his pleasure.
Along the lane slow waggons amble.
The sad-eyed calves awake and gamble;
The foal that lay so sorrowful
Is playing in the grasses cool.
By slanting ways, in slanting sun,
Through startled lapwings now we run
Along the pale green hazel-path,

Through April's lingering aftermath
Of lady's smock and lady's slipper;
We stay to watch a nesting dipper.
The rabbits eye us while we pass,
Out of the sorrel-crimson grass;
The blackbird sings, without a fear,
Where honeysuckle horns blow clear—
Cool ivory stained with true vermilion,
And here, within a silk pavilion,
Small caterpillars lie at ease.
The endless shadows of the trees
Are painted purple and cobalt;
Grandiloquent, the rook-files halt,
Each one aware of you and me,
And full of conscious dignity.
Our shoes are golden as we pass
With pollen from the pansied grass.
Beneath an elder—set anew
With large clean plates to catch the dew—
On fine white cheese and bread we dine.
The clear brook-water tastes like wine.
If all folk lived with labour sweet
Of their own busy hands and feet,
Such marketing, it seems to me,
Would make an end of poverty.

MARY WEBB

147 UNDER THE GREENWOOD TREE

UNDER the greenewood tree,
Who loves to lye with me,
And turne his merrie Note
Unto the sweet Bird's throte:
Come hither, come hither, come hither,
Heere shall he see no enemie
But Winter and rough Weather.

Who doth ambition shunne
And loves to live i' the Sunne,

Seeking the food he eates
And pleased with what he gets:
Come hither, come hither, come hither,
Heere shall he see no enemie
But Winter and rough Weather.

WILLIAM SHAKESPEARE

148

IN SUMMER

In somer when the shawes be sheyne,[1]
And leves be large and long,
Hit[2] is full merry in feyre foreste
To here the foulys[3] song.

To se the dere draw to the dale
And leve the hillės hee,
And shadow him in the levės grene
Under the green-woode tree.

Hit befell on Whitsontide
Early in a May mornyng,
The Sonne up fairė gan shyne,
And the briddis mery gan syng.

"This is a mery mornyng," said Litulle Johne,
"By Hym that dyed on tree;
A more mery man than I am one
Lyves not in Christiantė.

"Pluk up thi hert, my dere mayster,"
Litulle Johne can say,
"And thynk hit is a fulle fayre tyme
In a mornynge of May."

149

LUBBER BREEZE

The four sails of the mill
Like stocks stand still;

1 When the woods are fresh and fair 2 It 3 Small birds'

Their lantern-length is white
On blue more bright.

Unruffled is the mead,
Where lambkins feed
And sheep and cattle browse
And donkeys drowse.

Never the least breeze will
The wet thumb chill
That the anxious miller lifts,
Till the vane shifts.

The breeze in the great flour-bin
Is snug tucked in;
The lubber, while rats thieve,
Laughs in his sleeve.

T. STURGE MOORE

150

A SUMMER'S DAY

"THE ample heaven of fabrik sure,
In cleannes dois surpas
The chrystall and the silver pure,
Or clearest poleist[1] glas.

The shadow of the earth anon
Removes and drawès by,
Sine in the east, when it is gon,
Appears a clearer sky.

Quhilk sune[2] perceives the little larks,
The lapwing and the snyp,
And tune their sangs, like Nature's clarks
Our medow, mure and stryp.[3]

The time sa tranquil is and still,
That na where sall ye find,

[1] Polished [2] Which soon [3] O'er meadow, moor and stream

Saife on ane high and barren hill,
Ane aire of peeping wind.

All trees and simples[1] great and small,
That balmie liefe do beir,
Nor thay were painted on a wall,
Na mair they move or steir[2]. . ."

ALEXANDER HUME

151

LEISURE

WHAT is this life if, full of care,
We have no time to stand and stare?

No time to stand beneath the boughs
And stare as long as sheep or cows.

No time to see, when woods we pass,
Where squirrels hide their nuts in grass.

No time to see, in broad daylight,
Streams full of stars, like skies at night.

No time to turn at Beauty's glance,
And watch her feet, how they can dance.

No time to wait till her mouth can
Enrich that smile her eyes began.

A poor life this if, full of care,
We have no time to stand and stare.

WILLIAM H. DAVIES

152

THE HAPPY COUNTRYMAN

WHO can live in heart so glad
As the merry country lad?
Who upon a fair green balk[3]

[1] Herbs, wild flowers [2] Stir [3] A green bank left in ploughing

May at pleasure sit and walk,
And amid the azure skies
See the morning sun arise,—
While he hears in every spring
How the birds do chirp and sing:
Or before the hounds in cry
See the hare go stealing by:
Or along the shallow brook,
Angling with a baited hook,
See the fishes leap and play
In a blessèd sunny day:
Or to hear the partridge call,
Till she have her covey all:
Or to see the subtle fox,
How the villain plies the box:
After feeding on his prey,
How he closely sneaks away,
Through the hedge and down the furrow
Till he gets into his burrow:
Then the bee to gather honey,
And the little black-haired coney,
On a bank for sunny place,
With her forefeet wash her face:
Are not these, with thousands moe [1]
Than the courts of kings do know,
The true pleasing spirit's sights
That may breed love's delights? . . .

NICHOLAS BRETON

153

"O FOR A BOOKE"

O FOR a Booke and a shadie nooke,
eyther in-a-doore or out;
With the grene leaves whispering overhede,
or the Streete cryes all about.
Where I maie Reade all at my ease,
both of the Newe and Olde;

[1] More

For a jollie goode Booke whereon to looke,
is better to me than Golde.

154 GREEN BROOM

THERE was an old man lived out in the wood,
His trade was a-cutting of Broom, green Broom;
He had but one son without thrift, without good,
Who lay in his bed till 'twas noon, bright noon.

The old man awoke, one morning and spoke,
He swore he would fire the room, that room,
If his John would not rise and open his eyes,
And away to the wood to cut Broom, green Broom,

So Johnny arose, and he slipped on his clothes,
And away to the wood to cut Broom, green Broom,
He sharpened his knives, for once he contrives
To cut a great bundle of Broom, green Broom.

When Johnny passed under a lady's fine house,
Passed under a lady's fine room, fine room,
She called to her maid, "Go fetch me," she said,
"Go fetch me the boy that sells Broom, green Broom."

When Johnny came in to the lady's fine house,
And stood in the lady's fine room, fine room;
"Young Johnny," she said, "Will you give up your trade,
And marry a lady in bloom, full bloom?"

Johnny gave his consent, and to church they both went,
And he wedded the lady in bloom, full bloom,
At market and fair, all folks do declare,
There is none like the Boy that sold Broom, green Broom.

155 THE TWELVE OXEN

I HAVE twelfė oxen that be faire and brown,
And they go a grasing down by the town.

With hey! with how! with hoy!
Saweste not you mine oxen, you litill prety boy?

I have twelfe oxen, and they be faire and white,
And they go a grasing down by the dyke.
With hey! with how! with hoy!
Saweste not you mine oxen, you litill prety boy?

I have twelfe oxen, and they be faire and blak,
And they go a grasing down by the lake.
With hey! with how! with hoy!
Saweste not you mine oxen, you litill prety boy?

I have twelfe oxen, and they be faire and rede,
And they go a grasing down by the mede
With hey! with how! with hoy!
Saweste not you mine oxen, you litill prety boy?

156 LAVENDER'S BLUE

LAVENDER's blue, dilly dilly, lavender's green,
When I am king, dilly dilly, you shall be queen
Who told you so, dilly dilly, who told you so?
'Twas mine own heart, dilly dilly, that told me so.

Call up your men, dilly dilly, set them to work,
Some with a rake, dilly dilly, some with a fork,
Some to make hay, dilly dilly, some to thresh corn,
Whilst you and I, dilly dilly, keep ourselves warm. . . .

157 THE GARDEN

. . . WHAT wondrous life is this I lead!
Ripe apples drop about my head;
The luscious clusters of the vine
Upon my mouth do crush their wine;
The nectarine and curious peach
Into my hands themselves do reach;
Stumbling on melons, as I pass,
Ensnared with flowers, I fall on grass.

Meanwhile the mind, from pleasure less,
Withdraws into its happiness;
The mind, that ocean where each kind
Does straight its own resemblance find;
Yet it creates, transcending these,
Far other worlds and other seas,
Annihilating all that's made
To a green thought in a green shade.

Here at the fountain's sliding foot
Or at some fruit-tree's mossy root,
Casting the body's vest aside
My soul into the boughs does glide:
There, like a bird, it sits and sings,
Then whets [1] and claps its silver wings,
And, till prepared for longer flight,
Waves in its plumes the various light. . . .

Such was the happy Garden-state
While man there walked without a mate:
After a place so pure and sweet,
What other help could yet be meet!
But 'twas beyond a mortal's share
To wander solitary there:
Two paradises 'twere in one,
To live in Paradise alone. . . .

ANDREW MARVELL

158

CHERRY-RIPE

CHERRIE Ripe, Ripe, Ripe, I cry,
Full and faire ones; come and buy:
If so be you ask me where
They doe grow? I answer, There,
Where my *Julia's* lips doe smile;
There's the Land, or Cherrie Ile:
Whose Plantations fully show
All the yeare, where Cherries grow.

ROBERT HERRICK

[1] Preens

159 CHERRY-RIPE

THERE is a Garden in her face
Where Roses and white Lillies grow;
A heav'nly paradice is that place,
Wherein all pleasant fruits doe flow.
There Cherries grow, which none may buy,
Till *Cherry Ripe* themselves doe cry.

Those Cherries fayrely doe enclose
Of Orient Pearle a double row,
Which when her lovely laughter showes,
They look like Rose-buds filled with snow.
Yet them nor Peere nor Prince can buy,
Till *Cherry Ripe* themselves doe cry.

Her Eyes like Angels watch them still;
Her Browes like bended bowes doe stand,
Threat'ning with piercing frownes to kill
All that approach with eye or hand
These sacred Cherries to come nigh,
Till *Cherry Ripe* themselves doe cry.

THOMAS CAMPION

160 SONG

WHAT is there hid in the heart of a rose,
Mother-mine?
Ah, who knows, who knows, who knows?
A Man that died on a lonely hill
May tell you, perhaps, but none other will,
Little child.

What does it take to make a rose,
Mother-mine?
The God that died to make it knows
It takes the world's eternal wars,
It takes the moon and all the stars
It takes the might of heaven and hell

And the everlasting Love as well,
Little child.

ALFRED NOYES

161

THE MYSTERY

HE came and took me by the hand
Up to a red rose tree,
He kept His meaning to Himself
But gave a rose to me.
I did not pray Him to lay bare
The mystery to me,
Enough the rose was Heaven to smell,
And His own face to see.

RALPH HODGSON

162

THE ROSE

A ROSE, as fair as ever saw the North,
Grew in a little garden all alone;
A sweeter flower did Nature ne'er put forth,
Nor fairer garden yet was never known:

The maidens danced about it morn and noon,
And learnèd bards of it their ditties made;
The nimble fairies by the pale-faced moon
Watered the root and kissed her pretty shade.

But well-a-day!—the gardener careless grew;
The maids and fairies both were kept away,
And in a drought the caterpillars threw
Themselves upon the bud and every spray.

God shield the stock! If heaven send no supplies,
The fairest blossom of the garden dies.

WILLIAM BROWNE

163

SONG

ASK me no more, where Jove bestows
When June is past the fading rose;

For in your beauty's orient deep
These flowers, as in their causes, sleep.

Ask me no more, whither do stray
The golden atoms of the day;
For in pure love heaven did prepare
Those powders to enrich your hair.

Ask me no more, whither doth haste
The nightingale when May is past;
For in your sweet dividing throat
She winters and keeps warm her note.

Ask me no more, where those stars light[1]
That downwards fall in dead of night;
For in your eyes they sit and there
Fixèd become as in their sphere.

Ask me no more if east or west
The Phœnix builds her spicy nest;
For unto you at last she flies,
And in your fragrant bosom dies.

THOMAS CAREW

164 THE BOWER OF BLISS

(The "daintie Paradise of the Enchauntresse" whereinto the Palmer brought Sir Guyon.)

. . . AND in the midst of all, a fountaine stood,
Of richest substaunce that on earth might bee,
So pure and shiny, that the silver flood
Through every channell running, one might see;
Most goodly it with pure imageree
Was over-wrought, and shapes of naked boyes,
Of which some seemed with lively jolitee
To fly about, playing their wanton toyes,
Whiles others did them selves embay in liquid joyes.

[1] Stay

And over all, of purest gold was spred
A trayle of yvie in his native hew:
For the rich mettall was so colourèd,
That wight, who did not well-advised it vew,
Would surely deeme it to be yvie treu.
Lowe his lascivious arms adown did creep,
That themselves dipping in the silver dew,
Their fleecy flowres they tenderly did steepe,
Which drops of Cristall seemed for wantonnes to weepe.

Infinit streames continually did well
Out of this fountaine, sweet and faire to see,
The which into an ample laver fell,
And shortly grew to so great quantitie,
That like a little lake it seemed to bee;
Whose depth exceeded not three cubits hight,
That through the waves one might the bottom see,
All paved beneath with Jaspar shining bright
That seemd the fountaine in that sea did sayle upright.

And all the margent round about was set
With shady lawrell-trees, thence to defend
The sunny beames, which on the billows bet,
And those which therein bathèd, mote [1] offend . . .
Eftsoones they heard a most melodious sound,
Of all that mote delight a daintie eare,
Such as att once might not on living ground,
Save in this Paradise, be heard elsewhere:
Right hard it was, for wight, which did it heare,
To read, what manner musicke that mote bee:
For all that pleasing is to living eare,
Was there consorted in one harmonie,
Birdes, voyces, instruments, windes, waters, all agree.

The joyous birdes, shrouded in cheareful shade,
Their notes unto the voice attempred sweet;
Th' Angelicall soft trembling voyces made
To th' instruments divine respondence meet:

[1] Might

The silver sounding instruments did meet:
With the base murmure of the waters fall:
The waters fall with difference discreet,
Now soft, now loud, unto the wind did call:
The gentle warbling wind low answerèd to all.

EDMUND SPENSER

165 SMALL FOUNTAINS

. . . JARRING the air with rumour cool,
Small fountains played into a pool
With sound as soft as the barley's hiss
When its beard just sprouting is;
Whence a young stream, that trod on moss,
Prettily rimpled the court across.
And in the pool's clear idleness,
Moving like dreams through happiness,
Shoals of small bright fishes were;
In and out weed-thickets bent
Perch and carp, and sauntering went
With mounching jaws and eyes a-stare;
Or on a lotus leaf would crawl,
A brinded loach to bask and sprawl,
Tasting the warm sun ere it dipt
Into the water; but quick as fear
Back his shining brown head slipt
To crouch on the gravel of his lair,
Where the cooled sunbeams broke in wrack,
Spilt shattered gold about his back. . . .

LASCELLES ABERCROMBIE

166 THE INVITATION, TO JANE

BEST and brightest, come away!
Fairer far than this fair Day,
Which, like thee to those in sorrow,
Comes to bid a sweet good-morrow
To the rough Year just awake

In its cradle on the brake.
The brightest hour of unborn Spring,
Through the winter wandering,
Found, it seems, the halcyon Morn
To hoar February born;
Bending from Heaven, in azure mirth,
It kissed the forehead of the Earth,
And smiled upon the silent sea,
And bade the frozen streams be free,
And waked to music all their fountains,
And breathed upon the frozen mountains,
And like a prophetess of May
Strewed flowers upon the barren way,
Making the wintry world appear
Like one on whom thou smilest, dear. . . .

Radiant Sister of the Day,
Awake! arise! and come away!
To the wild woods and the plains,
And the pools where winter rains
Image all their roof of leaves,
Where the pine its garland weaves
Of sapless green and ivy dun
Round stems that never kiss the sun;
Where the lawns and pastures be,
And the sand-hills of the sea;—
Where the melting hoar-frost wets
The daisy-star that never sets,
The wind-flowers, and violets,
Which yet join not scent to hue,
Crown the pale year weak and new;
When the night is left behind
In the deep east, dun and blind,
And the blue noon is over us,
And the multitudinous
Billows murmur at our feet,
Where the earth and ocean meet,
And all things seem only one
In the universal sun.

PERCY BYSSHE SHELLEY

THE RECOLLECTION

. . . We wandered to the Pine Forest
That skirts the Oean's foam;
The lightest wind was in its nest,
The tempest in its home.
The whispering winds were half asleep,
The clouds were gone to play,
And on the bosom of the deep
The smile of Heaven lay;
It seemed as if the hour were one
Sent from beyond the skies,
Which scattered from above the sun
A light of Paradise.

We paused amid the pines that stood
The giants of the waste,
Tortured by storms to shapes as rude
As serpents interlaced;
And, soothed by every azure breath,
That under Heaven is blown,
To harmonies and hues beneath,
As tender as its own,
Now all the tree-tops lay asleep,
Like green waves on the sea,
As still as in the silent deep
The ocean woods may be.

How calm it was!—the silence there
By such a chain was bound
That even the busy woodpecker
Made stiller with her sound
The inviolable quietness;
The breath of peace we drew
With its soft motion made not less
The calm that round us grew.
There seemed from the remotest seat
Of the white mountain waste,
To the soft flower beneath our feet,
A magic circle traced,—

A spirit interfused around,
  A thrilling, silent life,
To momentary peace it bound
  Our mortal nature's strife;
And still I felt the centre of
  The magic circle there
Was one fair form that filled with love
  The lifeless atmosphere. . . .

PERCY BYSSHE SHELLEY

168 THE GOAT PATHS

THE crooked paths go every way
  Upon the hill—they wind about
  Through the heather in and out
Of the quiet sunniness.
And there the goats, day after day,
  Stray in sunny quietness,

Cropping here and cropping there,
  As they pause and turn and pass,
Now a bit of heather spray,
  Now a mouthful of the grass.

In the deeper sunniness,
  In the place where nothing stirs,
Quietly in quietness,
  In the quiet of the furze,
For a time they come and lie
Staring on the roving sky.

If you approach they run away,
  They leap and stare, away they bound,
  With a sudden angry sound,
To the sunny quietude;
  Crouching down where nothing stirs
  In the silence of the furze,
Couching down again to brood
In the sunny solitude.

If I were as wise as they,
I would stray apart and brood,
I would beat a hidden way
Through the quiet heather spray
To a sunny solitude;

And should you come I'd run away,
I would make an angry sound,
I would stare and turn and bound
To the deeper quietude,
To the place where nothing stirs
In the silence of the furze.

In that airy quietness
I would think as long as they;
Through the quiet sunniness
I would stray away to brood
By a hidden beaten way
In a sunny solitude,
I would think until I found
Something I can never find,
Something lying on the ground,
In the bottom of my mind.

JAMES STEPHENS

169 UNDER A WILTSHIRE APPLE TREE

SOME folks as can afford,
So I've heard say,
Set up a sort of cross
Right in the garden way
To mind 'em of the Lord.
But I, when I do see
Thik [1] apple tree
An' stoopin' limb
All spread wi' moss,
I think of Him

[1] This

And how He talks wi' me.
I think of God

And how He trod
That garden long ago;
He walked, I reckon, to and fro
And then sat down
Upon the groun'
Or some low limb
What suited Him,
Such as you see
On many a tree,
And on thik very one
Where I at set o' sun
Do sit and talk wi' He.

And, mornings, too, I rise and come
An' sit down where the branch be low;
A bird do sing, a bee do hum,
The flowers in the border blow,
And all my heart's so glad and clear
As pools be when the sun do peer,
As pools a-laughing in the light
When mornin' air is swep' an' bright,
As pools what got all Heaven in sight,
So's my heart's cheer
When He be near.

He never pushed the garden door,
He left no foot mark on the floor;
I never heard 'Un stir nor tread
And yet His Hand do bless my head,
And when 'tis time for work to start
I takes Him with me in my heart.
And when I die, pray God I see
At very last thik apple tree
An' stoopin' limb,
And think of Him
And all He been to me.

ANNA DE BARY

How like an Angel came I down!
How bright were all things here!
When first among His works I did appear
O how their Glory me did crown!
The world resembled His ETERNITY,
In which my soul did walk;
And every thing that I did see
Did with me talk.

The skies in their magnificence,
The lively, lovely air,
Oh how divine, how soft, how sweet, how fair!
The stars did entertain my sense,
And all the works of God, so bright and pure,
So rich and great did seem,
As if they ever must endure
In my esteem. . . .

The streets were paved with golden stones,
The boys and girls were mine,
Oh how did all their lovely faces shine!
The sons of men were holy ones,
In joy and beauty they appeared to me,
And every thing which here I found,
While like an Angel I did see,
Adorned the ground.

Rich diamond and pearl and gold
In every place was seen;
Rare splendours, yellow, blue, red, white and green,
Mine eyes did everywhere behold.
Great wonders clothed with glory did appear,
Amazement was my bliss,
That and my wealth was everywhere;
No joy to this! . . .

THOMAS TRAHERNE

171

SONG

How sweet I roamed from field to field
And tasted all the summer's pride,
Till I the Prince of Love beheld
Who in the sunny beams did glide!

He showed me lilies for my hair,
And blushing roses for my brow;
He led me through his gardens fair
Where all his golden pleasures grow.

With sweet May dews my wings were wet,
And Phoebus fired my vocal rage;
He caught me in his silken net,
And shut me in his golden cage.

He loves to sit and hear me sing,
Then, laughing, sports and plays with me;
Then stretches out my golden wing,
And mocks my loss of liberty.

William Blake

172

THE BOOK

Of this fair volume which we World do name
If we the sheets and leaves could turn with care,
Of Him who it corrects and did it frame,
We clear might read the art and wisdom rare:

Find out His power which wildest powers doth tame,
His providence extending everywhere,
His justice which proud rebels doth not spare,
In every page, no period of the same.

But silly we, like foolish children, rest
Well pleased with coloured vellum, leaves of gold,
Fair dangling ribbands, leaving what is best,
On the great Writer's sense ne'er taking hold;

Or, if by chance we stay our minds on aught,
It is some picture on the margin wrought.

WILLIAM DRUMMOND

173 TETHY'S FESTIVAL

ARE they shadows that we see?
And can shadows pleasures give?
Pleasures only shadows be,
Cast by bodies we conceive;
And are made the things we deem
In those figures which they seem.

But those pleasures vanish fast,
Which by shadows are exprest;
Pleasures are not, if they last;
In their passing is their best:
Glory is more bright and gay
In a flash, and so away.

Feed apace then, greedy eyes,
On the wonder you behold:
Take it sudden, as it flies,
Though you take it not to hold.
When your eyes have done their part
Thought must length'n it in the heart.

SAMUEL DANIEL

WAR

174 A WAR SONG TO ENGLISHMEN

PREPARE, prepare the iron helm of War,
Bring forth the lots, cast in the spacious orb;
The Angel of Fate turns them with mighty hands,
And casts them out upon the darkened earth!
Prepare, prepare!

Prepare your hearts for Death's cold hand! prepare
Your souls for flight, your bodies for the earth;
Prepare your arms for glorious victory;
Prepare your eyes to meet a holy God!
Prepare, prepare!

Whose fatal scroll is that? Methinks 'tis mine!
Why sinks my heart, why faltereth my tongue?
Had I three lives, I'd die in such a cause,
And rise, with ghosts, over the well-fought field.
Prepare, prepare!

The arrows of Almighty God are drawn!
Angels of Death stand in the lowering heavens!
Thousands of souls must seek the realms of light,
And walk together on the clouds of heaven!
Prepare, prepare!

Soldiers, prepare! Our cause is Heaven's cause;
Soldiers, prepare! Be worthy of our cause:
Prepare to meet our father's in the sky:
Prepare, O troops, that are to fall to-day!
Prepare, prepare!

Alfred shall smile, and make his harp rejoice;
The Norman William, and the learnèd Clerk,

And Lion Heart, and black-browed Edward, with
His loyal Queen, shall rise, and welcome us!
Prepare, prepare!

WILLIAM BLAKE

175 FOR SOLDIERS

YE buds of Brutus' land, courageous youths, now play your parts;
Unto your tackle stand, abide the brunt with valiant hearts.
For news is carried to and fro, that we must forth to warfare go:
Men muster now in every place, and soldiers are prest forth apace.
Faint not, spend blood,
To do your Queen and country good;
Fair words, good pay,
Will make men cast all care away.

The time of war is come, prepare your corslet, spear and shield;
Methinks I hear the drum strike doleful marches to the field;
Tantarâ, tantarâ, ye trumpets sound, which makes our hearts with joy abound.
The roaring guns are heard afar, and everything denounceth war.
Serve God; stand stout;
Bold courage brings this gear about.
Fear not; fate run [1];
Faint heart fair lady never won.

Ye curious [2] carpet-knights, that spend the time in sport and play;
Abroad and see new sights, your country's cause calls you away;
Do not to make your ladies' game, bring blemish to your worthy name.
Away to field and win renown, with courage beat your enemies down.
Stout hearts gain praise,
When dastards sail in Slander's seas;

[1] Risk, hazard, dare. [2] Dainty; luxurious.

Hap what hap shall,
We sure shall die but once for all.

Alarm methinks they cry, Be packing, mates, begone with speed;
Our foes are very nigh; shame have that man that shrinks at need!
Unto it boldly let us stand, God will give Right the upper hand.
Our cause is good, we need not doubt, in sign of coming give a shout.
March forth, be strong,
Good hap will come ere it be long.
Shrink not, fight well,
For lusty lads must bear the bell.

All you that will shun evil, must dwell in warfare every day;
The world, the flesh, and devil, always do seek our soul's decay;
Strive with these foes with all your might, so shall you fight a worthy fight.
That conquest doth deserve most praise, where vice do yield to virtue's ways.
Beat down foul sin,
A worthy crown then shall ye win;
If ye live well,
In heaven with Christ our souls shall dwell.

HUMPHREY GIFFORD

176 BATTLE-HYMN OF THE REPUBLIC

MINE eyes have seen the glory of the coming of the Lord;
He is trampling out the vintage where the grapes of wrath are stored;
He hath loosed the fateful lightning of His terrible swift sword;
His truth is marching on.

I have seen Him in the watch-fires of a hundred circling camps;
They have builded Him an altar in the evening dews and damps;

I can read his righteous sentence by the dim and flaring lamps;
His day is marching on.

I have read a fiery gospel, writ in burnished rows of steel:
"As ye deal with my contemners, so with you my grace shall deal;
Let the Hero, born of woman, crush the serpent with his heel,
Since God is marching on."

He has sounded forth the trumpet that shall never call retreat;
He is sifting out the hearts of men before His judgment-seat;
Oh, be swift, my soul, to answer Him! be jubilant, my feet!
Our God is marching on.

In the beauty of the lilies Christ was born across the sea,
With a glory in His bosom that transfigures you and me:
As He died to make men holy, let us die to make men free,
While God is marching on.

JULIA WARD HOWE

177 "I HEARD A SOLDIER"

I HEARD a soldier sing some trifle
Out in the sun-dried veldt alone:
He lay and cleaned his grimy rifle
Idly, behind a stone.

"If after death, love, comes a waking,
And in their camp so dark and still
The men of dust hear bugles, breaking
Their halt upon the hill,

"To me the slow, the silver pealing
That then the last high trumpet pours
Shall softer than the dawn come stealing,
For, with its call, comes yours!"

What grief of love had he to stifle,
Basking so idly by his stone,

That grimy soldier with his rifle
Out in the veldt, alone?

HERBERT TRENCH

178 THE DUG-OUT

WHY do you lie with your legs ungainly huddled,
And one arm bent across your sullen cold
Exhausted face? It hurts my heart to watch you,
Deep-shadowed from the candle's guttering gold;
And you wonder why I shake you by the shoulder;
Drowsy, you mumble and sigh and turn your head . . .
You are too young to fall asleep for ever;
And when you sleep you remind me of the dead.

SIEGFRIED SASSOON

179 NOCTURNE

BE thou at peace this night
Wherever be thy bed,
Thy slumbering be light,
The fearful dreams be dead
Within thy lovely head;
God keep thee in His sight.

No hint of love molest
Thy quiet mind again;
Night fold thee to her breast
And hush thy crying pain;
Let memory in vain
Conspire against thy rest.

So may thy thoughts be lost
In the full hush of sleep.
Lest any sight accost
Thine eyes to make them weep,
In darkness buried deep
For ever be my ghost.

EDWARD L. DAVISON

180 THE DEAD

THESE hearts were woven of human joys and cares,
Washed marvellously with sorrow, swift to mirth.
The years had given them kindness. Dawn was theirs,
And sunset, and the colours of the earth.

These had seen movement, and heard music; known
Slumber and waking; loved; gone proudly friended;
Felt the quick stir of wonder; sat alone;
Touched flowers and furs and cheeks. All this is ended.

There are waters blown by changing winds to laughter
And lit by the rich skies, all day. And after,
Frost, with a gesture, stays the waves that dance
And wandering loveliness. He leaves a white
Unbroken glory, a gathered radiance,
A width, a shining peace, under the night.

RUPERT BROOKE

181 THE END

AFTER the blast of lightning from the east,
The flourish of loud clouds, the Chariot throne;
After the drums of time have rolled and ceased,
And, from the bronze west, long retreat is blown—

Shall Life renew these bodies? Of a truth
All death will he annul, all tears assuage?—
Or fill these void veins full again with youth,
And wash, with an immortal water, Age?

When I do ask white Age, he saith, "Not so:
My head hangs weighed with snow."
And when I hearken to the Earth, she saith:
"My fiery heart sinks aching. It is death.
Mine ancient scars shall not be glorified.
Nor my titanic tears, the seas, be dried."

WILFRED OWEN

182 THE CROWNS

CHERRY and pear are white,
Their snows lie sprinkled on the land like light
On darkness shed.
Far off and near
The orchards toss their crowns of delight,
And the sun casts down
Another shining crown.

The wind tears and throws down
Petal by petal the crown
Of cherry and pear till the earth is white,
And all the brightness is shed
In the orchards far off and near,
That tossed by the road and under the green hill;
And the wind is fled.

Far, far off the wind
Has shaken down
A brightness that was as the brightness of cherry or pear
When the orchards shine in the sun.
—Oh there is no more fairness
Since this rareness,
The radiant blossom of English earth—is dead!

JOHN FREEMAN

183 CORONACH[1]

HE is gone on the mountain,
  He is lost to the forest,
Like a summer-dried fountain,
  When our need was the sorest.
The font, reappearing,
  From the rain-drops shall borrow,
But to us comes no cheering,
  To Duncan no morrow!

The hand of the reaper
  Takes the ears that are hoary,

1 Dirge, lament

But the voice of the weeper
Wails manhood in glory.
The autumn winds rushing
Waft the leaves that are serest,
But our flower was in flushing,
When blighting was nearest.

Fleet foot on the correi,[1]
Sage counsel in cumber,[2]
Red hand in the foray,
How sound is thy slumber!
Like the dew on the mountain,
Like the foam on the river,
Like the bubble on the fountain,
Thou art gone, and for ever.

SIR WALTER SCOTT

184 THE CHILDREN'S BELLS

WHERE are your Oranges?
Where are your Lemons?
What, are you silent now,
Bells of St. Clement's? *
You, of all bells that rang
Once in old London,
You, of all bells that sang,
Utterly undone?
You whom all children know
Ere they know letters,
Making Big Ben himself
Call you his betters?
Where are your lovely tones
Fruitful and mellow,
Full-flavoured orange-gold,
Clear lemon-yellow?

[1] Vast hill-hollow [2] Danger or defeat

(*When the half-muffled City Bells rang in commemoration of the Bell-Ringers who fell in the war, the bells of St. Clement Danes could not take part owing to a defect in the framework.)

Ring again, sing again,
Bells of St. Clement's!
Call as you swing again,
"Oranges! Lemons!"
Fatherless children
Are listening near you—
Sing for the children,
The fathers will hear you.

ELEANOR FARJEON

185 MEN WHO MARCH AWAY

WE be the King's men, hale and hearty,
Marching to meet one Buonaparty;
If he won't sail, lest the wind should blow,
We shall have marched for nothing, O!
Right fol-lol!

We be the King's men, hale and hearty,
Marching to meet one Buonaparty;
If he be sea-sick, says "No, no!"
We shall have marched for nothing, O!
Right fol-lol!

We be the King's men, hale and hearty,
Marching to meet one Buonaparty;
Never mind, mates; we'll be merry, though
We may have marched for nothing, O!
Right fol-lol!

THOMAS HARDY

186 BUDMOUTH DEARS

WHEN we lay where Budmouth Beach is,
O, the girls were fresh as peaches,
With their tall and tossing figures and their eyes of blue and brown!
And our hearts would ache with longing
As we paced from our sing-songing,
With a smart *Clink! Clink!* up the Esplanade and down.

They distracted and delayed us
By the pleasant pranks they played us,
And what marvel, then, if troopers, even of regiments of renown,
On whom flashed those eyes divine, O,
Should forget the countersign, O,
As we tore *Clink! Clink!* back to camp above the town.

Do they miss us much, I wonder,
Now that war has swept us sunder,
And we roam from where the faces smile to where the faces frown?
And no more behold the features
Of the fair fantastic creatures,
And no more *Clink! Clink!* past the parlours of the town?

Shall we once again there meet them?
Falter fond attempts to greet them?
Will the gay sling-jacket glow again beside the muslin gown?
Will they archly quiz and con us
With a sideway glance upon us,
While our spurs *Clink! Clink!* up the Esplanade and down?

THOMAS HARDY

187 TRAFALGAR

IN the wild October night-time, when the wind raved round the land,
And the Back-sea met the Front-sea, and our doors were blocked with sand,
And we heard the drub of Dead-man's Bay, where bones of thousands are,
We knew not what the day had done for us at Trafalgár.
(*All*) Had done,
Had done,
For us at Trafalgar!

"Pull hard, and make the Nothe, or down we go!" one says, says he.
We pulled; and bedtime brought the storm; but snug at home slept we.

Yet all the while our gallants after fighting through the day,
Were beating up and down the dark, sou'-west of Cadiz Bay.
The dark,
The dark,
Sou'-west of Cadiz Bay!

The victors and the vanquished then the storm it tossed and tore,
As hard they strove, those worn-out men, upon that surly shore;
Dead Nelson and his half-dead crew, his foes from near and far,
Were rolled together on the deep that night at Trafalgar!
The deep,
The deep,
That night at Trafalgar!

THOMAS HARDY

188 MESSMATES

HE gave us all a good-bye cheerily
At the first dawn of day;
We dropped him down the side full drearily
When the light died away.
It's a dead dark watch that he's a-keeping there,
And a long, long night that lags a-creeping there,
Where the Trades and the tides roll over him
And the great ships go by.

He's there alone with green seas rocking him
For a thousand miles round;
He's there alone with dumb things mocking him,
And we're homeward bound.
It's a long, lone watch that he's a-keeping there,
And a dead cold night that lags a-creeping there,
While the months and the years roll over him
And the great ships go by.

I wonder if the tramps come near enough
As they thrash to and fro,
And the battle-ships' bells ring clear enough
To be heard down below;

If through all the lone watch that he's a-keeping there,
And the long, cold night that lags a-creeping there,
The voices of the sailor-men shall comfort him
When the great ships go by.

HENRY NEWBOLT

189 SONG FOR ALL SEAS, ALL SHIPS

TO-DAY a rude brief recitative,
Of ships sailing the seas, each with its special flag or ship-signal,
Of unnamed heroes in the ships—of waves spreading and spreading far as the eye can reach,
Of dashing spray, and the winds piping and blowing,
And out of these a chant for the sailors of all nations.
Fitful, like a surge.

Of sea-captains young or old, and the mates, and of all intrepid sailors,
Of the few, very choice, taciturn, whom fate can never surprise nor death dismay,
Picked sparingly without noise by thee, old ocean, chosen by thee,
Thou sea that pickest and cullest the race in time, and unitest nations,
Suckled by thee, old husky nurse, embodying thee,
Indomitable, untamed as thee. . . .

Flaunt out, O sea, your separate flags of nations!
Flaunt out visible as ever the various ship-signals!
But do you reserve especially for yourself and for the soul of man one flag above all the rest,
A spiritual woven signal for all nations, emblem of man elate above death,
Token of all brave captains and all intrepid sailors and mates,
And all that went down doing their duty,
Reminiscent of them, twined from all intrepid captains young or old,
A pennant universal, subtly waving all time, o'er all, brave sailors,
All seas, all ships.

WALT WHITMAN

HOHENLINDEN

On Linden, when the sun was low,
All bloodless lay the untrodden snow;
And dark as winter was the flow
Of Iser, rolling rapidly.

But Linden saw another sight,
When the drum beat at dead of night
Commanding fires of death to light
The darkness of her scenery.

By torch and trumpet fast arrayed
Each horseman drew his battle-blade,
And furious every charger neighed
To join the dreadful revelry.

Then shook the hills with thunder riven;
Then rushed the steed, to battle driven;
And louder than the bolts of Heaven
Far flashed the red artillery.

But redder yet that light shall glow
On Linden's hills of stainèd snow;
And bloodier yet the torrent flow
Of Iser, rolling rapidly.

'Tis morn; but scarce yon level sun
Can pierce the war-clouds, rolling dun,
Where furious Frank and fiery Hun
Shout in their sulphurous canopy.

The combat deepens. On, ye Brave,
Who rush to glory or the grave!
Wave, Munich! all thy banners wave,
And charge with all thy chivalry!

Few, few shall part, where many meet!
The snow shall be their winding-sheet,

And every turf beneath their feet
Shall be a soldier's sepulchre.

THOMAS CAMPBELL

191 HAME, HAME, HAME

HAME, hame, hame, hame, fain wad I be:
O hame, hame, hame, to my ain countrie!

When the flower is in the bud, and the leaf is on the tree,
The lark shall sing me hame to my ain countrie.
Hame, hame, hame! O hame fain wad I be!
O hame, hame, hame to my ain countrie!

The green leaf o' loyalty's beginning now to fa';
The bonnie white rose it is withering an' a';
But we'll water it with the blude of usurping tyrannie,
And fresh it shall blaw in my ain countrie!

O, there's nocht now frae ruin my countrie can save,
But the keys o' kind heaven, to open the grave,
That a' the noble martyrs wha died for loyaltie
May rise again and fight for their ain countrie.

The great now are gane, who attempted to save;
The green grass is growing abune their grave;
Yet the sun through the mirk seems to promise to me—
I'll shine on ye yet in your ain countrie.

Hame, hame, hame, hame, fain wad I be;
O hame, hame, hame to my ain countrie!

ALLAN CUNNINGHAM

192 DARK ROSALEEN

O MY dark Rosaleen,
Do not sigh, do not weep!
The priests are on the ocean green,
They march along the deep.
There's wine from the royal Pope
Upon the ocean green,

And Spanish ale shall give you hope,
  My dark Rosaleen!
  My own Rosaleen!
Shall glad your heart, shall give you hope,
Shall give you health, and help, and hope,
  My dark Rosaleen!

Over hills and through dales
  Have I roamed for your sake;
All yesterday I sailed the sails
  On river and on lake.
The Erne, at its highest flood,
  I dashed across unseen,
For there was lightning in my blood,
  My dark Rosaleen!
  My own Rosaleen!
Oh! there was lightning in my blood,
Red lightning lightened through my blood,
  My dark Rosaleen!

All day long, in unrest,
  To and fro do I move.
The very soul within my breast
  Is wasted for you, love!
The heart in my bosom faints
  To think of you, my Queen,
My life of life, my saint of saints,
  My dark Rosaleen!
  My own Rosaleen!
To hear your sweet and sad complaints,
My life, my love, my saints of saints,
  My dark Rosaleen!

Woe and pain, pain and woe,
  Are my lot, night and noon,
To see your bright face clouded so,
  Like to the mournful moon.
But yet will I rear your throne
  Again in golden sheen;
'Tis you shall reign, shall reign alone

My dark Rosaleen!
My own Rosaleen!
'Tis you shall have the golden throne,
'Tis you shall reign, and reign alone,
My dark Rosaleen!

Over dews, over sands,
Will I fly for your weal:
Your holy delicate white hands
Shall girdle me with steel.
At home, in your emerald bowers,
From morning's dawn till e'en
You'll pray for me, my flower of flowers,
My dark Rosaleen!
My fond Rosaleen!
You'll think of me through daylight hours,
My virgin flower, my flower of flowers,
My dark Rosaleen!

I could scale the blue air,
I could plough the high hills,
Oh, I could kneel all night in prayer,
To heal your many ills!
And one beamy smile from you
Would float like light between
My toils and me, my own, my true,
My dark Rosaleen!
My fond Rosaleen!
Would give me life and soul anew,
A second life, a soul anew,
My dark Rosaleen!

Oh! the Erne shall run red
With redundance of blood,
The earth shall rock beneath our tread,
And flames wrap hill and wood,
And gun-peal and slogan-cry
Wake many a glen serene,
Ere you shall fade, ere you shall die,
My dark Rosaleen!

My own Rosaleen!
The Judgment Hour must first be nigh,
Ere you shall fade, ere you can die,
My dark Rosaleen!

JAMES CLARENCE MANGAN

193 MY LUVE'S IN GERMANY

"MY Luve's in Germany;
Send him hame, send him hame;
My Luve's in Germany,
Send him hame:
My Luve's in Germany,
Fighting for Royalty;
He may ne'er his Jeanie see;
Send him hame, send him hame;
He may ne'er his Jeanie see,
Send him hame.

"He's brave as brave can be,
Send him hame, send him hame;
He's brave as brave can be,
Send him hame.
He's brave as brave can be,
He wad rather fa' than flee;
But his life is dear to me,
Send him hame, send him hame;
Oh! his life is dear to me,
Send him hame.

"Our faes are ten to three,
Send him hame, send him hame;
Our faes are ten to three,
Send him hame.
Our faes are ten to three,
He maun either fa' or flee,
In the cause o' Loyalty;
Send him hame, send him hame;

In the cause o' Loyalty,
Send him hame."

"Your luve ne'er learnt to flee,
Bonnie Dame, winsome Dame;
Your luve ne'er learnt to flee,
Winsome Dame.
Your luve ne'er learnt to flee,
But he fell in Germany,
Fighting brave for Loyalty,
Mournfu' Dame, bonnie Dame,
Fighting brave for Loyalty,
Mournfu' Dame!"

"He'll ne'er come owre the sea,
Willie's slain, Willie's slain;
He'll ne'er come owre the sea,
Willie's gane!
He'll ne'er come owre the sea,
To his Love and ain Countrie—
This warld's nae mair for me,
Willie's gane, Willie's gane!
This warld's nae mair for me
Willie's slain!"

194 A WEARY LOT IS THINE

"A WEARY lot is thine, fair maid,
A weary lot is thine!
To pull the thorn thy brow to braid,
And press the rue for wine.
A lightsome eye, a soldier's mien,
A feather of the blue,
A doublet of the Lincoln green—
No more of me you knew,
My love!
No more of me you knew,

"This morn is merry June, I trow,
The rose is budding fain;

But she shall bloom in winter snow
Ere we two meet again."
He turned his charger as he spake
Upon the river shore,
He gave the bridle-reins a shake,
Said, "Adieu for evermore,
My love!
And adieu for evermore."

Sir Walter Scott

195 CHARLIE HE'S MY DARLING

An' Charlie he's my darling,
My darling, my darling!
Charlie he's my darling,
The young Chevalier!

'Twas on a Monday morning,
Right early in the year,
That Charlie cam' to our town,
The young Chevalier!

As he was walking up the street,
The city for to view,
O, there he spied a bonnie lass
The window lookin' through.

Sae light's he jimpèd up the stair,
An' tirlèd at the pin;
An' wha sae ready as hersel
To let the laddie in?

He set his Jenny on his knee,
A' in his Highland dress;
For brawlie weel he kenned the way
To please a lassie best.

It's up yon heathery mountain,
An' down yon scroggy glen,
We daur na gang a-milking
For Charlie an' his men!

An' Charlie he's my darling,
My darling, my darling!
Charlie he's my darling,
The young Chevalier!

196 THE FAREWELL

It was a' for our rightfu' king
We left fair Scotland's strand;
It was a' for our rightfu' king
We e'er saw Irish land,
My dear,
We e'er saw Irish land.

Now a' is done that man can do,
And a' is done in vain;
My love, and native land, farewell,
For I maun cross the main,
My dear,
For I maun cross the main,

He turned him right and round about
Upon the Irish shore;
And gae his bridle-reins a shake,
With Adieu for evermore,
My dear,
Adieu for evermore.

The sodger frae the wars returns,
The sailor frae the main;
But I hae parted frae my love,
Never to meet again,
My dear,
Never to meet again,

When day is gane, and night is come,
And a' folks bound to sleep;
I think on him that's far awa',

The lee-lang night, and weep,
My dear,
The lee-lang night, and weep,

ROBERT BURNS

197 THE FLOWERS OF THE FOREST

I'VE heard them lilting at our ewe-milking,
Lasses a-lilting before the dawn of day;
But now they are moaning on ilka green loaning:—
The Flowers of the Forest are a' wede away.

At bughts in the morning nae blythe lads are scorning;
The lasses are lanely, and dowie, and wae;
Nae daffing, nae gabbing, but sighing and sabbing,
Ilk ane lifts her leglin, and hies her away.

In hairst, at the shearing, nae youths now are jeering:
The bandsters are lyart, and runkled, and gray.
At fair or at preaching, nae wooing, nae fleeching—
The Flowers of the Forest are a' wede away.

At e'en, in the gloaming, nae swankies are roaming
'Bout stacks wi' th lasses at bogle to play;
But ilk ane sits drearie, lamenting her dearie—
The Flowers of the Forest are a' wede away.

Dool and wae for the order sent our lads to the Border!
The English, for ance, be guile wan the day;
The Flowers of the Forest, that fought aye the foremost,
The prime of our land, lie cauld in the clay.

We'll hear nae mair lilting at our ewe-milking;
Women and bairns are heartless and wae,
Sighing and moaning on ilka green loaning:
The Flowers of the Forest are a' wede away.

JEAN ELLIOT

198 "AS I WAS GOING"

As I was going by Charing Cross,
I saw a black man upon a black horse;
They told me it was King Charles the First;
Oh dear, my heart was ready to burst!

199 OF THE GREAT AND FAMOUS

EVER TO BE HONOURED KNIGHT, SIR FRANCIS DRAKE, AND OF MY LITTLE-LITTLE SELFE.

THE Dragon that our Seas did raise his Crest
And brought back heapes of gold unto his nest,
Unto his Foes more terrible than Thunder,
Glory of his age, After-ages' wonder,
Excelling all those that excelled before;
It's feared we shall have none such any more;
Effecting all he sole did undertake,
Valiant, just, wise, milde, honest, Godly *Drake*.
This man when I was little I did meete
As he was walking up Totnes' long street.
He asked me whose I was? I answered him.
He asked me if his good friend were within?
A faire red Orange in his hand he had,
He gave it me whereof I was right glad,
Takes and kist me, and prayes *God blesse my boy*:
Which I record *with comfort* to this day.
Could he on me have breathèd with his breath,
His gifts, Elias-like, after his death,
Then had I beene enabled for to doe
Many brave things I have a heart unto.
I have as great desire as e're had *hee*
To joy, annoy, friends, foes; but 'twill not be.

ROBERT HAYMAN

200 A LAMENTATION

ALL looks be pale, hearts cold as stone,
For Hally now is dead and gone.

Hally in whose sight,
Most sweet sight,
All the earth late took delight.
Every eye, weep with me,
Joys drowned in tears must be.

His ivory skin, his comely hair,
His rosy cheeks so clear and fair,
Eyes that once did grace
His bright face,
Now in him all want their place.
Eyes and hearts, weep with me,
For who so kind as he?

His youth was like an April flower,
Adorned with beauty, love, and power.
Glory strewed his way,
Whose wreaths gay
Now are all turnèd to decay.
Then, again, weep with me,
None feel more cause than we.

No more may his wished sight return.
His golden lamp no more can burn,
Quenched is all his flame,
His hoped fame
Now hath left him nought but name.
For him all weep with me,
Since more him none shall see.

THOMAS CAMPION

201 WHAT IF SOME LITTLE PAINE THE PASSAGE HAVE

. . . WHAT if some little paine the passage have,
That makes fraile flesh to feare the bitter wave?
Is not short paine well borne, that brings long ease,
And layes the soule to sleepe in quiet grave?

Sleep after toyle, port after stormie seas,
Ease after warre, death after live does greatly please. . . .

EDMUND SPENSER

202 HENRY BEFORE AGINCOURT:

OCTOBER 25, 1415

. . . OUR King went up upon a hill high
And looked down to the valleys low:
He saw where the Frenchmen came hastily
As thick as ever did hail or snow.
Then kneeled our King down, in that stound,[1]
And all his men on every side:
Every man made a cross and kissed the ground,
And on their feet fast gan abide.
Our King said, "Sirs, what time of the day?"
"My Liege," they said, "it is nigh Prime."
"Then go we to our journey,
By the grace of JESU, it is good time:
For saints that lie in their shrine
To GOD for us be praying.
All the Religious of England, in this time,
Ora pro nobis for us they sing."
ST. GEORGE was seen over the host:
Of very truth this sight men did see.
Down was he sent by the HOLY GHOST,
To give our King the victory. . . .

JOHN LYDGATE

203 ALEXANDER THE GREAT

FOUR men stood by the grave of a man,
The grave of Alexander the Proud:
They sang words without falsehood
Over the prince from fair Greece.

Said the first man of them:
"Yesterday there were around the king

[1] For a moment

The men of the world—a sad gathering!
Though to-day he is alone."

"Yesterday the king of the brown world
Rode upon the heavy earth:
Though to-day it is the earth
That rides upon his neck."

"Yesterday," said the third wise author,
"Philip's son owned the whole world:
To-day he has nought
Save seven feet of earth."

"Alexander the liberal and great
Was wont to bestow silver and gold:
To-day," said the fourth man,
"The gold is here, and it is nought."

Thus truly spoke the wise men
Around the grave of the high-king:
It was not foolish women's talk
What those four sang.

204 THE MYRTLE BUSH GREW SHADY

"The myrtle bush grew shady
  Down by the ford."—
"Is it even so?" said my lady.
  "Even so!" said my lord.
"The leaves are set too thick together
  For the point of a sword."

"The arras in your room hangs close,
  No light between!
You wedded one of those
  That see unseen."—
"Is it even so?" said the King's Majesty.
  "Even so!" said the Queen.

MARY COLERIDGE

205

THE FORT OF RATHANGAN

THE fort over against the oak-wood,
Once it was Bruidge's, it was Cathal's,
It was Aed's, it was Ailill's,
It was Conaing's, it was Cuiline's,
And it was Maelduin's;
The fort remains after each in his turn—
And the kings asleep in the ground.

DANCE, MUSIC AND BELLS

206 A PIPER

A PIPER in the streets to-day
Set up, and tuned, and started to play,
And away, away, away on the tide
Of his music we started; on every side
Doors and windows were opened wide,
And men left down their work and came,
And women with petticoats coloured like flame.
And little bare feet that were blue with cold,
Went dancing back to the age of gold,
And all the world went gay, went gay,
For half an hour in the street to-day.

SEUMAS O'SULLIVAN

207 THE LITTLE DANCERS

LONELY, save for a few faint stars, the sky
Dreams; and lonely, below, the little street
Into its gloom retires, secluded and shy.
Scarcely the dumb roar enters this soft retreat;
And all is dark, save where come flooding rays
From a tavern window: there, to the brisk measure
Of an organ that down in an alley merrily plays,
Two children, all alone and no one by,
Holding their tattered frocks, through an airy maze
Of motion, lightly threaded with nimble feet,
Dance sedately: face to face they gaze,
Their eyes shining, grave with a perfect pleasure.

LAURENCE BINYON

208 TWO NUT TREES

i

I HAD a little nut tree,
Nothing would it bear,

But a silver nutmeg,
And a golden pear.
The King of Spain's daughter
Came to visit me,
And all was because of
My little nut tree.
I skipped over water
I danced over sea,
And all the birds in the air
Could not catch me.

THOMAS ANON

ii

THE King of China's daughter
So beautiful to see
With her face like yellow water, left
Her nutmeg tree.
Her little rope for skipping
She kissed and gave it me—
Made of painted notes of singing-birds
Among the fields of tea.
I skipped across the nutmeg grove,—
I skipped across the sea;
But neither sun nor moon, my dear,
Has yet caught me.

EDITH SITWELL

209 WHEN THE GREEN WOODS LAUGH

WHEN the green woods laugh with the voice of joy,
And the dimpling stream runs laughing by;
When the air does laugh with our merry wit,
And the green hill laughs with the noise of it;

When the meadows laugh with lively green,
And the grasshopper laughs in the merry scene,

When Mary and Susan and Emily
With their sweet round mouths sing "Ha Ha, He!"

When the painted birds laugh in the shade,
Where our table with cherries and nuts is spread,
Come live, and be merry, and join with me,
To sing the sweet chorus of "Ha, Ha, He!"

WILLIAM BLAKE

210

FA LA LA

MY mistress frowns when she should play;
I'll please her with a *Fa la la.*
Sometimes she chides, but I straightway
Present her with a *Fa la la.*

You lovers that have loves astray
May win them with a *Fa la la.*
Quick music's best, for still they say
None pleaseth like your *Fa la la.*

211

IT WAS A LOVER

IT was a Lover, and his lasse,
With a hey, and a ho, and a hey nonino,
That ore the greene corne-field did passe,
In spring time, the onely pretty ring time,
When Birds do sing, *hey ding a ding, ding*:
Sweet Lovers love the spring.

Between the acres of the Rie,
With a hey, and a ho, and a hey nonino,
These prettie Country folks would lie,
In spring time, the onely pretty ring time,
When Birds do sing, *hey ding a ding, ding*:
Sweet Lovers love the spring.

This Carroll they began that houre,
With a hey, and a ho, and a hey nonino;
How that a life was but a Flower,

In spring time, the onely pretty ring time,
When Birds do sing, *hey ding a ding, ding*:
Sweet Lovers love the spring.

And therefore take the present time,
With a hey and a ho, and a hey nonino;
For love is crownèd with the prime
In spring time, the onely pretty ring time,
When birds do sing, *hey ding a ding, ding*:
Sweet Lovers love the spring.

WILLIAM SHAKESPEARE

212

HEY, NONNY NO!

Hey, nonny no!
Men are fools that wish to die!
Is't not fine to dance and sing
When the bells of death do ring?
Is't not fine to swim in wine,
And turn upon the toe,
And sing *Hey nonny no!*

When the winds blow and the seas flow?
Hey, nonny no!

213

TARANTELLA

Do you remember an Inn,
Miranda?
Do you remember an Inn?
And the tedding and the spreading
Of the straw for a bedding,
And the fleas that tease in the High Pyrenees,
And the wine that tasted of the tar?
And the cheers and the jeers of the young muleteers
(Under the dark of the vine verandah)?

Do you remember an Inn, Miranda,
Do you remember an Inn?
And the cheers and the jeers of the young muleteers
Who hadn't got a penny,
And who weren't paying any,
And the hammer at the doors and the Din?
And the Hip! Hop! Hap!
Of the clap
Of the hands to the twirl and the swirl
Of the girl gone chancing,
Glancing,
Dancing,
Backing and advancing,
Snapping of the clapper to the spin
Out and in—
And the Ting, Tong, Tang of the guitar!
Do you remember an Inn,
Miranda?
Do you remember an Inn?

Never more;
Miranda,
Never more.
Only the high peaks hoar:
And Aragon a torrent at the door.
No sound
In the walls of the Halls where falls
The tread
Of the feet of the dead to the ground.
No sound:
Only the boom
Of the far Waterfall like Doom.

HILAIRE BELLOC

214 "I LOVED A LASS"

I LOVED a lass, a fair one,
As fair as e'er was seen;
She was indeed a rare one,

Another Sheba Queen:
But, fool as then I was,
I thought she loved me too:
But now, alas! she has left me,
Falero, lero, loo! . . .

And as abroad we walkèd
As lovers' fashion is,
Oft as we sweetly talkèd
The sun would steal a kiss.
The wind upon her lips
Likewise most sweetly blew;
But now, alas! she has left me,
Falero, lero, loo!

Many a merry meeting
My love and I have had;
She was my only sweeting,
She made my heart full glad;
The tears stood in her eyes
Like to the morning dew:
But now, alas! she has left me,
Falero, lero, loo!

Her cheeks were like the cherry,
Her skin was white as snow;
When she was blithe and merry
She angel-like did show;
Her waist exceeding small,
The fives did fit her shoe:
But now, alas! she's left me,
Falero, lero, loo!

In summer time or winter
She had her heart's desire;
I still did scorn to stint her
From sugar, sack, or fire;
The world went round about,
No cares we ever knew:

But now, alas! she's left me,
Falero, lero, loo! . . .

No riches now can raise me,
No want make me despair;
No misery amaze me,
Nor yet for want I care.
I have lost a world itself,
My earthly heaven, adieu,
Since she, alas! hath left me,
Falero, lero loo. . . .

GEORGE WITHER

215 GREEN GRASS

A dis, a dis, a green grass,
A dis, a dis, a dis;
Come all you pretty fair maids
And dance along with us.

For we are going roving,
A roving in this land;
We take this pretty fair maid,
We take her by the hand.

She shall get a duke, my dear,
As duck do get a drake;
And she shall have a young prince,
For her own fair sake.

And if this young prince chance to die,
She shall get another;
The bells will ring, and the birds will sing,
And we clap hands together.

216 THE LINCOLNSHIRE POACHER

WHEN I was bound apprentice in famous Lincolnshire,
Full well I served my master for more than seven year,

Till I took up to poaching—as you shall quickly hear:
Oh, 'tis my delight on a shining night
In the season of the year!

As mé and my cómrade were setting of a snare,
Twas then we spied the gamekeeper, for him we did not care,
For we can wrestle and fight, my boys, and jump o'er anywhere:
Oh, 'tis my delight on a shining night
In the season of the year!

As me and my comrade were setting four or five,
And taking on 'em up again we caught a hare alive,
We took the hare alive, my boys, and through the woods did steer:
Oh, 'tis my delight on a shining night
In the season of the year!

I threw him on my shoulder, and then we trudged home,
We took him to a neighbour's house and sold him for a crown
We sold him for a crown, my boys, but I did not tell you where:
Oh, 'tis my delight on a shining night
In the season of the year!

Success to every gentleman that lives in Lincolnshire,
Success to every poacher that wants to sell a hare,
Bad luck to every gamekeeper that will not sell his deer: [1]
Oh, 'tis my delight on a shining night
In the season of the year!

217 THE MEN OF GOTHAM

SEAMEN three! What men be ye?
Gotham's three wise men we be.
Whither in your bowl so free?
To rake the moon from out the sea.
The bowl goes trim. The moon doth shine.
And our ballast is old wine—
And your ballast is old wine.

[1] Game

Who art thóu, so fast adrift?
I am he they call Old Care.
Here on board we will thee lift.
No: I may not enter there.
Wherefore so? 'Tis Jove's decree,
In a bowl Care may not be—
In a bowl Care may not be.

Fear ye not the waves that roll?
No; in charmèd bowl we swim.
What the charm that floats the bowl?
Water may not pass the brim.
The bowl goes trim. The moon doth shine.
And our ballast is old wine—
And your ballast is old wine.

THOMAS LOVE PEACOCK

218 EARLY MORNING MEADOW SONG

Now some may drink old vintage wine
To ladies gowned with rustling silk,
But we will drink to dairymaids,
And drink to them in rum and milk—
O, it's up in the morning early,
When the dew is on the grass,
And St. John's bell rings for matins,
And St. Mary's rings for mass!

The merry skylarks soar and sing,
And seem to Heaven very near—
Who knows what blessed inns they see,
What holy drinking songs they hear?
O, it's up in the morning early,
When the dew is on the grass,
And St. John's bell rings for matins,
And St. Mary's rings for mass!

The mushrooms may be priceless pearls
A queen has lost beside the stream;
But rum is melted rubies when
It turns the milk to golden cream!
O, it's up in the morning early,
When the dew is on the grass,
And St. John's bell rings for matins,
And St. Mary's rings for mass!

CHARLES DALMON

219 DABBLING IN THE DEW

OH, where are you going to, my pretty little dear
With your red rosy cheeks and your coal-black hair?
I'm going a-milking, kind sir, she answered me:
And it's dabbling in the dew makes the milkmaids fair!

Suppose I were to clothe you, my pretty little dear,
In a green silken gown and the amethyst rare?
O no, sir, O no, sir, kind sir, she answered me,
For it's dabbling in the dew makes the milkmaids fair!

Suppose I were to carry you, my pretty little dear,
In a chariot with horses, a grey gallant pair?
O no, sir, O no, sir, kind sir, she answered me,
For it's dabbling in the dew makes the milkmaids fair!

Suppose I were to feast you, my pretty little dear,
With dainties on silver, the whole of the year?
O no, sir, O no, sir, kind sir, she answered me,
For it's dabbling in the dew makes the milkmaids fair!

O but London's a city, my pretty little dear,
And all men are gallant and brave that are there—
O no, sir, O no, sir, kind sir, she answered me,
For it's dabbling in the dew makes the milkmaids fair!

O fine clothes and dainties and carriages so rare
Bring grey to the cheeks and silver to the hair;

What's a ring on the finger if rings are round the eye?
But it's dabbling in the dew makes the mailkmaids fair!

220 BONNY LASSIE O!

O THE evening's for the fair, bonny lassie O!
To meet the cooler air and walk an angel there,
With the dark dishevelled hair,
Bonny lassie O!

The bloom's on the brere, bonnie lassie O!
Oak apples on the tree; and wilt thou gang to see
The shed I've made for thee,
Bonny lassie O!

'Tis agen the running brook, bonnie lassie O!
In a grassy nook hard by, with a little patch of sky,
And a bush to keep us dry,
Bonny lassie O!

There's the daisy all the year, bonny lassie O!
There's the king-cup bright as gold, and the speedwell never cold,
And the arum leaves unrolled,
Bonny lassie O!

O meet me at the shed, bonny lassie O!
With the woodbine peeping in, and the roses like thy skin
Blushing, thy praise to win,
Bonny lassie O!

I will meet thee there at e'en, bonny lassie O!
When the bee sips in the bean, and grey willow branches lean,
And the moonbeam looks between,
Bonny lassie O!

JOHN CLARE

221 THE MAD MAID'S SONG

GOOD-MORROW to the Day so fair,
Good-morning, Sir, to you:

Good-morrow to mine own torn hair,
  Bedabled with the dew.

Good-morning to this Prim-rose too,
  Good-morrow to each maid,
That will with flowers the *Tomb* bestrew
  Wherein my Love is laid.

Ah! woe is me, woe, woe is me,
  Alack and welladay!
For pitty, Sir, find out that Bee
  Which bore my Love away.

Ile seek him in your Bonnet brave,
  Ile seek him in your eyes;
Nay, now, I think they've made his grave
  I' the bed of strawburies.

Ile seek him there; I know, ere this,
  The cold, cold Earth doth shake him;
But I will go, or send a kiss
  By you, Sir, to awake him.

Pray hurt him not, though he be dead,
  He knowes well who do love him,
And who with green-turfes reare his head,
  And who do rudely move him.

He's soft and tender (Pray take heed);
  With bands of Cowslips bind him,
And bring him home—but 'tis decreed
  That I shall never find him.

ROBERT HERRICK

222 TELL ME WHERE IS FANCIE BRED

TELL me where is Fancie bred,
Or in the heart or in the head?

How begot, how nourishèd?
Replie, replie!
It is engendered in the eyes,
With gazing fed; and Fancy dies
In the cradle where it lies.
Let us all ring Fancie's knell:
Ile begin it:
Ding, dong, bell.
All. *Ding, dong, bell.*

WILLIAM SHAKESPEARE

223

MUSIC

MUSIC, when soft voices die,
Vibrates in the memory—
Odours, when sweet violets sicken,
Live within the sense they quicken.

Rose leaves, when the rose is dead,
Are heaped for the belovèd's bed;
And so thy thoughts, when thou art gone,
Love itself shall slumber on.

PERCY BYSSHE SHELLEY

224

THE BELLS OF SHANDON

WITH deep affection and recollection
I often think of the Shandon bells,
Whose sounds so wild would, in the days of childhood,
Fling around my cradle their magic spells.
On this I ponder where'er I wander,
And thus grow fonder, sweet Cork, of thee;
With thy bells of Shandon,
That sound so grand on
The pleasant waters of the river Lee.

I've heard bells chiming full many a clime in,
Tolling sublime in cathedral shrine,
While at a glib rate brass tongues would vibrate;

But all their music spoke naught to thine;
For memory, dwelling on each proud swelling
Of thy belfry, knelling its bold notes free,
Made the bells of Shandon
Sound more grand on
The pleasant waters of the river Lee.

I've heard bells tolling old "Adrian's Mole" in,
Their thunder rolling from the Vatican,
And cymbals glorious, swinging uproarious
In the gorgeous turrets of Notre Dame;
But thy sounds were sweeter than the dome of Peter
Flings o'er the Tiber, pealing solemnly.
O! the bells of Shandon
Sound far more grand on
The pleasant waters of the river Lee.

There's a bell in Moscow; while on Tower and Kiosk, O!
In St. Sophia the Turkman gets,
And loud in air, calls men to prayer,
From the tapering summit of tall minarets.
Such empty phantom I freely grant them;
But there is an anthem more dear to me,—
'Tis the bells of Shandon,
That sound so grand on
The pleasant waters of the river Lee.

FRANCIS MAHONY (FATHER PROUT)

225 UPON A RING OF BELLS

BELLS have wide mouths and tongues, but are too weak,
Have they not help, to sing, or talk or speak.
But if you move them they will mak't appear,
By speaking they'l make all the Town to hear.
When Ringers handle them with Art and Skill,
They then the ears of their Observers fill,
With such brave Notes, they ting and tang so well
As to out strip all with their ding, dong, Bell.

Comparison

These Bells are like the Powers of my Soul;
Their Clappers to the Passions of my mind;
The Ropes by which my Bells are made to tole,
Are Promises (I by experience find.)
 My body is the Steeple where they hang,
My graces they which do ring ev'ry Bell:
Nor is there any thing gives such a tang,
When by these Ropes these Ringers ring them well.
 Let not my Bells these Ringers want, nor Ropes;
Yea let them have room for to swing and sway:
To toss themselves deny them not their Scopes.
Lord! in my Steeple give them room to play.
If they do tole, ring out, or chime all in,
They drown the tempting tinckling Voice of Vice:
Lord! when my Bells have gone, my Soul has bin
As 'twere a tumbling in this Paradice!
 Or if these Ringers do the Changes ring,
Upon my Bells, they do such Musick make,
My Soul then (Lord) cannot but bounce and sing,
So greatly her they with their Musick take.
But Boys (my Lusts) into my Belfry go,
And pull these Ropes, but do no Musick make
They rather turn my Bells by what they do,
Or by disorder make my Steeple shake.
 Then, Lord! I pray thee keep my Belfry Key,
Let none but Graces meddle with these Ropes:
And when these naughty Boys come, say them Nay.
From such Ringers of Musick there's no hopes.
 O Lord! If thy poor Child might have his will,
And might his meaning freely to thee tell;
He never of this Musick has his fill,
There's nothing to him like thy ding, dong, Bell.

JOHN BUNYAN

226 THE BELFRY

DARK is the stair, and humid the old walls
Wherein it winds, on worn stones, up the tower.

Only by loophole chinks at intervals
Pierces the late glow of this August hour.

Two truant children climb the stairway dark,
With joined hands, half in glee and half in fear,
The boy mounts brisk, the girl hangs back to hark
If the gruff sexton their light footsteps hear.

Dazzled at last they gain the belfry-room.
Barred rays through shutters hover across the floor
Dancing in dust; so fresh they come from gloom
That breathless they pause wondering at the door.

How hushed it is! what smell of timbers old
From cobwebbed beams! The warm light here and there
Edging a darkness, sleeps in pools of gold,
Or weaves fantastic shadows through the air.

How motionless the huge bell! Straight and stiff,
Ropes through the floor rise to the rafters dim.
The shadowy round of metal hangs, as if
No force could ever lift its gleamy rim.

A child's awe, a child's wonder, who shall trace
What dumb thoughts on its waxen softness write
In such a spell-brimmed, time-forgotten place,
Bright in that strangeness of approaching night?

As these two gaze, their fingers tighter press;
For suddenly the slow bell upward heaves
Its vast mouth, the cords quiver at the stress,
And ere the heart prepare, the ear receives

Full on its delicate sense the plangent stroke
Of violent, iron, reverberating sound.
As if the tower in all its stones awoke,
Deep echoes tremble, again in clangour drowned,

That starts without a whir of frighted wings
And holds these young hearts shaken, hushed, and thrilled,
Like frail reeds in a rushing stream, like strings
Of music, or like trees with tempest filled,

And rolls in wide waves out o'er the lone land,
Tone following tone toward the far-setting sun,
Till where in fields long shadowed reapers stand
Bowed heads look up, and lo, the day is done. . . .

LAURENCE BINYON

227

IL PENSEROSO

. . . SWEET bird that shunn'st the noise of folly,
Most musicall, most melancholy!
Thee chauntress of the Woods among
I woo to hear thy eeven-song;
And missing thee, I walk unseen
On the dry smooth-shaven green,
To behold the wandering moon
Riding near her highest noon,
Like one that had been led astray
Through the Heaven's wide pathles way,
And oft, as if her head she bowed,
Stooping through a fleecy cloud.

Oft on a Plat of rising ground,
I hear the far-off *Curfeu* sound
Over some wide-watered shoar,
Swinging slow with sullen roar:
Or if the Ayr will not permit,
Som still removèd place will fit,
Where glowing Embers through the room
Teach light to counterfeit a gloom,
Far from all resort of mirth,
Save the Cricket on the hearth,
Or the Belman's drousie charm
To bless the dores from nightly harm. . . .

JOHN MILTON

228 CHIMES

Brief, on a flying night,
From the shaken tower,
A flock of bells take flight,
And go with the hour.

Like birds from the cote to the gales,
Abrupt—O hark!
A fleet of bells set sails,
And go to the dark.

Sudden the cold airs swing,
Alone, aloud,
A verse of bells takes wing
And flies with the cloud.

Alice Meynell

229 CITIES DROWNED

Cities drowned in olden time
Keep, they say, a magic chime
Rolling up from far below
When the moon-led waters flow.

So within me, ocean deep,
Lies a sunken world asleep.
Lest its bells forget to ring,
Memory! set the tide a-swing!

Henry Newbolt

230 THE BELL-MAN

From noise of Scare-fires rest ye free,
From Murders—*Benedicite.*
From all mischances, that may fright
Your pleasing slumbers in the night:
Mercie secure ye all, and keep
The Goblin from ye, while ye sleep.
Past one aclock, and almost two,
My Masters all, *Good day to you!*

Robert Herrick

AUTUMN LEAVES: WINTER SNOW

231 TO MEADOWS

YE have been fresh and green,
Ye have been filled with flowers:
And ye the Walks have been
Where maids have spent their houres.

Ye have beheld, how they
With *Wicker Arks* did come
To kisse, and beare away
The richer Couslips home.

Ye have heard them sweetly sing
And seen them in a Round:
Each Virgin, like a Spring,
With Hony-succles crowned.

But now, we see, none here,
Whose silverie feet did tread,
And with dishevelled Haire,
Adorned this smoother Mead.

Like Unthrifts, having spent,
Your stock, and needy grown,
Ye are left here to lament
Your poore estates, alone.

ROBERT HERRICK

232 THE COTTAGER TO HER INFANT

THE days are cold, the nights are long,
The North wind sings a doleful song;

Then hush again upon my breast;
All merry things are now at rest,
    Save thee, my pretty love!

The kitten sleeps upon the hearth,
The crickets long have ceased their mirth;
There's nothing stirring in the house
Save one wee, hungry, nibbling mouse,
    Then why so busy thou?
Nay! start not at the sparkling light;
'Tis but the moon that shines so bright
    On the window-pane
    Bedropped with rain:
Then, little darling! sleep again,
    And wake when it is day.

DOROTHY WORDSWORTH

233

TO AUTUMN

SEASON of mists and mellow fruitfulness,
  Close bosom-friend of the maturing sun;
Conspiring with him how to load and bless
  With fruit the vines that round the thatch-eaves run;
To bend with apples the mossed cottage-trees,
  And fill all fruit with ripeness to the core;
    To swell the gourd, and plump the hazel shells
  With a sweet kernel; to set budding more,
  And still more, later flowers for the bees,
  Until they think warm days will never cease,
    For Summer has o'er-brimmed their clammy cells—
Who hath not seen thee oft amid thy store?
  Sometimes whoever seeks abroad may find
Thee sitting careless on a granary floor,
  Thy hair soft-lifted by the winnowing wind;
Or on a half-reaped furrow sound asleep,
  Drowsed with the fume of poppies, while thy hook
    Spares the next swath and all its twinèd flowers:
And sometimes like a gleaner thou dost keep

Steady thy laden head across a brook;
Or by a cyder-press, with patient look,
Thou watchest the last oozings hours by hours.

Where are the songs of Spring? Ay, where are they?
Think not of them, thou hast thy music too,—
While barred clouds bloom the soft-dying day,
And touch the stubble-plains with rosy hue;
Then in a wailful choir the small gnats mourn
Among the river-sallows, borne aloft
Or sinking as the light wind lives or dies;
And full-grown lambs loud bleat from hilly bourn;
Hedge-crickets sing; and now with treble soft
The red-breast whistles from a garden-croft;
And gathering swallows twitter in the skies.

John Keats

234

THE SOLITARY REAPER

Behold her, single in the field,
Yon solitary Highland Lass!
Reaping and singing by herself;
Stop here, or gently pass!
Alone she cuts and binds the grain,
And sings a melancholy strain;
O listen! for the vale profound
Is overflowing with the sound.

No nightingale did ever chaunt
More welcome notes to weary bands
Of travellers in some shady haunt,
Among Arabian sands:
A voice so thrilling ne'er was heard
In spring-time from the cuckoo bird.
Breaking the silence of the seas
Among the farthest Hebrides.

Will no one tell me what she sings?—
Perhaps the plaintive numbers flow
For old, unhappy, far-off things,

And battles long ago;
Or is it some more humble lay,
Familiar matter of to-day?
Some natural sorrow, loss, or pain,
That has been, and may be again?

Whate'er the theme, the maiden sang
As if her song could have no ending;
I saw her singing at her work,
And o'er the sickle bending;—
I listened, motionless and still;
And, as I mounted up the hill,
The music in my heart I bore
Long after it was heard no more.

WILLIAM WORDSWORTH

235 "THE HEAVING ROSES OF THE HEDGE ARE STIRRED"

THE heaving roses of the hedge are stirred
By the sweet breath of summer, and the bird
Makes from within his jocund voice be heard.

The winds that kiss the roses sweep the sea
Of uncut grass, whose billows rolling free
Half drown the hedges which part lea from lea.

But soon shall look the wondering roses down
Upon an empty field cut close and brown,
That lifts no more its height against their own.

And in a little while those roses bright,
Leaf after leaf, shall flutter from their height,
And on the reapèd fields lie pink and white.

And yet again the bird that sings so high
Shall ask the snow for alms with piteous cry;
Take fright in his bewildering bower, and die.

CANON DIXON

236

A Dirge

THE warm sun is failing, the bleak wind is wailing,
The bare boughs are sighing, the pale flowers are dying;
And the Year
On the earth her death-bed, in a shroud of leaves dead,
Is lying.
Come, Months, come away,
From November to May,
In your saddest array;
Follow the bier
Of the dead cold Year,
And like dim shadows watch by her sepulchre.

The chill rain is falling, the nipped worm is crawling,
The rivers are swelling, the thunder is knelling
For the Year;
The blithe swallows are flown, and the lizards each gone
To his dwelling.
Come, Months, come away;
Put on white, black, and grey;
Let your light sisters play—
Ye, follow the bier
Of the dead cold Year,
And make her grave green with tear on tear.

PERCY BYSSHE SHELLEY

237

"WHEN THAT I WAS AND A LITTLE TINY BOY"

WHEN that I was and a little tinie boy,
With hey, ho, the winde and the raine:
A foolish thing was but a toy,
For the raine it raineth every day.

But when I came to man's estate,
With hey, ho, the winde and the raine:
'Gainst Knaves and Theeves men shut their gate,
For the raine it raineth every day.

But when I came, alas, to wive,
With hey, ho, the winde and the raine:
By swaggering could I never thrive,
For the raine it raineth every day.

But when I came unto my beds,
With hey, ho, the winde and the raine,
With tos-pottes still had drunken heades,—
For the raine it raineth every day.

A great while ago the world begon,
With hey, ho, the winde and the raine,
But that's all one, our Play is done,
And we'll strive to please you every day.

William Shakespeare

238

SONG

The feathers of the willow
Are half of them grown yellow
Above the swelling stream;
And ragged are the bushes,
And rusty are the rushes
And wild the clouded gleam.

The thistle now is older,
His stalk begins to moulder,
His head is white as snow;
The branches all are barer,
The linet's song is rarer
The robin pipeth now.

Canon Dixon

239

FALL, LEAVES, FALL

Fall, leaves, fall; die, flowers, away;
Lengthen night and shorten day;

Every leaf speaks bliss to me,
Fluttering from the autumn tree.

I shall smile when wreaths of snow
Blossom where the rose should grow;
I shall sing when night's decay
Ushers in a drearier day.

EMILY BRONTË

240

THE SANDS OF DEE

"O MARY, go and call the cattle home,
And call the cattle home,
And call the cattle home
Across the sands of Dee;"
The western wind was wild and dank with foam,
And all alone went she.

The western tide crept up along the sand,
And o'er and o'er the sand,
And round and round the sand,
As far as eye could see.
The rolling mist came down and hid the land:
And never home came she.

"Oh! is it weed, or fish, or floating hair—
A tress of golden hair,
A drownèd maiden's hair
Above the nets at sea?
Was never salmon yet that shone so fair
Among the stakes on Dee."

They rowed her in across the rolling foam,
The cruel crawling foam,
The cruel hungry foam,
To her grave beside the sea:
But still the boatmen hear her call the cattle home
Across the sands of Dee.

CHARLES KINGSLEY

241 BREAK, BREAK, BREAK

BREAK, break break,
  On thy cold grey stones, O Sea!
And I would that my tongue could utter
  The thoughts that arise in me.

O well for the fisherman's boy,
  That he shouts with his sister at play!
O well for the sailor lad,
  That he sings in his boat on the bay!

And the stately ships go on
  To their haven under the hill;
But O for the touch of a vanished hand,
  And the sound of a voice that is still!

Break, break, break,
  At the foot of thy crags, O Sea!
But the tender grace of a day that is dead
  Will never come back to me.

ALFRED, LORD TENNYSON

242 ODE TO THE WEST WIND

I

O, WILD West Wind, thou breath of Autumn's being,
Thou, from whose unseen presence the leaves dead
Are driven, like ghosts from an enchanter fleeing,

Yellow, and black, and pale, and hectic red,
Pestilence-stricken multitudes: O, thou,
Who chariotest to their dark wintry bed

The wingèd seeds, where they lie cold and low,
Each like a corpse within its grave, until
Thine azure sister of the Spring shall blow

Her clarion o'er the dreaming earth, and fill
(Driving sweet buds like flocks to feed in air)
With living hues and odours plain and hill:

Wild Spirit, which art moving everywhere;
Destroyer and preserver; hear, O hear!

II

Thou on whose stream, mid the steep sky's commotion,
Loose clouds like earth's decaying leaves are shed,
Shook from the tangled boughs of Heaven and Ocean,

Angels of rain and lightning: there are spread
On the blue surface of thine aëry surge,
Like the bright hair uplifted from the head

Of some fierce Maenad, even from the dim verge
Of the horizon to the zenith's height
The locks of the approaching storm. Thou dirge

Of the dying year, to which this closing night
Will be the dome of a vast sepulchre,
Vaulted with all thy congregated might

Of vapours, from whose solid atmosphere
Black rain, and fire, and hail will burst: O hear!

III

Thou who didst waken from his summer dreams
The blue Mediterranean, where he lay,
Lulled by the coil of his crystàlline streams,

Beside a pumice isle in Baiae's bay,
And saw in sleep old palaces and towers
Quivering within the wave's intenser day,

All overgrown with azure moss and flowers
So sweet, the sense faints picturing them! Thou
For whose path the Atlantic's level powers

Cleave themselves into chasms, while far below
The sea-blooms and the oozy woods which wear
The sapless foliage of the ocean, know

Thy voice, and suddenly grow grey with fear,
And tremble and despoil themselves: O hear!

IV

If I were a dead leaf thou mightest bear;
If I were a swift cloud to fly with thee;
A wave to pant beneath thy power, and share

The impulse of thy strength, only less free
Than thou, O uncontrollable! If even
I were as in my boyhood, and could be

The comrade of thy wanderings over Heaven,
As then, when to outstrip thy skiey speed
Scarce seemed a vision; I would ne'er have striven

As thus with thee in prayer in my sore need.
Oh, lift me as a wave, a leaf, a cloud!
I fall upon the thorns of life! I bleed!

A heavy weight of hours has chained and bowed
One too like thee: tameless, and swift, and proud.

V

Make me thy lyre, even as the forest is:
What if my leaves are falling like its own!
The tumult of thy mighty harmonies

Will take from both a deep, autumnal tone,
Sweet though in sadness. Be thou, Spirit fierce,
My spirit! Be thou me, impetuous one!

Drive my dead thoughts over the universe
Like withered leaves to quicken a new birth!
And, by the incantation of this verse,

Scatter, as from an unextinguished hearth
Ashes and sparks, my words among mankind!
Be through my lips to unawakened earth

The trumpet of a prophecy! O, Wind,
If Winter comes, can Spring be far behind?

PERCY BYSSHE SHELLEY

243 THAT WIND

THAT wind, I used to hear it swelling;
With joy divinely deep;
You might have seen my hot tears welling,
But rapture made me weep.

I used to love on winter nights
To lie and dream alone
Of all the rare and real delights
My lonely years had known;

And oh!—above the best—of those
That coming time should bear,
Like heaven's own glorious stars they rose,
Still beaming bright and fair.

EMILY BRONTË

244 A FROSTY NIGHT

Mother. Alice, dear, what ails you,
Dazed and white and shaken?
Has the chill night numbed you?
Is it fright you have taken?

Alice. Mother I am very well,
I felt never better;
Mother, do not hold me so,
Let me write my letter.

Mother. Sweet, my dear, what ails you?
Alice. No, but I am well.

The night was cold and frosty,
There's no more to tell.

Mother. Ay, the night was frosty,
Coldly gaped the moon,
Yet the birds seemed twittering
Through green boughs of June.

Soft and thick the snow lay,
Stars danced in the sky,
Not all the lambs of May-day
Skip so bold and high.

Your feet were dancing, Alice,
You seemed to dance on air,
You looked a ghost or angel
In the starlight there.

Your eyes were frosted starlight,
Your heart, fire and snow.
Who was it said "I love you"?

Alice. Mother, let me go!

ROBERT GRAVES

245

IN A DREAR-NIGHTED DECEMBER

IN a drear-nighted December,
Too happy, happy tree,
Thy branches ne'er remember
Their green felicity:
The north cannot undo them
With a sleety whistle through them;
Nor frozen thawings glue them
From budding at the prime.

In a drear-nighted December,
Too happy, happy brook,
Thy bubblings ne'er remember
Apollo's summer look;

But with a sweet forgetting,
They stay their crystal fretting,
Never, never petting
About the frozen time.

Ah! would 'twere so with many
A gentle girl and boy!
But were there ever any
Writhed not at passèd joy?
To know the change and feel it,
When there is none to heal it
Nor numbèd sense to steal it,
Was never said in rhyme.

JOHN KEATS

246 A SONG OF WINTER

COLD cold!
Cold to-night is broad Moylurg,
Higher the snow than the mountain-range,
The deer cannot get at their food.

Cold till Doom!
The storm has spread over all:
A river is each furrow upon the slope,
Each ford a full pool.

A great tidal sea is each loch,
A full loch is each pool:
Horses cannot get over the ford of Ross,
No more can two feet get there.

The fish of Ireland are a-roaming,
There is no strand which the wave does not pound,
Not a town there is in the land,
Not a bell is heard, no crane talks.

The wolves of Cuan-wood get
Neither rest nor sleep in their lair,

The little wren cannot find
Shelter in her nest on the slope of Lon.

Keen wind and cold ice
Has burst upon the little company of birds,
The blackbird cannot get a lee to her liking,
Shelter for its side in Cuan-wood.

Cosy our pot on its hook,
Crazy the hut on the slope of Lon:
The snow has crushed the wood here,
Toilsome to climb up Ben-bo.

Glenn Rye's ancient bird
From the bitter wind gets grief;
Great her misery and her pain,
The ice will get into her mouth.

From flock and from down to rise—
Take it to heart!—were folly for thee;
Ice in heaps on every ford—
That is why I say "cold"!

247 COLD BLOWS THE WIND

CAULD blows the wind frae north to south,
And drift is driving sairly;
The sheep are couring [1] in the heugh,[2]
Oh sirs; it's winter fairly.
Now up in the morning's no' for me,
Up in the morning early;
I'd rather gae supperless to my bed,
Than rise in the morning early.

Loud rairs the blast amang the woods,
The branches tirling barely,
Amang the chimley taps it thuds,
And frost is nippin sairly.
Now up in the morning's no' for me,

[1] Cowering [2] Glen

Up in the morning early;
To sit a' the night I'd rather agree,
Than rise in the morning early.

The sun peeps o'er the southlan' hill,
Like ony tim'rous carlie [1];
Just blinks a wee, then sings again,
And that we find severely.
Now up in the morning's no' for me,
Up in the morning early;
When snaw blaws into the chimley cheek,
Wha'd rise in the morning early.

Nae linties [2] lilt on hedge or bush,
Poor things, they suffer sairly;
In cauldrife [3] quarters a' the night,
A' day they feed but sparely.
Now up in the morning's no' for me,
Up in the morning early;
Nae fate can be waur, [4] in winter time,
Than rise in the morning early.

JOHN HAMILTON

248

SKATING

. . . So through the darkness and the cold we flew,
And not a voice was idle; with the din
Smitten, the precipices rang aloud;
The leafless trees and every icy crag
Tinkled like iron; while far distant hills
Into the tumult sent an alien sound
Of melancholy not unnoticed, while the stars
Eastward were sparkling clear, and in the west
The orange sky of evening died away.
Not seldom from the uproar I retired
Into a silent bay, or sportively
Glanced sideway, leaving the tumultuous throng,

[1] Wee bit lassikin [2] No linnets [3] Freezing [4] Worse

To cut across the reflex of a star
That fled, and, flying still before me, gleamed
Upon the glassy plain; and oftentimes,
When we had given our bodies to the wind,
And all the shadowy banks on either side
Came sweeping through the darkness, spinning still
In rapid line of motion, then at once
Have I, reclining back upon my heels,
Stopped short; yet still the solitary cliffs
Wheeled by me—even as if the earth had rolled
With visible motion her diurnal round!
Behind me did they stretch in solemn train,
Feebler and feebler, and I stood and watched
Till all was tranquil as a dreamless sleep. . . .

WILLIAM WORDSWORTH

249 LONDON SNOW

WHEN men were all asleep the snow came flying,
In large white flakes falling on the city brown,
Stealthily and perpetually settling and loosely lying,
Hushing the latest traffic of the drowsy town;
Deadening, muffling, stifling its murmurs failing;
Lazily and incessantly floating down and down:
Silently sifting and veiling road, roof and railing;
Hiding difference, making unevenness even,
Into angles and crevices softly drifting and sailing.
All night it fell, and when full inches seven
It lay in the depth of its uncompacted lightness,
The clouds blew off from a high and frosty heaven;
And all woke earlier for the unaccustomed brightness
Of the winter dawning, the strange unheavenly glare:
The eye marvelled—marvelled at the dazzling whiteness;
The ear hearkened to the stillness of the solemn air;
No sound of wheel rumbling nor of foot falling,
And the busy morning cries came thin and spare.
Then boys I heard, as they went to school, calling,
They gathered up the crystal manna to freeze
Their tongues with tasting, their hands with snowballing;

Or rioted in a drift, plunging up to the knees;
Or peering up from under the white-mossed wonder,
"O look at the trees!" they cried, "O look at the trees!"
With lessened load a few carts creak and blunder,
Following along the white deserted way,
A country company long dispersed asunder:
When now already the sun, in pale display
Standing by Paul's high dome, spread forth below
His sparkling beams, and awoke the stir of the day.
For now doors open, and war is waged with the snow;
And trains of sombre men, past tale of number,
Tread long brown paths, as toward their toil they go:
But even for them awhile no cares encumber
Their minds diverted; the daily word is unspoken,
The daily thoughts of labour and sorrow slumber
At the sight of the beauty that greets them, for the charm
they have broken.

ROBERT BRIDGES

250 FOR SNOW

OH the falling Snow!
Oh the falling Snow!
Where does it all come from?
Whither does it go?
Never never laughing,
Never never weeping,
Falling in its Sleep,
Forever ever sleeping—
From what Sleep of Heaven
Does it flow, and go
Into what Sleep of Earth,
The falling falling Snow?

ELEANOR FARJEON

251 VELVET SHOES

LET us walk in the white snow
In a soundless space;

With footsteps quiet and slow,
At a tranquil pace,
Under veils of white lace.

I shall go shod in silk,
And you in wool,
White as a white cow's milk,
More beautiful
Than the breast of a gull.

We shall walk through the still town
In a windless peace;
We shall step upon white down,
Upon silver fleece,
Upon softer than these.

We shall walk in velvet shoes:
Wherever we go
Silence will fall like dews
On white silence below.
We shall walk in the snow.

ELEANOR WYLIE

252

LUCY GRAY

OFT I had heard of Lucy Gray:
And when I crossed the wild,
I chanced to see at break of day
The solitary child.

No mate, no comrade Lucy knew;
She dwelt on a wide moor,
The sweetest thing that ever grew
Beside a human door!

You yet may spy the fawn at play,
The hare upon the green;
But the sweet face of Lucy Gray
Will never more be seen.

"To-night will be a stormy night—
You to the town must go;
And take a lantern, Child, to light
Your mother through the snow."

"That, Father! will I gladly do:
'Tis scarcely afternoon—
The minster-clock has just struck two,
And yonder is the moon!"

At this the father raised his hook,
And snapped a faggot-band;
He plied his work;—and Lucy took
The lantern in her hand.

Not blither is the mountain roe:
With many a wanton stroke
Her feet disperse the powdery snow,
That rises up like smoke.

The storm came on before its time:
She wandered up and down;
And many a hill did Lucy climb:
But never reached the town.

The wretched parents all that night
Went shouting far and wide;
But there was neither sound nor sight
To serve them for a guide.

At day-break on a hill they stood
That overlook'd the moor;
And thence they saw the bridge of wood
A furlong from their door.

They wept—and, turning homeward, cried
"In heaven we all shall meet!"
—When in the snow the mother spied
The print of Lucy's feet.

Then downwards from the steep hill's edge
They tracked the footmarks small;
And through the broken hawthorn hedge,
And by the long stone-wall:

And then an open field they crossed,
The marks were still the same;
They tracked them on, nor ever lost;
And to the bridge they came:

They followed from the snowy bank
Those footmarks, one by one,
Into the middle of the plank;
And further there were none!

—Yet some maintain that to this day
She is a living child;
That you may see sweet Lucy Gray
Upon the lonesome wild.

O'er rough and smooth she trips along,
And never looks behind;
And sings a solitary song
That whistles in the wind.

WILLIAM WORDSWORTH

253 GONE WERE BUT THE WINTER COLD

"GANE were but the winter cauld
And gane were but the snaw,
I could sleep in the wild woods,
Where primroses blaw.

"Cauld's the snaw at my head,
And cauld at my feet,
And the finger o' death is at my e'en
Closing them to sleep,

"Let nane tell my father,
Or my mither sae dear;
I'll meet them baith in heaven
At the Spring o' the year."

ALLAN CUNNINGHAM

254 A CHILD'S WINTER EVENING

THE smothering dark engulfs relentlessly
With nightmare tread approaching steadfastly;
All horrors thicken as the daylight fails
And, is it wind, or some lost ghost that wails?

Tongue cannot tell the stories that beset,
With livid pictures blackness dense as jet,
Or that wild questioning—whence we are; and why;
If death is darkness; and why I am I.

The children look through the uneven pane
Out to the world, to bring them joy again;
But only snowflakes melting into mire
Without, within the red glow of the fire.

They long for something wonderful to break
This long-drawn winter wistfulness, and take
Shape in the darkness; threatening like Fate
There comes a hell-like crackling from the grate.

But hand in hand they urge themselves anear
And watch the cities burning bright and clear;
Faces diabolical and cliffs and halls
And strangely-pinnacled, molten castle walls.

Tall figures flicker on the ceiling stark
Then grimly fade into one ominous dark;
Dream terrors iron-bound throng on them apace,
And dusk with fire, and flames with shadows race.

GWEN JOHN

255 A CAROL FOR SAINT STEPHEN'S DAY

SEYNT STEVENE was a clerk,
In kyng Herowdės halle,
And servyd him of bred and cloth,
As every kyng befalle.

Stevyn out of Kechoun cam,
With boris hed on honde,
He saw a sterr was fayr and bryght
Over Bedlem stonde.

He kyst adoun the bores hed,
And went into the halle:
"I forsake the, kyng Herowde,
And thi werkės alle.

"I forsak the, kyng Herowde,
And thi werkės alle:
Ther is a chyld, in Bedlem born,
Is better than we alle."

"Quhat eylyt the, Stevene?
Quhat is the befalle?
Lakkyt the eyther mete or drynk
In kyng Herowdės halle?"

"Lakyt me neyther mete ne drynk
In kyng Herowdės halle;
Ther is a chyld, in Bedlem born,
Is better than we alle."

"Quhat eylyt the, Stevyn, art thu wod?
Or thu gynnyst to brede?
"Lakkyt the eyther gold or fe,
Or ony rychė wede?"

"Lakyt me neyther gold ne fe,
Ne non rychė wede;

Ther is a chyld, in Bedlem born,
Shal helpyn us at our nede."

"That is al so soth, Stevyn,
Al so soth, I wys,
As this capon crowė schel
That lyth her in myn dych."
That word was not so sonė seyd,
That wordė in that halle,
The capon crew, *Christus natus est!*
Among the lordes alle.

"Rysyt up, myn túrmentowres
Be to and al be on,
And ledyt Stevyn out of this town,
And stonyt hym wyth ston."

Tokyn hem Stevene,
And stonyd hym in the way:
And therfor is his evyn
On Crystės owyn day.

256 THE BURNING BABE

As I in hoary winter's night
Stood shivering in the snow,
Surprised I was with sudden heat,
Which made my heart to glow;
And lifting up a fearful eye
To view what fire was near,
A pretty babe all burning bright,
Did in the air appear:
Who, scorchèd with excessive heat,
Such floods of tears did shed,
As though his floods should quench his flames,
Which with his tears were fed:
"Alas!" quoth he, "but newly born,
In fiery heats I fry,[1]

[1] Burn

Yet none approach to warm their hearts
Or feel my fire, but I!
My faultless breast the furnace is,
The fuel wounding thorns;
Love is the fire, and sighs the smoke,
The ashes shames and scorns;
The fuel Justice layeth on,
And Mercy blows the coals;
The metal in this furnace wrought
Are men's defilèd souls:
For which, as now on fire I am,
To work them to their good,
So will I melt into a bath,
To wash them in my blood."
With this he vanished out of sight,
And swiftly shrunk away,
And straight I called unto my mind
That it was Christmas Day.

ROBERT SOUTHWELL

257 THE HOLLY AND THE IVY

THE holly and the ivy,
Now both are full-well grown,
Of all the trees that are in the wood,
The holly bears the crown.
O the rising of the sun,
The running of the deer,
The playing of the merry Organ,
Sweet singing in the quire.
Sweet singing in the quire.

The holly bears a blossom,
As white as lily-flower;
And Mary bore sweet Jesus Christ,
To be our sweet Saviour.
O the rising of the sun, . . .

The holly bears a berry,
As red as any blood;

And Mary bore sweet Jesus Christ,
To do poor sinners good.
O the rising of the sun, . . .

The holly bears a prickle,
As sharp as any thorn;
And Mary bore sweet Jesus Christ,
On Christmas Day in the morn.
O the rising of the sun, . . .

The holly bears a bark,
As bitter as any gall;
And Mary bore sweet Jesus Christ,
For to redeem us all.
O the rising of the sun, . . .

The holly and the ivy,
Now both are full well grown,
Of all the trees that are in the wood,
The holly bears the crown.

O the rising of the sun,
The running of the deer,
The playing of the merry Organ,
Sweet singing in the quire.
Sweet singing in the quire.

258 WELCOME YULE

. . . WOLCUM be thu, hevene kyng,
Wolcom, born in on morwenyng,
Wolcom for home [1] we shal syng,
Wolcum yol.

Wolcum be ye Stefne and Jon,
Wolcum Innocentes everychon,
Wolcum Thomas martyr on,
Wolcum yol.

[1] Him

Wolcum be ye, good newe yere,
Wolcum twelthe-day, bothe infer,[1]
Wolcum syentes lef [2] and der,
Wolcum yol.

Wolcum be ye Candylmesse,
Wolcum be ye qwyn of blys,
Wolcum both to mor and lesse,
Wolcum yol.

Wolcum be ye that arn her,[3]
Wolcum alle and mak good cher,
Wolcum alle another yer,
Wolcum yol.

259 NAY, IVY, NAY

Nay, Ivy, nay,
Hyt shal not be, I wys;
Let Holy hafe the maystry,
As the maner [4] ys.

HOLY stond in the halle,
Fayre to behold;
Ivy stond wythout the dore,
She ys ful sore a-cold.
Nay, Ivy, nay . . .

Holy and hys mery men,
They dawnsyn and they syng;
Ivy and hur maydenys,
They wepyn and they wryng.
Nay, Ivy, nay . . .

Ivy hath a kybe,[5]
She kaght yt wyth the colde,
So mot thay all haf ae,

[1] Together [2] Loved [3] Are here [4] Custom [5] Chilblain

That wyth Ivy hold.
Nay, Ivy, nay . . .

Holy hath berys,
As rede as any rose,
The foster [1] and the hunter
Kepe hem [2] fro the doos.
Nay, Ivy, nay . . .

Ivy hath berys,
As blake as any slo,
Ther com the oulë,
And ete hym as she goo.
Nay, Ivy, nay . . .

Holy hath byrdys,
A ful fayre flok,
The nyghtyngale, the poppynguy,
The gayntyl lavyrok.
Nay, Ivy, nay . . .

Gode Ivy [tell me]
What byrdys ast thu?[3]
Non but the howlat,
That kreye [4] how, how!

Nay, Ivy, nay.
Hyt shal not be, I wys,
Let Holy hafe the maystry,
As the maner ys.

260 TU-WHIT TO-WHO

WHEN Isicles hang by the wall,
And Dicke the shepheard blowes his naile,
And Tom beares Logges into the hall,
And Milke comes frozen home in paile:
When blood is nipt, and waies be fowle,

[1] Forester [2] Them [3] Hast Thou [4] Cries

Then nightly sings the staring Owle,
Tu-whit to-who
A merrie note,
While greasie Jone doth keele [1] the pot.

When all aloud the winde doth blow,
And coffing drownes the Parson's saw;
And birds sit brooding in the snow,
And Marrian's nose lookes red and raw;
When roasted Crabs [2] hisse in the bowle,
Then nightly sings the staring Owle,
Tu-whit to-who
A merrie note,
While greasy Jone doth keele the pot.

William Shakespeare

261 BLOW, BLOW, THOU WINTER WIND

Blow, blow, thou winter winde,
Thou art not so unkinde
As man's ingratitude;
Thy tooth is not so keene,
Because thou art not seene,
Although thy breath be rude.
Heigh ho! sing heigh ho, unto the green holly,
Most friendship is fayning, most Loving meere folly:
Then heigh ho, the holly,
This Life is most jolly.

Freize, freize, thou bitter skie,
That dost not bight so nigh
As benefitts forgot;
Though thou the waters warpe,
Thy sting is not so sharpe,
As friend remembered not.
Heigh ho! sing heigh ho, unto the green holly,
Most friendship is fayning, most Loving meere folly:
Then heigh ho, the holly,
This Life is most jolly.

William Shakespeare

[1] Skim [2] Apples

"LIKE STARS UPON
SOME GLOOMY GROVE"

262 SPRING QUIET

Gone were but the Winter,
Come were but the Spring,
I would go to a covert
Where the birds sing.

Where in the whitethorn
Singeth a thrush,
And a robin sings
In the holly-bush.

Full of fresh scents,
Are the budding boughs
Arching high over
A cool green house:

Full of sweet scents,
And whispering air
Which sayeth softly:
"We spread no snare;

"Here dwell in safety,
Here dwell alone,
With a clear stream
And a mossy stone.

"Here the sun shineth
Most shadily;
Here is heard an echo
Of the far sea,
Though far off it be."

Christina Rossetti

263 A WIDOW BIRD

. . . A WIDOW bird sat mourning for her love
Upon a wintry bough;
The frozen wind crept on above,
The freezing stream below.

There was no leaf upon the forest bare,
No flower upon the ground,
And little motion in the air
Except the mill-wheel's sound.

PERCY BYSSHE SHELLEY

264 ECHO'S LAMENT FOR NARCISSUS

SLOW, slow, fresh fount, keep time with my salt tears;
Yet, slower yet; O faintly, gentle springs;
List to the heavy part the music bears;
Woe weeps out her division when she sings.
Droop herbs and flowers;
Fall grief in showers,
Our beauties are not ours;
O, I could still,
Like melting snow upon some craggy hill,
Drop, drop, drop, drop,
Since nature's pride is now a withered daffodil.

BEN JONSON

265 THIS LIFE

THIS Life, which seems so fair,
Is like a bubble blown up in the air
By sporting children's breath,
Who chase it everywhere,
And strive who can most motion it bequeath.
And though it sometimes seem of its own might
Like to an eye of gold to be fixed there,
And firm to hover in that empty height,

That only is because it is so light.
But in that pomp it doth not long appear;
For when 'tis most admirèd—in a thought,
Because it erst[1] was nought, it turns to nought.

William Drummond

266 SWEET CONTENT

Art thou poor, yet hast thou golden slumbers?
O, sweet content!
Art thou rich, yet is thy mind perplexed?
O, punishment!
Dost thou laugh to see how fools are vexed
To add to golden numbers golden numbers?
O, sweet content! O, sweet, O sweet content!

Work apace, apace, apace, apace;
Honest labour bears a lovely face;
Then hey nonny, hey nonny, nonny!

Canst drink the waters of the crispèd spring?
O, sweet content!
Swimm'st thou in wealth, yet sink'st in thine own tears?
O, punishment!
Then he that patiently want's burden bears,
No burden bears, but is a king, a king!
O, sweet content! O, sweet, O, sweet content!

Work apace, apace, apace, apace;
Honest labour bears a lovely face;
Then hey nonny, hey nonny, nonny!

Thomas Dekker

267 OH, SWEET CONTENT

Oh, sweet content, that turns the labourer's sweat
To tears of joy, and shines the roughest face;

[1] Once

How often have I sought you high and low,
And found you still in some lone quiet place;

Here, in my room, when full of happy dreams,
With no life heard beyond that merry sound
Of moths that on my lighted ceiling kiss
Their shadows as they dance and dance around;

Or in a garden, on a summer's night,
When I have seen the dark and solemn air
Blink with the blind bats' wings, and heaven's bright face
Twitch with the stars that shine in thousands there.

WILLIAM H. DAVIES

268 RARELY, RARELY, COMEST THOU

RARELY, rarely comest thou,
Spirit of Delight!
Wherefore hast thou left me now
Many a day and night?
Many a weary night and day
'Tis since thou art fled away.

How shall ever one like me
Win thee back again?
With the joyous and the free
Thou wilt scoff at pain.
Spirit false! thou hast forgot
All but those who need thee not.

As a lizard with the shade
Of a trembling leaf,
Thou with sorrow art dismayed;
Even the sighs of grief
Reproach thee, that thou art not near,
And reproach thou wilt not hear.

Let me set my mournful ditty
To a merry measure;

Thou wilt never come for pity,
Thou wilt come for pleasure;
Pity then will cut away,
Those cruel wings, and thou wilt stay.

I love all that thòu lovest,
Spirit of Delight!
The fresh Earth in new leaves drest,
And the starry night,
Autumn evening, and the morn
When the golden mists are born.

I love snow, and all the forms
Of the radiant frost;
I love waves, and winds, and storms,
Everything almost
Which is Nature's, and may be
Untainted by man's misery.

I love tranquil solitude
And such society
As is quiet, wise, and good;
Between thee and me
What difference? but thou dost possess
The things I seek, not love them less.

I love Love—though he has wings,
And like light can flee,
But above all other things,
Spirit, I love thee—
Thou art love and life! Oh, come,
Make once more my heart thy home!

PERCY BYSSHE SHELLEY

269

BIRTHRIGHT

LORD RAMESES of Egypt sighed
Because a summer evening passed;
And little Ariadne cried

That summer fancy fell at last
To dust; and young Verona died
When beauty's hour was overcast.

Theirs was the bitterness we know
Because the clouds of hawthorn keep
So short a state, and kisses go
To tombs unfathomably deep,
While Rameses and Romeo
And little Adriadne sleep.

JOHN DRINKWATER

270

O SORROW!

. . ."O SORROW,
Why dost borrow
The natural hue of health, from vermeil lips?—
To give maiden blushes
To the white rose bushes?
Or is't thy dewy hand the daisy tips?

"O Sorrow,
Why dost borrow
The lustrous passion from a falcon-eye?—
To give the glow-worm light?
Or, on a moonless night,
To tinge, on siren shores, the salt sea-spry?

"O Sorrow,
Why dost borrow
The mellow ditties from a mourning tongue?—
To give at evening pale
Unto the nightingale,
That thou mayst listen the cold dews among?

"O Sorrow,
Why dost borrow
Heart's lightness from the merriment of May?—
A lover would not tread

A cowslip on the head,
Though he should dance from eve till peep of day—
Nor any drooping flower
Held sacred for thy bower,
Wherever he may sport himself and play.

To Sorrow,
I bade good-morrow,
And thought to leave her far away behind;
But cheerly, cheerly,
She loves me dearly;
She is so constant, to me, and so kind:
I could deceive her
And so leave her,
But oh! she is so constant and so kind. . . .

"Come then, Sorrow!
Sweetest Sorrow!
Like an own babe I nurse thee on my breast:
I thought to leave thee
And deceive thee,
But now of all the world I love thee best.

"There is not one,
No, no, not one
But thee to comfort a poor lonely maid;
Thou art her mother,
And her brother,
Her playmate, and her wooer in the shade.". . .

John Keats

271

WHEN THE LAMP IS SHATTERED

When the lamp is shattered,
The light in the dust lies dead—
When the cloud is scattered,
The rainbow's glory is shed.
When the lute is broken,

Sweet tones are remembered not;
When the lips have spoken,
Loved accents are soon forgot.

As music and splendour
Survive not the lamp and the lute,
The heart's echoes render
No song when the spirit is mute:—
No song but sad dirges,
Like the wind through a ruined cell,
Or the mournful surges
That ring the dead seaman's knell.

When hearts have once mingled
Love first leaves the well-built nest;
The weak one is singled
To endure what it once possessed.
O Love, who bewailest
The frailty of all things here,
Why choose you the frailest
For your cradle, your home, and your bier?

Its passions will rock thee
As the storm rocks the ravens on high:
Bright reason will mock thee,
Like the sun from a wintry sky.
From thy nest every rafter
Will rot, and thine eagle home
Leave thee naked to laughter,
When leaves fall and cold winds come.

PERCY BYSSHE SHELLEY

272

ONCE

HE sees them pass
As the light is graying
Each lad and lass
In their beauty gaying
And a voice in his aching heart is saying:

"Once—once even I
Was straight as these,
As clear of eye,
And as apt to please
When I tuned my voice to balladries.

Now my eyes are dim,
Their old fires forsaking,
And each wasted limb
As a branch is shaking,
And my grief-bowed heart will soon be breaking.

—Ah, if One comes not
Beckoning nigh
To that land where hums not
One small fly,
These Strong and Fair shall be as I."

Eric N. Batterham

273 UPON THE IMAGE OF DEATH

Before my face the picture hangs
That dailie should put me in minde
Of those cold qualms and bitter pangs
That shortly I am like to finde:
But yet, alas! full little I
Do think hereon, that I must die.

I often look upon a face
Most uglie, grislie, bare, and thin;
I often view the hollow place
Where eyes and nose have sometime been;
I see the bones across that lie;
Yet little think, that I must die.

I read the label underneathe,
That telleth me whereto I must:
I see the sentence eke that saithe
"Remember, man, that thou art duste;"

But yet, alas, but seldom I
Do think indeed, that I must die!

Continually at my bed's head
An hearse doth hang, which doth me tell
That I, ere morning, may be dead,
Though now I feel myself full well:
But yet, alas, for all this, I
Have little minde that I must die!

The gowne which I do use to weare,
The knife, wherewith I cut my meate,
And eke that old and ancient chair
Which is my only usual seate,
All these do tell me I must die;
And yet my life amende not I!

My ancestors are turned to clay,
And many of my mates are gone;
My youngers daily drop away;—
And can I think to 'scape alone?
No, no, I know that I must die;
And yet my life amende not I!

Not Solomon, for all his wit,
Nor Samson, though he were so strong,
No king, nor ever person yet,
Could 'scape, but Death laid him along!
Wherefore I know that I must die;
And yet my life amende not I!

Though all the east did quake to hear
Of Alexander's dreadful name,
And all the west did likewise fear
The sound of Julius Caesar's fame,
Yet both my death in duste now lie;
Who then can 'scape, but he must die?

If none can 'scape Death's dreadful darte,
If rich and poor his beck obey,
If strong, if wise, if all do smarte,
Then I to 'scape shall have no way.
O grant me grace, O God, that I
My life may mende, sith I must die!

ROBERT SOUTHWELL

274 ADIEU! FAREWELL EARTH'S BLISS!

ADIEU! farewell earth's bliss!
This world uncertain is:
Fond are life's lustful joys,
Death proves them all but toys.
None from his darts can fly:
I am sick, I must die—
Lord, have mercy on us!

Rich men, trust not in wealth,
Gold cannot buy you health;
Physic himself must fade;
All things to end are made;
The plague full swift goes by:
I am sick, I must die—
Lord, have mercy on us!

Beauty is but a flower
Which wrinkles will devour:
Brightness falls from the air;
Queens have died young and fair;
Dust hath closed Helen's eye:
I am sick, I must die—
Lord, have mercy on us!

Strength stoops unto the grave;
Worms feed on Hector brave;
Swords may not fight with fate;

Earth still holds ope her gate;
Come! come! the bells do cry:
I am sick, I must die—
Lord, have mercy on us!

Wit with his wantonness,
Tasteth death's bitterness;
Hell's executioner
Hath no ears for to hear
What vain art can reply.
I am sick, I must die—
Lord, have mercy on us!

Haste, therefore, each degree
To welcome destiny!
Heaven is our heritage;
Earth but a player's stage.
Mount we unto the sky!
I am sick, I must die—
Lord, have mercy on us!

THOMAS NASH

275 MESSAGES

WHAT shall I your true-love tell,
Earth-forsaking maid?
What shall I your true-love tell,
When life's spectre's laid?

"Tell him that, our side the grave,
Maid may not conceive
Life should be so sad to have,
That's so sad to leave!"

What shall I your true-love tell,
When I come to him?
What shall I your true-love tell—
Eyes growing dim!

"Tell him this, when you shall part
From a maiden pined;
That I see him with my heart,
Now my eyes are blind."

What shall I your true-love tell?
Speaking-while is scant.
What shall I your true-love tell,
Death's white postulant?

"Tell him—love, with speech at strife,
For last utterance saith:
I, who loved with all my life,
Love with all my death."

FRANCIS THOMPSON

276

DOUBTS

WHEN she sleeps, her soul, I know,
Goes a wanderer on the air,
Wings where I may never go,
Leaves her lying, still and fair,
Waiting, empty, laid aside,
Like a dress upon a chair. . . .
This I know, and yet I know
Doubts that will not be denied.

For if the soul be not in place,
What has laid trouble in her face?
And, sits there nothing ware and wise
Behind the curtains of her eyes,
What is it, in the self's eclipse,
Shadows, soft and passingly,
About the corners of her lips,
The smile that is essential she?

And if the spirit be not there,
Why is fragrance in the hair?

RUPERT BROOKE

277

HARK

HARK! now everything is still,
The screech-owl and the whistler shrill
Call upon our dame aloud,
And bid her quickly don her shroud.

Much you had of land and rent;
Your length in clay's now competent.
A long war disturbed your mind;
Here your perfect peace is signed.
Of what is't fools make such vain keeping?—
Sin their conception, their birth weeping,
Their life a general mist of error,

Their death a hideous storm of terror.
Strew your hair with powders sweet,
Don clean linen, bathe your feet,
And (the foul fiend more to check)
A crucifix let bless your neck:
'Tis now full tide 'tween night and day;
End your groan, and come away.

JOHN WEBSTER

278

A LYKE-WAKE DIRGE

THIS ae nighte, this ae nighte,
Every nighte and alle,
Fire and sleet and candle-lighte,
And Christe receive thy saule.

When thou from hence away art past,
Every nighte and alle,
To Whinny-muir thou comest at last;
And Christe receive thy saule.

If ever thou gavest hosen and shoon,
Every night and alle,
Sit thee down and put them on;
And Christe receive thy saule.

If hosen and shoon thou ne'er gav'st nane,
Every nighte and alle,
The whinnes sall prick thee to the bare bane;
And Christe receive thy saule.

From Whinny-muir that thou may'st pass,
Every nighte and alle,
To Brig o' Dread thou comest at last,
And Christe receive thy saule.

From Brig o' Dread that thou may'st pass,
Every nighte and alle,
To Purgatory fire thou com'st at last,
And Christe receive thy saule.

If ever thou gavest meat or drink,
Every nighte and alle,
The fire sall never make thee shrink;
And Christe receive thy saule.

If meat and drink thou ne'er gav'st nane,
Every nighte and alle,
The fire will burn thee to the bare bane,
And Christe receive thy saule.

This ae nighte, this ae nighte,
Every nighte and alle,
Fire and sleet and candle-lighte,
And Christe receive thy saule.

279 HE IS THE LONELY GREATNESS

He is the lonely greatness of the world—
(His eyes are dim),
His power it is holds up the Cross
That holds up Him.

He takes the sorrow of the threefold hour—
(His eyelids close),

Round Him and round, the wind—His Spirit—where
It listeth blows.

And so the wounded greatness of the World
In silence lies—
And death is shattered by the light from out
Those darkened eyes.

MADELEINE CARON ROCK

280 "O SING UNTO MY ROUNDELAY"

O SING unto my roundelay,
O drop the briny tear with me,
Dance no more at holyday
Like a running river be!
My love is dead,
Gone to his death-bed,
All under the willow-tree.

Black his cryne [1] as the winter night,
White his rode [2] as the summer snow,
Red his face as the morning light,
Cold he lies in the grave below:
My love is dead,
Gone to his death-bed,
All under the willow-tree. . . .

See, the white moon shines on high;
Winter is my true-love's shroud,
Whiter than the morning sky,
Whiter than the evening cloud.
My love is dead,
Gone to his death-bed,
All under the willow-tree. . . .

With my hands I'll dent [3] the briars
Round his holy corse to gre; [4]
Ouph [5] and fairy, light your fires,

[1] Locks [2] Skin [3] Set [4] Grow [5] Elf

Here my body still shall be.
My love is dead,
Gone to his death-bed,
All under the willow-tree. . . .

THOMAS CHATTERTON

281 FEAR NO MORE

FEARE no more the heate o' th' Sun,
Nor the fureous Winters rages,
Thou thy worldly task hast don,
Home art gon, and tane thy wages.
Golden Lads and Girles all must,
As Chimney-Sweepers, come to dust.

Feare no more the frowne o' th' Great,
Thou art past the Tirants stroake,
Care no more to cloath, and eate,
To thee the Reede is as the Oake:
The Scepter, Learning, Physicke must,
All follow this, and come to dust.

Feare no more the Lightning flash,
Nor the all-dreaded Thunder-stone,
Feare not Slander, Censure rash,
Thou hast finished joy and mone.
All Lovers young, all Lovers must,
Consigne to thee, and come to dust. . . .

WILLIAM SHAKESPEARE

282 A LAND DIRGE

CALL for the robin-redbreast and the wren,
Since o'er shady groves they hover,
And with leaves and flowers do cover
The friendless bodies of unburied men.
Call unto his funeral dole
The ant, the field-mouse, and the mole,

To rear him hillocks that shall keep him warm,
And (when gay tombs are robbed) sustain no harm;
But keep the wolf far thence, that's foe to men,
For with his nails he'll dig them up again.

JOHN WEBSTER

283

THE GRAVE OF LOVE

I DUG, beneath the cypress shade,
What well might seem an elfin's grave;
And every pledge in earth I laid,
That erst thy false affection gave.

I pressed them down the sod beneath;
I placed one mossy stone above;
And twined the rose's fading wreath
Around the sepulchre of love.

Frail as thy love, the flowers were dead
Ere yet the evening sun was set:
But years shall see the cypress spread,
Immutable as my regret.

THOMAS LOVE PEACOCK

284

THE BURIAL

ALL the flowers of the spring
Meet to perfume our burying;
These have but their growing prime,
And man does flourish but his time.
Survey our progress from our birth—
We are set, we grow, we turn to earth,
Courts adieu, and all delights,
All bewitching appetites!
Sweetest breath and clearest eye,
Like perfumes go out and die;
And consequently this is done
As shadows wait upon the sun.

Vain the ambition of kings
Who seek by trophies and dead things
To leave a living name behind,
And weave but nets to catch the wind.

JOHN WEBSTER

285

ON THE TOMBS IN WESTMINSTER ABBEY

MORTALITY, behold and fear!
What a change of flesh is here!
Think how many royal bones
Sleep within these heaps of stones;
Here they lie had realms and lands,
Who now want strength to stir their hands;
Where from their pulpits sealed with dust
They preach:—"In greatness is no trust."
Here's an acre sown indeed
With the richest royallest seed
That the Earth did e'er suck in
Since the first man died for sin:
Here the bones of birth have cried:—
"Though gods they were, as men they died!"
Here are sands, ignoble things,
Dropt from the ruined sides of Kings:
Here's a world of pomp and state
Buried in dust, once dead by fate.

FRANCIS BEAUMONT

286

A FUNERALL SONG

(*Lamenting Syr Phillip Sidney*)

COME to me, grief, for ever;
Come to me, tears, day and night;
Come to me, plaint, ah, helpless;
Just grief, heart tears, plaint worthy.

Go from me dread to die now;
Go from me care to live more;

Go from me joys all on earth;
Sidney, O Sidney is dead.

He whom the court adornèd,
He whom the country courtesied,
He who made happy his friends,
He that did good to all men.

Sidney, the hope of land strange,
Sidney, the flower of England,
Sidney, the spirit heroic,
Sidney is dead, O dead.

Dead? no, no, but renownèd,
With the Anointed onèd;[1]
Honour on earth at his feet,
Bliss everlasting his seat.

Come to me, grief, for ever;
Come to me, tears, day and night;
Come to me, plaint, ah, helpless;
Just grief, heart tears, plaint worthy.

287 ON JOHN DONNE'S BOOK OF POEMS

I SEE in his last preached and printed Booke,
His Picture in a sheet. In Pauls I looke,
And see his Statue in a sheete of stone,
And sure his body in the grave hath one.
Those sheetes present him dead; these, if you buy,
You have him living to Eternity.

JOHN MARRIOT

288 O, LIFT ONE THOUGHT

STOP, Christian passer-by!—Stop, child of God,
And read with gentle breast. Beneath this sod

[1] Made one

A poet lies, or that which once seemed he.
O, lift one thought in prayer for S.T.C.;
That he who many a year with toil of breath
Found death in life, may here find life in death.
Mercy for praise—to be forgiven for fame
He asked, and hoped, through Christ. Do thou the same!

SAMUEL TAYLOR COLERIDGE

289

ELEGY

To the Memory of an unfortunate Lady.

. . . MOST souls, 'tis true, but peep out once an age,
Dull, sullen prisoners in the body's cage;
Dim lights of life, that burn a length of years,
Useless, unseen, as lamps in sepulchres;
Like eastern kings, a lazy state they keep,
And close confined to their own palace, sleep. . . .
Yet shall thy grave with rising flowers be dressed,
And the green turf lie lightly on thy breast:
There shall the morn her earliest tears bestow,
There the first roses of the year shall blow;
While angels with their silver wings o'ershade
The ground, now sacred by thy relics made.

So peaceful rests, without a stone, a name,
What once had beauty, titles, wealth and fame.
How loved, how honoured once, avails thee not
To whom related, or by whom begot;
A heap of dust alone remains of thee:
'Tis all thou art, and all the proud shall be!

Poets themselves must fall, like those they sung,
Deaf the praised ear, and mute the tuneful tongue.
Ev'n he whose soul now melts in mournful lays
Shall shortly want the generous tear he pays;
Then from his closing eyes thy form shall part,
And the last pang shall tear thee from his heart:
Life's idle business at one gasp be o'er,
The Muse forgot, and thou beloved no more!

ALEXANDER POPE

290 UPON A CHILD THAT DIED

HERE she lies, a pretty bud,
Lately made of flesh and blood:
Who, as soone, fell fast asleep,
As her little eyes did peep.
Give her strewings; but not stir
The earth, that lightly covers her.

ROBERT HERRICK

291 THE TURNSTILE

AH! sad wer we as we did peäce
The wold church road, wi' downcast feäce,
The while the bells, that mwoaned so deep
Above our child a-left asleep,
Wer now a-zingèn all alive
Wi' tother bells to meäke the vive.
But up at woone pleäce we come by,
'Twer hard to keep woone's two eyes dry;
On Steän-cliff road, 'ithin the drong,
Up where, as vo'k do pass along,
The turnèn stile, a-païnted white,
Do sheen by day an' show by night.

Vor always there, as we did goo
To church, thik stile did let us drough,
Wi' spreadèn eärms that wheeled to guide
Us each in turn to tother zide.
An' vu'st ov all the traïn he took
My wife, wi' winsome gaït an' look;
An' then zent on my little maïd,
A-skippen onward, over-jaÿ'd
To reach ageän the pleäce o' pride,
Her comely mother's left han' zide.
An' then, a-wheelèn roun', he took
On me, 'ithin his third white nook.
An' in the fourth, a-sheäken wild,
He zent us on our giddy child.

But eesterday he guided slow
My downcast Jenny, vull o' woe,
An' then my little maïd in black,
A-walken softly on her track;
An' after he'd a-turned ageän,
To let me goo along the leäne,
He had noo little bwoy to vill
His last white eärms, an' they stood still.

WILLIAM BARNES

292 THE EXEQUY

. . . SLEEP on, my Love, in thy cold bed
Never to be disquieted!
My last good-night! Thou wilt not wake
Till I thy fate shall overtake:
Till age, or grief, or sickness must
Marry my body to that dust
It so much loves; and fill the room
My heart keeps empty in that tomb.
Stay for me there: I will not fail
To meet thee in that hollow vale.
And think not much of my delay:
I am already on the way,
And follow thee with all the speed
Desire can make, or sorrows breed.
Each minute is a short degree
And every hour a step towards thee. . . .

HENRY KING

293 "I FOUND HER OUT THERE"

I FOUND her out there
On a slope few see,
That falls westwardly
To the salt-edged air,
Where the ocean breaks
On the purple strand,

And the hurricane shakes
The solid land.

I brought her here,
And have laid her to rest
In a noiseless nest
No sea beats near.
She will never be stirred
In her loamy cell
By the waves long heard
And loved so well.

So she does not sleep
By those haunted heights
The Atlantic smites
And the blind gales sweep,
Whence she often would gaze
At Dundagel's famed head,
While the dipping blaze
Dyed her face fire-red;

And would sigh at the tale
Of sunk Lyonnesse,
As a wind-tugged tress
Flapped her cheek like a flail;
Or listen at whiles
With a thought-bound brow
To the murmuring miles
She is far from now.

Yet her shade, maybe,
Will creep underground
Till it catch the sound
Of that western sea
As it swells and sobs
Where she once domiciled,
And joys in its throbs
With the heart of a child.

THOMAS HARDY

294 I NEVER SHALL LOVE THE SNOW AGAIN

I NEVER shall love the snow again
Since Maurice died:
With corniced drift it blocked the lane
And sheeted in a desolate plain
The country side.

The trees with silvery rime bedight
Their branches bare.
By day no sun appeared; by night
The hidden moon shed thievish light
In the misty air.

We fed the birds that flew around
In flocks to be fed:
No shelter in holly or brake they found.
The speckled thrush on the frozen ground
Lay frozen and dead.

We skated on stream and pond; we cut
The crinching snow
To Doric temple or Arctic hut;
We laughed and sang at nightfall, shut
By the fireside glow.

Yet grudged we our keen delights before
Maurice should come.
We said, In-door or out-of-door
We shall love life for a month or more,
When he is home.

They brought him home; 'twas two days late
For Christmas day:
Wrapped in white, in solemn state,
A flower in his hand, all still and straight
Our Maurice lay.

And two days ere the year outgave
We laid him low.

The best of us truly were not brave,
When we laid Maurice down in his grave
Under the snow.

ROBERT BRIDGES

295 THE COMFORTERS

WHEN I crept over the hill, broken with tears,
When I crouched down in the grass, dumb in despair,
I heard the soft croon of the wind bend to my ears,
I felt the light kiss of the wind touching my hair.

When I stood lone on the height my sorrow did speak,
As I went down the hill, I cried and I cried,
The soft little hands of the rain stroking my cheek,
The kind little feet of the rain ran by my side.

When I went to thy grave, broken with tears,
When I crouched down in the grass, dumb in despair,
I heard the sweet croon of the wind soft in my ears,
I felt the kind lips of the wind touching my hair.

When I stood lone by thy cross, sorrow did speak,
When I went down the long hill, I cried and I cried,
The soft little hands of the rain stroked my pale cheek,
The kind little feet of the rain ran by my side.

DORA SIGERSON SHORTER

296 THE CHILDLESS FATHER

"UP, Timothy, up with your staff and away!
Not a soul in the village this morning will stay;
The hare has just started from Hamilton's grounds,
And Skiddaw is glad with the cry of the hounds."

—Of coats and of jackets grey, scarlet, and green,
On the slopes of the pastures all colours were seen;
With their comely blue aprons, and caps white as snow,
The girls on the hills made a holiday show.

Fresh sprigs of green boxwood, not six months before,
Filled the funeral basin at Timothy's door;
A coffin through Timothy's threshold had passed;
One child did it bear, and that child was his last.

Now fast up the dell came the noise and the fray,
The horse and the horn, and the "hark! hark away!"
Old Timothy took up his staff, and he shut,
With a leisurely motion, the door of his hut.

Perhaps to himself at that moment he said,
"The key I must take, for my Helen is dead."
But of this in my ears not a word did he speak,
And he went to the chase with a tear on his cheek.

WILLIAM WORDSWORTH

297 "LYDIA IS GONE THIS MANY A YEAR"

LYDIA is gone this many a year,
Yet when the lilacs stir,
In the old gardens far or near,
This house is full of her.

They climb the twisted chamber stair;
Her picture haunts the room;
On the carved shelf beneath it there,
They heap the purple bloom.

A ghost so long has Lydia been,
Her cloak upon the wall,
Broidered, and gilt, and faded green,
Seems not her cloak at all.

The book, the box on the mantle laid,
The shells in a pale row,
Are those of some dim little maid,
A thousand years ago.

And yet the house is full of her,
She goes and comes again;
And longings thrill, and memories stir,
Like lilacs in the rain.

Out in their yards the neighbours walk,
Among the blossoms tall;
Of Anne, of Phyllis do they talk,
Of Lydia not at all.

LIZETTE WOODWORTH REESE

298 REMEMBRANCE

COLD in the earth—and the deep snow piled above thee,
Far, far removed, cold in the dreary grave!
Have I forgot, my only Love, to love thee,
Severed at last by Time's all-severing wave?

Now—when alone—do my thoughts no longer hover
Over the mountains, on that northern shore,
Resting their wings where heath and fern-leaves cover
Thy noble heart for ever, ever more?

Cold in the earth—and fifteen wild Decembers,
From those brown hills, have melted into spring:
Faithful, indeed, is the spirit that remembers
After such years of change and suffering!

Sweet Love of youth, forgive, if I forget thee,
While the world's tide is bearing me along;
Other desires and other hopes beset me,
Hopes which obscure, but cannot do thee wrong!

No later light has lightened up my heaven,
No second morn has ever shone for me;
All my life's bliss from thy dear life was given,
All my life's bliss is in the grave with thee.

But, when the days of golden dreams had perished,
And even Despair was powerless to destroy;
Then did I learn how existence could be cherished,
Strengthened, and fed, without the aid of joy.

Then did I check the tears of useless passion—
Weaned my young soul from yearning after thine;
Sternly denied its burning wish to hasten
Down to that tomb already more than mine.

And, even yet, I dare not let it languish,
Dare not indulge in memory's rapturous pain;
Once drinking deep of that divinest anguish,
How could I seek the empty world again?

EMILY BRONTË

299

SONG

WHEN I am dead, my dearest,
Sing no sad songs for me;
Plant thou no roses at my head,
Nor shady cypress-tree:
Be the green grass above me
With showers and dewdrops wet;
And if thou wilt, remember,
And if thou wilt, forget.

I shall not see the shadows,
I shall not feel the rain;
I shall not hear the nightingale
Sing on, as if in pain:
And dreaming through the twilight
That doth not rise nor set,
Haply I may remember
And haply may forget.

CHRISTINA ROSSETTI

300

"WHERE SHALL THE LOVER REST"

WHERE shall the lover rest
Whom the fates sever

From his true maiden's breast
  Parted for ever?
Where, through groves deep and high
  Sounds the far billow,
Where early violets die
  Under the willow.
    Eleu loro
  Soft shall be his pillow.

There through the summer day
  Cool streams are laving:
There, while the tempests sway,
  Scarce are boughs waving;
There thy rest shalt thou take,
  Parted for ever,
Never again to wake
  Never, O never!
    Eleu loro
  Never, O never!

SIR WALTER SCOTT

301

REMEMBER

REMEMBER me when I am gone away,
  Gone far away into the silent land;
  When you can no more hold me by the hand,
Nor I half turn to go yet turning stay.
Remember me when no more day by day
  You tell me of our future that you planned:
  Only remember me; you understand
It will be late to counsel then or pray.

Yet if you should forget me for a while
  And afterwards remember, do not grieve:
  For if the darkness and corruption leave
  A vestige of the thoughts that once I had,
Better by far you should forget and smile
  Than that you should remember and be sad.

CHRISTINA ROSSETTI

302 READEN OV A HEAD-STWONE

As I wer readen ov a stwone,
In Grenly church-yard, all alwone,
A little maïd ran up, wi' pride
To zee me there; an' pushed azide
A bunch o' bennets, that did hide
  A verse her father, as she zaïd,
  Put up above her mother's head
    To tell how much he loved her.

The verse wer short, but very good,
I stood an' larn'd en where I stood:—
"Mid [1] God, dear Meäry, gi'e me greäce
"To vind, lik' thee, a better pleäce,
"Where I, oonce mwore, mid zee thy feäce;
  "An' bring thy children up, to know
  "His word, that they mid come an' show
    "Thy soul how much I loved thee."

"Where's father, then," I zaid, "my child?"
"Dead, too," she answered wi' a smile;
"An' I an' brother Jem do bide
"At Betty White's, o'tother zide
  "O' road." "Mid He, my chile," I cried,
  "That's father to the fatherless,
  "Become thy father now, an' bless
    "An' keep, an' leäd, an' love thee."

—Though she've a-lost, I thought, so much,
Still He don't let the thoughts o't touch
Her litsome heart, by day or night;
An' zoo, if we could teäke it right,
Do show He'll meäke his burdens light
  To weaker souls; an' that his smile,
    Is sweet upon a harmless chile,
    When they be dead that loved it.

WILLIAM BARNES

[1] May

303 GOLDEN SLUMBERS

GOLDEN slumbers kiss your eyes,
Smiles awake you when you rise.
Sleep, pretty wantons, do not cry,
And I will sing a lullaby.
Rock them, rock them, lullaby.

Care is heavy, therefore sleep you;
You are care, and care must keep you.
Sleep, pretty wantons, do not cry,
And I will sing a lullaby:
Rock them, rock them, lullaby.

THOMAS DEKKER

304 MATER DOLOROSA

I'D a dream to-night
As I fell asleep,
O! the touching sight
Makes me still to weep:
Of my little lad,
Gone to leave me sad,
Ay, the child I had,
But was not to keep.

As in heaven high,
I my child did seek,
There in train came by
Children fair and meek,
Each in lily white,
With a lamp alight;
Each was clear to sight,
But they did not speak.

Then, a little sad,
Came my child in turn,
But the lamp he had
O it did not burn!

He, to clear my doubt,
Said, half-turned about,
"Your tears put it out;
Mother, never mourn."

WILLIAM BARNES

305 WEEP YOU NO MORE

WEEP you no more, sad fountains!
What need you flow so fast?
Look how the snowy mountains
Heaven's sun doth gently waste!
But my sun's heavenly eyes
View not your weeping,
That now lies sleeping
Softly, now softly lies
Sleeping.

Sleep is a reconciling,
A rest that peace begets:
Doth not the sun rise smiling
When fair at even he sets?
Rest you then, rest, sad eyes!
Melt not in weeping,
While she lies sleeping
Softly, now softly lies
Sleeping.

306 FAERY SONG

SHED no tear—O shed no tear!
The flower will bloom another year.
Weep no more—O weep no more!
Young buds sleep in the root's white core.
Dry your eyes—O dry your eyes!

For I was taught in Paradise
To ease my breast of melodies—
Shed no tear.

Overhead—look overhead
'Mong the blossoms white and red,—
Look up, look up—I flutter now
On this flush pomegranate bough—
See me—'tis this silvery bill
Ever cures the good man's ill—
Shed no tear—O shed no tear!
The flower will bloom another year.
Adieu—Adieu—I fly, adieu,
I vanish in the heaven's blue—
Adieu, Adieu!

JOHN KEATS

307 THE WORLD OF LIGHT

THEY are all gone into the world of light!
And I alone sit lingering here;
Their very memory is fair and bright,
And my sad thoughts doth clear.

It glows and glitters in my cloudy breast
Like stars upon some gloomy grove,
Or those faint beams in which this hill is drest
After the Sun's remove.

I see them walking in an Air of glory,
Whose light doth trample on my days;
My days, which are at best but dull and hoary,
Mere glimmering and decays.

O holy hope! and high humility,
High as the Heavens above!
These are your walks, and you have showed them me,
To kindle my cold love.

Dear, beauteous Death! the Jewel of the Just!
Shining nowhere but in the dark;
What mysteries do lie beyond thy dust,
Could man outlook that mark!

He that hath found some fledge bird's nest may know
At first sight if the bird be flown;
But what fair Well or Grove he sings in now,
That is to him unknown.

And yet, as Angels in some brighter dreams
Call to the soul, when man doth sleep,
So some strange thoughts transcend our wonted themes,
And into glory peep. . . .

HENRY VAUGHAN

308 SILENT IS THE HOUSE

SILENT is the house: all are laid asleep:
One alone looks out o'er the snow-wreaths deep,
Watching every cloud, dreading every breeze
That whirls the wildering drift, and bends the groaning trees.

Cheerful is the hearth, soft the matted floor;
Not one shivering gust creeps through pane or door;
The little lamp burns straight, its rays shoot strong and far:
I trim it well, to be the wanderer's guiding-star.

Frown, my haughty sire; chide, my angry dame;
Set your slaves to spy; threaten me with shame!
But neither sire, nor dame, nor prying serf shall know,
What angel nightly tracks that waste of frozen snow.

What I love shall come like visitant of air,
Safe in secret power from lurking human snare;
What loves me, no word of mine shall e'er betray,
Though for faith unstained my life must forfeit pay.

Burn, then, little lamp; glimmer straight and clear—
Hush! a rustling wing stirs, methinks, the air:

He for whom I wait, thus ever comes to me;
Strange Power! I trust thy might; trust thou my constancy.

EMILY BRONTË

309 THE MISTRESS OF VISION

. . . SECRET was the garden;
Set i' the pathless awe
Where no star its breath can draw.
Life, that is its warden,
Sits behind the fosse of death. Mine eyes saw not, and I saw.

It was a mazeful wonder;
Thrice three times it was enwalled
With an emerald—
Sealèd so asunder.
All its birds in middle air hung a-dream, their music thralled.

The Lady of fair weeping,
At the garden's core,
Sang a song of sweet and sore
And the after-sleeping;
In the land of Luthany, and the tracts of Elenore.

With sweet-pangèd singing,
Sang she through a dream-night's day;
That the bowers might stay,
Birds bate their winging,
Nor the wall of emerald float in wreathèd haze away. . . .

Her song said that no springing
Paradise but evermore
Hangeth on a singing
That has chords of weeping,
And that sings the after-sleeping
To souls which wake too sore.
"But woe the singer, woe!" she said; "beyond the dead his singing-lore,
All its art of sweet and sore
He learns, in Elenore!"

Where is the land of Luthany,
Where is the tract of Elenore?
I am bound therefor.

"Pierce thy heart to find the key;
With thee take
Only what none else would keep;
Learn to dream when thou dost wake,
Learn to wake when thou dost sleep.
Learn to water joy with tears,
Learn from fears to vanquish fears;
To hope, for thou dar'st not despair,
Exult, for that thou dar'st not grieve;
Plough thou the rock until it bear;
Know, for thou else couldst not believe;
Lose, that the lost thou may'st receive;
Die, for none other way canst live.
When earth and heaven lay down their veil,
And that apocalypse turns thee pale;
When thy seeing blindeth thee
To what thy fellow-mortals see;
When their sight to thee is sightless;
Their living, death; their light, most lightless;
Search no more—
Pass the gates of Luthany, tread the region Elenore."

Where is the land of Luthany,
And where the region Elenore?
I do faint therefor.
"When to the new eyes of thee
All things by immortal power,
Near or far,
Hiddenly
To each other linkèd are,
That thou canst not stir a flower
Without troubling of a star;
When thy song is shield and mirror
To the fair snake-curlèd Pain,
Where thou dar'st affront her terror

That on her thou may'st attain
Perséan conquest; seek no more,
O seek no more!
Pass the gates of Luthany, tread the region Elenore."

So sang she, so wept she,
Through a dream-night's day;
And with her magic singing kept she—
Mystical in music—
The garden of enchanting
In visionary May;
Songless from my spirits' haunting,
Thrice-threefold walled with emerald from our mortal mornings grey. . . .

FRANCIS THOMPSON

FAR

310 TOM O' BEDLAM

THE moon's my constant mistress,
And the lovely owl my marrow;
The flaming drake,
And the night-crow, make
Me music to my sorrow.

I know more than Apollo;
For oft, when he lies sleeping,
I behold the stars
At mortal wars,
And the rounded welkin weeping.

The moon embraces her shepherd,
And the Queen of Love her warrior;
While the first does horn
The stars of the morn,
And the next the heavenly farrier.

With a heart of furious fancies,
Whereof I am commander:
With a burning spear,
And a horse of air,
To the wilderness I wander;

With a Knight of ghosts and shadows,
I summoned am to Tourney:
Ten leagues beyond
The wide world's end;
Methinks it is no journey.

311 THE NIGHT-PIECE

HER Eyes the Glow-worme lend thee,
The Shooting Starres attend thee;
And the Elves also,
Whose little eyes glow,
Like the sparks of fire, befriend thee.

No *will-o'-th'-Wispe* mis-light thee;
Nor Snake, or Slow-worme bite thee:
But on, on thy way
Not making a stay,
Since Ghost ther's none to affright thee.

Let not the darke thee cumber;
What through the Moon does slumber?
The Starres of the night
Will lend thee their light,
Like Tapers cleare without number. . . .

ROBERT HERRICK

312 MY PLAID AWA'

"MY plaid awa', my plaid awa',
And ore the hill and far awa',
And far awa' to Norrowa,
My plaid shall not be blown awa'."

The elphin knight sits on yon hill,
Ba, ba, lilli ba,
He blowes it east, he blowes it west,
He blowes it where he lyketh best. . .
"My plaid awa', my plaid awa',
And ore the hill and far awa'."

313 BUCKEE BENE

BUCKEE, Buckee, biddy Bene,
Is the way now fair and clean?

Is the goosey gone to nest?
And the foxy gone to rest?
Shall I come away?

314 WHAT'S IN THERE?

FAHT's in there?
Gold and money.
Fahr's[1] my share o't?
The moosie ran awa' wi't.
Fahr's the moosie?
In her hoosie.
Fahr's her hoosie?
In the wood.
Fahr's the wood?
The fire burnt it.
Fahr's the fire?
The water quenched it.
Fahr's the water?
The broon bull drank it.
Fahr's the broon bull?
Back a Burnie's hill.
Fahr's Burnie's hill?
A' claid wi' snaw.
Fahr's the snaw?
The sun meltit it.
Fahr's the sun?
Heigh, heigh up i' the air!"

315 THE WEE WEE MAN

As I was wa'king all alone,
Between a water and a wa',
And there I spy'd a Wee Wee Man,
And he was the least that ere I saw.

His legs were scarce a shathmont's length
And thick and timber was his thigh;

[1] Where's

Between his brows there was a span,
  And between his shoulders there was three.

He took up a meikle stane,
  And he flang't as far as I could see;
Though I had been a Wallace wight,
  I couldna' liften't to my knee.

"O Wee Wee Man, but thou be strang!
  O tell me where thy dwelling be?"
"My dwelling's down at yon bonny bower;
  O will you go with me and see?"

On we lap, and awa' we rade,
  Till we came to yon bonny green;
We lighted down for to bait our horse,
  And out there came a lady fine.

Four and twenty at her back,
  And they were a' clad out in green;
Though the King of Scotland had been there,
  The warst o' them might hae been his queen.

On we lap, and awa' we rade,
  Till we came to yon bonny ha',
Whare the roof was o' the beaten gould,
  And the floor was o' the cristal a'.

When we came to the stair-foot,
  Ladies were dancing, jimp and sma',
But in the twinkling of an eye,
  My Wee Wee Man was clean awa'.

316 I SAW A PEACOCK

I SAW a peacock with a fiery tail
I saw a blazing comet drop down hail
I saw a cloud wrappèd with ivy round
I saw an oak creep on along the ground

I saw a pismire swallow up a whale
I saw the sea brim full of ale
I saw a Venice glass five fathom deep
I saw a well full of men's tears that weep
I saw red eyes all of a flaming fire
I saw a house bigger than the moon and higher
I saw the sun at twelve o'clock at night
I saw the Man that saw this wondrous sight.

317

GIRAFFE AND TREE

Upon a dark ball spun in Time
Stands a Giraffe beside a Tree:
Of what immortal stuff can that
The fading picture be?

So, thought I, standing beside my love
Whose hair, a small black flag,
Broke on the universal air
With proud and lovely brag:

It waved among the silent hills,
A wind of shining ebony
In Time's bright glass, where mirrored clear
Stood the Giraff beside a Tree.

Walter J. Turner

318

THE WATER LADY

Alas, the moon should ever beam
To show what man should never see!
I saw a maiden on a stream,
And fair was she!

I stayed awhile, to see her throw
Her tresses back, that all beset
The fair horizon of her brow
With clouds of jet.

I stayed a little while to view
Her cheek, that wore in place of red
The bloom of water, tender blue,
Daintily spread.

I stayed to watch, a little space,
Her parted lips if she would sing;
The waters closed above her face
With many a ring.

And still I stayed a little more,
Alas! she never comes again;
I throw my flowers from the shore,
And watch in vain.

I know my life will fade away,
I know that I must vainly pine,
For I am made of mortal clay,
But she's divine!

THOMAS HOOD

319 THE SONG OF WANDERING AENGUS

I WENT out to the hazel wood,
Because a fire was in my head,
And cut and peeled a hazel wand,
And hooked a berry to a thread;
And when white moths were on the wing,
And moth-like stars were flickering out,
I dropped the berry in a stream
And caught a little silver trout.

When I had laid it on the floor
I went to blow the fire a-flame,
But something rustled on the floor,
And someone called me by my name:
It had become a glimmering girl
With apple blossom in her hair

Who called me by my name and ran
And faded through the brightening air.

Though I am old with wandering
Through hollow lands and hilly lands,
I will find out where she has gone,
And kiss her lips and take her hands;
And walk among long dappled grass,
And pluck till time and times are done
The silver apples of the moon,
The golden apples of the sun.

W. B. YEATS

320 THE WAY THROUGH THE WOODS[1]

THEY shut the road through the woods
Seventy years ago.
Weather and rain have undone it again,
And now you would never know
There was once a road through the woods
Before they planted the trees.
It is underneath the coppice and heath,
And the thin anemones.
Only the keeper sees
That, where the ring-dove broods,
And the badgers roll at ease,
There was once a road through the woods.

Yet, if you enter the woods
Of a summer evening late,
When the night-air cools on the trout-ringed pools
Where the otter whistles his mate
(They fear not men in the woods,
Because they see so few),
You will hear the beat of a horse's feet,
And the swish of a skirt in the dew,
Steadily cantering through

The misty solitudes,
As though they perfectly knew
The old lost road through the woods . . .
But there is no road through the woods!

RUDYARD KIPLING

321 THE FALLOW DEER AT THE LONELY HOUSE

ONE without looks in to-night
  Through the curtain-chink
From the sheet of glistening white;
One without looks in to-night
  As we sit and think
  By the fender-brink.

We do not discern those eyes
  Watching in the snow;
Lit by lamps of rosy dyes
We do not discern those eyes
  Wondering, aglow,
  Fourfooted, tiptoe.

THOMAS HARDY

322 DEER

SHY in their herding dwell the fallow deer.
They are spirits of wild sense. Nobody near
Comes upon their pastures. There a life they live,
Of sufficient beauty, phantom, fugitive,
Treading as in jungles free leopards do,
Printless as eyelight, instant as dew.
The great kine are patient, and home-coming sheep
Know our bidding. The fallow deer keep
Delicate and far their counsels wild,
Never to be folded reconciled
To the spoiling hand as the poor flocks are;
Lightfoot, and swift, and unfamiliar,

These you may not hinder, unconfined
Beautiful flocks of the mind.

JOHN DRINKWATER

323 THE TWO SWANS

(A FAIRY TALE)

IMMORTAL Imogen, crowned queen above
The lilies of thy sex, vouchsafe to hear
A fairy dream in honour of true love—
True above ills, and frailty, and all fear—
Perchance a shadow of his own career
Whose youth was darkly prisoned and long twined
By serpent-sorrow, till white Love drew near,
And sweetly sang him free, and round his mind
A bright horizon threw, wherein no grief may wind.

I saw a tower builded on a lake,
Mocked by its inverse shadow, dark and deep—
That seemed a still intenser night to make,
Wherein the quiet waters sunk to sleep,—
And, whatsoe'er was prisoned in that keep,
A monstrous Snake was warden:—round and round
In sable ringlets I beheld him creep,
Blackest amid black shadows, to the ground,
Whilst his enormous head the topmost turret crowned:

From whence he shot fierce light against the stars,
Making the pale moon paler with affright;
And with his ruby eye out-threatened Mars—
That blazed in the mid-heavens, hot and bright—
Nor slept, nor winked, but with a steadfast spite
Watched their wan looks and tremblings in the skies;
And that he might not slumber in the night,
The curtain-lids were plucked from his large eyes,
So he might never drowse, but watch his secret prize.

Prince or princess in dismal durance pent,
Victims of old Enchantment's love or hate,

Their lives must all in painful sighs be spent,
Watching the lonely waters soon and late,
And clouds that pass and leave them to their fate,
Or company their grief with heavy tears:—
Meanwhile that Hope can spy no golden gate
For sweet escapement, but in darksome fears
They weep and pine away as if immortal years.

No gentle bird with gold upon its wing
Will perch upon the grate—the gentle bird
Is safe in leafy dell, and will not bring
Freedom's sweet keynote and commission-word
Learned of a fairy's lips, for pity stirred—
Lest while he trembling sings, untimely guest!
Watched by that cruel Snake and darkly heard,
He leave a widow on her lonely nest,
To press in silent grief the darlings of her breast.

No gallant knight, adventurous, in his bark,
Will seek the fruitful perils of the place,
To rouse with dipping oar the waters dark
That bear that serpent-image on their face.
And Love, brave Love, though he attempt the base,
Nerved to his loyal death, he may not win
His captive lady from the strict embrace
Of that foul Serpent, clasping her within
His sable folds—like Eve enthralled by the old Sin.

But there is none—no knight in panoply,
Nor Love, intrenched in his strong steely coat:
No little speck—no sail—no helper nigh,
No sign—no whispering—no plash of boat:—
The distant shores show dimly and remote,
Made of a deeper mist,—serene and grey,—
And slow and mute the cloudy shadows float
Over the gloomy wave, and pass away,
Chased by the silver beams that on their marges play.

And bright and silvery the willows sleep
Over the shady verge—no mad winds tease

Their hoary heads; but quietly they weep
Their sprinkling leaves—half fountains and half trees;
There lilies be—and fairer than all these,
A solitary Swan her breast of snow
Launches against the wave that seems to freeze
Into a chaste reflection, still below,
Twin-shadow of herself wherever she may go.

And forth she paddles in the very noon
Of solemn midnight, like an elfin thing
Charmed into being by the argent moon—
Whose silver light for love of her fair wing
Goes with her in the shade, still worshipping
Her dainty plumage:—all around her grew
A radiant circlet, like a fairy ring;
And all behind, a tiny little clue
Of light, to guide her back across the waters blue.

And sure she is no meaner than a fay
Redeemed from sleepy death, for beauty's sake,
By old ordainment:—silent as she lay,
Touched by a moonlight wand I saw her wake,
And cut her leafy slough and so forsake
The verdant prison of her lily peers,
That slept amidst the stars upon the lake—
A breathing shape—restored to human fears,
And new-born love and grief—self-conscious of her tears.

And now she clasps her wings around her heart,
And near that lonely isle begins to glide,
Pale as her fears, and oft-times with a start
Turns her impatient head from side to side
In universal terrors—all too wide
To watch; and often to that marble keep
Upturns her pearly eyes, as if she spied
Some foe, and crouches in the shadows steep
That in the gloomy wave go diving fathoms deep.

And well she may, to spy that fearful thing
All down the dusky walls in circlets wound;

Alas! for what rare prize, with many a ring
Girding the marble casket round and round?
His folded tail, lost in the gloom profound,
Terribly darkeneth the rocky base;
But on the top his monstrous head is crowned
With prickly spears, and on his doubtful face
Gleam his unwearied eyes, red watchers of the place.

Alas! of the hot fires that nightly fall,
No one will scorch him in those orbs of spite,
So he may never see beneath the wall
That timid little creature, all too bright,
That stretches her fair neck, slender and white,
Invoking the pale moon, and vainly tries
Her throbbing throat, as if to charm the night
With song—but, hush—it perishes in sighs,
And there will be no dirge sad-swelling, though she dies!

She droops—she sinks—she leans upon the lake,
Fainting again into a lifeless flower;
But soon the chilly springs anoint and wake
Her spirit from its death, and with new power
She sheds her stifled sorrows in a shower
Of tender song, timed to her falling tears—
That wins the shady summit of that tower,
And, trembling all the sweeter for its fears,
Fills with imploring moan that cruel monster's ears.

And, lo! the scaly beast is all deprest,
Subdued like Argus by the might of sound—
What time Apollo his sweet lute addrest
To magic converse with the air, and bound
The many monster eyes, all slumber-drowned:—
So on the turret-top that watchful Snake
Pillows his giant head, and lists profound,
As if his wrathful spite would never wake,
Charmed into sudden sleep for Love and Beauty's sake!

His prickly crest lies prone upon his crown,
And thirsty lip from lip disparted flies,

To drink that dainty flood of music down—
His scaly throat is big with pent-up sighs—
And whilst his hollow ear entrancèd lies,
His looks for envy of the charmèd sense
Are fain to listen, till his steadfast eyes,
Stung into pain by their own impotence,
Distil enormous tears into the lake immense.

Oh, tuneful Swan! oh, melancholy bird!
Sweet was that midnight miracle of song,
Rich with ripe sorrow, needful of no word
To tell of pain, and love, and love's deep wrong—
Hinting a piteous tale—perchance how long
Thy unknown tears were mingled with the lake,
What time disguised thy leafy mates among—
And no eye knew what human love and ache
Dwelt in those dewy leaves, and heart so nigh to break.

Therefore no poet will ungently touch
The water-lily, on whose eyelids dew
Trembles like tears; but ever hold it such
As human pain may wander through and through,
Turning the pale leaf paler in its hue—
Wherein life dwells, transfigured, not entombed,
By magic spells. Alas! who ever knew
Sorrow in all its shades, leafy and plumed,
Or in gross husks of brutes eternally inhumed?

And now the wingèd song has scaled the height
Of that dark dwelling, builded for despair,
And soon a little casement flashing bright
Widens self-opened into the cool air—
That music like a bird may enter there
And soothe the captive in his stony cage;
For there is nought of grief, or painful care,
But plaintive song may happily engage
From sense of its own ill, and tenderly assuage.

And forth into the light, small and remote,
A creature, like the fair son of a king,

Draws to the lattice in his jewelled coat
Against the silver moonlight glistening,
And leans upon his white hand listening
To that sweet music that with tenderer tone
Salutes him, wondering what kindly thing
Is come to soothe him with so tuneful moan,
Singing beneath the walls as if for him alone!

And while he listens, the mysterious song,
Woven with timid particles of speech,
Twines into passionate words that grieve along
The melancholy notes, and softly teach
The secrets of true love,—that trembling reach
His earnest ear, and through the shadows dun
He missions like replies and each to each
Their silver voices mingle into one,
Like blended streams that make one music as they run

"Ah, Love! my hope is swooning in my heart,—"
"Ay, sweet! my cage is strong and hung full high—"
"Alas! our lips are held so far apart,
Thy words come faint,—they have so far to fly!—"
"If I may only shun that serpent-eye!—"
"Ah me! that serpent-eye doth never sleep;—"
"Then nearer thee, Love's martyr, I will die!—"
"Alas, alas! that word has made me weep!
For pity's sake remain safe in thy marble keep!"

"My marble keep! it is my marble tomb—"
"Nay, sweet! but thou hast there thy living breath—"
"Aye to expend in sighs for this hard doom;—"
"But I will come to thee and sing beneath,
And nightly so beguile this serpent wreath;—"
"Nay, I will find a path from these despairs."
"Ah! needs then thou must tread the back of death,
Making his stony ribs thy stony stairs.—
Behold his ruby eye, how fearfully it glares!"

Full sudden at these words, the princely youth
Leaps on the scaly back that slumbers, still

Unconscious of his foot, yet not for ruth,
But numbed to dulness by the fairy skill
Of that sweet music (all more wild and shrill
For intense fear) that charmed him as he lay—
Meanwhile the lover nerves his desperate will,
Held some short throbs by natural dismay,
Then, down the serpent-tracks begins his darksome way.

Now dimly seen—now toiling out of sight,
Eclipsed and covered by the envious wall;
Now fair and spangled in the sudden light,
And clinging with wide arms for fear of fall:
Now dark and sheltered by a kindly pall
Of dusky shadow from his wakeful foe;
Slowly he winds adown—dimly and small,
Watched by the gentle Swan that sings below,
Her hope increasing, still, the larger he doth grow.

But nine times nine the Serpent folds embrace
The marble walls about—which he must tread
Before his anxious foot may touch the base:
Long is the dreary path, and must be sped!
But Love, that holds the mastery of dread,
Braces his spirit, and with constant toil
He wins his way, and now, with arms outspread,
Impatient plunges from the last long coil:
So may all gentle Love ungentle Malice foil!

The song is hushed, the charm is all complete,
And two fair Swans are swimming on the lake:
But scarce their tender bills have time to meet,
When fiercely drops adown that cruel Snake—
His steely scales a fearful rustling make,
Like autumn leaves that tremble and foretell
The sable storm;—the plumy lovers quake—
And feel the troubled waters pant and swell,
Heaved by the giant bulk of their pursuer fell.

His jaws, wide yawning like the gates of Death,
His horrible pursuit—his red eyes glare

The waters into blood—his eager breath
Grows hot upon their plumes:—now, minstrel fair!
She drops her ring into the waves, and there
It widens all around, a fairy ring
Wrought of the silver light—the fearful pair
Swim in the very midst, and pant and cling
The closer for their fears, and tremble wing to wing.

Bending their course over the pale grey lake,
Against the pallid East, wherein light played
In tender flushes, still the baffled Snake
Circled them round continually, and bayed
Hoarsely and loud, forbidden to invade
The sanctuary ring: his sable mail
Rolled darkly through the flood, and writhed and made
A shining track over the waters pale,
Lashed into boiling foam by his enormous tail,

And so they sailed into the distance dim,
Into the very distance—small and white,
Like snowy blossoms of the spring that swim
Over the brooklets—followed by the spite
Of that huge Serpent, that with wild affright
Worried them on their course, and sore annoy,
Till on the grassy marge I saw them 'light,
And change, anon, a gentle girl and boy,
Locked in embrace of sweet unutterable joy!

Then came the Morn, and with her pearly showers
Wept on them, like a mother, in whose eyes
Tears are no grief; and from his rosy bowers
The Oriental sun began to rise,
Chasing the darksome shadows from the skies;
Wherewith that sable Serpent far away
Fled, like a part of night—delicious sighs
From waking blossoms purified the day,
And little birds were singing sweetly from each spray.

THOMAS HOOD

324 THE EARL OF MAR'S DAUGHTER

It was intill a pleasant time,
  Upon a simmer's day,
The noble Earl of Mar's daughter
  Went forth to sport and play.

As thus she did amuse hersell,
  Below a green aik tree,
There she saw a sprightly doo [1]
  Set on a tower sae hie,

"O Cow-me-doo, my love sae true,
  If ye'll come down to me,
Ye'se hae a cage o' guid red gowd
  Instead o' simple tree:

"I'll put gowd hingers [2] roun' your cage,
  And siller roun' your wa';
I'll gar [3] ye shine as fair a bird
  As ony o' them a'."

But she hadnae these words well spoke,
  Nor yet these words well said,
Till Cow-me-doo flew frae the tower
  And lighted on her head.

Then she has brought this pretty bird
  Hame to her bowers and ha',
And made him shine as fair a bird
  As ony o' them a'.

When day was gane, and night was come,
  About the evening tide
This lady spied a sprightly youth
  Stand straight up by her side.

"From whence came ye, young man?" she said;
  "That does suprise me sair;

[1] Dove [2] Trappings [3] Make

My door was bolted right secure,
What way hae ye come here?"

"O had[1] your tongue, ye lady fair,
Lat a' folly be;
Mind ye not on your turtle-doo
Last day ye brought wi' thee?"

"O tell me mair, young man," she said,
"This does surprise me now;
What country hae ye come frae?
What pedigree are you?"

"My mither lives on foreign isles,
She has nae mair but me;
She is a queen o' wealth and state,
And birth and high degree.

"Likewise well skilled in magic spells,
As ye many plainly see,
And she transformed me to yon shape,
To charm such maids as thee.

"I am a doo the live-lang day,
A sprightly youth at night;
This aye gars me appear mair fair
In a fair maiden's sight.

"And it was but this verra day
That I came ower the sea;
Your lovely face did me enchant;
I'll live and dee wi' thee."

"O Cow-me-doo, my luve sae true,
Nae mair frae me ye'se gae";
"That's never my intent, my luve,
As ye said, it shall be sae. . ."

[1] Hold

325 THE BROOMFIELD HILL

Brome, brome on hill,
The gentle brome on hill, hill,
Brome, brome on Hive hill,
The gentle brome on Hive hill,
The brome stands on Hive hill-a . . .

"O WHERE were ye, my milk-white steed,
That I hae coft [1] sae dear,
That wadna' watch and waken me
When there was maiden here?"

"I stampèd wi' my foot, master,
And gard my bridle ring,
But na kin thing wald waken ye,
Till she was past and gane."

"And wae betide ye, my gay goss-hawk,
That I did love sae dear,
That wadna' watch and waken me
When there was maiden here."

"I clappèd wi' my wings, master,
And aye my bells I rang,
And aye cryed, Waken, waken, master,
Before the ladye gang."

"But haste and haste, my guide white steed,
To come the maiden till,
Or a' the birds of gude green wood
Of your flesh shall have their fill."

"Ye need no burst your gude white steed
Wi' racing o'er the howm; [2]
Nae bird flies faster through the wood,
Than she fled through the broom."

[1] Bought [2] The green margin of a river

Toll no bell for me, dear Father, dear Mother,
Waste no sighs;
There are my sisters, there is my little brother
Who plays in the place called Paradise,
Your children all, your children for ever;
But I, so wild,
Your disgrace, with the queer brown face, was never,
Never, I know, but half your child!

In the garden at play, all day, last summer,
Far and away I heard
The sweet "tweet-tweet" of a strange new-comer,
The dearest, clearest call of a bird.
It lived down there in the deep green hollow,
My own old home, and the fairies say
The word of a bird is a thing to follow,
So I was away a night and a day.

One evening, too, by the nursery fire,
We snuggled close and sat round so still,
When suddenly as the wind blew higher,
Something scratched on the window-sill,
A pinched brown face peered in—I shivered;
No one listened or seemed to see;
The arms of it waved and the wings of it quivered,
Whoo—I knew it had come for me!
Some are as bad as bad can be!
All night long they danced in the rain,
Round and round in a dripping chain,
Threw their caps at the window-pane,
Tried to make me scream and shout
And fling the bedclothes all about:
I meant to stay in bed that night,
And if only you had left a light
They would never have got me out!

Sometimes I wouldn't speak, you see,
Or answer when you spoke to me,
Because in the long, still dusks of Spring

You can hear the whole world whispering;
  The shy green grasses making love,
  The feathers grow on the dear grey dove,
  The tiny heart of the redstart beat,
  The patter of the squirrel's feet,
The pebbles pushing in the silver streams,
The rushes talking in their dreams,
  The swish-swish of the bat's black wings,
  The wild-wood bluebell's sweet ting-tings,
    Humming and hammering at your ear,
    Everything there is to hear
In the heart of hidden things.
  But not in the midst of the nursery riot,
  That's why I wanted to be quiet,
    Couldn't do my sums, or sing,
    Or settle down to anything.
  And when, for that, I was sent upstairs
  I *did* kneel down to say my prayers;
But the King who sits on your high church steeple
Has nothing to do with us fairy people!

'Times I pleased you, dear Father, dear Mother,
  Learned all my lessons and liked to play,
And dearly I loved the little pale brother
  Whom some other bird must have called away.
Why did they bring me here to make me
  Not quite bad and not quite good,
Why, unless They're wicked, do They want, in spite, to take me
      Back to Their wet, wild wood?
Now, every night I shall see the windows shining,
  The gold lamp's glow, and the fire's red gleam,
While the best of us are twining twigs and the rest of us are
    whining
      In the hollow by the stream.
Black and chill are Their nights on the wold;
  And They live so long and They feel no pain:
I shall grow up, but never grow old,
I shall always, always be very cold,
      I shall never come back again!

CHARLOTTE MEW

327 THE HOST OF THE AIR

O'Driscoll drove with a song
The wild duck and the drake
From the tall and the tufted reeds
Of the drear Hart Lake.

And he saw how the reeds grew dark
At the coming of night tide,
And dreamed of the long dim hair
Of Bridget his bride.

He heard while he sang and dreamed
A piper piping away,
And never was piping so sad,
And never was piping so gay.

And he saw young men and young girls
Who danced on a level place
And Bridget his bride among them,
With a sad and a gay face.

The dancers crowded about him,
And many a sweet thing said,
And a young man brought him red wine
And a young girl white bread.

But Bridget drew him by the sleeve,
Away from the merry bands,
To old men playing at cards
With a twinkling of ancient hands.

The bread and the wine had a doom,
For these were the host of the air;
He sat and played in a dream
Of her long dim hair.

He played with the merry old men
And thought not of evil chance,
Until one bore Bridget his bride
Away from the merry dance.

He bore her away in his arms,
The handsomest young man there,
And his neck and his breast and his arms
Were drowned in her long dim hair.

O'Driscoll scattered the cards
And out of his dream awoke:
Old men and young men and young girls
Were gone like a drifting smoke;

But he heard high up in the air
A piper piping away,
And never was piping so sad,
And never was piping so gay.

William Butler Yeats

328 THE LOVE-TALKER

I met the Love-Talker one eve in the glen,
He was handsomer than any of our handsome young men,
His eyes were blacker than the sloe, his voice sweeter far
Then the crooning of old Kevin's pipes beyond in Coolnagar.

I was bound for the milking with a heart fair and free—
My grief! my grief! that bitter hour drained the life from me;
I thought him human lover, though his lips on mine were cold,
And the breath of death blew keen on me within his hold.

I know not what way he came, no shadow fell behind,
But all the sighing rushes swayed beneath a faery wind,
The thrush ceased its singing, a mist crept about,
We two clung together—with the world shut out.

Beyond the ghostly mist I could hear my cattle low,
The little cow from Ballina, clean as driven snow,
The dun cow from Kerry, the roan from Inisheer,
Oh, pitiful their calling—and his whispers in my ear!

His eyes were a fire; his words were a snare;
I cried my mother's name, but no help was there;

I made the blessed Sign; then he gave a dreary moan,
A wisp of cloud went floating by, and I stood alone.

Running ever through my head, is an old-time rune—
"Who meets the Love-Talker must weave her shroud soon."
My mother's face is furrowed with the salt tears that fall,
But the kind eyes of my father are the saddest sight of all.

I have spun the fleecy lint, and now my wheel is still,
The linen length is woven for my shroud fine and chill,
I shall stretch me on the bed where a happy maid I lay—
Pray for the soul of Mairė Og at dawning of the day!

Ethna Carbery

329 MARIANA

With blackest moss the flower-plots
Were thickly crusted, one and all:
The rusted nails fell from the knots
That held the pear to the garden-wall.
The broken sheds looked sad and strange:
Unlifted was the clinking latch;
Weeded and worn the ancient thatch
Upon the lonely moated grange.
She only said, "My life is dreary,
He cometh not," she said;
She said, "I am aweary, aweary,
I would that I were dead!"

Her tears fell with the dews at even;
Her tears fell ere the dews were dried;
She could not look on the sweet heaven,
Either at morn or eventide.
After the flitting of the bats,
When thickest dark did trance the sky,
She drew her casement-curtain by,
And glanced athwart the glooming flats.
She only said, "The night is dreary,
He cometh not," she said;

She said, "I am aweary, aweary,
I would that I were dead!"

Upon the middle of the night,
Waking she heard the night-fowl crow:
The cock sung out an hour ere light:
From the dark fen the oxen's low
Came to her: without hope of change,
In sleep she seemed to walk forlorn,
Till cold winds woke the grey-eyed morn
About the lonely moated grange.
She only said, "The day is dreary,
He cometh not," she said;
She said, "I am aweary, aweary,
I would that I were dead!"

About a stone-cast from the wall
A sluice with blackened water slept,
And o'er it many, round and small,
The clustered marish-mosses crept.
Hard by a poplar shook alway,
All silver-green with gnarled bark:
For leagues no other tree did mark
The level waste, the rounding grey.
She only said, "My life is dreary,
He cometh not," she said;
She said, "I am aweary, aweary,
I would that I were dead!"

And ever when the moon was low,
And the shrill winds were up and away,
In the white curtain, to and fro,
She saw the gusty shadow sway.
But when the moon was very low,
And wild winds bound within their cell,
The shadow of the popular fell
Upon her bed, across her brow.
She only said, "The night is dreary,
He cometh not," she said;

She said, "I am aweary, aweary,
I would that I were dead!"

All day within the dreamy house,
The doors upon their hinges creaked;
The blue fly sung in the pane; the mouse
Behind the mouldering wainscot shrieked,
Or from the crevice peered about.
Old faces glimmered thro' the doors,
Old footsteps trod the upper floors,
Old voices called her from without.
She only said, "My life is dreary,
He cometh not," she said;
She said, "I am aweary, aweary,
I would that I were dead!"

The sparrow's chirrup on the roof,
The slow clock ticking, and the sound
Which to the wooing wind aloof
The poplar made, did all confound
Her sense; but most she loathed the hour
When the thick-moted sunbeam lay
Athwart the chambers, and the day
Was sloping toward his western bower.
Then, said she, "I am very dreary,
He will not come," she said;
She wept, "I am aweary, aweary,
Oh God, that I were dead!"

ALFRED, LORD TENNYSON

330

KEITH OF RAVELSTON

THE murmur of the mourning ghost
That keeps the shadowy kine,
"Oh, Keith of Ravelston,
The sorrows of thy line!"

Ravelston, Ravelston,
The merry path that leads

Down the golden morning hill,
And thro' the silver meads;

Ravelston, Ravelston,
The stile beneath the tree,
The maid that kept her mother's kine,
The song that sang she!

She sang her song, she kept her kine,
She sat beneath the thorn
When Andrew Keith of Ravelston
Rode thro' the Monday morn.

His henchmen sing, his hawk-bells ring,
His belted jewels shine!
Oh, Keith of Ravelston,
The sorrows of thy line!

Year after year, where Andrew came,
Comes evening down the glade,
And still there sits a moonshine ghost
Where sat the sunshine maid.

Her misty hair is faint and fair,
She keeps the shadowy kine;
Oh, Keith of Ravelston,
The sorrows of thy line!

I lay my hand upon the stile,
The stile is lone and cold,
The burnie that goes babbling by
Says naught that can be told.

Yet, stranger! here, from year to year,
She keeps her shadowy kine;
Oh, Keith of Ravelston,
The sorrows of thy line!

Step out three steps, where Andrew stood—
Why blanch thy cheeks for fear

The ancient stile is not alone,
'Tis not the burn I hear!

She makes her immemorial moan,
She keeps her shadowy kine;
Oh, Keith of Ravelston,
The sorrows of thy line!

SYDNEY DOBELL

331 UNWELCOME

WE were young, we were merry, we were very very wise,
And the door stood open at our feast,
When there passed us a woman with the West in her eyes,
And a man with his back to the East.

O, still grew the hearts that were beating so fast,
The loudest voice was still.
The jest died away on our lips as they passed,
And the rays of July struck chill.

The cups of red wine turned pale on the board,
The white bread black as soot.
The hound forgot the hand of her lord,
She fell down at his foot.

Low let me lie, where the dead dog lies,
Ere I sit me down again at a feast,
When there passes a woman with the West in her eyes,
And a man with his back to the East.

MARY COLERIDGE

332 ON YES TOR

BENEATH our feet, the shuddering bogs
Made earthquakes of their own,
For greenish-grizzled furtive frogs
And lizards lithe and brown;

And high to east and south and west,
Girt round the feet with gorse,
Lay, summering, breast by giant breast,
The titan brood of tors;

Golden and phantom-pale they lay,
Calm in the cloudless light,
Like gods that, slumbering, still survey
The obsequious infinite.

Plod, plod, through herbage thin or dense;
Past chattering rills of quartz;
Across brown bramble-coverts, whence
The shy black ouzel darts;

Through empty leagues of broad, bare lands,
Beneath the empty skies,
Clutched in the grip of those vast hands,
Cowed by those golden eyes,

We fled beneath their scornful stare,
Like terror-hunted dogs,
More timid than the lizards were,
And shyer than the frogs.

EDMUND GOSSE

333 THE WITCHES' SONG

"I HAVE beene all day looking after
A raven feeding upon a quarter;
And, soone as she turned her back to the south,
I snatched this morsell out of her mouth." . . .

"I last night lay all alone
O' the ground, to heare the madrake grone;
And pluckt him up, though he grew full low:
And, as I had done, the cocke did crow." . . .

"And I ha' been plucking (plants among)
Hemlock, henbane, adders-tongue,
Night-shade, moone-wort, libbards-bane;
And twise by the dogges was like to be tane." . . .

"Yes: I have brought, to helpe your vows,
Hornèd poppie, cypresse boughes.
The fig-tree wild, that grows on tombes,
And juice that from the larch-tree comes,
The basiliske's bloud, and the viper's skin;
And now our orgies let's begin."

BEN JONSON

334 THE RAVEN

ONCE upon a midnight dreary, while I pondered, weak and
weary,
Over many a quaint and curious volume of forgotten lore,—
While I nodded, nearly napping, suddenly there came a tapping,
As of some one gently rapping. rapping at my chamber door.
" 'Tis some visitor," I muttered, "tapping at my chamber door;
Only this and nothing more."

Ah, distinctly I remember it was in the bleak December,
And each seperate dying ember wrought its ghost upon the
floor.
Eagerly I wished the morrow;—vainly I had sought to borrow
From my books surcease of sorrow—sorrow for the lost Lenore,
For the rare and radiant maiden whom the angels name Lenore:
Nameless here for evermore.

And the silken sad uncertain rustling of each purple curtain
Thrilled me—filled me with fantastic terrors never felt before;
So that now, to still the beating of my heart, I stood repeating,
" 'Tis some visitor entreating entrance at my chamber door—
Some late visitor entreating entrance at my chamber door;
This it is and nothing more."

Presently my soul grew stronger; hesitating then no longer,
"Sir," said I, "or Madam, truly your forgiveness I implore;
But the fact is I was napping, and so gently you came rapping,
And so faintly you came tapping, tapping at my chamber door,
That I scarce was sure I heard you"—here I opened wide the door:—
Darkness there and nothing more.

Deep into that darkness peering, long I stood there wondering, fearing,
Doubting, dreaming, dreams no mortals ever dared to dream before;
But the silence was unbroken, and the stillness gave no token,
And the only word there spoken was the whispered word, "Lenore?"
This I whispered, and an echo murmured back the word, "Lenore":
Merely this and nothing more.

Back into the chamber turning, all my soul within me burning,
Soon again I heard a tapping somewhat louder than before.
"Surely," said I, "surely that is something at my window lattice;
Let me see, then, what thereat is, and this mystery explore:
Let my heart be still a moment and this mystery explore;
'Tis the wind and nothing more."

Open here I flung the shutter, when, with many a flirt and flutter,
In there stepped a stately Raven of the saintly days of yore.
Not the least obeisance made he; not a minute stopped or stayed he;
But, with mien of lord or lady, perched above my chamber door,
Perched upon a bust of Pallas just above my chamber door:
Perched, and sat, and nothing more.

Then this ebony bird beguiling my sad fancy into smiling
By the grave and stern decorum of the countenance it wore,—
"Though thy crest be shorn and shaven, thou," I said, "art sure no craven,

Ghastly grim and ancient Raven wandering from the Nightly shore:
Tell me what thy lordly name is on the Night's Plutonian shore!"
Quoth the Raven, "Nevermore."

Much I marvelled this ungainly fowl to hear discourse so plainly,
Though its answer little meaning—little relevancy bore;
For we cannot help agreeing that no living human being
Ever yet was blessed with seeing bird above his chamber door—
Bird or beast upon the sculptured bust above his chamber door,
With such name as "Nevermore."

But the Raven, sitting lonely on the placid bust, spoke only
That one word, as if his soul in that one word he did outpour.
Nothing further then he uttered, not a feather then he fluttered,
Till I scarcely more than muttered,—"Other friends have flown before;
On the morrow *he* will leave me, as my Hopes have flown before."
Then the bird said, "Nevermore."

Startled at the stillness broken by reply so aptly spoken,
"Doubtless," said I, "what it utters is its, only stock and store,
Caught from some unhappy master whom unmerciful Disaster
Followed fast and followed faster till his songs one burden bore:
Till the dirges of his Hope that melancholy burden bore
Of 'Never-nevermore.'"

But the Raven still beguiling all my sad soul into smiling,
Straight I wheeled a cushioned seat in front of bird and bust and door;
Then, upon the velvet sinking, I betook myself to linking
Fancy unto fancy, thinking what this ominous bird of yore,
What this grim, ungainly, ghastly, gaunt, and ominous bird of yore
Meant in croaking "Nevermore."

This I sat engaged in guessing, but no syllable expressing
To the fowl whose fiery eyes now burned into my bosom's core;
This and more I sat divining, with my head at ease reclining

On the cushion's velvet lining that the lamplight gloated o'er,
But whose velvet violet lining with the lamplight gloating o'er
She shall press, ah, nevermore!

Then, methought, the air grew denser, perfumed from an unseen censer
Swung by seraphim whose foot-falls tinkled on the tufted floor.
"Wretch," I cried, "thy God hath lent thee—by these angels he hath sent thee
Respite—respite and nepenthe from thy memories of Lenore!
Quaff, oh quaff this kind nepenthe, and forget this lost Lenore!"
Quoth the Raven, "Nevermore."

"Prophet!" said I, "thing of evil! prophet still, if bird or devil!
Whether Tempter sent or whether tempest tossed thee here ashore,
Desolate, yet all undaunted, on this desert land enchanted,
On this home by Horror haunted—tell me truly, I implore:
Is there—*is* there balm in Gilead?—tell me—tell me, I implore!"
Quoth the Raven, "Nevermore."

"Prophet!" said I, "thing of evil—prophet still, if bird or devil!
By that Heaven that bends above us, by that God we both adore,
Tell this soul with sorrow laden if, within the distant Aidenn,
It shall clasp a sainted maiden whom the angels name Lenore:
Clasp a rare and radiant maiden whom the angels name Lenore!"
Quoth the Raven, "Nevermore."

"Be that word our sign of parting, bird or fiend!" I shrieked, upstarting
"Get thee back into the tempest and the Night's Plutonian shore!
Leave no black plume as a token of that lie thy soul hath spoken!
Leave my loneliness unbroken! quit the bust above my door!
Take thy beak from out my heart, and take thy form from off my door!"
Quoth the Raven, "Nevermore."

And the Raven, never flitting, still is sitting, still is sitting
On the pallid bust of Pallas just above my chamber door;
And his eyes have all the seeming of a demon's that is dreaming,
And the lamp-light o'er him streaming throws his shadow on the
floor;
And my soul from out that shadow that lies floating on the
floor
Shall be lifted—nevermore!

EDGAR ALLAN POE

335 THE WITCHES' BALLAD

O, I HAE come from far away,
From a warm land far away,
A southern land across the sea,
With sailor-lads about the mast,
Merry and canny, and kind to me.

And I hae been to yon town
To try my luck in yon town;
Nort, and Mysie, Elspie too.
Right braw we were to pass the gate,
Wi' gowden-clasps on girdles blue.

Mysie smiled wi' miminy mouth,
Innocent mouth, miminy mouth;
Elspie wore a scarlet gown.
Nort's grey eyes were unco' gleg.[1]
My Castile comb was like a crown.

We walk'd abreast all up the street,
Into the market up the street;
Our hair with marigolds was wound,
Our bodices with love-knots laced,
Our merchandise with tansy bound.

Nort had chickens, I had cocks;
Gamesome cocks, loud-crowing cocks;

[1] Wild and lively

Mysie ducks, and Elspie drakes,—
For a wee groat or a pound
We lost nae time wi' gives and takes.

—Lost nae time for well we knew,
In our sleeves full well we knew,
When the gloaming came that night,
Duck nor drake, nor hen nor cock
Would be found by candle-light.

And when our chaffering all was done,
All was paid for, sold and done,
We drew a glove on ilka hand,
We sweetly curtsied, each to each.
And deftly danced a saraband.

The market-lassies looked and laughed,
Left their gear, and looked and laughed;
They made as they would join the game,
But soon their mithers, wild and wud,[1]
With whack and screech they stopped the same.

Sae loud the tongues o' randies [2] grew,
The flytin' [3] and the skirlin' grew,
At all the windows in the place,
Wi' spoons or knives, wi' needle or awl,
Was thrust out every hand and face.

And down each stair they thronged anon,
Gentle, semple, thronged anon;
Souter [4] and tailor, frowsy Nan,
The ancient widow young again,
Simpering behind her fan.

Without a choice, against their will,
Doited, [5] dazed, against their will,
The market lassie and her mither,
The farmer and his husbandman,
Hand in hand dance a' thegither.

[1] Furious [2] Carousers [3] Brawling [4] Cobbler [5] Spellbound

Slow at first, but faster soon,
Still increasing, wild and fast,
Hoods and mantles, hats and hose,
Blindly doffed and cast away,
Left them naked, heads and toes.

They would have torn us limb from limb,
Dainty limb from dainty limb;
But never one of them could win
Across the line that I had drawn
With bleeding thumb a-widdershin.

But there was Jeff the provost's son,
Jeff the provost's only son;
There was Father Auld himsel',
The Lombard frae the hostelry,
And the lawyer Peter Fell.

All goodly men we singled out,
Waled [1] them well, and singled out,
And drew them by the left hand in;
Mysie the priest, and Elspie won
The Lombard, Nort the lawyer carle,
I mysel' the provost's son.

Then, with cantrip [2] kisses seven,
Three times round with kisses seven,
Warped and woven there spun we
Arms and legs and flaming hair,
Like a whirlwind on the sea.

Like a wind that sucks the sea,
Over and in and on the sea,
Good sooth it was a mad delight;
And every man of all the four
Shut his eyes and laughed outright.

[1] Chose [2] Witching

Laughed as long as they had breath,
  Laughed while they had sense or breath;
And close about us coiled a mist
Of gnats and midges, wasps and flies,
Like the whirlwind shaft it rist.

Drawn up I was right off my feet,
  Into the mist and off my feet;
And, dancing on each chimney-top,
I saw a thousand darling imps
Keeping time with skip and hop.

And on the provost's brave ridge-tile,
  On the provost's grand ridge-tile,
The Blackamoor first to master me
I saw, I saw that winsome smile,
The mouth that did my heart beguile,
And spoke the great Word over me,
In the land beyond the sea.

I called his name, I called aloud,
  Alas! I called on him aloud;
And then he filled his hand with stour,[1]
And threw it towards me in the air;
My mouse flew out, I lost my pow'r!

My lusty strength, my power were gone;
  Power was gone, and all was gone.
He will not let me love him more!
Of bell and whip and horse's tail
He cares not if I find a store.

But I am proud if he is fierce!
  I am as proud as he is fierce;
I'll turn about and backward go,
If I meet again that Blackamoor,
And he'll help us then, for he shall know
I seek another paramour.

[1] Dust: reek

And we'll gang once more to yon town,
Wi' better luck to yon town;
We'll walk in silk and cramoisie,
And I shall wed the provost's son
My lady of the town I'll be!

For I was born a crowned king's child,
Born and nursed a king's child,
King o' the land ayont the sea,
Where the Blackamoor kissed me first,
And taught me art and glamourie.

Each one in her wame shall hide
Her hairy mouse, her wary mouse,
Fed on madwort and agramie,—
Wear amber beads between her breasts,
And blind-worm's skin about her knee.

The Lombard shall be Elspie's man,
Elspie's gowden husband-man;
Nort shall take the lawyer's hand;
The priest shall swear another vow;
We'll dance again the saraband!

William Bell Scott

336

ANNAN WATER

Annan Water's wading deep,
"And my Love Annie's wondrous bonny;
And I am loath she should wet he feet,
Because I love her best of ony."

He's loupen on his bonny gray,
He rode the right gate [1] and the ready; [2]
For all the storm he wadna stay,
For seeking of his bonny lady.

And he has ridden o'er field and fell,
Through moor, and moss, and many a mire;

[1] Road [2] Nearest

His spurs of steel were sair to bide,
And from her four feet flew the fire.

"My bonny gray, now play your part!
If ye be the steed that wins my dearie,
With corn and hay ye'll be fed for aye,
And never spur shall make you wearie."

The gray was a mare, and a right gude mare;
But when she wan the Annan Water,
She should not have ridden the ford that night
Had a thousand marks been wadded at her.

"O boatman, boatman, put off your boat,
Put off your boat for golden money!"
But for all the gold in fair Scotland,
He dared not take him through to Annie.

"O I was sworn so late yestreen,
Not by a single oath, but mony!
I'll cross the drumly stream to-night,
Or never could I face my honey."

The side was steep, and the bottom deep,
From bank to brae the water pouring;
The bonny gray mare she swat for fear,
For she heard the Water-Kelpy roaring.

He spurred her forth into the flood,
I wot she swam both strong and steady;
But the stream was broad, and her strength did fail,
And he never saw his bonny lady!

337

SONG

AH! County Guy, the hour is nigh:
The sun has left the lea,
The orange flower perfumes the bower,
The breeze is on the sea,
The lark, his lay who thrilled all day,

Sits hushed his partner nigh:
Breeze, bird, and flower, confess the hour,
But where is County Guy?—

The village maid steals through the shade,
Her shepherd's suit to hear;
To beauty shy, by lattice high,
Sings high-born Cavalier;
The star of Love, all stars above,
Now reigns o'er earth and sky,
And high and low the influence know—
But where is County Guy?

SIR WALTER SCOTT

338 DEADMAN'S DIRGE

PRAYER unsaid, and Mass unsung,
Deadman's dirge must still be rung:
Dingle-dong, the dead-bells sound!
Mermen chant his dirge around!

Wash him bloodless, smooth him fair,
Stretch his limbs, and sleek his hair:
Dingle-dong, the dead-bells go!
Mermen swing them to and fro!

In the wormless sand shall he
Feast for no foul glutton be:
Dingle-dong, the dead-bells chime!
Mermen keep the tone and time!

We must with a tombstone brave
Shut the shark out from his grave:
Dingle-dong, the dead-bells toll!
Mermen dirgers ring his knoll!

Such a slab will we lay o'er him,
All the dead shall rise before him:
Dingle-dong, the dead bells boom!
Mermen lay him in his tomb!

GEORGE DARLEY

339 BOATS AT NIGHT

How lovely is the sound of oars at night
  And unknown voices, borne through windless air,
From shadowy vessels floating out of sight
  Beyond the harbour lantern's broken glare
To those piled rocks that make on the dark wave
  Only a darker stain. The splashing oars
Slide softly on as in an echoing cave
  And with the whisper of the unseen shores
Mingle their music, till the bell of night
  Murmurs reverberations low and deep
That droop towards the land in swooning flight
  Like whispers from the lazy lips of sleep.
The oars grow faint. Below the cloud-dim hill
The shadows fade and now the bay is still.

EDWARD SHANKS

340 A VOICE SINGS

HEAR, sweet spirit, hear the spell,
Lest a blacker charm compel!
So shall the midnight breezes swell
With thy deep long-lingering knell.

And at evening evermore,
In a chapel on the shore,
Shall the chaunters, sad and saintly,
Yellow tapers burning faintly,
Doleful masses chaunt for thee,
  Miserere Domine!

Hark, the cadence dies away
  On the quiet moonlight sea:
The boatmen rest their oars; and say,
  Miserere Domine!

SAMUEL TAYLOR COLERIDGE

341 THE WANDERING SPECTRE

WAE's me, wae's me,
The acorn's not yet
Fallen from the tree
That's to grow the wood,
That's to make the cradle,
That's to rock the bairn,
That's to grow a man,
That's to lay me.

342 LUCIFER IN STARLIGHT

ON a starred night Prince Lucifer uprose.
Tired of his dark dominion swung the fiend
Above the rolling ball in cloud part screened,
Where sinners hugged their spectre of repose.
Poor prey to his hot fit of pride were those.
And now upon his western wing he leaned,
Now his huge bulk o'er Afric's sands careened,
Now the black planet shadowed Arctic snows.
Soaring through wider zones that pricked his scars
With memory of the old revolt from Awe,
He reached a middle height, and at the stars,
Which are the brain of heaven, he looked, and sank.
Around the ancient track marched rank on rank,
The army of unalterable law.

GEORGE MEREDITH

343 THERE WAS A KNIGHT

THERE was a knicht riding frae the east
Jennifer gentle an' rosemaree.
Who had been wooing at monie a place,
As the doo [1] flies owre the mulberry tree.

He cam' unto a widow's door,
And speird [2] whare her three dochters were.

[1] Dove [2] Asked

"The auldest ane's to a washing gane,
The second's to a baking gane.

"The youngest ane's to a wedding gane,
And it will be nicht or [1] she be hame."

He sat him doun upon a stane,
Till thir three lasses cam' tripping hame.

The auldest ane she let him in,
And pinned the door wi' a siller pin.

The second ane she made his bed,
And laid saft pillows unto his head.

The youngest ane was bauld [2] and bricht,
And she tarried for words wi' this unco knicht.—

"Gin ye will answer me questions ten,
The morn ye sall me made my ain:—

"O what is higher nor [3] the tree?
And what is deeper nor the sea?

"Or what is heavier nor the lead?
And what is better nor the bread?

"Or what is whiter nor the milk?
Or what is safter nor the silk?

"Or what is sharper nor a thorn?
Or what is louder nor a horn?

"Or what is greener nor the grass?
Or what is waur [4] nor a woman was?"

"O heaven is higher nor the tree,
And hell is deeper nor the sea.

[1] Ere [2] Bold [3] Than [4] Worse

"O sin is heavier nor the lead,
The blessing's better nor the bread.

"The snaw is whiter nor the milk,
And the down is safter nor the silk.

"Hunger is sharper nor a thorn,
And shame is louder nor a horn.

"The pies are greener nor the grass,
And Clootie's waur nor a woman was."

As sure as she the fiend did name,
Jennifer gentle an' rosemaree,
He flew awa' in a blazing flame,
As the doo flies owre the mulberry tree.

344 THE FALSE KNIGHT UPON THE ROAD

"O WHARE are ye gaun?"
Quo' the fause knicht upon the road:
"I'm gaun to the scule."
Quo' the wee boy, and still he stude.

"What is that upon your back?"
Quo' the fause knicht upon the road:
"Atweel [1] it is my bukes."
Quo' the wee boy, and still he stude.

"What's that ye've got in your arm?"
Quo' the fause knicht upon the road:
"Atweel it is my peit." [2]
Quo' the wee boy, and still he stude.

"Wha's aucht [3] they sheep?"
Quo' the fause knicht upon the road:
"They're mine and my mither's."
Quo' the wee boy, and still he stude.

[1] Why, sure [2] Peat for school fire [3] Who owns

"How monie o' them are mine?"
Quo' the fause knicht upon the road:
"A' they that hae blue tails."
Quo' the wee boy, and still he stude.

"I wiss ye were on yon tree:"
Quo' the fause knicht upon the road:
"And a gude ladder under me."
Quo' the wee boy, and still he stude.

"And the ladder for to break:"
Quo' the fause knicht upon the road:
"And *you* for to fa' down."
Quo' the wee boy, and still he stude.

"I wiss ye were in yon sie:"
Quo' the fause knicht upon the road:
"And a gude bottom-[1] under me."
Quo' the wee boy, and still he stude.

"And the bottom for to break:"
Quo' the fause knicht upon the road:
"And *ye* to be drowned."
Quo' the wee boy, and still he stude.

345 CHRISTABEL

'TIS the middle of night by the castle clock,
And the owls have awakened the crowing cock;
Tu-whit!———Tu-whoo!
And hark, again! the crowing cock,
How drowsily it crew.

Sir Leoline, the Baron rich,
Hath a toothless mastiff bitch;
From her kennel beneath the rock
She maketh answer to the clock,
Four for the quarters, and twelve for the hour;

[1] Vessel, ship

Ever and aye, by shine and shower,
Sixteen short howls, not over loud;
Some say, she sees my lady's shroud.

Is the night chilly and dark?
The night is chilly, but not dark.
The thin gray cloud is spread on high,
It covers but not hides the sky.
The moon is behind, and at the full;
And yet she looks both small and dull.
The night is chill, the cloud is gray:
'Tis a month before the month of May,
And the Spring comes slowly up this way.

The lovely lady, Christabel,
Whom her father loves so well,
What makes her in the wood so late,
A furlong from the castle gate?
She had dreams all yesternight
Of her own betrothed knight;
And she in the midnight wood will pray
For the weal of her lover that's far away.

She stole along, she nothing spoke,
The sighs she heaved were soft and low,
And naught was green upon the oak
But moss and rarest mistletoe:
She kneels beneath the hugh oak tree,
And in silence prayeth she.

The lady sprang up suddenly,
The lovely lady, Christabel!
It moaned as near, as near can be,
But what it is she cannot tell.—
On the other side it seems to be,
Of the huge, broad-breasted, old oak tree.

The night is chill; the forest bare;
Is it the wind that moaneth bleak?
There is not wind enough in the air
To move away the ringlet curl

From the lovely lady's cheek—
There is not wind enough to twirl
The one red leaf, the last of its clan,
That dances as often as dance it can,
Hanging so light, and hanging so high,
On the topmost twig that looks up at the sky.

Hush, beating heart of Christabel!
Jesu, Maria, shield her well!
She folded her arms beneath her cloak,
And stole to the other side of the oak.
What sees she there?

There she sees a damsel bright,
Drest in a silken robe of white,
That shadowy in the moonlight shone:
The neck that made that white robe wan—
Her stately neck, and arms were bare;
Her blue-veined feet unsandaled were,
And wildly glittered here and there
The gems entangled in her hair. . . .

SAMUEL TAYLOR COLERIDGE

346 THE FRUIT PLUCKER

ENCINCTURED with a twine of leaves,
That leafy twine his only dress,
A lovely Boy was plucking fruits,
By moonlight, in a wilderness.
The moon was bright, the air was free,

And fruits and flowers together grew
On many a shrub and many a tree:
And all put on a gentle hue,
Hanging in the shadowy air
Like a picture rich and rare.

It was a climate where, they say,
The night is more beloved than day.

But who that beauteous Boy beguiled,
That beauteous Boy to linger here?
Alone, by night, a little child,
In place so silent and so wild—
Has he no friend, no loving mother near?

SAMUEL TAYLOR COLERIDGE

347 THE HAUNTED PALACE

In the greenest of our valleys
By good angels tenanted,
Once a fair and stately palace—
Radiant palace—reared its head.
In the monarch's Thought's dominion
It stood there!
Never seraph spread a pinion
Over fabric half so fair.

Banners yellow, glorious, golden,
On its roof did float and flow,
(This—all this—was in the olden
Time long ago),
And every gentle air that dallied
In that sweet day,
Along the ramparts plumed and pallid
A wingèd odour went away.

Wanderers, in that happy valley,
Through two luminous windows saw
Spirits moving musically,
To a lute's well-tunèd law,
Round about a throne, where sitting
(Porphyrogene),
In state his glory well befitting,
The ruler of the realm was seen.

And all with pearl and ruby glowing
Was the fair palace door,
Through which came flowing, flowing, flowing,

And sparkling evermore,
A troop of Echoes, whose sweet duty
Was but to sing,
In voices of surpassing beauty,
The wit and wisdom of their king.

But evil things, in robes of sorrow,
Assailed the monarch's high estate.
(Ah, let us mourn, for never morrow
Shall dawn upon him desolate!)
And round about his home, the glory,
That blushed and bloomed,
Is but a dim-remembered story
Of the old time entombed.

And travellers, now, within that valley,
Through the red-litten windows see
Vast forms, that move fantastically
To a discordant melody;
While, like a ghastly rapid river,
Through the pale door
A hideous throng rush out for ever,
And laugh—but smile no more.

EDGAR ALLEN POE

348 THE HOUSE OF RICHESSE

NEIGHBOURING THE GATE OF HELL INTO WHICH MAMMON LED THE ELFIN KNIGHT

. . . THAT houses forme within was rude and strong,
Like an huge cave, hewne out of rocky clift,
From whose rough vaut the ragged breaches hong,
Embost with massy gold of glorious gift,
And with rich metall loaded every rift,
That heavy ruine they did seeme to threat;
And over them *Arachne* high did lift
Her cunning web, and spred her subtile net,
Enwrappèd in fowle smoke and clouds more blacke then jet

Both roofe, and floore, and wals were all of gold,
But overgrowne with dust and old decay,
And hid in darkenesse, that none could behold
The hew thereof: for vew of chearefull day
Did never in that house it selfe display,
But a faint shadow of uncertain light;
Such as a lamp, whose life does fade away:
Or as the Noone cloathèd with clowdy night,
Does shew to him that walkes in feare and sad affright.

In all that rowme was nothing to be seene,
But hugh great yron chests and coffers strong,
All bard with double bends,[1] that none could weene
Them to efforce by violence or wrong;
On every side they placèd were along.
But all the ground which sculs was scatterèd,
And dead mens bones, which round about were flong,
Whose lives, it seemèd, whilome there were shed,
And their vile carcases now left unburièd. . . .

EDMUND SPENSER

[1] Bands

349 THE OLD CITY

THOU hast come from the old city,
From the gate and the tower,
From King and priest and serving man
And burnished bower,
From beggar's whine and barking dogs,
From Prison sealed—
Thou hast come from the old city
Into the field.

The gables in the old city
Are stooping awry,
They gloom upon the muddy lanes
And smother the sky
And nightly through those mouldy lanes,
Moping and slow,

They who builded the old city
The cold ghosts go.

There is plague in the old city,
And the priests are sped
To graveyard and vault
To bury the dead;
Brittle bones and dusty breath
To death must yield—
Fly, fly, from the old city
Into the field!

RUTH MANNING-SANDERS

350

THE TWO SPIRITS

First Spirit. O THOU, who plumed with strong desire
Wouldst float above the earth, beware!
A Shadow tracks thy flight of fire—
Night is coming!
Bright are the regions of the air,
And among the winds and beams
It were delight to wander there—
Night is coming!

Second Spirit. The deathless stars are bright above;
If I would cross the shade of night,
Within my heart is the lamp of love,
And that is day!
And the moon will smile with gentle light
On my golden plumes where'er they move;
The meteors will linger round my flight;
And make night day.

First Spirit. But if the whirlwinds of darkness waken
Hail, and lightning, and stormy rain;
See, the bounds of the air are shaken—
Night is coming!
The red swift clouds of the hurricane
Yon declining sun have overtaken,

The clash of the hail sweeps over the plain—
Night is coming!

Second Spirit. I see the light, and I hear the sound;
I'll sail on the flood of the tempests dark,
With the calm within and the light around
Which makes night day:
And thou, when the gloom is deep and stark,
Look from thy dull earth, slumber-bound,
My moon-like flight thou then may'st mark
On high, far away.

* * *

Some say there is a precipice
Where one vast pine is frozen to ruin
O'er piles of snow and chasms of ice
'Mid Alpine mountains;
And that the languid storm pursuing
That wingèd shape, for ever flies
Round those hoar branches, aye renewing
Its aëry fountains.

Some say, when nights are dry and clear,
And the death-dews sleep on the morass,
Sweet whispers are heard by the traveller,
Which make night day;
And a silver shape, like his early love, doth pass
Up-borne by her wild and glittering hair,
And when he awakes on the fragrant grass,
He finds night day.

PERCY BYSSHE SHELLEY

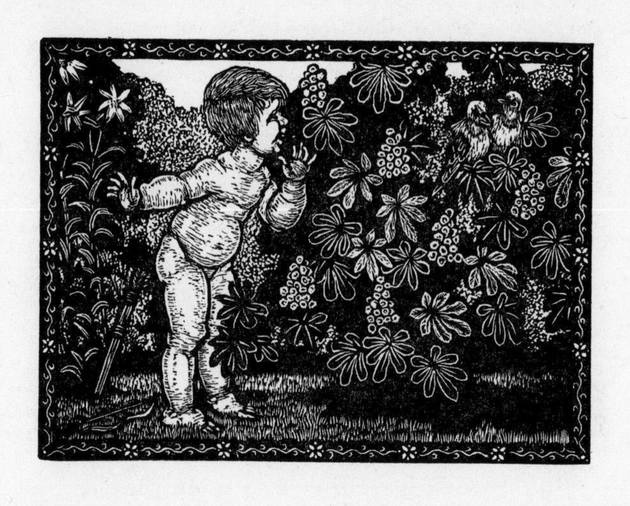

LILY BRIGHT AND SHINE-A

351 SILLY SWEETHEART

SILLY Sweetheart, say not nay,
Come away:
All I tell is sweet and merry;
Soon rings evensong, and soon
Where was blossom hangs a berry;
Where was darkness shines a moon.
Prythee, Sweetheart, then I say,
Come, come away!

O away,
Come away:
Maids there are with cheeks like roses,
Thine are roses in the snow.
Fie, the lass whose dainty nose is
Tilted not as one I know.
Nought heeds she, Alackaday!
My, "Come, come away!"

O away,
Come away:
Honeycomb by bees made sweet is;
Dew on apple, bloom on plum;
Hearken, my heart's lightest beat is
Drumming, drumming; haste and come
Say not nay, then;
Make no stay, then;
Dance thy dainty foot and straying
Come, come away!

352 HERE COMES A LUSTY WOOER

"HERE comes a lusty wooer,
My a dildin, my a daldin;

Here comes a lusty wooer,
Lily bright and shine-a."

"Pray who do you woo?
My a dildin, my a daldin;
Pray who do you woo?
Lily bright and shine-a."

"Woo! Your fairest daughter!
My a dildin, my a daldin;
Woo! your fairest daughter!
Lily bright and shine-a."

"There! there! she is for you,
My a dildin, my a daldin;
There! there! she is for you,
Lily bright and shine-a."

353 THREE KNIGHTS FROM SPAIN

We are three Brethren come from Spain,
All in French garlands;
We are come to court your daughter Jane,
And adieu to you, my darlings.

My daughter Jane!—she is too young,
All in French garlands;
She cannot bide your flattering tongue,
And adieu to you, my darlings.

Be she young, or be she old,
All in French garlands;
'Tis for a bride she must be sold,
And adieu to you, my darlings.

A bride, a bride, she shall not be,
All in French garlands;
Till she go through this world with me,
And adieu to you, my darlings.

Then shall you keep your daughter Jane,
All in French garlands;

Come once, we come not here again,
And adieu to you, my darlings.

Turn back, turn back, you Spanish Knights,
All in French garlands;
Scour, scour your spurs, till they be bright,
And adieu to you, my darlings.

Sharp shine our spurs, all richly wrought,
All in French garlands;
In towns afar our spurs were bought
And adieu to you, my darlings.

Smell my lilies, smell my roses,
All in French garlands;
Which of my maidens do you choose?
And adieu to you, my darlings.

Not she. Not she. Thy youngest, Jane!
All in French garlands;
We ride—and ride not back again,
And adieu to you, my darlings.

In every pocket a thousand pound,
All in French garlands;
On every finger a gay gold ring,
And adieu to you, my darlings.
And adieu to you, my darlings.

354 THE WHUMMIL BORE

Seven lang years I hae served the King,
Fa fa fa fa lilly:
And I never got a sight of his daughter but ane:
With my glimpy, glimpy, glimpy eedle,
Lillum too tee a ta too a tee a ta a tally.

I saw her thro' a whummil bore,
Fa fa fa fa lilly:

And I ne'er got a sight of her no more.
With my glimpy, glimpy, glimpy eedle,
Lillum too tee a ta too a tee a ta a tally.

Twa was putting on her gown,
Fa fa fa fa lilly:
And ten was putting pins therein.
With my glimpy, glimpy, glimpy eedle,
Lillum too tee a ta too a tee a ta a tally.

Twa was putting on her shoon,
Fa fa fa fa lilly:
And twa was buckling them again.
With my glimpy, glimpy, glimpy eedle,
Lillum too tee a ta too a tee a ta a tally.

Five was combing down her hair,
Fa fa fa fa lilly:
And I ne'er got a sight of her nae mair.
With my glimpy, glimpy, glimpy eedle,
Lillum too tee a ta too a tee a ta a tally.

Her neck and breast was like the snow,
Fa fa fa fa lilly:
Then from the bore I was forced to go.
With my glimpy, glimpy, glimpy eedle,
Lillum too tee a ta too a tee a ta a tally.

355 HEY, WULLY WINE

Hey, Wully wine, and How, Wully wine,
I hope for hame ye'll no' incline;
Ye'll better light, and stay a' night,
And I'll gie thee a lady fine.

I maun ride hame, I maun ride hame,
And bide nae langer here;
The road is lang, the mirk soon on,
And howlets mak' me fear.

Light down, and bide wi' us a' night,
  We'll choose for ye a bonnie lass,
Ye'll get your wield and pick o' them a'
  And the time it soon awa' will pass.

Wha will ye gie, if I wi' ye bide,
To be my bonny bonny bride,
And lie down lovely by my side?

I'll gie thee Kate o' Dinglebell,
A bonny body like yersell.

I'll stick her high in yon pear-tree
Sweet and meek, and sae is she:
I lo'ed her ance, but she's no' for me,
Yet I thank ye for your courtesy.

I'll gie thee Rozie o' the Cleugh,
I'm sure she'll please thee weel eneugh.

Up wi' her on the bare bane dyke,
She'll be rotten or [1] I'll be ripe:
She's made for some ither, and no' me,
Yet I thank ye for your courtesy.

Then I'll gie ye Nell o' sweet Sprinkell,
Owre Galloway she bears the bell.

I'll set her up in my bed-head,
And feed her wi' new milk and bread;
She's for nae ither, but just for me,
Sae I thank ye for your courtesy.

356 DOWN IN YONDER MEADOW

Down in yonder meadow where the green grass grows,
Pretty Pollie Pillicote bleaches her clothes.
She sang, she sang, she sang, oh, so sweet,

[1] Ere

She sang, *Oh, come over!* across the street.
He kissed her, he kissed her, he bought her a gown,
A gown of rich cramasie out of the town.
He bought her a gown and a guinea gold ring,
A guinea, a guinea, a guinea gold ring;
Up street, and down, shine the windows made of glass,
Oh, isn't Pollie Pillicote a braw young lass?
Cherries in her cheeks, and ringlets her hair,
Hear her singing *Handy, Dandy* up and down the stair.

357 QUOTH JOHN TO JOAN

QUOTH John to Joan, Will thou have me:
I prithee now, wilt? and I'll marry thee,
My cow, my calf, my house, my rents,
And all my lands and tenements:
Oh, say, my Joan, will not that do?
I cannot come every day to woo.

I've corn and hay in the barn hard-by,
And three fat hogs pent up in the sty,
I have a mare and she is coal black,
I ride on her tail to save my back.
Then, say, my Joan, will not that do?
I cannot come every day to woo.

I have a cheese upon the shelf,
And I cannot eat it all myself;
I've three good marks that lie in a rag,
In a nook of the chimney, instead of a bag.
Then, say, my Joan, will not that do?
I cannot come every day to woo.

To marry I would have thy consent,
But faith I never could compliment;
I can say nought but "Hoy, gee ho!"
Words that belong to the cart and the plough.
Oh, say, My Joan, will not that do?
I cannot come every day to woo.

358 MY MISTRESS IS AS FAIR AS FINE

My mistress is as fair as fine,
Milk-white fingers, cherry nose.
Like twinkling day-stars look her eyne,
Lightening all things where she goes.
Fair as Phoebe, though not so fickle,
Smooth as glass, though not so brickle.

My heart is like a ball of snow
Melting at her lukewarm sight;
Her fiery lips like night-worms glow,
Shining clear as candle-light.
Neat she is, no feather lighter;
Bright she is, no daisy whiter.

359 DIAPHENIA

Diaphenia, like the daffadowndilly,
White as the sun, fair as the lily,
Heigh ho, how I do love thee!
I do love thee as my lambs
Are belovèd of their dams—
How blest were I if thou wouldst prove me.

Diaphenia, like the spreading roses,
That in thy sweets all sweets encloses,
Fair sweet, how I do love thee!
I do love thee as each flower
Loves the sun's life-giving power,
For, dead, thy breath to life might move me.

Diaphenia, like to all things blessèd,
When all thy praises are expressèd,
Dear joy, how I do love thee!
As the birds do love the Spring,
Or the bees their careful king.
Then in requite, sweet virgin, love me!

Henry Constable

360 AEGLAMOUR'S LAMENT

HERE she was wont to go, and here, and here!
Just where those daisies, pinks, and violets grow:
The world may find the spring by following her;
For other print her airy steps ne'er left:
Her treading would not bend a blade of grass,
Or shake the downy blow-ball from his stalk;
But like the soft west-wind she shot along;
And where she went, the flowers took thickest root
As she had sowed them with her odourous foot.

BEN JONSON

361 MY TRUE-LOVE HATH MY HEART

MY true-love hath my heart, and I have his,
By just exchange one for the other given;
I hold his dear, and mine he cannot miss;
There never was a better bargain driven.

His heart in me keeps me and him in one,
My heart in him his thoughts and senses guides;
He loves my heart, for once it was his own;
I cherish his because in me it bides.

His heart his wound receivèd from my sight,
My heart was wounded with his wounded heart;
For as from me on him his heart did light,
So still methought in me his heart did smart.

Both equal hurt, in this change sought our bliss,
My true-love hath my heart, and I have his.

SIR PHILIP SIDNEY

362 A BIRTHDAY

MY heart is like a singing bird
Whose nest is in a watered shoot;

My heart is like an apple-tree
  Whose boughs are bent with thickest fruit.

My heart is like a rainbow shell
  That paddles in a halcyon sea;
My heart is gladder than all these
  Because my love is come to me.

Raise me a dais of silk and down;
  Hang it with vair and purple dyes;
Carve it in doves and pomegranates,
  And peacocks with a hundred eyes;
Work it in gold and silver grapes,
  In leaves and silver fleurs-de-lys;
Because the birthday of my life
  Is come, my love is come to me.

CHRISTINA ROSSETTI

363

LIFE OF LIFE

"VOICE IN THE AIR, SINGING"

LIFE of Life! thy lips enkindle
  With their love the breath between them
And thy smiles before they dwindle
  Make the cold air flare; then screen them
In those looks, where whoso gazes
Faints, entangled in their mazes.

Child of Light! thy limbs are burning
  Through the vest which seeks to hide them;
As the radiant lines of morning
  Through the clouds ere they divide them;
And this atmosphere divinest
Shrouds thee wheresoe'er thou shinest.

Fair are others; none beholds thee,
  But thy voice sounds low and tender
Like the fairest, for it folds thee
  From the sight, that liquid splendour,

And all feel, yet see thee never,
As I feel now, lost for ever!

Lamp of Earth! where'er thou movest
Its dim shapes are clad with brightness,
And the souls of whom thou lovest
Walk upon the winds with lightness,
Till they fail, as I am failing,
Dizzy, lost, yet unbewailing! . . .

PERCY BYSSHE SHELLEY

364 A SONNET OF THE MOON

LOOK how the pale Queen of the silent night
Doth cause the Ocean to attend upon her,
And he, as long as she is in his sight,
With his full tide is ready her to honour:

But when the silver waggon of the Moon
Is mounted up so high he cannot follow,
The sea calls home his crystal waves to moan,
And with low ebb doth manifest his sorrow.

So you that are the sovereign of my heart,
Have all my joys attending on your will,
My joys low-ebbing when you do depart,
When you return, their tide my heart doth fill.

So as you come, and as you do depart,
Joys ebb and flow within my tender heart.

CHARLES BEST

365 THE OUTLAW OF LOCH LENE

O MANY a day have I made good ale in the glen,
That came not of stream or malt, like the brewing of men:
My bed was the ground; my roof, the green-wood above;
And the wealth that I sought, one far kind glance from my Love.

Alas, on that night when the horses I drove from the field
That I was not near from terror my angel to shield!
She stretched forth her arms; her mantel she flung to the wind,
And swam o'er Loch Lene, her outlawed lover to find.

O would that a freezing sleet-winged tempest did sweep,
And I and my love were alone, far off on the deep;
I'd ask not a ship, or a bark, or a pinnace, to save—
With her hand round my waist, I'd fear not the wind or the wave.

'Tis down by the lake where the wild tree fringes its sides,
The maid of my heart, my fair one of Heaven resides:
I think, as at eve she wanders its mazes among,
The birds go to sleep by the sweet wild twist of her song.

JEREMIAH JOHN CALLANAN

366 O WHAT IF THE FOWLER

O WHAT if the fowler my blackbird has taken?
The roses of dawn blossom over the sea;
Awaken, my blackbird, awaken, awaken,
And sing to me out of my red fuchsia tree!

O what if the fowler my blackbird has taken?
The sun lifts his head from the lip of the sea—
Awaken, my blackbird, awaken, awaken,
And sing to me out of my red fuchsia tree!

O what if the fowler my blackbird has taken?
The mountain grows white with the birds of the sea;
But down in my garden forsaken, forsaken,
I'll weep all the day by my red fuchsia tree!

CHARLES DALMON

367 WHITHER AWAY?

"WHERE are you going, Master mine?"
"Mistress of mine, farewell!

Pledge me a cup of golden wine!
Light shall be dark and darkness shine
Before I tell!"

"O go you by the firwoods blue?
And by the Fairies' Trysting Tree?"
"No, for the path is grown with rue
And nightshade's purple fruit, since you
Walked there with me!"

"O go you by the pastures high—
A grassy road and daisies fair?"
"No, for I saw them fade and die
On the bright evening, love, that I
Sat with you there."

MARY COLERIDGE..

368 BONNY BARBARA ALLAN

IT was in and about the Martinmas time,
When the green leaves were a falling,
That Sir John Graeme, in the West Country,
Fell in love with Barbara Allan.

He sent his man down through the town,
To the place where she was dwelling:
"O haste and come to my master dear,
Gin ye be Barbara Allan."

O hooly, hooly [1] rose she up,
To the place where he was lying,
And when she drew the curtain by;—
"Young man, I think, you're dying."

"O it's I'm sick, and very, very sick,
And 'tis a' for Barbara Allan."—

[1] Slowly, softly

"O the better for me ye's never be,
Tho your heart's blood were a spilling.

"O dinna ye mind, young man," said she,
"When ye was in the tavern a-drinking,
That ye made the healths gae round and round,
And slighted Barbara Allan?"

He turned his face unto the wall,
And death was with him dealing:
"Adieu, adieu, my dear friends all,
And be kind to Barbara Allan."

She had not gane a mile but twa,
When she heard the dead-bell ringing,
And every jow that the dead-bell gied,
It cryed, *Woe to Barbara Allan!*

"O mother, mother, make my bed!
O make it saft and narrow!
Since my love died for me to-day,
I'll die for him to-morrow."

369 PROUD MAISIE

PROUD Maisie is in the wood,
Walking so early;
Sweet Robin sits on the bush,
Singing so rarely.

"Tell me, thou bonny bird,
When shall I marry me?"
"When six braw gentlemen
Kirkward shall carry ye."

"Who makes the bridal bed,
Birdie, say truly?"
"The grey-headed sexton
That delves the grave duly."

"The glowworm o'er grave and stone
Shall light thee steady;
The owl from the steeple sing
Welcome, proud lady."

SIR WALTER SCOTT

370

A LEAVE TAKING

LET us go hence, my songs; she will not hear.
Let us go hence together without fear;
Keep silence now, for singing-time is over,
And over all old things and all things dear.
She loves not you nor me as all we love her.
Yea, though we sang as angels in her ear,
She would not hear.

Let us rise up and part; she will not know.
Let us go seaward as the great winds go,
Full of blown sand and foam; what help is here?
There is no help, for all these things are so,
And all the world is bitter as a tear.
And how these things are, though ye strove to show,
She would not know.

Let us go hence and rest; she will not love.
We gave love many dreams and days to keep,
Flowers without scent, and fruits that would not grow,
Saying, "If thou wilt, thrust in thy sickle and reap."
All is reaped now; no grass is left to mow;
And we that sowed, though all we fell on sleep,
She would not weep.

Let us go hence and rest; she will not love.
She shall not hear us if we sing hereof,
Nor see love's ways, how sore they are and steep.
Come hence, let be, lie still; it is enough.
Love is a barren sea, bitter and deep;
And though she saw all heaven in flower above,
She would not love.

Let us give up, go down; she will not care.
Though all the stars made gold of all the air,
And the sea moving saw before it move
One moon-flower making all the foam-flowers fair;
Though all those waves went over us, and drove
Deep down the stifling lips and drowning hair,
She would not care.

Let us go hence, go hence; she will not see.
Sing all once more together; surely she,
She, too, remembering days and words that were,
Will turn a little toward us, sighing; but we,
We are hence, we are gone, as though we had not been there.
Nay, and though all men seeing had pity on me,
She would not see.

ALGERNON CHARLES SWINBURNE

371

THE UNQUIET GRAVE

"THE wind doth blow to-day, my love,
And a few small drops of rain;
I never had but one true love,
In cold grave she was lain.

"I'll do as much for my true love
As any young man may;
I'll sit and mourn all at her grave
For a twelvemonth and a day."

The twelvemonth and a day being up,
The dead began to speak:
"Oh who sits weeping on my grave,
And will not let me sleep?"

" 'Tis I, my love, sits on your grave,
And will not let you sleep;
For I crave one kiss of your clay-cold lips,
And that is all I seek."

"You crave one kiss of my clay-cold lips;
But my breath smells earthy strong;
If you have one kiss of my clay-cold lips,
Your time will not be long.

"'Tis down in yonder garden green,
Love, where we used to walk,
The finest flower that ere was seen
Is withered to a stalk.

"The stalk is withered dry, my love,
So will our hearts decay;
So make yourself content, my love,
Till God calls you away."

372 A LAMENT: 1547

"Departe, departe, departe—
Allace! I most departe
From hir that hes my hart,
With hairt full soir;
Aganis my will in deid,
And can find no remeid:
I wait the pains of deid—
Can do no moir. . . .

"Adew, my ain sueit thing,
My joy and comforting,
My mirth and sollesing
Of erdly gloir:
Fair weill, my lady bricht,
And my remembrance rycht;
Fair weill and haif gud nycht:
I say no moir."

Alexander Scott

373 I DIED TRUE

Lay a garland on my hearse
Of the dismal yew;

Maidens, willow branches bear;
Say I died true.
My love was false, but I was firm
From my hour of birth.
Upon my buried body lie
Lightly, gentle earth!

JOHN FLETCHER

374

SONG

How should I your true love know
From another one?
By his Cockle hat and staffe,
And his Sandal shoone.

He is dead and gone, Lady,
He is dead and done,—
At his head a grasse-greene Turfe,
At his heeles a stone.

White his Shrowd as the Mountain Snow,
Larded with sweet flowers:
Which bewept to the grave did not go,
With true-love showres.

WILLIAM SHAKESPEARE

375

IT WAS THE TIME OF ROSES

It was not in the winter
Our loving lot was cast:
It was the time of roses—
We plucked them as we passed!

That churlish season never frowned
On early lovers yet!
O, no—the world was newly crowned
With flowers, when first we met.

'Twas twilight, and I bade you go,
But still you held me fast:

It was the time of roses—
We plucked them as we passed.". . .

THOMAS HOOD

376

AULD ROBIN GRAY

WHEN the sheep are in the fauld, and the kye [1] at hame,
And a' the warld to rest are gane,
The waes o' my heart fa' in showers frae my ee,
While my gudeman [2] lies sound by me.

Young Jamie lo'ed me weel, and sought for his bride,
But saving a croun he had naething else beside:
To make the croun a pund, young Jamie gaed to sea,
And the croun and the pund were baith for me.

He hadna been awa a week but only twa,
When my father brak his arm, and the cow was stown awa;
My mother she fell sick, and my Jamie at the sea—
And auld Robin Gray came a-courtin' me.

My father couldna work, and my mother couldna spin;
I toiled day and night, but their bread I couldna win;
Auld Rob maintained them baith, and wi' tears in his ee
Said, "Jennie, for their sakes, O, marry me!"

My heart it said nay; I look'd for Jamie back;
But the wind it blew high, and the ship it was a wrack;
His ship it was a wrack. . . . Why didna Jamie dee?
Or why do I live to cry, Wae's me?

My father urgit sair: my mother didna speak,
But she looked in my face till my heart was like to break:
They gi'ed him my hand, but my heart was at the sea,
Sae auld Robin Gray he was gudeman to me.

I hadna been a wife a week but only four,
When mournfu' as I sat on the stane at the door,

[1] Cows [2] Husband

I saw my Jamie's wraith, for I couldna think it he—
Till he said, "I'm come home to marry thee."

O, sair, sair did we greet,[1] and muckle[2] did we say;
We took but ae kiss, and I bad him gang away:
I wish that I were dead, but I'm no like to dee;
And why was I born to say, Wae's me!

I gang like a ghaist, and I carena to spin;
I daurna think on Jamie, for that wad be a sin;
But I'll do my best a gude wife aye to be,
For auld Robin Gray, he is kind unto me.

LADY ANNE LINDSAY

377 THE LAWLANDS O' HOLLAND

"THE love that I hae chosen,
I'll therewith be content;
The saut sea sall be frozen
Before that I repent.
Repent it sall I never
Until the day I dee;
But the Lawlands o' Holland
Hae twinned my love and me.

"My love he built a bonny ship,
And set her to the main,
Wi' twenty-four brave mariners
To sail her out and hame.
But the weary wind began to rise,
The sea began to rout,
And my love and his bonny ship
Turned withershins about.

"There sall nae mantle cross my back,
No kaim gae in my hair,
Neither sall coal nor candle-light
Shine in my bower mair;

[1] Weep [2] Much

Nor sall I choose anither love,
  Until the day I dee,
Sin' the Lawlands o' Holland,
  Hae twinned my love and me."

"Noo haud your tongue, my daughter dear,
  Be still, and bide content;
There's ither lads in Galloway;
  Ye needna sair lament."
"O there is nane in Galloway,
  There's nane at a' for me.
I never lo'ed a lad but ane,
  And he's drowned in the sea."

378 THE CHURCHYARD ON THE SANDS

My love lies in the gates of foam,
  The last dear wreck of shore;
The naked sea-marsh binds her home,
  The sand her chamber door.

The gray gull flaps the written stones,
  The ox-birds chase the tide;
And near that narrow field of bones
  Great ships at anchor ride.

Black piers with crust of dripping green,
  One foreland, like a hand,
O'er intervals of grass between
  Dim lonely dunes of sand.

A church of silent weathered looks,
  A breezy reddish tower,
A yard whose wounded resting-nooks
  Are tinged with sorrel flower.

In peace the swallow's eggs are laid
  Along the belfry walls;

The tempest does not reach her shade,
  The rain her silent halls.

But sails are sweet in summer sky,
  The lark throws down a lay;
The long salt levels steam and dry,
  The cloud-heart melts away.

And patches of the sea-pink shine,
  The pied crows poise and come;
The mallow hangs, the bind-weeds twine,
  Where her sweet lips are dumb.

The passion of the wave is mute;
  No sound or ocean shock;
No music save the thrilling flute
  That marks the curlew flock. . . .

LORD DE TABLEY

379

ROSE AYLMER

AH, what avails the sceptred race,
  Ah, what the form divine!
What every virtue, every grace!
  Rose Aylmer, all were thine.
Rose Aylmer, whom these wakeful eyes
  May weep, but never see,
A night of memories and sighs
  I consecrate to thee.

WALTER SAVAGE LANDOR

380

TO HELEN

HELEN, thy beauty is to me
  Like those Nicæan barks of yore,
That gently, o'er a perfumed sea,
  The weary, wayworn wanderer bore
  To his own native shore.

On desperate seas long wont to roam,
Thy hyacinth hair, thy classic face,
Thy Naiad air, have brought me home
To the glory that was Greece
And the grandeur that was Rome.

Lo! in yon brilliant window-niche
How statue-like I see thee stand,
The agate lamp within thy hand!
Ah, Psyche, from the regions which
Are Holy Land!

EDGAR ALLAN POE

381 "THERE IS A LADY SWEET AND KIND"

THERE is a Lady sweet and kind,
Was never face so pleased my mind;
I did but see her passing by,
And yet I love her till I die.

Her gesture, motion, and her smiles,
Her wit, her voice, my heart beguiles,
Beguiles my heart, I know not why,
And yet I love her till I die. . . .

Cupid is wingèd and doth range,
Her country so my love doth change:
But change she earth, or change she sky,
Yet will I love her till I die.

382 "LOVE NOT ME FOR COMELY GRACE"

LOVE not me for comely grace,
For my pleasing eye or face,
Not for any outward part:

No, nor for my constant heart!
For these may fail or turn to ill:
So thou and I shall sever:
Keep therefore a true woman's eye,
And love me still, but know not why!
So hast thou the same reason still
To doat upon me ever.

383 NOW WOLDE

Now wolde I faine some merthes [1] make,
All only for my lady sake,
When her I see;
But now I am so far fro her
It will not be.

Though I be far out of her sight
I am her man both day and night
And so will be.
Therefore wolde; as I love her,
She lovèd me.

When she is mery, then I am glad;
When she is sory, then I am sad;
And causè why,[2]
For he liveth not that loveth her
As well as I.

She saith that she hath seen it written
That "seldom seen is soon forgotten";
It is not so.
For in good feith, save only her,
I love no mo.[3]

384 EGYPT'S MIGHT IS TUMBLED DOWN

Egypyt's might is tumbled down
Down a-down the deeps of thought;

[1] Praises [2] Good reason why [3] More

Greece is fallen and Troy town,
Glorious Rome hath lost her crown,
Venice' pride is nought.

But the dreams their children dreamed
Fleeting, unsubstantial, vain,
Shadowy as the shadows seemed,
Airy nothing, as they deemed,
These remain.

MARY COLERIDGE

385

DREAM LOVE

YOUNG Love lies sleeping
In May-time of the year.
Among the lilies,
Lapped in the tender light:
White lambs come grazing,
White doves come building there;
And round about him
The May-bushes are white.

Soft moss the pillow
For oh, a softer cheek;
Broad leaves cast shadow
Upon the heavy eyes:
There winds and waters
Grow lulled and scarcely speak;
There twilight lingers
The longest in the skies.

Young Love lies dreaming;
But who shall tell the dream?
A perfect sunlight
On rustling forest tips;
Or perfect moonlight
Upon a rippling stream;
Or perfect silence,
Or song of cherished lips.

Burn odours round him
To fill the drowsy air;
Weave silent dances
Around him to and fro;
For oh, in waking
The sights are not so fair,
And song and silence
Are not like these below.

Young Love lies dreaming
Till summer days are gone,—
Dreaming and drowsing
Away to perfect sleep:
He sees the beauty
Sun hath not looked upon,
And tastes the fountain
Unutterably deep.

Him perfect music
Doth hush unto his rest,
And through the pauses
The perfect silence calms.
Oh, poor the voices
Of earth from east to west,
And poor earth's stillness
Between her stately palms.

Young Love lies drowsing
Away to poppied death;
Cool shadows deepen
Across the sleeping face:
So fails the summer
With warm, delicious breath;
And what hath autumn
To give us in its place?

Draw close the curtains
Of branched evergreen;
Change cannot touch them
With fading fingers sere:

Here the first violets
  Perhaps will bud unseen,
And a dove, may be,
  Return to nestle here.

CHRISTINA ROSSETTI

386 AT COMMON DAWN

AT common dawn there is a voice of bird
So sweet, 'tis kin to pain;
For love of earthly life it needs be heard,
And lets not sleep again.

This bird I did one time at midnight hear
In wet November wood
Say to himself his lyric faint and clear
As one at daybreak should.

He ceased; the covert breathed no other sound,
Nor moody answer made;
But all the world at beauty's worship found,
Was waking in the glade.

VIVIAN LOCKE ELLIS

“ECHO THEN SHALL
AGAIN TELL HER
I FOLLOW”

387 GLYCINE'S SONG

A SUNNY shaft did I behold,
From sky to earth it slanted:
And poised therein a bird so bold—
Sweet bird, thou wert enchanted!

He sank, he rose, he twinkled, he trolled
Within that shaft of sunny mist;
His eyes of fire, his beak of gold,
All else of amethyst!

And thus he sang: "Adieu! adieu!
Love's dreams prove seldom true.
The blossoms, they make no delay:
The sparkling dew-drops will not stay.
Sweet month of May,
We must away;
Far, far away!
To-day! to-day!"

SAMUEL TAYLOR COLERIDGE

388 THE CRYSTAL CABINET

THE Maiden caught me in the wild,
Where I was dancing merrily;
She put me into her Cabinet,
And locked me up with a golden key.

This Cabinet is formed of Gold
And Pearl and Crystal shining bright,
And within it opens into a World
And a little lovely Moony Night.

Another England there I saw
Another London with its Tower,
Another Thames and other Hills,
And another pleasant Surrey Bower.

Another Maiden like herself,
Translucent, lovely, shining clear,
Threefold each in the other closed—
O, what a pleasant trembling fear!

O, what a smile! a Threefold Smile
Filled me, that like a flame I burned;
I bent to kiss the lovely Maid,
And found a Threefold Kiss returned.

I strove to seize the inmost form
With ardour fierce and hands of flame,
But burst the Crystal Cabinet,
And like a Weeping Babe became—

A Weeping Babe upon the wild,
And Weeping Woman pale reclined,
And in the outward air again
I filled with woes the passing wind.

WILLIAM BLAKE

389 THE CHASE

ART thou gone in haste?
I'll not forsake thee;
Runn'st thou ne'er so fast?
I'll overtake thee:
O'er the dales, o'er the downs,
Through the green meadows,
From the fields through the towns,
To the dim shadows.

All along the plain,
To the low fountains,
Up and down again

From the high mountains;
Echo then shall again
Tell her I follow,
And the floods to the woods
Carry my holla!
Holla!
Ce! la! ho! ho! hu!

WILLIAM ROWLEY

390

TONY O!

OVER the bleak and barren snow
A voice there came a-calling;
"Where are you going to, Tony O!
Where are you going this morning?"

"I am going where there are rivers of wine,
The mountains bread and honey;
There Kings and Queens do mind the swine,
And the poor have all the money."

COLIN FRANCIS

391

ROMANCE

WHEN I was but thirteen or so
I went into a golden land,
Chimborazo, Cotopaxi
Took me by the hand.

My father died, my brother too,
They passed like fleeting dreams.
I stood where Popocatapetl
In the sunlight gleams.

I dimly heard the master's voice
And boys far-off at play,
Chimborazo, Cotopaxi
Had stolen me away.

I walked in a great golden dream
To and fro from school—

Shining Popocatapetl
The dusty streets did rule.

I walked home with a gold dark boy,
And never a word I'd say,
Chimborazo, Cotopaxi
Had taken my speech away:

I gazed entranced upon his face
Fairer than any flower—
O shining Popocateptl
It was thy magic hour:

The houses, people, traffic seemed
Thin fading dreams by day,
Chimborazo, Cotopaxi
They had stolen my soul away!

WALTER J. TURNER

392 HALLO MY FANCY

IN melancholic fancy,
Out of myself,
In the vulcan dancy,
All the world surveying,
Nowhere staying,
Just like a fairy elf;
Out o'er the tops of highest mountains skipping,
Out o'er the hill, the trees and valleys tripping,
Out o'er the ocean seas, without an oar or shipping,—
Hallo my fancy, whither wilt thou go?

Amidst the misty vapours
Fain would I know
What doth cause the tapers;
Why the clouds benight us
And affright us,
While we travel here below;
Fain would I know what makes the roaring thunder,

And what these lightnings be that rend the clouds asunder,
And what these comets are on which we gaze and wonder—
Hallo my fancy, whither wilt thou go?

Fain would I know the reason,
Why the little ant,
All the summer season,
Layeth up provision
On condition
To know no winter's want.
And how housewives, that are so good and painful,
Do unto their husbands prove so good and gainful;
And why the lazy drones to them do prove disdainful—
Hallo my fancy, whither wilt thou go? . . .

Amidst the foamy ocean,
Fain would I know
What doth cause the motion,
And returning
In its journeying,
And doth so seldom swerve?
And how the little fishes that swim beneath salt waters,
Do never blind their eye; methinks it is a matter
An inch above the reach of old Erra Pater!—
Hallo my fancy, whither wilt thou go?

Fain would I be resolvèd
How things are done;
And where the bull was calvèd
Of bloody Phalaris,
And where the tailor is
That works to the man i' the moon!
Fain would I know how Cupid aims so rightly;
And how the little fairies do dance and leap so lightly,
And where fair Cynthia makes her ambles nightly—
Hallo my fancy, whither wilt thou go?

In conceit like Phæton
I'll mount Phoebus' chair
Having ne'er a hat on,

All my hair a-burning
In my journeying;
Hurrying through the air.
Fain would I hear his fiery horses neighing
And see how they on foamy bits are playing,
All the stars and planets I will be surveying!—
Hallo my fancy, whither wilt thou go?

O from what ground of nature
Doth the pelican,
That self devouring creature
Prove so froward
And untoward,
Her vitals for to strain!
And why the subtle fox, while in death's wounds a-lying,
Do not lament his pangs by howling and by crying,
And why the milk-swan doth sing when she's a-dying—
Hallo my fancy, whither wilt thou go?

Fain would I conclude this,
At least make essay;
What similitude is:
Why fowls of a feather
Flock and fly together,
And lambs know beasts of prey;
How Nature's alchemists, these small laborious creatures,
Acknowledge still a prince in ordering their matters,
And suffer none to live who slothing lose their features—
Hallo my fancy, wither wilt thou go? . . .

To know this world's centre
Height, depth, breadth and length,
Fain would I adventure
To search the hid attractions
Of magnetic actions
And adamantine strength.
Fain would I know, if in some lofty mountain,
Where the moon sojourns, if there be tree or fountain;
If there be beasts of prey, or yet be fields to hunt in—
Hallo my fancy, wither wilt thou go? . . .

Hallo my fancy, hallo,
Stay, stay at home with me,
I can no longer follow,
For thou hast betrayed me,
And bewrayed me;
It is too much for thee.
Stay, stay at home with me, leave off thy lofty soaring;
Stay then at home with me, and on thy books be poring;
For he that goes abroad, lays little up in storing—
Thou'rt welcome my fancy, welcome home to me.

WILLIAM CLELAND

393

SONNET

THERE was an Indian, who had known no change,
Who strayed content along a sunlit beach
Gathering shells. He heard a sudden strange
Commingled noise: looked up; and gasped for speech.
For in the bay, where nothing was before,
Moved on the sea, by magic, huge canoes,
With bellying clothes on poles, and not one oar,
And fluttering coloured signs and clambering crews.

And he, in fear, this naked man alone,
His fallen hands forgetting all their shells,
His lips gone pale, knelt low behind a stone,
And stared, and saw, and did not understand,
Columbus's doom-burdened caravels
Slant to the shore, and all their seamen land.

J. C. SQUIRE

394

ON FIRST LOOKING INTO CHAPMAN'S HOMER

MUCH have I travelled in the realms of gold,
And many goodly states and kingdoms seen:
Round many western islands have I been
Which bards in fealty to Apollo hold.

Oft of one wide expanse had I been told
That deep-browed Homer ruled as his demesne;
Yet did I never breathe its pure serene
Till I heard Chapman speak out loud and bold:

Then felt I like some watcher of the skies
When a new planet swims into his ken;
Or like stout Cortez, when with eagle eyes

He stared at the Pacific—and all his men
Looked at each other with a wild surmise—
Silent, upon a peak in Darien.

JOHN KEATS

395 "TO SEA"

To sea, to sea! The calm is o'er;
The wanton water leaps in sport,
And rattles down the pebbly shore;
The dolphin wheels, the sea-cows snort,
And unseen Mermaids' pearly song
Comes bubbling up, the weeds among.
Fling broad the sail, dip deep the oar:
To sea, to sea! the calm is o'er.

To sea, to sea! our wide-winged bark
Shall billowy cleave its sunny way,
And with its shadow, fleet and dark,
Break the caved Tritons' azure day,
Like mighty eagle soaring light
O'er antelopes on Alpine height.
The anchor heaves, the ship swings free,
The sails swell full. To sea, to sea!

THOMAS LOVELL BEDDOES

396 BERMUDAS

WHERE the remote Bermudas ride,
In the Ocean's bosom unespied,
From a small boat, that rowed along,

The listening winds received this song:

"What should we do but sing His praise,
That led us through the watery maze,
Unto an isle so long unknown,
And yet far kinder than our own?
Where He the huge sea-monsters wracks
That lift the deep upon their backs,
He lands us on a grassy stage,
Safe from the storms' and prelates' rage:
He gave us this eternal Spring
Which here enamels everything,
And sends the fowls to us in care
On daily visits through the air:
He hangs in shades the orange bright,
Like golden lamps in a green night,
And does in the pomegranates close
Jewels more rich than Ormus shows;
He makes the figs our mouths to meet,
And throws the melons at our feet;
But apples plants of such a price
No tree could ever bear them twice.
With cedars, chosen by His hand
From Lebanon, He stores the land,
And makes the hollow seas, that roar,
Proclaim the ambergris on shore.
He cast (of which we rather boast)
The Gospel's pearl upon our coast;
And in these rocks for us did frame
A temple where to sound His name.
Oh! let our voice His praise exalt,
Till it arrive at Heaven's vault,
Which, thence (perhaps) rebounding, may
Echo beyond the Mexique bay."

Thus sung they, in the English boat,
A holy and a cheerful note;
And all the way, to guide their chime,
With falling oars they kept the time.

ANDREW MARVELL

397 THE OLD SHIPS

I HAVE seen old ships sail like swans asleep
Beyond the village which men still call Tyre,
With leaden age o'ercargoed, dipping deep
For Famagusta and the hidden sun
That rings black Cyprus with a lake of fire;
And all those ships were certainly so old—
Who knows how oft with squat and noisy gun,
Questing brown slaves or Syrian oranges,
The pirate Genoese
Hell-raked them till they rolled
Blood, water, fruit and corpses up the hold.
But now through friendly seas they softly run,
Painted the mid-sea blue or shore-sea green,
Still patterned with the vine and grapes in gold.

But I have seen
Pointing her shapely shadows from the dawn
And image tumbled on a rose-swept bay
A drowsy ship of some yet older day;
And, wonder's breath indrawn,
Thought I—who knows—who knows—but in that same
(Fished up beyond Aeaea, patched up new
—Stern painted brighter blue—)
That talkative, bald-headed seaman came
(Twelve patient comrades sweating at the oar)
From Troy's doom-crimson shore,
And with great lies about his wooden horse
Set the crew laughing, and forgot his course.
It was so old a ship—who knows, who knows?
—And yet so beautiful, I watched in vain
To see the mast burst open with a rose,
And the whole deck put on its leaves again.

JAMES ELROY FLECKER

398 THE RIME OF THE ANCIENT MARINER

In Seven Parts

Argument: *How a Ship having passed the Line is driven by storms to the cold Country towards the South Pole; and how from thence she made her course to the Tropical Latitude of the great Pacific Ocean; and of the strange things that befell; and in what manner the Ancient Mariner came back to his own Country.*

Part I

It is an ancient Mariner,
And he stoppeth one of three.
"By thy long grey beard and glittering eye,
Now wherefore stopp'st thou me?

The Bridegroom's doors are opened wide,
And I am next of kin;
The guests are met, the feast is set:
May'st hear the merry din."

He holds him with his skinny hand,
"There was a ship," quoth he.
"Hold off! unhand me, grey-beard loon!"
Eftsoons his hand dropt he.

He holds him with his glittering eye—
The Wedding-Guest stood still,
And listens like a three years' child:
The Mariner hath his will.

The Wedding-Guest sat on a stone:
He cannot choose but hear;
And thus spake on that ancient man,
The bright-eyed Mariner.

"The ship was cheered, the harbour cleared,
Merrily did we drop
Below the kirk, below the hill,
Below the lighthouse top.

The Sun came up upon the left,
Out of the sea came he!
And he shone bright, and on the right
Went down into the sea.

Higher and higher every day,
Till over the mast at noon—"
The Wedding-Guest here beat his breast,
For he heard the loud bassoon.

The bride hath paced into the hall,
Red as a rose is she;
Nodding their heads before her goes
The merry minstrelsy.

The Wedding-Guest he beat his breast,
Yet he cannot choose but hear;
And thus spake on that ancient man,
The bright-eyed Mariner.

"And now the STORM-BLAST came, and he
Was tyrannous and strong:
He struck with his o'ertaking wings,
And chased us south along.

With sloping masts and dipping prow,
As who pursued with yell and blow
Still treads the shadow of his foe,
And forward bends his head,
The ship drove fast, loud roared the blast,
And southward aye we fled.

And now there came both mist and snow,
And it grew wondrous cold:
And ice, mast-high, came floating by,
As green as emerald.

And through the drifts the snow cliffs
Did send a dismal sheen:
Nor shapes of men nor beasts we ken—
The ice was all between.

The ice was here, the ice was there,
The ice was all around:
It cracked and growled, and roared and howled,
Like noises in a swound!

At length did cross an Albatross,
Thorough the fog it came;
As if it had been a Christian soul,
We hailed it in God's name.

It ate the food it ne'er had eat,
And round and round it flew.
The ice did split with a thunder-fit;
The helmsman steered us through!

And a good south wind sprung up behind;
The Albatross did follow,
And every day, for food or play,
Came to the mariner's hollo!

In mist or cloud, on mast or shroud,
It perched for vespers nine;
Whiles all the night, through fog-smoke white,
Glimmered the white Moon-shine."

"God save thee, ancient Mariner!
Form the fiends, that plague thee thus!—
Why look'st thou so?"
—"With my cross-bow
I shot the ALBATROSS."

PART II

The Sun now rose upon the right:
Out of the sea came he,
Still hid in mist, and on the left
Went down into the sea.

And the good south wind still blew behind,
But no sweet bird did follow,

Nor any day for food or play
Came to the mariner's hollo!

And I had done a hellish thing,
And it would work 'em woe:
For all averred, I had killed the bird
That made the breeze to blow.
Ah wretch! said they, the bird to slay,
That made the breeze to blow!

Nor dim nor red, like God's own head,
The glorious Sun uprist:
Then all averred, I had killed the bird
That brought the fog and mist.
'Twas right, said they, such birds to slay,
That bring the fog and mist.

The fair breeze blew, the white foam flew.
The furrow followed free;
We were the first that ever burst
Into that silent sea.

Down dropt the breeze, the sails dropt down,
'Twas sad as sad could be;
And we did speak only to break
The silence of the sea!

All in a hot and copper sky,
The bloody Sun, at noon,
Right up above the mast did stand,
No bigger than the Moon.

Day after day, day after day,
We stuck, nor breath nor motion;
As idle as a painted ship
Upon a painted ocean.

Water, water, every where,
And all the boards did shrink;
Water, water, every where,
Nor any drop to drink.

The very deep did rot: O Christ!
That ever this should be!
Yea, slimy things did crawl with legs
Upon the slimy sea.

About, about, in reel and rout
The death-fires danced at night;
The water, like a witch's oils,
Burnt green, and blue, and white.

And some in dreams assurèd were
Of the Spirit that plagued us so;
Nine fathom deep he had followed us
From the land of mist and snow.

And every tongue, through utter drought,
Was withered at the root;
We could not speak, no more than if
We had been choked with soot.

Ah! well a-day! what evil looks
Had I from old and young!
Instead of the cross, the Albatross
About my neck was hung.

Part III

"There passed a weary time. Each throat
Was parched, and glazed each eye.
A weary time! a weary time!
How glazed each weary eye,
When looking westward, I beheld
A something in the sky.

At first it seemed a little speck,
And then it seemed a mist;
It moved and moved, and took at last
A certain shape, I wist.

A speck, a mist, a shape, I wist!
And still it neared and neared:

As if it dodged a water-sprite,
It plunged and tacked and veered.

With throats unslaked, with black lips baked,
We could nor laugh nor wail;
Through utter drought all dumb we stood!
I bit my arm, I sucked the blood,
And cried, A sail! a sail!

With throats unslaked, with black lips baked,
Agape they heard me call:
Gramercy! they for joy did grin,
And all at once their breath drew in,
As they were drinking all.

See! see! (I cried) she tacks no more!
Hither to work us weal;
Without a breeze, without a tide,
She steadies with upright keel!

The western wave was all a-flame,
The day was well nigh done!
Almost upon the western wave
Rested the broad bright Sun;
When that strange shape drove suddenly
Betwixt us and the Sun.

And straight the Sun was flecked with bars,
(Heaven's Mother send us grace!)
As if through a dungeon-grate he peered
With broad and burning face.

Alas! (thought I, and my heart beat loud)
How fast she nears and nears!
Are those *her* sails that glance in the Sun,
Like restless gossameres?

Are those *her* ribs through which the Sun
Did peer, as through a grate?

And is that Woman all her crew?
Is that a DEATH? and are there two?
Is DEATH that woman's mate?

Her lips were red, *her* looks were free,
Her locks were yellow as the gold:
Her skin was as white as leprosy,
The Night-mare LIFE-IN-DEATH was she,
Who thicks man's blood with cold.

The naked hulk alongside came,
And the twain were casting dice;
"The game is done! I've won! I've won!"
Quoth she, and whistles thrice.

The Sun's rim dips: the stars rush out:
At one stride comes the dark;
With far-heard whisper, o'er the sea,
Off shot the spectre-bark.

We listened and looked sideways up!
Fear at my heart, as at a cup,
My life-blood seemed to sip!
The stars were dim, and thick the night,
The steersman's face by his lamp gleamed white;

From the sails the dew did drip—
Till clomb above the eastern bar
The hornèd Moon, with one bright star
Within the nether tip.

One after one, by the star-dogged Moon,
Too quick for groan or sigh,
Each turned his face with a ghastly pang,
And cursed me with his eye.

Four times fifty living men,
(And I heard nor sigh nor groan)
With heavy thump, a lifeless lump,
They dropped down one by one.

The souls did from their bodies fly,—
They fled to bliss or woe!
And every soul, it passed me by,
Like the whizz of my cross-bow!"

Part IV

"I fear thee, ancient Mariner!
I fear thy skinny hand!
And thou art long, and lank, and brown,
As is the ribbed sea-sand.

I fear thee and thy glittering eye,
And thy skinny hand, so brown."—
"Fear not, fear not, thou Wedding-Guest!
This body dropt not down.

Alone, alone, all, all alone,
Alone on a wide wide sea!
And never a saint took pity on
My soul in agony.

The many men, so beautiful!
And they all dead did lie:
And a thousand thousand slimy things
Lived on; and so did I.

I looked upon the rotting sea,
And drew my eyes away;
I looked upon the rotting deck,
And there the dead men lay.

I looked to heaven, and tried to pray;
But or ever a prayer had gusht,
A wicked whisper came, and made
My heart as dry as dust.

I closed my lids, and kept them close,
And the balls like pulses beat;
For the sky and the sea, and the sea and the sky
Lay like a load on my weary eye,
And the dead were at my feet.

The cold sweat melted from their limbs,
Nor rot nor reek did they:
The look with which they looked on me
Had never passed away.

An orphan's curse would drag to hell
A spirit from on high;
But oh! more horrible than that
Is the curse in a dead man's eye!
Seven days, seven nights, I saw that curse,
And yet I could not die.

The moving Moon went up the sky,
And no where did abide:
Softly she was going up,
And a star or two beside—

Her beams bemocked the sultry main,
Like April hoar-frost spread;
But where the ship's huge shadow lay,
The charmèd water burnt alway
A still and awful red.

Beyond the shadow of the ship,
I watched the water-snakes:
They moved in tracks of shining white,
And when they reared, the elfish light
Fell off in hoary flakes.

Within the shadow of the ship
I watched their rich attire:
Blue, glossy green, and velvet black,
They coiled and swam; and every track
Was a flash of golden fire.

O happy living things! no tongue
Their beauty might declare:
A spring of love gushed from my heart,
And I blessed them unaware:
Sure my kind saint took pity on me,
And I blessed them unaware.

The self-same moment I could pray;
And from my neck so free
The Albatross fell off, and sank
Like lead into the sea.

Part V

Oh sleep! it is a gentle thing,
Beloved from pole to pole!
To Mary Queen the praise be given!
She sent the gentle sleep from Heaven,
That slid into my soul.

The silly buckets on the deck,
That had so long remained,
I dreamt that they were filled with dew;
And when I awoke, it rained.

My lips were wet, my throat was cold,
My garments all were dank;
Sure I had drunken in my dreams,
And still my body drank.

I moved, and could not feel my limbs:
I was so light—almost
I thought that I had died in sleep,
And was a blessèd ghost.

And soon I heard a roaring wind:
It did not come anear;
But with its sound it shook the sails,
That were so thin and sere.

The upper air burst into life!
And a hundred fire-flags sheen,
To and fro they were hurried about!
And to and fro, and in and out,
The wan stars danced between.

And the coming wind did roar more loud,
And the sails did sigh like sedge;

And the rain poured down from one black cloud;
The Moon was at its edge.

The thick black cloud was cleft, and still
The Moon was at its side:
Like waters shot from some high crag,
The lightning fell with never a jag,
A river steep and wide.

The loud wind never reached the ship,
Yet now the ship moved on!
Beneath the lightning and the Moon
The dead men gave a groan.

They groaned, they stirred, they all uprose,
Nor spake, nor moved their eyes;
It had been strange, even in a dream,
To have seen those dead men rise.

The helmsman steered, the ship moved on;
Yet never a breeze up-blew;
The mariners all 'gan work the ropes,
Where they were wont to do;
They raised their limbs like lifeless tools—
We were a ghastly crew.

The body of my brother's son
Stood by me, knee to knee:
The body and I pulled at one rope,
But he said nought to me."—

"I fear thee, ancient Mariner!"—
"Be calm, thou Wedding-Guest!
'Twas not those souls that fled in pain,
Which to their corses came again,
But a troop of spirits blest:

For when it dawned—they dropped their arms,
And clustered round the mast;
Sweet sounds rose slowly through their mouths,
And from their bodies passed.

Around, around, flew each sweet sound,
Then darted to the Sun;
Slowly the sounds came back again,
Now mixed, now one by one.

Sometimes a-dropping from the sky
I heard the sky-lark sing;
Sometimes all little birds that are,
How they seemed to fill the sea and air
With their sweet jargoning!

And now 'twas like all instruments,
Now like a lonely flute;
And now it is an angel's song,
That makes the heavens be mute.

It ceased; yet still the sails made on
A pleasant noise till noon,
A noise like of a hidden brook
In the leafy month of June,
That to the sleeping woods all night
Singeth a quiet tune.

Till noon we silently sailed on,
Yet never a breeze did breathe:
Slowly and smoothly went the ship,
Moved onward from beneath.

Under the keel nine fathom deep,
From the land of mist and snow,
The spirit slid: and it was he
That made the ship to go.
The sails at noon left off their tune,
And the ship stood still also.

The Sun, right up above the mast,
Had fixed her to the ocean;
But in a minute she 'gan stir,
With a short uneasy motion—

Backwards and forwards half her length
With a short uneasy motion.

Then like a pawing horse let go,
She made a sudden bound:
It flung the blood into my head,
And I fell down in a swound.

How long in that same fit I lay,
I have not to declare;
But ere my living life returned,
I heard and in my soul discerned
Two voices in the air.

"Is it he?" quoth one, "Is this the man?
By him who died on cross,
With his cruel bow he laid full low
The harmless Albatross.

The spirit who bideth by himself
In the land of mist and snow,
He loved the bird that loved the man
Who shot him with his bow."

The other was a softer voice,
As soft as honey-dew:
Quoth he, "The man hath penance done,
And penance more will do."

Part VI

First Voice. "But tell me, tell me! speak again,
Thy soft response renewing—
What makes that ship drive on so fast?
What is the ocean doing?"

Second Voice. "Still as a slave before his lord,
The ocean hath no blast;
His great bright eye most silently
Up to the Moon is cast—

If he may know which way to go;
For she guides him smooth or grim.
See, brother, see! how graciously
She looketh down on him."

First Voice. "But why drives on that ship so fast,
Withouten wave or wind?"

Second Voice. "The air is cut away before,
And closes from behind.

Fly, brother, fly! more high, more high!
Or we shall be belated:
For slow and slow that ship will go,
When the Mariner's trance is abated."—

I woke and we were sailing on
As in a gentle weather:
'Twas night, calm night, the moon was high;
The dead men stood together.

All stood together on the deck,
For a charnel-dungeon fitter:
All fixed on me their stony eyes,
That in the Moon did glitter.

The pang, the curse, with which they died,
Had never passed away:
I could not draw my eyes from theirs,
Nor turn them up to pray.

And now this spell was snapt: once more
I viewed the ocean green,
And looked far forth, yet little saw
Of what had else been seen—

Like one, that on a lonesome road
Doth walk in fear and dread,
And having once turned round walks on,
And turns no more his head;

Because he knows, a frightful fiend
Doth close behind him tread.

But soon there breathed a wind on me,
Nor sound nor motion made:
Its path was not upon the sea,
In ripple or in shade.

It raised my hair, it fanned my cheek
Like a meadow-gale of spring—
It mingled strangely with my fears,
Yet it felt like a welcoming.

Swiftly, swiftly flew the ship,
Yet she sailed softly too:
Sweetly, sweetly blew the breeze—
On me alone it blew.

Oh! dream of joy! is this indeed
The light-house top I see?
Is this the hill? is this the kirk?
Is this mine own countree?

We drifted o'er the harbour-bar,
And I with sobs did pray—
O let me be awake, my God!
Or let me sleep alway.

The harbour-bay was clear as glass,
So smoothly it was strewn!
And on the bay the moonlight lay,
And the shadow of the Moon.

The rock shone bright, the kirk no less,
That stands above the rock:
The moonlight steeped in silentness
The steady weathercock.

And the bay was white with silent light,
Till rising from the same,

Full many shapes, that shadows were,
In crimson colours came.

A little distance from the prow
Those crimson shadows were:
I turned my eyes upon the deck—
Oh, Christ! what saw I there!

Each corse lay flat, lifeless, and flat,
And, by the holy rood!
A man all light, a seraph-man,
On every corse there stood.

This seraph-band, each waved his hand:
It was a heavenly sight!
They stood as signals to the land,
Each one a lovely light;

This seraph-band, each waved his hand,
No voice did they impart—
No voice; but oh! the silence sank
Like music on my heart.

But soon I heard the dash of oars,
I heard the Pilot's cheer;
My head was turned perforce away,
And I saw a boat appear.

The Pilot and the Pilot's boy,
I heard them coming fast:
Dear Lord in Heaven! it was a joy
The dead men could not blast.

I saw a third—I heard his voice:
It is the Hermit good!
He singeth loud his godly hymns
That he makes in the wood.
He'll shrieve my soul, he'll wash away
The Albatross's blood.

Part VII

This Hermit good lives in that wood
Which slopes down to the sea.
How loudly his sweet voice he rears!
He loves to talk with marineres
That come from a far countree.

He kneels at morn, and noon, and eve—
He hath a cushion plump:
It is the moss that wholly hides
The rotted old oak-stump.

The skiff-boat neared: I heard them talk,
"Why, this is strange, I trow!
Where are those lights so many and fair,
That signal made but now?"

"Strange, by my faith!" the Hermit said—
"And they answered not our cheer!
The planks looked warped! and see those sails,
How thin they are and sere!
I never saw aught like to them,
Unless perchance it were

Brown skeletons of leaves that lag
My forest-brook along;
When the ivy-tod is heavy with snow,
And the owlet whoops to the wolf below,
That eats the she-wolf's young."

"Dear Lord! it hath a fiendish look—
(The Pilot made reply)
I am a-feared"—"Push on, push on!"
Said the Hermit cheerily.

The boat came closer to the ship,
But I nor spake nor stirred;
The boat came close beneath the ship,
And straight a sound was heard.

Under the water it rumbled on,
Still louder and more dread:
It reached the ship, it split the bay;
The ship went down like lead.

Stunned by that loud and dreadful sound,
Which sky and ocean smote,
Like one that hath been seven days drowned
My body lay afloat;
But swift as dreams, myself I found
Within the Pilot's boat.

Upon the whirl, where sank the ship,
The boat spun round and round;
And all was still, save that the hill
Was telling of the sound.

I moved my lips—the Pilot shrieked
And fell down in a fit;
The holy Hermit raised his eyes,
And prayed where he did sit.

I took the oars: the Pilot's boy,
Who now doth crazy go,
Laughed loud and long, and all the while
His eyes went to and fro.
"Ha! ha!" quoth he, "full plain I see,
The Devil knows how to row."

And now, all in my own countree,
I stood on the firm land!
The Hermit stepped forth from the boat,
And scarcely he could stand.

"O shrieve me, shrieve me, holy man!"
The Hermit crossed his brow.
"Say quick," quoth he, "I bid thee say—
What manner of man art thou?"

Forthwith this frame of mine was wrenched
With a woful agony,

Which forced me to begin my tale;
And then it left me free.

Since then, at an uncertain hour,
That agony returns:
And till my ghastly tale is told,
This heart within me burns.

I pass, like night, from land to land;
I have strange power of speech;
That moment that his face I see,
I know the man that must hear me:
To him my tale I teach.

What loud uproar bursts from that door!
The wedding-guests are there:
But in the garden-bower the bride
And bride-maids singing are:
And hark the little vesper bell,
Which biddeth me to prayer!

O Wedding-Guest! this soul hath been
Alone on a wide wide sea:
So lonely 'twas, that God himself
Scarce seemèd there to be.

O sweeter than the marriage-feast,
'Tis sweeter far to me,
To walk together to the kirk
With a goodly company!—

To walk together to the kirk,
And all together pray,
While each to his great Father bends,
Old men, and babes, and loving friends
And youths and maidens gay!

Farewell, farewell! but this I tell
To thee, thou Wedding-Guest!

He prayeth well, who loveth well
Both man and bird and beast.

He prayeth best, who loveth best
All things both great and small;
For the dear God who loveth us,
He made and loveth all."—

The Mariner, whose eye is bright,
Whose beard with age is hoar,
Is gone: and now the Wedding-Guest
Turned from the bridegroom's door.

He went like one that hath been stunned,
And is of sense forlorn:
A sadder and a wiser man,
He rose the morrow morn.

SAMUEL TAYLOR COLERIDGE

399 THE CHILD AND THE MARINER

THIS sailor knows of wondrous lands afar,
More rich than Spain, when the Phoenicians shipped
Silver for common ballast, and they saw
Horses at silver mangers eating grain;
This man has seen the wind blow up a mermaid's hair
Which, like a golden serpent, reared and stretched
To feel the air away beyond her head. . . .
He many a tale of wonder told: of where,
At Argostoli, Cephalonia's sea
Ran over the earth's lip in heavy floods;
And then again of how the strange Chinese
Conversed much as our homely Blackbirds sing.
He told us how he sailed in one old ship
Near that volcano Martinique, whose power
Shook like dry leaves the whole Caribbean seas;
And made the sun set in a sea of fire
Which only half was his; and dust was thick
On deck, and stones were pelted at the mast. . . .

He told how isles sprang up and sank again,
Between short voyages, to his amaze;
How they did come and go, and cheated charts;
Told how a crew was cursed when one man killed
A bird that perched upon a moving barque;
And how the sea's sharp needles, firm and strong,
Ripped open the bellies of big, iron ships;
Of mighty icebergs in the Northern seas,
That haunt the far horizon like white ghosts.
He told of waves that lift a ship so high.
That birds could pass from starboard unto port
Under her dripping keel.

Oh, it was sweet

To hear that seaman tell such wondrous tales. . . .

WILLIAM H. DAVIES

400 THE PARROTS

SOMEWHERE, somewhen I've seen,
But where or when I'll never know,
Parrots of shrilly green
With crests of shriller scarlet flying
Out of black cedars as the sun was dying
Against cold peaks of snow.

From what forgotten life
Of other worlds I cannot tell
Flashes that screeching strife:
Yet the shrill colour and shrill crying
Sing through my blood and set my heart replying
And jangling like a bell.

WILFRID GIBSON

401 OZYMANDIAS OF EGYPT

I MET a traveller from an antique land
Who said: Two vast and trunkless legs of stone
Stand in the desert. . . . Near them, on the sand,
Half sunk, a shattered visage lies, whose frown

And wrinkled lip, and sneer of cold command
Tell that its sculptor well those passions read
Which yet survive, stamped on these lifeless things,
The hand that mocked them, and the heart that fed:
And on the pedestal these words appear:
"My name is Ozymandias, king of kings:
Look on my works, ye Mighty, and despair!"
Nothing beside remains. Round the decay
Of that colossal wreck, boundless and bare
The lone and level sands stretch far away.

PERCY BYSSHE SHELLEY

402 ST. ANTHONY'S TOWNSHIP

THE trees of the elder lands,
Give ear to the march of Time,
To his steps that are heavy and slow
In the streets of ruined cities
That were great awhile ago—
Skeletons bare to the skies
Or mummies hid in the sands,
Wasting to rubble and lime.
Ancient are they and wise;

But the gum-trees down by the creek,
Gnarled, archaic and grey,
Are even as wise as they.
They have learned in a score of years
The lore that their brethren know;
For they saw a town arise,
Arise and pass.

There are pits by the dry, dead river,
Whence the diggers won their gold,
A circle traced in the grass,
A hearthstone long a-cold,
A path none come to seek—
The trail of the pioneers—
Where the sheep wind to and fro;

And the rest is a tale that is told
By voices quavering and weak
Of men grown old.

GILBERT SHELDON

403

SILENCE

THERE is a silence where hath been no sound,
There is a silence where no sound may be,
In the cold grave—under the deep—deep sea,
Or in wide desert where no life is found,
Which hath been mute, and still must sleep profound;
No voice is hushed—no life treads silently,
But clouds and cloudy shadows wander free,
That never spoke, over the idle ground:
But in green ruins, in the desolate walls
Of antique palaces, where Man hath been,
Though the dun fox, or wild hyaena, calls,
And owls, that flit continually between,
Shriek to the echo, and the low winds moan,
There the true Silence is, self-conscious and alone.

THOMAS HOOD

404

KUBLA KHAN

IN Xanadu did Kubla Khan
A stately pleasure-dome decree:
Where Alph, the sacred river, ran
Through caverns measureless to man
Down to a sunless sea.
So twice five miles of fertile ground
With walls and towers were girdled round:
And here were gardens bright with sinuous rills
Where blossomed many an incense-bearing tree;
And here were forests ancient as the hills,
Enfolding sunny spots of greenery.

But oh! that deep romantic chasm which slanted
Down the green hill athwart a cedarn cover!

A savage place! as holy and enchanted
As e'er beneath a waning moon was haunted
By woman wailing for her demon-lover!
And from this chasm, with ceaseless turmoil seething,
As if this earth in fast thick pants were breathing,
A mighty fountain momently was forced:
Amid whose swift half-intermitted burst
Huge fragments vaulted like rebounding hail,
Or chaffy grain beneath the thresher's flail:

And 'mid these dancing rocks at once and ever
It flung up momently the sacred river.
Five miles meandering with a mazy motion
Through wood and dale the sacred river ran,
Then reached the caverns measureless to man,
And sank in tumult to a lifeless ocean:
And 'mid this tumult Kubla heard from far
Ancestral voices prophesying war!
    The shadow of the dome of pleasure
    Floated midway on the waves;
    Where was heard the mingled measure
    From the fountain and the caves.
  It was a miracle of rare device,
  A sunny pleasure-dome with caves of ice!

    A damsel with a dulcimer
    In a vision once I saw:
    It was an Abyssinian maid,
    And on her dulcimer she played,
    Singing of Mount Abora.
    Could I revive within me
    Her symphony and song,
  To such a deep delight 'twould win me,
  That with music loud and long
  I would build that dome in air,
  That sunny dome! those caves of ice!
  And all who heard should see them there,
  And all should cry, Beware! Beware!
  His flashing eyes, his floating hair!

Weave a circle round him thrice,
And close your eyes with holy dread,
For he on honey-dew hath fed,
And drunk the milk of Paradise. . . .

SAMUEL TAYLOR COLERIDGE

405

LOST LOVE

HIS eyes are quickened so with grief,
He can watch a grass or leaf
Every instant grow; he can
Clearly through a flint wall see,
Or watch the startled spirit flee
From the throat of a dead man.
Across two countries he can hear,
And catch your words before you speak.
The woodlouse, or the maggot's weak
Clamour rings in his sad ear;
And noise so slight it would surpass
Credence:—drinking sound of grass,
Worm talk, clashing jaws of moth
Chumbling holes in cloth:
The groan of ants who undertake
Gigantic loads for honour's sake,
Their sinews creak, their breath comes thin:
Whir of spiders when they spin,
And minute whispering, mumbling, sighs
Of idle grubs and flies.
This man is quickened so with grief,
He wanders god-like or like thief
Inside and out, below, above,
Without relief seeking lost love.

ROBERT GRAVES

406

ECSTASY

I SAW a frieze on whitest marble drawn
Of boys who sought for shells along the shore,

Their white feet shedding pallor in the sea,
The shallow sea, the spring-time sea of green
That faintly creamed against the cold, smooth pebbles. . . .

One held a shell unto his shell-like ear
And there was music carven in his face,
His eyes half-closed, his lips just breaking open
To catch the lulling, mazy, coralline roar
Of numberless caverns filled with singing seas.

And all of them were hearkening as to singing
Of far-off voices thin and delicate,
Voices too fine for any mortal wind
To blow into the whorls of mortal ears—
And yet those sounds flowed from their grave, sweet faces.

And as I looked I heard that delicate music,
And I became as grave, as calm, as still
As those carved boys. I stood upon that shore,
I felt the cool sea dream around my feet,
My eyes were staring at the far horizon. . . .

WALTER J. TURNER

407 THE SEA OF DEATH

. . . AND there were spring-faced cherubs that did sleep
Like water-lilies on that motionless deep,
How beautiful! with bright unruffled hair
On sleek unfretted brows, and eyes that were
Buried in marble tombs, a pale eclipse!
And smile-bedimpled cheeks, and pleasant lips,
Meekly apart, as if the soul intense
Spake out in dreams of its own innocence. . . .
So lay they garmented in torpid light,
Under the pall of a transparent night,
Like solemn apparitions lulled sublime
To everlasting rest,—and with them Time
Slept, as he sleeps upon the silent face
Of a dark dial in a sunless place.

408 THE FROZEN OCEAN

THE sea would flow no longer,
It wearied after change,
It called its tide and breakers in,
From where they might range.

It sent an icy message
To every wave and rill;
They lagged, they paused, they stiffened,
They froze, and were still.

It summoned in its currents,
They reached not where they led;
It bound its foaming whirlpools.
"Not the old life," it said,

"Not fishes for the fisherman,
Not bold ships as before,
Not beating loud for ever
Upon the seashore,

"But cold white foxes stepping
On to my hard proud breast,
And a bird coming sweetly
And building a nest.

"My icebergs shall be mountains,
My silent fields of snow
Unmarked shall join the lands' snowfields—
Where, no man shall know."

VIOLA MEYNELL

409 THE END OF THE WORLD

THE snow had fallen many nights and days;
The sky was come upon the earth at last,
Sifting thinly down as endlessly
As though within the system of blind planets
Something had been forgot or overdriven.
The dawn now seemed neglected in the grey

Where mountains were unbuilt and shadowless trees
Rootlessly paused or hung upon the air.
There was no wind, but now and then a sigh
Crossed that dry falling dust and rifted it
Through crevices of slate and door and casement.
Perhaps the new moon's time was even past.
Outside, the first white twilights were too void
Until a sheep called once, as to a lamb,
And tenderness crept everywhere from it;
But now the flock must have strayed far away.
The lights across the valley must be veiled,
The smoke lost in the greyness or the dusk.
For more than three days now the snow had thatched
That cow-house roof where it had ever melted
With yellow stains from the beasts' breath inside;
But yet a dog howled there, though not quite lately.
Someone passed down the valley swift and singing,
Yes, with locks spreaded like a son of morning;
But if he seemed too tall to be a man
It was that men had been so long unseen,
Or shapes loom larger through a moving snow.
And he was gone and food had not been given him.
When snow slid from an overweighted leaf,
Shaking the tree, it might have been a bird
Slipping in sleep or shelter, whirring wings;
Yet never bird fell out, save once a dead one—
And in two days the snow had covered it.
The dog had howled again—or thus it seemed
Until a lean fox passed and cried no more.
All was so safe indoors where life went on
Glad of the close enfolding snow—O glad
To be so safe and secret at its heart,
Watching the strangeness of familiar things.
They knew not what dim hours went on, went by,
For while they slept the clock stopt newly wound
As the cold hardened. Once they watched the road,
Thinking to be remembered. Once they doubted
If they had kept the sequence of the days,
Because they heard not any sound of bells.

A butterfly, that hid until the Spring
Under a ceiling's shadow, dropt, was dead.
The coldness seemed more nigh, the coldness deepened
As a sound deepens into silences;
It was of earth and came not by the air;
The earth was cooling and drew down the sky.
The air was crumbling. There was no more sky.
Rails of a broken bed charred in the grate,
And when he touched the bars he thought the sting
Came from their heat—he could not feel such cold . . .
She said, "O do not sleep,
Heart, heart of mine, keep near me. No, no; sleep.
I will not lift his fallen, quiet eyelids,
Although I know he would awaken then—
He closed them thus but now of his own will.
He can stay with me while I do not lift them."

GORDON BOTTOMLEY

OLD TALES AND BALLADRY

FLANNAN ISLE

"Though three men dwell on Flannan Isle
To keep the lamp alight,
As we steered under the lee, we caught
No glimmer through the night."—

A passing ship at dawn had brought
The news; and quickly we set sail,
To find out what strange thing might ail
The keepers of the deep-sea light.

The Winter day broke blue and bright,
With glancing sun and glancing spray,
While o'er the swell our boat made way,
As gallant as a gull in flight.

But as we neared the lonely Isle,
And looked up at the naked height,
And saw the lighthouse towering white,
With blinded lantern, that all night
Had never shot a spark
Of comfort through the dark,
So ghostly in the cold sunlight
It seemed, that we were struck the while
With wonder all too dread for words.

And as into the tiny creek
We stole beneath the hanging crag,
We saw three queer, black, ugly birds—
Too big, by far, in my belief,
For cormorant or shag—
Like seamen sitting bolt-upright
Upon a half-tide reef:

But, as we neared, they plunged from sight,
Without a sound, or spurt of white.

And still too mazed to speak,
We landed; and made fast the boat;
And climbed the track in single file,
Each wishing he were safe afloat,
On any sea, however far,
So it be far from Flannan Isle:
And still we seemed to climb, and climb,
As though we'd lost all count of time,
And so must climb for evermore.
Yet, all too soon, we reached the door
The black, sun-blistered lighthouse-door,
That gaped for us ajar.

As, on the threshold, for a spell,
We paused, we seemed to breathe the smell
Of limewash and of tar,
Familiar as our daily breath,
As though 'twere some strange scent of death:
And so, yet wondering, side by side,
We stood a moment, still tongue-tide:
And each with black foreboding eyed
The door, ere we should fling it wide,
To leave the sunlight for the gloom:
Till, plucking courage up, at last,
Hard on each other's heels we passed,
Into the living-room.

Yet, as we crowded through the door,
We only saw a table, spread
For dinner, meat and cheese and bread;
But, all untouched; and no one there:
As though, when they sat down to eat,
Ere they could even taste,
Alarm had come; and they in haste
Had risen and left the bread and meat:
For at the table-head a chair
Lay tumbled on the floor.

We listened; but we only heard
The feeble cheeping of a bird
That starved upon its perch:
And, listening still, without a word,
We set about our hopeless search.

We hunted high, we hunted low;
And soon ransacked the empty house;
Then o'er the Island, to and fro,
We ranged, to listen and to look
In every cranny, cleft or nook
That might have hid a bird or mouse:
But, though we searched from shore to shore,
We found no sign in any place:
And soon again stood face to face
Before the gaping door:
And stole into the room once more
As frightened children steal.
Ay: though we hunted high and low,
And hunted everywhere,
Of the three men's fate we found no trace
Of any kind in any place,
But a door ajar, and an untouched meal,
And an overtoppled chair.
And as we listened in the gloom
Of that forsaken living-room—
A chill clutch on our breath—
We thought how ill-chance came to all
Who kept the Flannan Light:
And how the rock had been the death
Of many a likely lad:
How six had come to a sudden end,
And three had gone stark mad:
And one whom we'd all known as friend
Had leapt from the lantern one still night,
And fallen dead by the lighthouse wall:
And long we thought
On the three we sought,
And of what might yet befall.

Like curs a glance has brought to heel,
We listened, flinching there:
And looked, and looked, on the untouched meal,
And the overtoppled chair.

We seemed to stand for an endless while,
Though still no word was said,
Three men alive on Flannan Isle,
Who thought on three men dead.

WILFRED GIBSON

411 THE GOLDEN VANITY

THERE was a gallant ship, and a gallant ship was she,
Eck iddle du, and the Lowlands low;
And she was called The Goulden Vanitie.
As she sailed to the Lowlands low.

She had not sailed a league, a league but only three,
When she came up with a French gallee.
As she sailed to the Lowlands low.

Out spoke the little cabin-boy, out spoke he;
"What will you give me if I sink that French gallee?
As ye sail to the Lowlands low."

"I'll give thee gold, and I'll give thee fee,
And my eldest daughter thy wife shall be
If you sink her off the Lowlands low."

"Then row me up ticht in a black bull's skin,
And throw me oer deck-buird, sink I or swim.
As ye sail to the Lowlands low."

So they've rowed him up ticht in a black bull's skin,
And have thrown him oer deck-buird, sink he or swim.
As they sail to the Lowlands low.

About, and about, and about went he,
Until he cam up with the French gallee.
As they sailed to the Lowlands low.

O some were playing cards, and some were playing dice,
The boy he had an auger bored holes two at twice;
He let the water in, and it dazzled in their eyes,
As they sailed to the Lowlands low.

Then some they ran with cloaks, and some they ran with caps,
To try if they could stap the saut-water draps.
As they sailed to the Lowlands low.

About, and about, and about went he,
Until he cam back to The Goulden Vanitie.
As they sailed to the Lowlands low.

"Now throw me oer a rope and pu me up on buird,
And prove unto me as guid as your word.
As we sail to the Lowlands low."

"We'll no throw ye oer a rope, nor pu you up on buird,
Nor prove unto you as guid as our word.
As we sail to the Lowlands low."

"You promised me gold, and you promised me fee,
Your eldest daughter my wife she should be.
As we sail to the Lowlands low."

"You shall have gold, and you shall have fee,
But my eldest daughter your wife shall never be.
As we sail to the Lowlands low."

Out spoke the little cabin-boy, out spoke he;
"Then hang me, I'll sink ye as I sunk the French gallee.
As ye sail to the Lowlands low."

The boy he swam round all by the starboard side,
When they pu'd him up on buird it's there he soon died;
They threw him o'er deck-buird to go down with the tide,
And sink off the Lowlands low.

412 BROWN ROBYN

It fell upon a Wednesday
Brown Robyn's men went to sea,

But they saw neither moon nor sun,
Nor starlight with their ee.

"We'll cast kevels us amang,
See what the unhappy man may be":
The kevel fell on Brown Robyn,
The master-man was hee.

"It is nae wonder," said Brown Robyn,
"Altho I dinna thrive;
[For if the deidly sins be seven,
Befallen me hae five.]

"But tie me to a plank o wude,
And throw me in the sea;
And if I sink, ye may bid me sink,
But if I swim, lat me bee."

They've tyed him to a plank o wude,
And thrown him in the sea;
He didna sink, tho they bade him sink;
He swimd, and they lat him be—

He hadna been into the sea
An hour but barely three,
Till by and came Our Blessed Lady,
Her dear young son her wi.

"Will ye gang to your men again?
Or will ye gang wi me?
Will ye gang to the high heavens,
Wi my dear son and me?"

"I winna gang to my men again,
For they woud be feared at mee;
But I woud gang to the high heavens,
Wi thy dear son and thee."

"It's for nae honour ye did to me, Brown Robyn,
It's for nae guid ye did to mee;

But a' is for your fair confession
  You've made upon the sea."

413 ONE FRIDAY MORN

One Friday morn when we set sail,
  Not very far from land,
We there did espy a fair pretty maid
  With a comb and a glass in her hand, her hand, her hand,
  With a comb and a glass in her hand.
    While the raging seas did roar,
      And the stormy winds did blow,
    While we jolly sailor-boys were up into the top,
    And the land-lubbers lying down below, below, below,
    And the land-lubbers lying down below.

Then up starts the captain of our gallant ship,
  And a brave young man was he:
"I've a wife and a child in fair Bristol town,
  But a widow I fear she will be."
    And the raging seas did roar,
      And the stormy winds did blow.

Then up starts the mate of our gallant ship,
  And a bold young man was he:
"Oh! I have a wife in fair Portsmouth town,
  But a widow I fear she will be."
    And the raging seas did roar,
      And the stormy winds did blow.

Then up starts the cook of our gallant ship,
  And a gruff old soul was he:
"Oh! I have a wife in fair Plymouth town,
  But a widow I fear she will be."
    And the raging seas did roar,
      And the stormy winds did blow.

And then up spoke the little cabin-boy,
  And a pretty little boy was he;

"Oh! I am more grieved for my daddy and my mammy
Than you for your wives all three."
And the raging seas did roar,
And the stormy winds did blow.

Then three times round went our gallant ship,
And three times round went she;
And three times round went our gallant ship,
And she sank to the bottom of the sea. . . .

And the raging seas did roar,
And the stormy winds did blow.
While we jolly sailor-boys were up into the top,
And the land-lubbers lying down below, below, below,
And the land-lubbers lying down below.

414

THE SHIP

THERE was no song nor shout of joy
Nor beam of moon or sun,
When she came back from the voyage
Long ago begun;
But twilight on the waters
Was quiet and grey,
And she glided steady, steady and pensive,
Over the open bay.

Her sails were brown and ragged,
And her crew hollow-eyed,
But their silent lips spoke content
And their shoulders pride;
Though she had no captives on her deck,
And in her hold
There were no heaps of corn or timber
Or silks or gold.

J. C. SQUIRE

415 THE MOON-CHILD

A LITTLE lonely child am I
  That have not any soul:
God made me as the homeless wave,
  That has no goal.

A seal my father was, a seal
  That once was man;
My mother loved him tho' he was
  'Neath mortal ban.

He took a wave and drownèd her,
  She took a wave and lifted him:
And I was born where shadows are
  In sea-depths dim.

All through the sunny blue-sweet hours
  I swim and glide in waters green:
Never by day the mournful shores
  By me are seen.

But when the gloom is on the wave
  A shell unto the shore I bring:
And then upon the rocks I sit
    And plaintive sing.

I have no playmate but the tide
  The seaweed loves with dark brown eyes:
The night-waves have the stars for play,
  For me but sighs.

FIONA MACLEOD

416 THE MERMAID

To yon fause stream that, by the sea,
  Hides mony an elf and plum,[1]
And rives wi' fearful din the stanes,
  A witless knicht did come.

[1] Pool

The day shines clear. Far in he's gane,
Whar shells are silver bright;
Fishes war loupin'[1] a' aroun'
An' sparklin' to the light.

When, as he laved, sounds came sae sweet
Frae ilka rock ajee;[2]
The brief[3] was out; 'twas him it doomed
The mermaid's face to see.

Frae 'neath a rock sune, sune she rose,
An' stately on she swam,
Stopped i' the midst, and becked and sang
For him to stretch his han';

Gowden glist the yellow links
That roun' her neck she'd twine;
Her een war o' the skyie blue,
Her lips did mock the wine.

The smile upon her bonnie cheek
Was sweeter than the bee;
Her voice excelled the birdie's sang
Upon the birchen tree.

Sae couthie, couthie did she look,
And meikle had she fleeched;[4]
Out shot his hand—alas! alas!
Fast in the swirl he screeched.

The mermaid leuched;[5] her brief was dane;
The kelpie's blast was blawin':
Fu' low she dived, ne'er cam' again;
For deep, deep was the fawin'.

Aboon the stream his wraith was seen:
Warlocks tirled lang at gloamin':
That e'en was coarse;[6] the blast blew hoarse
Ere lang the waves war foamin'.

[1] Leaping [2] Crooked, awry [3] Spell
[4] Charmed and cozened [5] Laughed [6] Foul

417 QUO' THE TWEED

Quo' the Tweed to the Till,
"What gars ye gang sae still?"
Quo' the Till to the Tweed,
"Though ye rin wi' speed,
And I rin slaw,
For ilka ane that ye droon,
I droon twa."

418 SIR PATRICK SPENCE

The king sits in Dumferling toune,
Drinking the blude-reid wine:
"O whar will I get a guid sailor,
To sail this schip of mine?"

Up and spak an eldlern knicht,
Sat at the king's richt kne;
"Sir Patrick Spence is the best sailor
That sails upon the se."

The king has written a braid letter,
And signed it wi his hand,
And sent it to Sir Patrick Spence,
Was walking on the sand.

The first line that Sir Patrick red,
A loud lauch lauched he;
The next line that Sir Patrick red,
The teir blinded his ee.

"O wha is this has done this deid,
This ill deid don to me,
To send me out this time o' the yeir,
To sail upon the se!

"Mak haste, mak haste, my mirry men all,
Our guid schip sails the morne:"
"O say na sae, my master deir,
Fir I feir a deadlie storme.

"Late, late yestreen I saw the new moone,
Wi' the auld moone in hir arme,
And I feir, I feir, my deir master,
That we will cum to harme."

O our Scots nobles wer richt laith [1]
To weet [2] their cork-heil'd schoone;
Bot lang owre [3] a' the play wer playd,
Thair hats they swam aboone.

O lang, lang may their ladies sit
Wi' thair fans into their hand,
Or eir they se Sir Patrick Spence
Cum sailing to the land.

O lang, lang may the ladies stand,
Wi' thair gold kems in their hair,
Waiting for thair ain deir lords,
For they'll se thame na mair.

Haf owre, haf owre to Aberdour,
It's fiftie fadom deip,
And thair lies guid Sir Patrick Spence,
Wi' the Scots lords at his feit.

419 ALLISON GROSS

O Allison Gross, that lives in yon towr,
The ugliest witch i the north country,
Has trysted me ae day up till her bowr,
An monny fair speech she made to me.

She stroaked my head, an she kembed my hair,
An she set me down saftly on her knee;
Says, Gin [4] ye will be my luver so true,
Sae monny braw things as I woud you gi'e.

She showed me a mantle o red scarlet,
Wi gouden flowrs an fringes fine;

[1] Right [2] Wet [3] But long ere [4] If

Says, Gin ye will be my luver so true,
This goodly gift it sal be thine.

"Awa, awa, ye ugly witch,
Haud far awa, an lat me be;
I never will be your luver sae true,
An I wish I were out o your company."

She neist brought a sark o the saftest silk,
Well wrought wi pearles about the ban;
Says, Gin you will be my ain true love,
This goodly gift you sal comman.

She showd me a cup of the good red gold,
Well set wi jewls sae fair to see;
Says, Gin you will be my luver sae true,
This goodly gift I will you gi'e.

"Awa, awa, ye ugly witch,
Haud far awa, and lat me be;
For I woudna ance kiss your ugly mouth
For a' the gifts that ye could gi'e."

She's turnd her right and roun about,
And thrice she blaw on a grass-green horn,
An she sware by the moon and the stars aboon,
That she'd gar me rue the day I was born.

Then out has she taen a silver wand,
An she's turned her three times roun an roun;
She's mutterd sich words till my strength it faild,
An I fell down senceless upon the groun.

She's turnd me into an ugly worm,
And gard me writhle about the tree;
An ay, on ilka Saturdays night,
My sister Maisry came to me,

Wi silver bason an silver kemb,
To kemb my heady upon her knees;

But or I had kissd her ugly mouth,
I'd rather a writhled about the tree.

But as it fell out on last Hallow-even,
When the seely court was ridin by,
The queen lighted down on a gowany bank,
Nae far frae the tree where I wont to lye.

She took me up in her milk-white han,
An she's stroakd me three times oer her knee;
She chang'd me again to my ain proper shape,
An I nae mair maun writhle about the tree.

420 SIR HUGH, OR, THE JEW'S DAUGHTER

FOUR and twenty bonny boys
Were playing at the ba',
And by it came him sweet Sir Hugh,
And he playd o'er them a'.

He kicked the ba' with his right foot,
And catchd it wi' his knee,
And throuch-and-thro the Jew's window
He gard the bonny ba' flee.

He's doen him to the Jew's castell,
And walkd it round about;
And there he saw the Jew's daughter,
At the window looking out.

"Throw down the ba', ye Jew's daughter,
Throw down the ba' to me!"
"Never a bit," says the Jew's daughter,
"Till up to me come ye."

"How will I come up? How can I come up?
How can I come to thee?
For as ye did to my auld father
The same ye'll do to me."

She's gane till her father's garden,
  And pu'd an apple red and green;
'T was a' to wyle him—sweet Sir Hugh,
  And to entice him in.

She's led him in through ae dark door,
  And sae has she thro nine;
She's laid him on a dressing-table,
  And stickit him like a swine.

And first came out the thick, thick blood,
  And syne came out the thin,
And syne came out the bonny heart's blood;
  There was nae mair within.

She's rowd him in a cake o' lead,
  Bade him lie still and sleep;
She's thrown him in Our Lady's draw-well,
  Was fifty fathom deep.

When bells were rung, and mass was sung,
  And a' the bairns came hame,
When every lady gata hame her son,
  The Lady Maisry gat nane.

She's ta'en her mantle her about,
  Her coffer [1] by the hand,
And she's gane out to seek her son,
  And wanderd o'er the land.

She's doen her to the Jew's castell,
  Where a' were fast asleep:
"Gin ye be there, my sweet Sir Hugh,
  I pray you to me speak."

She's doen her to the Jew's garden,
  Thought he had been gathering fruit:
"Gin ye be there, my sweet Sir Hugh,
  I pray you to me speak!"

[1] Hand-bag

She neard Our Lady's deep draw-well,
Was fifty fathom deep:
"Whareer ye be, my sweet Sir Hugh,
I pray you to me speak."

"Gae hame, gae hame, my mither dear,
Prepare my winding sheet,
And at the birks[1] o' merry Lincoln
The morn I will you meet."

Now Lady Maisry is gane hame,
Made him a winding sheet,
And at the birks o' merry Lincoln
The dead corpse did her meet.

And a' the bells o' merry Lincoln
Without men's hands were rung,
And a' the books o' merry Lincoln
Were read without man's tongue,

When bells war rung, and mass was sung
And a' man bound for bed,
Every mither had her son,
But sweet Sir Hugh was dead.

421 EDWARD

"Why does your brand so drop wi' blood,
Edward, Edward,
Why does your brand so drop wi' blood,
And why so sad go ye O?"
"O I have killed my hawk so good,
Mother, mother,
O I have killed my hawk so good,
And I had no more but he O."

"Your hawk's blood was never so red,
Edward, Edward,

[1] Birch-wood

Your hawk's blood was never so red,
My dear son I tell thee O."
"O I have killed my red-roan steed,
Mother, mother,
O I have killed my red-roan steed,
That erst was so fair and free O."

"Your steed was old, and ye have got more,
Edward, Edward,
Your steed was old, and ye have got more,
Some other grief you bear O."
"O I have killed my father dear,
Mother, mother,
O I have killed my father dear,
Alas, and woe is me O!"

"And what penance will ye do for that,
Edward, Edward?
And what penance will ye do for that?
My dear son, now tell me O."
"I'll set my foot in yonder boat,
Mother, mother,
I'll set my foot in yonder boat,
And I'll fare over the sea O."

"And what will ye do wi' your towers and your hall,
Edward, Edward?
And what will ye do wi' your towers and your hall,
That were so fair to see O?"
"I'll let them stand till they down fall,
Mother, mother,
I'll let them stand till they down fall,
For here never more may I be O."

"And what will ye leave to your bairns and your wife,
Edward, Edward?
And what will ye leave to your bairns and your wife,
When ye go over the sea O?"
"The world's wide, let them beg their life,
Mother, mother,

The world's wide, let them beg their life,
  For them never more will I see O."

"And what will ye leave to your own mother dear,
            Edward, Edward?
And what will ye leave to your own mother dear?
  My dear son, now tell me O."
"The curse of hell from me shall ye bear,
            Mother, mother,
The curse of hell from me shall ye bear,
  Such counsels ye gave to me O."

422 THE LAIRD O' LOGIE

I WILL sing, if ye will hearken,
  If ye will hearken unto me;
The King has ta'en a poor prisoner,
  The wanton laird of Young Logie.

Young Logie's laid in Edinburgh chapel,
  Carmichael's the keeper o' the key;
I heard a May [1] lamenting sair
  A' for the laird of Young Logie.

"Lament, lament, na, May Margaret,
  And o' your weeping let me be;
For ye maun to the king yoursell,
  And ask the life of Young Logie."

May Margaret has kilted her green cleiding,[2]
  And she's currlld back her yellow hair;
"If I canna get young Logie's life,
  Farewell to Scotland for ever mair!"

When she came before the king,
  She knelit low doon on her knee:
"It's what's your will wi' me, May Margaret,
  And what needs a' this courtesie?"

[1] The young wife [2] Skirts of bright green

"A boon, a boon, my noble leige,
  A boon, a boon, I beg o' thee!
And the first boon that I come to crave,
  It's to grant me the life o' Young Logie."

"O na, O na, May Margaret,
  Na, in sooth it mauna [1] be;
For the [2] morn, ere I taste meat or drink,
  Hee [3] hangèd shall Young Logie be."

She has stolen the king's redding-kaim,[4]
  Likewise the queen her wedding-knife;
And sent the tokens to Carmichael,
  To cause Young Logie get [5] his life.

She sent him a purse o' the red gowd,
  Another o' the white monie;
And sent him a pistol for each hand,
  And bade him shoot when he gat free.

When he came to the Tolbooth stair,
  There he let his volley flee,
It made the king in his chamber start,
  E'en in the bed where he might be.

"Gae out, gae out, my merrie men a',
  And gar Carmichael come speak wi' me,
For I'll lay my life the pledge o' that,
  That yon's the volley of Young Logie."

When Carmichael came before the king,
  He fell low down upon his knee;
The very first word that the king spake,
  Was, "Where's the laird o' Young Logie?"

Carmichael turn'd him round about,
  I wat the salt tear blinded his ee,
"There came a token frae your grace,
  Has ta'en the laird awa frae me."

[1] Must not [2] This [3] High [4] Hair-comb [5] Save

"Hast thou played me that Carmichael?—
Hast thou played me that?" quoth he;
"The morn the Justice Court's to stand,
And Logic's place ye maun supplie."

Carmichael's awa to May Margaret's bower,
Even as fast as he may dree;
"O if Young Logie be within,
Tell him to come and speak with me."

May Margaret's turn'd her round about,
I wat a loud laughter gae she:
"The egg is chipp'd, the bird is flown,
Ye'll see nae mair o' Young Logie."

Tane [1] is shipped at the pier o' Leith,
T'other at the Queen's Ferrie,
And she's gotten a father to her bairn,
The wanton laird of Young Logie.

423 FAIR ANNIE

THE reivers [2] they stole Fair Annie,
As she walked by the sea;
But a noble knight was her ransom soon,
Wi' gowd and white monie.[3]

She bided in strangers' land wi' him,
And none knew whence she cam;
She lived in the castle wi' her love,
But never told her name.—

"It's narrow, narrow, mak your bed,
And learn to lie your lane; [4]
For I'm gaun owre the sea, Fair Annie,
A braw Bride to bring hame.

[1] The one [2] Raiders [3] Gold and silver
[4] Alone

Wi' her I will get gowd and gear,
Wi' you I ne'er gat nane.

"But wha will bake my bridal bread,
Or brew my bridal ale?
And what will welcome my bright Bride,
That I bring owre the dale?"

"It's I will bake your bridal bread,
And brew your bridal ale;
And I will welcome your bright Bride,
That you bring owre the dale."

"But she that welcomes my bright Bride
Maun gang like maiden fair;
She maun lace on her robe sae jimp,
And comely braid her hair.

"Bind up, bind up your yellow hair,
And tie it on your neck;
And see you look as maiden-like
As the day that first we met."

"O how can I gang maiden-like,
When maiden I am nane?
Have I not borne six sons to thee,
And am wi' child again?"

"I'll put cooks into my kitchen,
And stewards in my hall,
And I'll have bakers for my bread,
And brewers for my ale;
But you're to welcome my bright Bride,
That I bring owre the dale."

Three months and a day were gane and past,
Fair Annie she gat word
That her love's ship was come at last,
Wi' his bright young Bride aboard.

She's ta'en her young son in her arms,
  Anither in her hand;
And she's gane up to the highest tower.
  Looks over sea and land.

"Come doun, come doun, my mother dear,
  Come aff the castle wa'!
I fear if langer ye stand there,
  Ye'll let yoursell doun fa'."

She's ta'en a cake o' the best bread,
  A stoup o' the best wine,
And a' the keys upon her arm,
  And to the yett is gane. [1]

"O ye're welcome hame, my ain gude lord,
  To your castles and your towers;
Ye're welcome hame, my ain gude lord,
  To your ha's,[2] but and your bowers.
And welcome to your hame, fair lady!
  For a' that's here is yours."

"O whatna lady's that, my lord,
  That welcomes you and me?
Gin [3] I be lang about this place,
  Her friend I mean to be."—

Fair Annie served the lang tables
  Wi' the white bread and the wine;
But ay she drank the wan water
  To keep her colour fine.

And she gaed by the first table,
  And smiled upon them a';
But ere she reached the second table,
  The tears began to fa'.

She took a napkin lang and white,
  And hung it on a pin;

[1] To the gate is gone [2] Hails [3] If

It was to wipe away the tears,
As she gaed out and in.

When bells were rung and mass was sung,
And a' men bound for bed,
The bridegroom and the bonny Bride
In ae [1] chamber were laid.—

Fair Annie's ta'en a harp in her hand,
To harp thir twa [2] asleep;
But ay, as she harpit and she sang,
Fu' sairly did she weep.

"O gin my sons were seven rats,
Rinnin' on the castle wa',
And I mysell a grey grey cat,
I soon wad worry them a'!

"O gin my sons were seven hares,
Rinnin' owre yon lily lea,
And I mysell a good greyhound,
Soon worried they a' should be!"—

Then out and spak the bonny young Bride,
In bride-bed where she lay:
"That's like my sister Annie," she says;
"Wha is it doth sing and play?

"I'll put on my gown," said the new-come Bride
"And my shoes upon my feet;
I will see wha doth sae sadly sing,
And what is it gars her greet.[3]

"What ails you, what ails you, my housekeeper,
Tha ye mak sic a mane? [4]
Has ony wine-barrell cast its girds,
Or is a' your white bread gane?"

"It isna because my wine is spilt,
Or that my white bread's gane;

[1] One [2] The twain [3] Make her weep [4] Such lament

But because I've lost my true love's love,
And he's wed to anither ane."

"Noo tell me wha was your father?" she says,
"Noo tell me wha was your mother?
And had ye ony sister?" she says,
"And had ye ever a brother?"

"The Earl of Wemyss was my father,
The Countess of Wemyss my mother,
Young Elinor she was my sister dear,
And Lord John he was my brother."

"If the Earl of Wemyss was your father,
I wot sae was he mine;
And it's O my sister Annie!
Your love ye sallna tyne.[1]

"Tak your husband, my sister dear;
You ne'er were wrangd for me,
Beyond a kiss o' his merry mouth
As we cam owre the sea.

"Seven ships, loaded weel,
Cam owre the sea wi' me;
Ane o' them will tak me hame,
And six I'll gie to thee."

424 HELEN OF KIRCONNELL

. . . I WISH I were where Helen lies,
Night and day on me she cries;
O that I were where Helen lies,
On fair Kirconnell lea!

Curst be the heart that thought the thought,
And curst the hand that fired the shot,
When in my arms burd Helen dropt,
And died to succour me!

[1] Shall not lose

O think na ye my heart was sair
When my love dropt down and spak nae mair;
There did she swoon, wi' meickle care,
On fair Kirconnell lea.

As I went down the water side,
None but my foe to be my guide,
None but my foe to be my guide,
On fair Kirconnell lea;

I lighted down, my sword to draw,
I hackèd him in pieces sma',
I hackèd him in pieces sma',
For her that died for me.

O Helen fair, beyond compare,
I'll make a garland of thy hair
Shall bind my heart for evermair,
Until the day I die.

O that I were where Helen lies,
Night and day on me she cries;
Out of my bed she bids me rise,
Says, "Haste and come to me!"

O Helen fair! O Helen chaste!
If I were with thee I were blest,
Where thou lies low, and takes thy rest
On fair Kirconnell lea.

I wish my grave were growing green,
A winding-sheet drawn ower my e'en,
And I in Helen's arms lying
On fair Kirconnell lea.

I wish I were where Helen lies,
Night and day on me she cries;
And I am weary of the skies,
For her sake that died for me.

425 THE BONNIE BOWER

The Lament of the Border Widow

My love he built me a bonnie bower,
And clad it a' wi' lily flower;
A brawer bower ye ne'er did see,
Than my true-love he built for me.

There came a man, by middle day,
He spied his sport, and went away;
And brought the king that very night,
Who brake my bower, and slew my knight.

He slew my knight, to me sae dear;
He slew my knight, and poin'd his gear:[1]
My servants all for life did flee,
And left me in extremitie.

I sewed his sheet, making my mane;
I watched the corpse, mysel alane;
I watched his body night and day;
No living creature came that way.

I took his body on my back,
And whiles I gaed, and whiles I sat;
I digged a grave, and laid him in,
And happed him with the sod sae green.

But think na' ye my heart was sair,
When I laid the moul' on his yellow hair?
O, think na' ye my heart was wae,
When I turned about, away to gae?

Nae living man I'll love again,
Since that my lovely knight is slain;
Wi' ae lock o' his yellow hair
I'll chain my heart for evermair.

[1] Seized his all

426 **WEEP NO MORE**

WEEP no more, nor sigh nor groan,
Sorrow calls no time that's gone:
Violets plucked, the sweetest rain
Makes not fresh nor grow again;
Trim thy locks, look cheerfully,
Fate's hidden ends eyes cannot see.
Joys as wingèd dreams fly fast,
Why should sadness longer last?
Grief is but a wound to woe;
Gentlest fair, mourn, mourn no moe.[1]

JOHN FLETCHER

427 **"THE TWA SISTERS"**

THERE were twa sisters sat in a bowr;
Binnorie, O Binnorie:
There came a knight to be their wooer
By the bonny mill-dams of Binnorie.

He courted the eldest wi' glove an ring,
But he lovd the youngest above a' thing.[2]

He courted the eldest wi' brotch an knife,
But lovd the youngest as his life.

The eldest she was vexèd sair,
An' much envi'd her sister fair.

Into[3] her bowr she could not rest,
Wi' grief an spite she almos brast.

Upon a morning fair an' clear,
She cried upon her sister dear:—

"O sister, come to yon sea stran,
An see our father's ships come to lan."

She's ta'en her by the milk-white han,
An led her down to yon sea stran.

[1] More [2] Everything [3] Within

The youngest stood upon a stane,
The eldest came an threw her in.

She tooke her by the middle sma,'
An dashed her bonny back to the jaw.[1]

"O sister, sister, tak my han,
And Ise mack [2] you heir to a' my lan.

"O sister, sister, tak my middle,
An yes get [3] my goud and my gouden girdle.

"O sister, sister, save my life,
An I swear Ise never be nae man's wife."

"Foul fa' the han that I should tacke,
It twin'd me an my wardles make.[4]

"Your cherry cheeks an yellow hair
Gars me gae maiden for evermair."

Sometimes she sank, an sometimes she swam,
Till she came down yon bonny mill-dam.

O out it came the miller's son.
An' saw the fair maid swimmin in.

"O father, father, draw your dam,
Here's either a mermaid or a swan."

The miller quickly drew the dam,
An there he found a drown'd woman.

You couldna see her yellow hair
For gold and pearle that were so rare.

You couldna see her middle sma'
For gouden girdle that was sae braw.

[1] And dashed her backwards into the waves
[2] And I'll make [3] You shall have
[4] It parted me and my world's mate

You couldna see her fingers white,
For gouden rings that was sae gryte.[1]

An by there came a harper fine,
That harpèd to the king at dine.

When he did look that lady upon,
He sigh'd and made a heavy moan.

He's taen three locks o' her yellow hair,
An wi' them strung his harp sae fair.

The first tune he did play and sing,
Was, "Farewell to my father the king."

The nextin tune that he play'd syne,
Was, "Farewell to my mother the queen."

The lastin tune that he play'd then,
Was, "Wae to my sister, fair Ellen."

428 SWEET WILLIAM AND MAY MARGARET

THERE came a ghost to Margret's door,
With many a grievous groan;
And aye he tirlèd at the pin,
But answer made she none. . . .

"Is that my father Philip?
Or is't my brother John?
Or is't my true-love Willie,
From Scotland new come home?"

'Tis not thy father Philip,
Nor yet thy brother John,
But 'tis thy true-love Willie,
From Scotland new come home.

[1] Great

"O sweet Margret, O dear Margret,
  I pray thee speak to me;
Give me my faith and troth, Margret,
  As I gave it to thee."

"Thy faith and troth thou's never get,
  Nor yet will I thee lend,
Till that thou come within my bower
  And kiss me cheek and chin."

"If I shou'd come within thy bower,
  I am no earthly man;
And shou'd I kiss thy ruby lips,
  Thy days would not be lang.

"O sweet Margret, O dear Margret,
  I pray thee speak to me;
Give me my faith and troth, Margret,
  As I give it to thee."

"Thy faith and troth thou's never get,
  Nor yet will I thee lend,
Till thou take me to yon kirk-yard,
  And wed me with a ring."

"My bones are buried in yon kirk-yard
  Afar beyond the sea;
And it is but my spirit, Margret,
  That's now speaking to thee."

She stretched out her lily-white hand,
  And, for to do her best:
"Hae, there's your faith and troth, Willie;
  God send your soul good rest." . . .

Now she has kilted her robes o' green
  A piece below her knee,
And a' the live-lang winter night
  The dead corp followed she.

"Is there any room at your head, Willie,
Or any room at your feet?
Or any room at your side, Willie,
Wherein that I may creep?"

"There's nae room at my head, Margret,
There's nae room at my feet;
There's nae room at my side, Margret,
My coffin's made so meet."

Then up and crew the red, red cock,
And up and crew the grey;
" 'Tis time, 'tis time, my dear Margret,
That you were gane awa'."

429 THE WIFE OF USHER'S WELL

There lived a wife at Usher's Well
And a wealthy wife was she;
She had three stout and stalwart sons,
And sent them o'er the sea.

They hadna been a week from her,
A week but barely ane,
Whan word came to the carline wife
That her three sons were gane.

They hadna been a week from her,
A week but barely three,
Whan word came to the carline wife
That her sons she'd never see.

"I wish the wind may never cease,
Nor fashes in the flood,[1]
Till my three sons come hame to me,
In earthly flesh and blood."—

[1] Travail on the deep

It fell about the Martinmass,
When nights are lang and mirk,
The carline wife's three sons came hame,
And their hats were o the birk.

It neither grew in syke[1] nor ditch,
Nor yet in ony sheugh;
But at the gates o' Paradise
That birk grew fair enough. . . .

"Blow up the fire, my maidens,
Bring water from the well;
For a' my house shall feast this night.
Since my three sons are well."

And she has made to them a bed,
She's made it large and wide;
And she's ta'en her mantle her about,
Sat down at the bedside.

Up then crew the red, red cock,
And up and crew the grey;
The eldest to the youngest said,
" 'Tis time we were away!"

The cock he hadna crawed but once,
And clapped his wings at a',
When the youngest to the eldest said,
"Brother, we must awa'.

"The cock doth craw, the day doth daw,
The channerin worm doth chide;
Gin we be mist out o' our place,
A sair pain we maun bide.

"Lie still, lie still but a little wee while,
Lie still but if we may;

[1] Marsh

Gin my mother should miss us when she wakes
  She'll go mad ere it be day.

"Fare ye weel, my mother dear!
  Fareweel to barn and byre!
And fare ye well, the bonny lass
  That kindles my mother's fire!"

EVENING AND DREAM

430 **DREAM-PEDLARY**

If there were dreams to sell,
What would you buy?
Some cost a passing bell;
Some a light sigh,
That shakes from Life's fresh crown
Only a rose-leaf down.
If there were dreams to sell,
Merry and sad to tell,
And the crier rang the bell,
What would you buy?

A cottage lone and still,
With bowers nigh,
Shadowy, my woes to still,
Until I die.
Such peace from Life's fresh crown
Fain would I shake me down.
Were dreams to have at will,
This would best heal my ill,
This would I buy.

THOMAS LOVELL BEDDOES

431 **THE EVENING SUN**

The evening sun was sinking down
On low green hills and clustered trees;
It was a scene as fair and lone
As ever felt the soothing breeze

That cools the grass when day is gone,
And gives the waves a brighter blue,

And makes the soft white clouds sail on—
  Like spirits of ethereal dew

Which all the morn had hovered o'er
  The azure flowers, where they were nursed,
And now return to Heaven once more,
  Where their bright glories shone at first.

EMILY BRONTË

432 TO THE EVENING STAR

THOU fair-haired angel of the evening,
Now, whilst the sun rests on the mountains, light
Thy bright torch of love; thy radiant crown
Put on, and smile upon our evening bed!
Smile on our loves, and, while thou drawest the
Blue curtains of the sky, scatter thy silver dew
On every flower that shuts its sweet eyes
In timely sleep. Let thy west wind sleep on
The lake; speak silence with thy glimmering eyes,
And wash the dusk with silver. Soon, full soon,
Dost thou withdraw; then the wolf rages wide,
And the lion glares thro' the dun forest:
The fleeces of the flocks are covered with
Thy sacred dew: protect them with thine influence.

WILLIAM BLAKE

433 TO DAISIES, NOT TO SHUT SO SOON

SHUT not so soon; the dull-eyed night
  Hath not as yet begun
To make a seisure on the light,
  Or to seale up the Sun.

No Marigolds yet closèd are;
  No shadowes great appeare:
Nor doth the early Shepheard's Starre
  Shine like a spangle here.

Stay but till my *Julia* close
  Her life-begetting eye;
And let the whole world then dispose
  It selfe to live or dye.

ROBERT HERRICK

434 OF THE GOING DOWN OF THE SUN

WHAT, hast thou run thy Race? Art going down?
Thou seemest angry, why dost on us frown?
Yea wrap thy heads with Clouds, and hide thy face,
As threatning to withdraw from us thy Grace?
Oh leave us not! When once thou hid'st thy head,
Our Hórizon with darkness will be spread.
Tell's, who hath thee offended? Turn again:
Alas! too late—Entreaties are in vain! . . .

JOHN BUNYAN

435 VIRTUE

SWEET day, so cool, so calm, so bright
  The bridal of the earth and skie:
The dew shall weep thy fall to-night,
      For thou must die.

Sweet rose, whose hue angry and brave
  Bids the rash gazer wipe his eye,
Thy root is ever in its grave,
      And thou must die.

Sweet spring, full of sweet days and roses,
  A box where sweets compacted lie,
My music shows ye have your closes,
      And all must die.

Only a sweet and vertuous soul,
  Like seasond timber, never gives;

But though the whole world turn to coal,
Then chiefly lives.

GEORGE HERBERT

436 NIGHT

THE sun descending in the west,
The evening star does shine;
The birds are silent in their nest,
And I must seek for mine.
The moon, like a flower,
In heaven's high bower,
With silent delight
Sits and smiles on the night.

Farewell green fields and happy groves,
Where flocks have took delight.
Where lambs have nibbled, silent moves
The feet of angels bright;
Unseen they pour blessing,
And joy without ceasing,
On each bud and blossom,
And each sleeping bosom.

They look in every thoughtless nest,
Where birds are covered warm;
They visit caves of every beast,
To keep them all from harm.
If they see any weeping,
That should have been sleeping,
They pour sleep on their head,
And sit down by their bed.

When wolves and tygers howl for prey,
They pitying stand and weep;
Seeking to drive their thirst away,
And keep them from the sheep.
But if they rush dreadful,
The angels, most heedful,

Receive each mild spirit,
New worlds to inherit.

And there the lion's ruddy eyes
Shall flow with tears of gold,
And pitying the tender cries,
And walking round the fold,
Saying, "Wrath, by his meekness,
And by his health, sickness
Is driven away
From our immortal day.

"And now beside thee, bleating lamb,
I can lie down and sleep;
Or think on him who bore thy name,
Graze after thee and weep.
For, washed in life's river,
My bright mane for ever
Shall shine like the gold,
As I guard o'er the fold."

WILLIAM BLAKE

437 NURSE'S SONG

WHEN the voices of children are heard on the green
And laughing is heard on the hill,
My heart is at rest within my breast
And everything else is still.

"Then come home, my children, the sun is gone down,
And the dews of night arise;
Come, come, leave off play, and let us away
Till the morning appears in the skies."

"No, no, let us play, for it is yet day
And we cannot go to sleep;
Besides, in the sky the little birds fly,
And the hills are all covered with sheep."

"Well, well, go and play till the light fades away,
And then go home to bed."
The little ones leaped and shouted and laughed
And all the hills ecchoèd.

WILLIAM BLAKE

438 THE EVENING PRIMROSE

WHEN once the sun sinks in the west,
And dew-drops pearl the evening's breast;
Almost as pale as moonbeams are,
Or its companionable star,
The evening primrose opes anew
Its delicate blossoms to the dew;
And, shunning hermit of the light,
Wastes its fair bloom upon the night;
Who, blindfold to its fond caresses,
Knows not the beauty he possesses.
Thus it blooms on till night is bye
And day looks out with open eye,
Abashed at the gaze it cannot shun,
It faints and withers, and is done.

JOHN CLARE

439 "TIME, YOU OLD GIPSY MAN"

TIME, you old gipsy man,
Will you not stay,
Put up your caravan
Just for one day?

All things I'll give you
Will you be my guest,
Bells for your jennet
Of silver the best,
Goldsmiths shall beat you
A great golden ring
Peacocks shall bow to you,

Little boys sing,
Oh, and sweet girls will
Festoon you with may.
Time, you old gipsy,
Why hasten away?

Last week in Babylon,
Last night in Rome,
Morning, and in the crush
Under Paul's dome;
Under Paul's dial
You tighten your rein—
Only a moment,
And off once again;
Off to some city
Now blind in the womb,
Off to another
Ere that's in the tomb.

Time, you old gipsy man,
Will you not stay,
Put up your caravan
Just for one day?

RALPH HODGSON

440 AFTERWARDS

WHEN the Present has latched its postern behind my tremulous
stay,
And the May month flaps its glad green leaves like wings,
Delicate-filmed as new-spun silk, will the neighbours say,
"He was a man who used to notice such things"?

If it be in the dusk when, like an eyelid's soundless blink,
The dewfall-hawk comes crossing the shades to alight
Upon the wind-warped upland thorn, a gazer may think,
"To him this must have been a familiar sight."

If I pass during some nocturnal blackness, mothy and warm,
When the hedgehog travels furtively over the lawn,

One may say, "He strove that such innocent creatures should
come to no harm,
But he could do little for them; and now he is gone."

If, when hearing that I have been stilled at last, they stand at
the door,
Watching the full-starred heavens that winter sees,
Will this thought rise on those who will meet my face no more,
"He was one who had an eye for such mysteries"?

And will any say when my bell of quittance is heard in the gloom,
And a crossing breeze cuts a pause in its outrollings,
Till they rise again, as they were a new bell's boom,
"He hears it not now, but used to notice such things"?

THOMAS HARDY

441 STEPPING WESTWARD

"WHAT, you are stepping westward?"—"Yea."
—'Twould be a wildish destiny,
If we, who thus together roam
In a strange land, and far from home,
Were in this place the guests of chance;
Yet who would stop, or fear to advance,
Though home or shelter he had none,
With such a sky to lead him on?

The dewy ground was dark and cold;
Behind, all gloomy to behold;
And stepping westward seemed to be
A kind of heavenly destiny;
I liked the greeting; 'twas a sound
Of something without place or bound;
And seemed to give me spiritual right
To travel through that region bright.

The voice was soft, and she who spake
Was walking by her native lake;
The salutation had to me

The very sound of courtesy;
Its power was felt; and while my eye
Was fixed upon the glowing sky,
The echo of the voice enwrought
A human sweetness with the thought
Of travelling through the world that lay
Before me in my endless way.

WILLIAM WORDSWORTH

442

FOLDING THE FLOCKS

SHEPHERDS all, and Maidens fair,
Fold your Flocks up; for the Air
'Gins to thicken, and the Sun
Already his great course hath run.
See the Dew-drops how they kiss
Every little Flower that is:
Hanging on their Velvet Heads,
Like a Rope of Cristal Beads.
See the heavy Clouds low falling,
And bright *Hesperus* down calling
The dead Night from under Ground,
At whose rising, Mists unsound,
Damps and Vapours fly apace,
Hov'ring o'er the smiling Face
Of these Pastures, where they come,
Striking dead both Bud and Bloom;
Therefore, from such Danger, lock
Ev'ry one his lovèd Flock;
And let your Dogs lie loose without,
Lest the Wolf come as a scout
From the Mountain, and, ere day,
Bear a Lamb or Kid away;
Or the crafty, thievish Fox
Break upon your simple Flocks:
To secure yourself from these
Be not too secure in ease;
Let one Eye his watches keep,
While the other Eye doth sleep;

So shall you good Shepherds prove,
And deserve your Master's love.
Now, good night! may Sweetest Slumbers
And soft Silence fall in numbers
On your Eye-lids: So, farewell;
Thus I end my Evening knell.

JOHN FLETCHER

443 TO THE NIGHT

SWIFTLY walk over the western wave,
Spirit of Night!
Out of the misty eastern cave,
Where, all the long and lone daylight,
Thou wovest dreams of joy and fear,
Which make thee terrible and dear,—
Swift be thy flight!

Wrap thy form in a mantle gray,
Star-inwrought;
Blind with thine hair the eyes of Day;
Kiss her until she be wearied out,
Then wander o'er city, and sea, and land,
Touching all with thine opiate wand—
Come, long-sought!

When I arose and saw the dawn,
I sighed for thee;
When light rode high, and the dew was gone,
And noon lay heavy on flower and tree,
And the weary Day turned to his rest,
Lingering like an unloved guest,
I sighed for thee.

Thy brother Death came, and cried,
Wouldst thou me?
Thy sweet child Sleep, the filmy-eyed,
Murmured like a noon-tide bee,
Shall I nestle near thy side?

Wouldst thou me?—And I replied
No, not thee!

Death will come when thou art dead,
Soon, too soon—
Sleep will come when thou art fled;
Of neither would I ask the boon
I ask of thee, belovèd Night—
Swift be thine approaching flight,
Come soon, soon!

PERCY BYSSHE SHELLEY

444 LIGHT THE LAMPS UP, LAMPLIGHTER!

(FOR A LAMPLIGHTER, A GRANDMOTHER, THE ANGEL GABRIEL, AND ANY NUMBER OF OTHERS)

LIGHT the lamps up, Lamplighter,
The people are in the street—
Without a light
They have no sight,
And where will they plant their feet?
Some will tread in the gutter,
And some in the mud—oh dear!
Light the lamps up, Lamplighter,
Because the night is here.

Light the candles, Grandmother,
The children are going to bed—
Without a wick
They'll stumble and stick,
And where will they lay their head?
Some will lie on the staircase,
And some in the hearth—oh dear!
Light the candles, Grandmother,
Because the night is here.

Light the stars up, Gabriel,
The cherubs are out to fly—

If heaven is blind
How will they find
Their way across the sky?
Some will splash in the Milky Way,
Or bump on the moon—oh dear!
Light the stars up, Gabriel,
Because the night is here.

ELEANOR FARJEON

445 WILL YOU COME?

WILL you come?
Will you come?
Will you ride
So late
At my side?
O, will you come?

Will you come?
Will you come
If the night
Has a moon,
Full and bright?
O, will you come?

Would you come?
Would you come
If the noon
Gave light,
Not the moon?
Beautiful, would you come?

Would you have come?
Would you have come
Without scorning,
Had it been
Still morning?
Beloved, would you have come?

If you come
Haste and come.
Owls have cried;
It grows dark
To ride.
Beloved, beautiful, come!

EDWARD THOMAS

446 COME!

WULL ye come in eärly Spring,
Come at Easter, or in Mäy?
Or when Whitsuntide mid bring
Longer light to show your wäy?
Wull ye come, if you be true,
Vor to quicken love anew?
Wull ye call in Spring or Fall?
Come now soon by zun or moon?
Wull ye come?

Come wi' väice to väice the while
All their words be sweet to hear;
Come that feäce to feäce mid smile,
While their smiles do seem so dear;
Come within the year to seek
Woone you have sought woonce a week?
Come while flow'rs be on the bow'rs,
And the bird o' songs a-heärd.
Wull ye come?
Ess come *to* ye, an' come *vor* ye, is my word,
I wull come.

WILLIAM BARNES

447 HYMN TO DIANA

QUEEN and huntress, chaste and fair,
Now the sun is laid to sleep,

Seated in thy silver chair,
State in wonted manner keep;
Hesperus entreats thy light,
Goddess excellently bright.

Earth, let not thy envious shade
Dare itself to interpose;
Cynthia's shining orb was made
Heaven to clear when day did close:
Bless us then with wishèd sight,
Goddess excellently bright.

Lay thy bow of pearl apart,
And thy crystal shining quiver;
Give unto the flying hart
Space to breathe, how short soever:
Thou that mak'st a day of night,
Goddess excellently bright.

BEN JONSON

448 THE CLOUDS HAVE LEFT THE SKY

THE clouds have left the sky,
The wind hath left the sea,
The half-moon up on high
Shrinketh her face of dree.

She lightens on the comb
Of leaden waves, that roar
And thrust their hurried foam
Up on the dusky shore.

Behind the western bars
The shrouded day retreats,
And unperceived the stars
Steal to their sovran seats.

And whiter grows the foam,
The small moon lightens more;

And as I turn me home,
My shadow walks before.

ROBERT BRIDGES

449 WITH HOW SAD STEPS

WITH how sad steps, O Moon, thou climb'st the skies!
How silently, and with how wan a face!
What! may it be that even in heavenly place
That busy archer his sharp arrows tries?
Sure, if that long-with-love-acquainted eyes
Can judge of love, thou feel'st a lover's case:
I read it in thy looks; thy languished grace
To me, that feel the like, thy state descries.

Then, even of fellowship, O Moon, tell me,
Is constant love deemed there but want of wit?
Are beauties there as proud as here they be?
Do they above love to be loved, and yet
Those lovers scorn whom that love doth possess?
Do they call virtue there ungratefulness?

SIR PHILIP SIDNEY

450 IN DISPRAISE OF THE MOON

I WOULD not be the Moon, the sickly thing,
To summon owls and bats upon the wing;
For when the noble Sun is gone away,
She turns his night into a pallid day.

She hath no air, no radiance of her own,
That world unmusical of earth and stone.
She wakes her dim, uncoloured, voiceless hosts,
Ghost of the Sun, herself the sun of ghosts.

The mortal eyes that gaze too long on her
Of Reason's piercing ray defrauded are.

Light in itself doth feed the living brain;
That light, reflected, but makes darkness plain.

MARY COLERIDGE

451 THE WANING MOON

AND like a dying lady, lean and pale,
Who totters forth, wrapt in a gauzy veil,
Out of her chamber, led by the insane
And feeble wanderings of her fading brain,
The moon arose up in the murky East,
A white and shapeless mass.—

PERCY BYSSHE SHELLEY

452 WE'LL GO NO MORE A-ROVING

So, we'll go no more a-roving
So late into the night,
Though the heart be still as loving,
And the moon be still as bright.

For the sword outwears its sheath,
And the soul wears out the breast,
And the heart must pause to breathe,
And love itself have rest.

Though the night was made for loving,
And the day returns too soon,
Yet we'll go no more a-roving
By the light of the moon.

GEORGE GORDON, LORD BYRON

453 SONG OF THE NIGHT AT DAY-BREAK

ALL my stars forsake me,
And the dawn-winds shake me.
Where shall I betake me?

Whither shall I run
Till the set of sun,
Till the day be done?

To the mountain-mine,
To the boughs o' the pine,
To the blind man's eyne,

To a brow that is
Bowed upon the knees,
Sick with memories.

ALICE MEYNELL

454 THE NIGHT WILL NEVER STAY

THE night will never stay,
The night will still go by,
Though with a million stars
You pin it to the sky;
Though you bind it with the blowing wind
And buckle it with the moon,
The night will slip away
Like sorrow or a tune.

ELEANOR FARJEON

455 LINES FOR A BED AT KELMSCOTT MANOR

"THE wind's on the wold
And the night is a-cold,
And Thames runs chill
Twixt mead and hill,
But kind and dear
Is the old house here,
And my heart is warm
Midst winter's harm.
Rest then and rest,
And think of the best
Twixt summer and spring

When all birds sing
In the town of the tree,
And ye lie in me
And scarce dare move
Lest earth and its love
Should fade away
Ere the full of the day.

I am old and have seen
Many things that have been,
Both grief and peace,
And wane and increase.
No tale I tell
Of ill or well,
But this I say,
Night treadeth on day,
And for worst and best
Right good is rest."

WILLIAM MORRIS

456 ROCK, BALL, FIDDLE

HE that lies at the stock,
Shall have the gold rock;
He that lies at the wall,
Shall have the gold ball;
He that lies in the middle,
Shall have the gold fiddle.

457 BEFORE SLEEPING

MATTHEW, Mark, Luke, and John,
Bless the bed that I lie on.
Before I lay me down to sleep
I give my soul to Christ to keep.
Four corners to my bed,
Four angels there aspread,
Two to foot, and two to head,

And four to carry me when I'm dead.
I go by sea, I go by land,
The Lord made me with His right hand.
If any danger come to me,
Sweet Jesus Christ deliver me.
He's the branch and I'm the flower,
Pray God send me a happy hour,
And if I die before I wake,
I pray that Christ my soul will take.

458 ON A QUIET CONSCIENCE

CLOSE thine eyes, and sleep secure;
Thy soul is safe, thy body sure.
He that guards thee, he that keeps,
Never slumbers, never sleeps.
A quiet conscience in the breast
Has only peace, has only rest.
The wisest and the mirth of kings
Are out of tune unless she sings:
Then close thine eyes in peace and sleep secure,
No sleep so sweet as thine, no rest so sure.

CHARLES I.

459 SONG

WHILE Morpheus thus does gently lay
His powerful charge upon each part
Making thy spirits even obey
The silver charms of his dull art;

I, thy Good Angel, from thy side,—
As smoke doth from the altar rise,
Making no noise as it doth glide,—
Will leave thee in this soft surprise;

And from the clouds will fetch thee down
A holy vision, to express

Thy right unto an earthly crown;
No power can make this kingdom less.

But gently, gently, lest I bring
A start in sleep by sudden flight,
Playing aloof, and hovering,
Till I am lost unto the sight.

This is a motion still and soft;
So free from noise and cry,
That Jove himself, who hears a thought,
Knows not when we pass by.

HENRY KILLIGREW

460

THE EVE OF SAINT MARK

UPON a Sabbath-day, it fell;
Twice holy was the Sabbath-bell,
That called the folk to evening prayer;
The city streets were clean and fair
From wholesome drench of April rains;
And, on the western window panes,
The chilly sunset faintly told
Of unmatured green vallies cold,
Of the green thorny bloomless hedge,
Of rivers new with spring-tide sedge,
Of primroses by sheltered rills,
And daisies on the aguish hills.
Twice holy was the Sabbath-bell:
The silent streets were crowded well
With staid and pious companies,
Warm from their fire-side oratories;
And moving, with demurest air,
To even-song, and vesper-prayer.
Each archèd porch, and entry low,
Was filled with patient folk and slow,
With whispers hush, and shuffling feet,
While played the organ loud and sweet.
The bells had ceased, the prayers begun,

And Bertha had not yet half done
A curious volume, patched and torn,
That all day long, from earliest morn,
Had taken captive her two eyes,
Among its golden broideries;
Perplexed her with a thousand things,—
The stars of Heaven, and angels' wings,
Martyrs in a fiery blaze,
Azure saints in silver rays,
Moses' breastplate, and the seven
Candlesticks John saw in Heaven,
The winged Lion of Saint Mark,
And the Covenantal Ark,
With its many mysteries,
Cherubim and golden mice.

Bertha was a maiden fair,
Dwelling in the old Minster-square;
From her fire-side she could see,
Sidelong, its rich antiquity,
Far as the Bishop's garden-wall;
Where sycamores and elm-trees tall,
Full-leaved the forest had outstript,
By no sharp north-wind ever nipt,
So sheltered by the mighty pile,
Bertha arose, and read awhile,
With forehead 'gainst the window-pane,
Again she tryed, and then again,
Until the dusk eve left her dark
Upon the legend of St. Mark.
From plaited lawn-frill, fine and thin,
She lifted up her soft warm chin,
With aching neck and swimming eyes,
And dazed with saintly imageries.

All was gloom, and silent all,
Save now and then the still foot-fall
Of one returning homewards late,
Past the echoing minster-gate.

The clamorous daws, that all the day
Above tree-tops and towers play,
Pair by pair had gone to rest,
Each in its ancient belfry-nest,
Where asleep they fall betimes,
To music of the drowsy chimes.

All was silent, all was gloom,
Abroad and in the homely room:
Down she sat, poor cheated soul!
And struck a lamp from the dismal coal;
Leaned forward, with bright drooping hair
And slant book, full against the glare.
Her shadow, in uneasy guise,
Hovered about, a giant size,
On ceiling-beam and old oak chair,
The parrot's cage, and panel square;
And the warm angled winter screen,
On which were many monsters seen,
Called doves of Siam, Lima mice,
And legless birds of Paradise,
Macaw, and tender Avadavat,
And silken-furred Angora cat.
Untired she read, her shadow still
Glowered about, as it would fill
The room with wildest forms and shades,
As though some ghostly queen of spades
Had come to mock behind her back,
And dance, and ruffle her garments black.
Untired she read the legend page,
Of holy Mark, from youth to age,
On land, on sea, in pagan chains,
Rejoicing for his many pains.
Sometimes the learned eremite,
With golden star, or dagger bright,
Referred to pious poesies
Written in smallest crow-quill size
Beneath the text; and thus the rhyme
Was parcelled out from time to time:—

" 'Gif ye wol stonden[1] hardie wight—
Amiddès of the blackè night—
Righte in the churchè porch, pardie
Ye wol behold a companie
Approchen thee full dolourouse:
For soothe to sain from everich house
Be it in city or villàge
Wol come the Phantom and imàge
Of ilka[2] gent and ilka carle
Whom coldè Deathè hath in parle
And wol some day that very year
Touchen with foulè venime spear
And sadly do them all to die.—
Hem all shalt thou see verilie—
And everichon shall by thee pass
All who must die that year, Alas.'

"Als[3] writith he of swevenis,[4]
Men han beforne they wake in bliss,
Whanne that hir friendès thinke hem bound
In crimpèd shroude farre under grounde;
And how a litling child mote be
A saint er its nativitie,
Gif that the modre—God her blesse!—
Kepen in solitarinesse,
And kissen devoute the holy croce—
Of Goddès love, and Sathan's force,—
He writith; and thinges many mo,
Of swichè things I may not show.
Bot I must tellen verilie
Somdel of Saintè Cicilie,
And chieflie what he auctoriethe
Of Saintè Markis life and dethe:"

At length her constant eyelids come
Upon the fervent martyrdom;
Then lastly to his holy shrine,

[1] If you will stand [2] Every [3] Likewise [4] Visions

Exalt amid the tapers' shine
At Venice. . . .

JOHN KEATS

461 LAID IN MY QUIET BED

LAID in my quiet bed, in study as I were,
I saw within my troubled head a heap of thoughts appear;
And every thought did shew so lively in mine eyes,
That now I sighed, and then I smiled, as cause of thought did rise.
I saw the little boy in thought how oft that he
Did wish of God, to scape the rod, a tall young man to be.
The young man eke that feels his bones with pains opprest,
How he would be a rich old man, to live and lie at rest.
The rich old man that sees his end draw on so sore,
How he would be a boy again, to live so much the more.
Whereat full oft I smiled, to see how all these three,
From boy to man, from man to boy, would chop and change degree. . . .

HENRY HOWARD, EARL OF SURREY

462 AT NIGHT

HOME, home from the horizon far and clear,
Hither the soft wings sweep;
Flocks of the memories of the day draw near
The dovecote doors of sleep.

Oh, which are they that come through sweetest light
Of all these homing birds?
Which with the straightest and the swiftest flight?
Your words to me, your words!

ALICE MEYNELL

463 ECHO

COME to me in the silence of the night;
Come in the speaking silence of a dream;

Come with soft rounded cheeks and eyes as bright
As sunlight on a stream;
Come back in tears,
O memory, hope, love of finished years.

O dream how sweet, too sweet, too bitter sweet,
Whose wakening should have been in Paradise,
Where souls brimfull of love abide and meet;
Where thirsting longing eyes
Watch the slow door
That opening, letting in, lets out no more.

Yet come to me in dreams, that I may live
My very life again though cold in death:
Come back to me in dreams, that I may give
Pulse for pulse, breath for breath:
Speak low, lean low,
As long ago, my love, how long ago.

CHRISTINA ROSSETTI

464 THE SHADOW OF NIGHT

How strange it is to wake
And watch while others sleep,
Till sight and hearing ache
For objects that may keep
The awful inner sense
Unroused, lest it should mark
The life that haunts the emptiness
And horror of the dark.

How strange the distant bay
Of dogs; how wild the note
Of cocks that scream for day,
In homesteads far remote;
How strange and wild to hear
The old and crumbling tower,
Amidst the darkness, suddenly
Take life and speak the hour. . . .

The nightingale is gay,
For she can vanquish night;
Dreaming, she sings of day,
Notes that make darkness bright:
But when the refluent gloom
Suddens the gaps of song,
We charge on her the dolefulness,
And call her crazed with wrong.

COVENTRY PATMORE

465

OUT IN THE DARK

OUT in the dark over the snow
The fallow fawns invisible go
With the fallow doe;
And the winds blow
Fast as the stars are slow.

Stealthily the dark haunts round
And, when the lamp goes, without sound
At a swifter bound
Then the swiftest hound,
Arrives, and all else is drowned;

And I and star and wind and deer,
Are in the dark together,—near,
Yet far,—and fear
Drums on my ear
In that sage company drear.

How weak and little is the light,
All the universe of sight,
Love and delight,
Before the might,
If you love it not, of night.

EDWARD THOMAS

466

NOCTURNE

THE red flame flowers bloom and die,
The embers puff a golden spark.

Now and again a horse's eye
  Shines like a topaz in the dark.

A prowling jackal jars the hush,
  The drowsy oxen chump and sigh—
The ghost moon lifts above the bush
  And creeps across the starry sky.

Low in the south the "Cross" is bright,
  And sleep comes dreamless, undefiled,
Here in the blue and silver night,
  In the star-chamber of the Wild.

CROSBIE GARSTIN

467

THE ANGEL

I DREAMT a Dream! what can it mean?
And that I was a maiden Queen
Guarded by an Angel mild:
Witless woe was ne'er beguiled!

And I wept both night and day,
And he wiped my tears away;
And I wept both day and night,
And hid from him my heart's delight.

So he took his wings and fled;
Then the morn blushed rosy red;
I dried my tears, and armed my fears
With ten thousand shields and spears.

Soon my Angel came again;
I was armed, he came in vain;
For the time of youth was fled,
And grey hairs were on my head.

WILLIAM BLAKE

368

"ANGEL SPIRITS OF SLEEP"

ANGEL spirits of sleep,
White-robed, with silver hair,

In your meadows fair,
Where the willows weep,
And the sad moonbeam
On the gliding stream
Writes her scattered dream:

Angel spirits of sleep,
Dancing to the weir
In the hollow roar
Of its waters deep;
Know ye how men say
That ye haunt no more
Isle and grassy shore
With your moonlit play;
That ye dance not here,
White-robed spirits of sleep,
All the summer night
Threading dances light?

ROBERT BRIDGES

469 A DREAM

ONCE a dream did weave a shade
O'er my Angel-guarded bed,
That an Emmet lost its way
Where on grass methought I lay.

Troubled, 'wildered, and forlorn,
Dark, benighted, travel-worn,
Over many a tangled spray,
All heart-broke I heard her say:

"O my children! do they cry?
Do they hear their father sigh?
Now they look abroad to see:
Now return and weep for me."

Pitying, I dropped a tear;
But I saw a glow-worm near,

Who replied: "What wailing wight
Calls the watchman of the night?

"I am set to light the ground,
While the beetle goes his round:
Follow now the beetle's hum;
Little wanderer, hie thee home."

WILLIAM BLAKE

470 THE LAND OF DREAMS

AWAKE, awake, my little Boy!
Thou wast thy Mother's only joy:
Why dost thou weep in thy gentle sleep?
Awake! thy Father does thee keep.

"O, what land is the Land of Dreams,
What are its mountains, and what are its streams?
O Father! I saw my Mother there,
Among the Lillies by waters fair.

"Among the lambs clothèd in white,
She walked with her Thomas in sweet delight.
I wept for joy, like a dove I mourn;
O! when shall I again return?"

Dear Child, I also by pleasant streams
Have wandered all night in the Land of Dreams,
But tho' calm and warm the waters wide,
I could not get to the other side.

"Father, O Father! what do we here,
In this Land of unbelief and fear?
The Land of Dreams is better far
Above the light of the Morning Star."

WILLIAM BLAKE

THE GARDEN

471[1] I KNOW A LITTLE GARDEN-CLOSE

I KNOW a little garden-close
Set thick with lily and red rose,
Where I would wander if I might
From dewy dawn to dewy night,
And have one with me wandering.

And though within it no birds sing,
And though no pillared house is there,
And though the apple boughs are bare
Of fruit and blossom, would to God,
Her feet upon the green grass trod,
And I beheld them as before.

There comes a murmur from the shore,
And in the close two fair streams are,
Drawn from the purple hills afar,
Drawn down unto the restless sea;
Dark hills whose heath-bloom feeds no bee,
Dark shores no ship has ever seen,
Tormented by the billows green
Whose murmur comes unceasingly
Unto the place for which I cry.

For which I cry both day and night,
For which I let slip all delight,
Whereby I grow both deaf and blind,
Careless to win, unskilled to find,
And quick to lose what all men seek.

Yet tottering as I am, and weak,
Still have I left a little breath

To seek within the jaws of death
An entrance to that happy place,
To seek the unforgotten face,
Once seen, once kissed, once reft from me
Anight the murmuring of the sea.

WILLIAM MORRIS

472

FOLLOW

FOLLOW thy fair sun, unhappy shadow,
Though thou be black as night,
And she made all of light,
Yet follow thy fair sun, unhappy shadow.

Follow her whose light thy light depriveth,
Though here thou liv'st disgraced,
And she in heaven is placed,
Yet follow her whose light the world reviveth.

Follow those pure beams whose beauty burneth,
That so have scorchèd thee,
As thou still black must be,
Till her kind beams thy black to brightness turneth.

Follow her while yet her glory shineth:
There comes a luckless night,
That will dim all her light;
And this the black unhappy shade divineth.

Follow still since so thy fates ordainèd;
The Sun must have his shade,
Till both at once do fade—
The Sun still proud, the shadow still disdainèd.

THOMAS CAMPION

473

UP-HILL

DOES the road wind up-hill all the way?
Yes, to the very end.
Will the day's journey take the whole long day?
From morn to night, my friend.

But is there for the night a resting-place?
  A roof for when the slow dark hours begin.
May not the darkness hide it from my face?
  You cannot miss that inn.

Shall I meet other wayfarers at night?
  Those who have gone before.
Then must I knock or call when just in sight?
  They will not keep you standing at the door.

Shall I find comfort, travel-sore and weak?
  Of labour you shall find the sum.
Will there be beds for me and all who seek?
  Yea, beds for all who come.

CHRISTINA ROSSETTI

474 LOVE

LOVE bade me welcome; yet my soul drew back,
    Guilty of dust and sin.
But quick-eyed Love, observing me grow slack
    From my first entrance in,
Drew nearer to me, sweetly questioning
    If I lacked anything.

"A guest," I answered, "worthy to be here":
    Love said, "You shall be he."
"I, the unkind, ungrateful? Ah, my dear!
    I cannot look on Thee."
Love took my hand, and smiling did reply,
    "Who made the eyes but I?"

"Truth, Lord; but I have marred them; let my shame
    Go where it doth deserve."
"And know you not," says Love, "who bore the blame?"
    "My dear, then I will serve."
"You must sit down," says Love, "and taste my meat."
    So I did sit and eat.

GEORGE HERBERT

475 A ROYAL GUEST

. . . YET if His Majesty our sovereign lord
Should of his own accord
Friendly himself invite,
And say, "I'll be your guest to-morrow night,"
How should we stir ourselves, call and command
All hands to work! "Let no man idle stand!

"Set me fine Spanish tables in the hall,
See they be fitted all;
Let there be room to eat,
And order taken that there want no meat.
See every sconce and candlestick made bright,
That without tapers they may give a light.

"Look to the presence: are the carpets spread,
The dazie [1] o'er the head,
The cushions in the chairs,
And all the candles lighted on the stairs?
Perfume the chambers, and in any case
Let each man give attendance in his place!"

Thus, if the king were coming, would we do,
And 'twere good reason too;
For 'tis a duteous thing
To show all honour to an earthly king,
And after all our travail and our cost,
So he be pleased, to think no labour lost.

But at the coming of the King of Heaven
All's set at six and seven:
We wallow in our sin,
Christ cannot find a chamber in the inn.
We entertain Him always like a stranger,
And, as at first, still lodge Him in a manger.

[1] Canopy over dais

EVE

Eve, with her basket, was
Deep in the bells and grass,
Wading in bells and grass
Up to her knees,
Picking a dish of sweet
Berries and plums to eat,
Down in the bells and grass
Under the trees.

Mute as a mouse in a
Corner the cobra lay,
Curled round a bough of the
Cinnamon tall. . . .
Now to get even and
Humble proud heaven and—
Now was the moment or
Never at all.

"Eva!" Each syllable
Light as a flower fell,
"Eva!" he whispered the
Wondering maid,
Soft as a bubble sung
Out of a linnet's lung,
Soft and most silverly
"Eva!" he said.

Picture that orchard sprite,
Eve, with her body white,
Supple and smooth to her
Slim finger tips,
Wondering, listening,
Listening, wondering,
Eve with a berry
Half-way to her lips.

Oh, had our simple Eve
Seen through the make-believe!
Had she but known the

Pretender he was!
Out of the boughs he came,
Whispering still her name,
Tumbling in twenty rings
Into the grass.

Here was the strangest pair
In the world anywhere,
Eve in the bells and grass
Kneeling, and he
Telling his story low. . . .
Singing birds saw them go
Down the dark path to
The Blasphemous Tree.

Oh, what a clatter when
Titmouse and Jenny Wren
Saw him successful and
Taking his leave!
How the birds rated him,
How they all hated him!
How they all pitied
Poor motherless Eve!

Picture her crying,
Outside in the lane,
Eve, with no dish of sweet
Berries and plums to eat,
Haunting the gate of the
Orchard in vain. . . .
Picture the lewd delight
Under the hill to-night—
"Eva!" the toast goes round,
"Eva!" again.

RALPH HODGSON

477

EVE

"WHILE I sit at the door,
Sick to gaze within,

Mine eye weepeth sore
For sorrow and sin:
As a tree my sin stands
To darken all lands;
Death is the fruit it bore.

"How have Eden bowers grown
Without Adam to bend them!
How have Eden flowers blown,
Squandering their sweet breath,
Without me to tend them!
The Tree of Life was ours,
Tree twelvefold-fruited,
Most lofty tree that flowers,
Most deeply rooted:
I chose the Tree of Death.

"Hadst thou but said me nay,
Adam, my brother,
I might have pined away;
I, but none other:
God might have let thee stay
Safe in our garden
By putting me away
Beyond all pardon.

"I, Eve, sad mother
Of all who must live,
I, not another,
Plucked bitterest fruit to give
My friend, husband, lover.
O wanton eyes run over;
Who but I should grieve?—
Cain hath slain his brother:
Of all who must die mother,
Miserable Eve!"
Thus she sat weeping,
Thus Eve our mother,
Where one lay sleeping

Slain by his brother.
Greatest and least
Each piteous beast
To hear her voice
Forgot his joys
And set aside his feast.

The mouse paused in his walk
And dropped his wheaten stalk;
Grave cattle wagged their heads
In rumination;
The eagle gave a cry
From his cloud station:
Larks on thyme beds
Forbore to mount or sing;
Bees drooped upon the wing;
The raven perched on high
Forgot his ration;
The conies in their rock,
A feeble nation,
Quaked sympathetical;
The mocking-bird left off to mock;
Huge camels knelt as if
In deprecation;
The kind hart's tears were falling;
Chattered the wistful stork;
Dove-voices with a dying fall
Cooed desolation
Answering grief by grief.
Only the serpent in the dust,
Wriggling and crawling,
Grinned an evil grin and thrust
His tongue out with its fork.

CHRISTINA ROSSETTI

478

ADAM

ADAM lay i-bowndyn,
bowndyn in a bond.

Fowre thowsand wynter
thowt he not to long;

And al was for an appil,
an appil that he tok,
As clerkes fyndyn wretyn
in here Book.

Ne hadde the appil takė ben,
the appil taken ben,
Ne hadde never our lady
a ben hevene qwen.

Blyssid be the tyme
that appil takė was!
Therefore we mown syngyn
Deo gracias.

479 THE SEVEN VIRGINS

ALL under the leaves and the leaves of life
I met with virgins seven,
And one of them was Mary mild,
Our Lord's mother of Heaven.

"Oh, what are you seeking, you seven fair maids
All under the leaves of life?
Come tell, come tell, what seek you
All under the leaves of life?"

"We're seeking for no leaves, Thomas,
But for a friend of thine;
We're seeking for sweet Jesus Christ,
To be our guide and thine."

"Go down, go down, to yonder town,
And sit in the gallery,
And there you'll see sweet Jesus Christ
Nailed to a big yew-tree."

So down they went to yonder town
As fast as foot could fall,
And many a grievous bitter tear
From the virgins' eyes did fall.

"O peace, Mother, O peace, Mother,
Your weeping doth me grieve:
I must suffer this," He said,
"For Adam and for Eve.

"O Mother, take you John Evangelist
All for to be your son,
And he will comfort you sometimes,
Mother, as I have done."

"O come, thou John Evangelist,
Thou'rt welcome unto me;
But more welcome my own dear Son,
Whom I nursèd on my knee."

Then he laid his head on His right shoulder,
Seeing death it struck Him nigh—
"The Holy Ghost be with your soul,
I die, Mother dear, I die." . . .

480 LULLY, LULLEY

Lully, lalley, lully, lulley;
The faucon hath borne my make[1] away.

He bare him up, he bare him down,
He bare him in to an orchard browne.

In that orchard there was an halle
That was hanged with purpill and pall.

And in that hall there was a bede,[2]
Hit was hanged with gold so rede.

[1] Mate [2] Bed

And in that bede there lithe a knyght,
His woundes bleding day and night.

By that bede side kneleth a may,
And she wepeth both night and day.

And by that bede side there stondeth a stone,
Corpus Christi wretyen there on.

481

BALME

. . . THERE grew a goodly tree him faire beside,
Loaden with fruit and apples rosie red,
As they in pure vermilion had beene dide,
Whereof great vertues over all were red:[1]
For happie life to all, which thereon fed,
And life eke everlasting did befall:
Great God it planted in that blessed sted
With his almightie hand, and did it call
The tree of life, the crime of our first father's fall.

In all the world like was not to be found,
Save in that soile, where all good things did grow,
And freely sprong out of the fruitfull ground,
As incorrupted Nature did them sow,
Till that dread Dragon all did overthrow.
Another like faire tree eke grew thereby,
Whereof who so did eat, eftsoones did know
Both good and ill: O mornefull memory:
That tree through one man's fault hath doen us all to dy.

From that first tree forth flowd, as from a well,
A trickling streame of Balme, most soveraine
And daintie deare, which on the ground still fell,
And overflowèd all the fertill plaine,
And it had deawèd bene with timely raine:
Life and long health that gratious ointment gave,
And deadly woundes could heale, and reare againe
The senselesse corse appointed for the grave.
Into that same he fell: which did from death him save. . . .

EDMUND SPENSER

[1] Told

482 MY MASTER HATH A GARDEN

My master hath a garden, full-filled with divers flowers,
Where thou mayst gather posies gay, all times and hours,
Here nought is heard
But paradise-bird,
Harp, dulcimer, and lute,
With cymbal,
And timbrel,
And the gentle sounding flute.

Oh! Jesus, Lord, my heal and weal, my bliss complete,
Make thou my heart thy garden-plot, true, fair and neat
That I may hear
This music clear,
Harp, dulcimer, and lute,
With cymbal,
And timbrel,
And the gentle sounding flute.

483 THIS IS THE KEY

This is the Key of the Kingdom:
In that Kingdom is a city;
In that city is a town;
In that town there is a street;
In that street there winds a lane;
In that lane there is a yard;
In that yard there is a house;
In that house there waits a room;
In that room an empty bed;
And on that bed a basket—
A Basket of Sweet Flowers:
Of Flowers, of Flowers;
A Basket of Sweet Flowers.

Flowers in a Basket;
Basket on the bed;
Bed in the chamber;
Chamber in the house;

House in the weedy yard;
Yard in the winding lane;
Lane in the broad street;
Street in the high town;
Town in the city;
City in the Kingdom—
This is the Key of the Kingdom;
Of the Kingdom this is the Key.

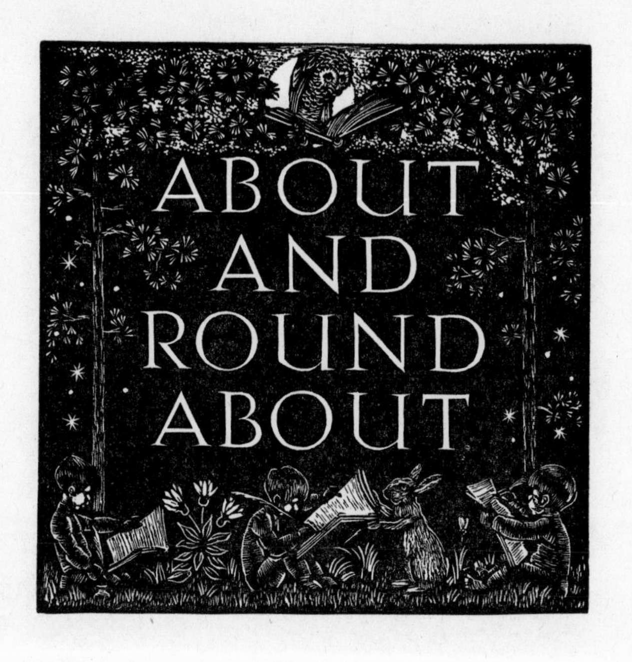
ABOUT
AND
ROUND
ABOUT

ABOUT AND ROUNDABOUT

In the margins of Nahum Tarune's The Other Worlde *I found many things in his own handwriting about (and roundabout) the poems contained in it. Some of them I copied out at the time. Others of my own making were added afterwards. These were all included in the first edition of* Come Hither, *which appeared in* 1923.

In this new edition no change has been made in its contents up to page 493, *apart from the correction of certain copying mistakes. But from here onward many new poems and rhymes have been added, and always with the intention of carrying on the theme or meaning or of adding to the interest of the poems to which they refer in the earlier part of the book.*

By the kindness and courtesy, too, of readers of the original edition I have now been able to put right a certain number of my first blunders and inaccuracies, though, it may be, others as flagrant still remain. Moreover, many entirely new notes have been added—the consequence being that whereas in 1923 *this section of the book filled* 171 *pages, it has now overflowed into* 304; *with a fresh crop, I fear, of such weeds as disfigured the originals! For these I must ask to be as generously excused.*

But why have taken any such risk? The fact is that in the making of notes—of which to some minds there should be no beginning—it is difficult to find an end. For many reasons. At every reading of a poem—though it may have been familiar from early childhood—some hitherto hidden delicacy of rhythm or intonation may be revealed; new shades of meaning show themselves; and even difficulties may become apparent which were before unheeded. Indeed what is read on the printed page is merely so many words; they may mean much or little to the reader, but in either case it is he alone who out of them can create a poem, *and therefore* his *poem. And this poem changes for him, as he himself changes with the years.*

A poem, too, is a blossoming in words of a language at a certain time in its history, and words stand for things, objects, actions, as well as ideas. It was the work also of one man living in a certain place and period and setting and state of being and often in a bye-gone century. Is it waste of pains, then, even when one is young, to attempt not only to realise this but to illustrate it in some degree, and so to cross again and again over the slender bridge between poetry and actuality, between the world of the imagination and the world without? There will not be less to be seen on either side by becoming familiar with both of them. And much, alas, that was of the very being of our early English poetry and particularly that of the folk, of the people, is rapidly vanishing away.

Still, it must be confessed that some of the pages that follow are not only without rhyme, but with very little detectible reason. An even larger number are, in fact, confessions of ignorance. For of all the boys in a school, it is the dunce who—if only he were encouraged—could ask the most questions. He may by no means be the best at answering them for himself: but the attempt to do so, even when it is made with so little method and so much at random as it has been here, is its own reward.

And last, owing to the pleasant custom of printing poetry so that, in intention at least, it cannot be mistaken for prose, any reader of the following pages who has a natural distaste for any annotator, can easily skip from rhyme to rhyme, dream on from poem to poem; and ignore everything else.

1. "This is the Key."

This jingle (like Nos. 15, 16 and others) is one of hundreds of nursery or dandling rhymes which I found in Mr. Nahum's book. Compared with more formal poems they are like the least (and loveliest) of the wild flowers—pimpernel, eyebright, thyme, woodruff, and others even tinier, even quieter, but revealing their own private and complete little beauty if looked at closely. Who made them, how old they are; nobody knows. But when Noah's Ark stranded on the slopes of Mount Ararat, maybe a blossoming weed or two was nodding at the open third-storey window out of which over the waters of the flood the dove had followed the raven, and there, rejoicing in the sunshine and the green, sat

Japheth's wife dandling little Magog on her lap, and crooning him some such lullaby.

3.

On the one side is printed the old Scots, and on the other the best I can do to put it into the English of our own time. According to the dictionary the thistle-cock that cries shame on the sleepers still drowsing in their beds is the corn-bunting—a cousin of the yellow-hammer. He has a small harsh monotonous voice as if for the very purpose. Whereas the nightingale might seem to cry, "Nay, nay: it is in dreams you wander. Happy ones! Sleep on; sleep on."

But for most of us sleep keeps strangely to its hours; and though nearly all children of seven have spent about three long years abed, few of us have slept straight on even from one day's dark into another. Not so William Foxley. He was pot-maker in the Mint, then in the Tower of London. He fell asleep one day—the 27th of April, 1546—and continued to sleep for fourteen days and nights. Not even a visit from Henry VIII. and his royal physician stirred his slumbers. Having awakened at last, however, he returned to the busy world; and continued his pot-making for forty years after.

4. "I passed by his Garden."

Whatever fate befell the Sluggard, I should like to have taken a walk in his *garden*, among those branching thistles, green thorns and briers. Maybe he sailed off at last to the Isle of Nightmare, or to the land where it is always afternoon, or was wrecked in Yawning Gap. He must, at any rate, have had an even heavier head than Dr. Watts supposed if he never so much as lifted it from his pillow to brood awhile on that still, verdurous scene. And the birds!

Indeed, to lie, between sleep and wake, when daybreak is brightening of an April or a May morning, and so listen to the far-away singing of a thrush or to the whistling of a robin or a wren is to seem to be transported back into the garden of Eden. Dreamers, too, may call themselves travellers.

Mr. Nahum's picture to this rhyme was of a man in rags looking into a small round mirror or looking-glass, but at what you couldn't see.

6. "THE MERCHANT BOWS" (line 7)

—(as do the happy to the New Moon, for luck), for his merchandise is being wafted over the sea under the guidance of the Seaman's, or Ship, or Lode, or Pole Star. It shines in the constellation of the Little Bear, and "is the cheefe marke whereby mariners governe their course in saylings by nyghte." To find the "marke," look towards the north some cloudless night for the constellation of Seven Stars called the Plough or the Dipper or Charles's Wain (or Waggon), which "enclyneth his ravisshinge courses abouten the soverein heighte of the worlde" day and night throughout the year. Its hinder stars (Dubhe and Merak) are named "the pointers," because if you follow the line of them with the eye into the empty skies, the next brightish star it will alight on *is* the Seaman's Star. Close beside the second of the seven is a mere speck of a star. And that is called by country people Jack-by-the-middle-horse. On this same star looked Shakespeare—as did the 1st Carrier in his *Henry IV.*: "Heigh-ho, an't be not foure by the day, Ile be hanged. Charles' waine is over the near Chimney, and yet our horse not packt"; and as did his 2nd Gentleman in *Othello*:

Montano. What from the Cape can you discerne at Sea?
1st Gentleman. Nothing at all, it is a high-wrought Flood: I cannot 'twixt the Heaven, and the Maine
Descry a Saile. . .
2nd Gentleman. . . . Do but stand upon the Foaming Shore,
The chidden Billow seemes to pelt the Clowds,
The wind-shaked-Surge, with high and monstrous Maine,
Seemes to cast water on the burning Beare,
And quench the Guards of the ever-fixèd Pole.
I never did like mollestation view
On the enchafèd Flood. . . .

Faintly shimmering, too, in the northern heavens is that other numerous starry cluster, known the world over as *Seven*—to us as the Seven Sisters or the Pleiades. A strange seven; for only six stars are now clearly visible to the naked eye, one having vanished, it would seem, within human memory. When? where? —none can tell. They play in light as close together as dewdrops in a cobweb hung from thorn to thorn, and near-by them, on winter's cold breast burns the most marvellous of the constellations—the huntsman Orion, the Dog-star at his heels.

"Seek him that maketh the Seven Stars and Orion, and turneth the shadow of death into the morning, and maketh the day dark with night . . ."

8. "Bird prune thy wing."

It is as pleasant an occupation to watch a bird "pruning" or preening its feathers—stretching out each delicately pinioned wing in turn—as it is to eye a cat washing his face. Assuredly no human nurse ever went so many times over the same ear of one of her charges (or used so little moisture) as he seems to do over one of his own. Forty-eight was my own black house-cat's score when last I watched him at his toilet—and even then he looked no different! Preening (and cats nibble their fur as well as tongue it) is more than merely smoothing and rearranging, for it not only removes damaged feathers, but at the same time oils the sound ones.

9. "Bare Winter suddenly was changed to Spring."

In Marche, and in Aprill, from morning to night;
  In sowing and setting, good huswives delight.
To have in their garden, or some other plot:
  To trim up their house, and to furnish their pot. . . .

At Spring (for the sommer) sowe garden ye shall,
  At harvest (for winter) or sowe not at all.
Oft digging, removing and weeding (ye see)
  Makes herbe the more holesome and greater to bee. . . .

New set doo aske watering with pot or with dish,
  New sowne doo not so, if ye doo as I wish.
Though cunning with dible, rake, mattock and spade,
  By line and by leavell, trim garden is made.

Who soweth too lateward, hath seldom good seed,
 Who soweth too soone, little better shall speed.
Apt time and the season so divers to hit,
 Let aier and laier helpe practise and wit. . . .

THOMAS TUSSER.

"LIKE A CHILD, HALF IN TENDERNESS AND MIRTH."

At a first reading, perhaps, this line will not appear to flow so smoothly as the rest. But linger an instant on the word *child,* and you will have revealed to yourself one of Shelley's, and indeed one of every poet's loveliest devices with words—to let the music of his verse accord with its meaning, and at the same time to please and charm the ear with a slight variation from the regular beat and accent of the metre. So, too, in the middle lines of the next stanza. This variation, which is called rhythm, is the very proof of its writer's sincerity. For if the sound of his verse (or of his voice) ring false, he cannot have completely realised what he was writing or saying. When a man says what he means, he says it *as if he meant it.* The *tune* of what he says sounds right. When a man does *not* mean what he says, he finds it all but impossible to say it as if he did. The *tune* goes wrong.

Just so with reading. One must catch the tune (the intonation) to ensure the meaning. Four brief rules from a gay and tiny *Compendious English Grammar* of 1780 may be of help:

(1) . . . Observe well the pauses, accents and emphases; and never stop but where the sense will admit of it.

(2) Humour your voice a little, according to the subject. . . .

(3) Do not read too fast, lest [in lip or mind] you get a habit of stammering; adding or omitting words; and be sure that your understanding keep pace with your tongue.

(4) In reading Verse, pronounce every word just as if it were prose, observing the stops with great exactness, and giving each word its proper accent; and if it be not harmonious, the Poet, and not the Reader, is to blame.

This scrap of rhyme also contains sound advice: its "each idle gait" meaning all lounging and laziness:

Give your attention as you read,
And frequent pauses take.
Think seriously; and take good heed
That you no dogs' ears make.
Don't wet the fingers as you turn
The pages one by one;
Never touch prints; observe; and learn
Each idle gait to shun.

But in general, if these rules are followed, there can be little danger of reading like a parrot, or like a small boy in his first breeches at a Dame's school. To *think* while one reads; that is the main thing: so that at last the eyes forget the words and fix themselves with a burning interest and delight upon the objects for which the words are music and symbol. That at least is not to be, as Sidney says,—just

. . . like a child that some fair book doth find,
With gilded leaves or coloured vellum plays,
Or, at the most, on some fair pictures stays,
But never heeds the fruit of writer's mind.

13. "Comes dancing from the East."

There is a story about this dancing in Mrs. Wright's *Rustic Speech and Folklore*. It is the story of a woman who lived in a district called Hockley, in the parish of Broseley. She said that she had heard of such "dancing" but did not believe it to be true, "till on Easter morning last, I got up early, and then I saw the sun dance, and dance, and dance, three times, and I called to my husband and said, *'Rowland, Rowland, get up and see the sun dance!'* I used," she said, "not to believe it, but now I can never doubt more." The neighbours agreed with her that the sun did dance on Easter morning, and that some of them had seen it. "Seeing," goes the old proverb, "is believing"—which is true no less of the "inward" than the outward eye. I once tried to comfort a little boy who was unhappy because there was a Bear under his bed. Candlestick in hand, I talked and talked, and *proved* that there wasn't a real bear for miles and miles around, except, of course, at the Zoological Gardens, and there —black, brown, sloth, spectacled, grizzly and polar alike—all of them, poor creatures, were cabined, cribbed and shut up in barred cages. He listened, tears still shining in his eyes, his small face sharp and clear. "Why certainly, certainly *not,*" I ended, "there can't be a real bear for miles around!" He smiled as if pitying me. "Ah yes," he answered with a die-away sob, "but, you see, you's talking of *real* bears, and mine *isn't* real."

14. "See the clear sun . . ."

and here the motto on an old sun-dial:

Here stand I ever lonely amidst the flowers tall,
While o'er my figured bosom faint shadows slowly fall.
And to the busy world without whose life by hours I keep
I say, 'Tis time to rise: and then, 'Tis time to sleep.

"Us Idle Wenches."

It was a jolly bed in sooth,
Of oak as strong as Babel.
And there slept Kit and Sall and Ruth
As sound as maids are able.

Ay—three in one—and there they dreamed,
Their bright young eyes hid under;
Nor hearkened when the tempest streamed
Nor recked the rumbling thunder.

For marvellous regions strayed they in,
Each moon-far from the other—
Ruth in her childhood, Kit in heaven,
And Sall with ghost for lover.

But soon as ever sun shone sweet,
And birds sang, Praise for rain, O—
Leapt out of bed three pair of feet
And danced on earth again, O!

17. Old May Song.

This, like No. 2, and the next song must be as old as the dew-ponds on the Downs. They were wont to be sung, I have read, by five or six men, with a fiddle, or flute, or clarionet accompaniment. When I was a boy I can remember one First of May seeing a Jack-in-the-Green in the street—a man in a kind of wicker cage hung about with flowers and leaves—with Maid Marian, Friar Tuck and the rest, dressed up, and dancing beside him. A great friend of mine, when she was a little girl of eight, was so frightened at sight of this leafy prancing creature on her way to school that she turned about and ran for a mile without stopping.

18. And gone to-morrow.

Yesterday returneth not;
Perchance to-morrow cometh not;
There is to-day; misuse it not.

19. The Daisy.

There is far too little of Geoffrey Chaucer's—that most lovable, shrewd, compassionate, and natural of poets—in this book. There was much more of him, I noticed, in Mr. Nahum's Tome II. At first sight his words look a little strange; but not for long; and if every dotted letter is made a syllable of, his rhythm will flow like water over bright green waterweed.

It is a curious, though little, thing, that while, among the one hundred and seventy varieties of flowers mentioned by Shakespeare, there are no less than about fifty-seven several references to the rose, twenty-one to the green grass, eighteen to the violet, and even to the serviceable but rank nettle a round dozen, he has but a scant five to Chaucer's beloved daisy. Flowers, it is true, as says Canon Ellacombe (who collected all such references into his delightful book, *Plant-lore and Garden-craft of Shakespeare*), never sweeten the Plays for their own sake alone, and foxgloves, snowdrops and forget-me-nots find no place there at all.

On reading this over again I began to wonder if any *other* reason than that given above could be found for the absence of all mention of these three familiar flowers in the *Plays*. With this result—which I owe chiefly to *British Flowering Plants:*

In none of the early English poets is mention made of the *Snowdrop;* and the wild snowdrop appears to be an escape, a runaway, from monastery gardens. About 180 years ago, it was recorded as flourishing at the foot of Herefordshire Beacon. The earliest reference to the flower in the Oxford English Dictionary is of 1664: "Those purely white flowers that appear about the end of Winter, and are commonly call'd a Snow Drop." Quite possibly, then, Shakespeare never set eyes on this frail green-flecked lovely thing, nid-nodding in the icy blasts of January.

Foxgloves, however, had been so called for at least seven centuries before he was born, and must have been a familiar flower in England in the late sixteenth century. But it has a rooted distaste for lime and chalk, and so is not found in north-east Gloucestershire. How about Stratford? I appealed to a friend, Miss Eleanor Doorly, living at Warwick, who very kindly made enquiries for me. It appears that foxgloves are to be found near Stratford, but only by the elect, so to speak, and in occasional clumps. There were foxgloves at Lapworth, for example, in the summer of last year [1927]. But none now grows on the bank that Oberon knew, with its thyme, oxlip, violet, musk rose and eglantine; and in South Warwickshire what foxgloves there are tend to disappear. They have been transplanted, maybe, and die of homesickness. It is possible, then, that Shakespeare when a child never saw a foxglove either; and it is what we see early in life that comes back easiest later. How else can we explain its absence, say, from *A Midsummer Night's Dream*?—its natural earthly paradise.

As for the *Forget-me-not,* it is only within the last hundred years or so that this name has been applied to the Great Water Scorpion Grass. There is a legend from the German to account for the name. A Knight in armour and his Lady were straying beside a deep and rapid river. She espied a pretty pale flower growing in midstream, and entreated the Knight to pluck her a spray of it. He leapt in and perished, having adjured her with his last breath, as he flung the spray toward the bank, *"Vergeiss mein nicht!"*—Forget me not!

But apart from the fact that this is the "blue and bright-eyed floweret of the *brook,*" and flourishes no more in deep water than a sailor does on land; to some tastes, Mouse-ear, which is all that *Myosotis* means, may seem a better name for it than the sentimental one borrowed from abroad.

Shakespeare, then, if he had referred to this particular flower, would not have so named it. None the less, there was a flower in his time with this name—it is mentioned in Gerard's *Herbal*—the ground-pine or "herbe-ivie." It is a sticky, hairy little plant with a pungent flavour of turpentine, and is never very happy far from chalk. Kent, then, might boast of its unforgetableness, but hardly South Warwickshire. So he never mentioned that either.

Having thus (joyfully) disposed of these three examples, it occurred to me to return to *Plant Lore* again, in case any other quite familiar flower had—poor soul—escaped Shakespeare's mention. And I found to my dismay that while honourable place has been given to the eryngo, to coloquintida and the pomegranate; while onions, pignuts, rhubarb, cabbage, potatoes, and turnips have won their niche (the last three in *The Merry Wives*); bindweed, cornflower, dandelion, London Pride, buttercup, and *Sweet William!* had bloomed for him in vain. The absence of the buttercup can be easily explained (though no explanation, of course, is *necessary*); but what of the others?

And now to return to Chaucer's *daisy:*

"A yellow cup, it hath," says Pliny, "and the same is crowned, as it were with a garland, consisting of five and fifty little leaves, set round about it in manner of fine pales. These be flowers of the meadow, and most of such are of no use at all." No use at all—except only to make skylark of every heart whose owner has eyes in his head for a daisy's simple looks, its marvellous workmanship, and the sheer happiness of their multitudes wide open in the sun or round-headed and adrowse in the evening twilight.

But of all the daisies in poetry surely this from *The Second Brother,* by Thomas Beddoes, is not only the loveliest, but has the strangest setting:

> . . . . I . . . say
> How thou art like the daisy in Noah's meadow,
> On which the foremost drop of rain fell warm

And soft at evening; so the little flower
Wrapped up its leaves, and shut the treacherous water
Close to the golden welcome of its breast,—
Delighting in the touch of that which led
The shower of oceans, in whose billowy drops
Tritons and lions of the sea were warring,
And sometimes ships on fire sunk in the blood
Of their own inmates; others were of ice,
And some had islands rooted in their waves,
Beasts on their rocks, and forest-powdering winds,
And showers tumbling on their tumbling self,—
And every sea of every ruined star
Was but a drop in the world-melting flood. . . .

Chaucer's painted portrait is well known. So is that in his own words in the *Canterbury Tales.* But here is another, less familiar, by Robert Greene—of "Sir Jeffrey Chaucer," as he calls him. Water chamlet is a rich coloured silken plush, and a whittell is a knife:

His stature was not very tall,
Leane he was, his legs were small,
Hosed within a stock of red
A buttoned bonnet on his head,
From under which did hang, I weene,
Silver haires both bright and sheene,
His beard was white, trimmèd round,
His count'nance blithe and merry found,
A Sleevelesse Iacket large and wide,
With many pleights and skirts Side,
Of water Chamlet did he weare,
A whittell by his belt he beare,
His shooes were cornèd broad before,
His Inkhorne at his side he wore,
And in his hand he bore a booke,
Thus did this auntient Poet looke.

Few poets have been so much *delighted in* as Chaucer. He reminds one of the picture of Genius doffing his hat to Dame

Nature in the MS. of *Roman de la Rose* in the British Museum, while the green things of Spring are enamelling the walled garden in which they meet; blue sky is over all, and the swallows are flying.

Caxton, his first printer, said that his poems were "full of plesaunce"; Dryden, that "he was a perpetual fountain of good sense." Waller praised his "matchless strain." "His words," said Hazlitt, "point as an index to the objects they refer to like the eye or finger"—alert, quick, direct.

Southey referred to him as "Father Chaucer"; Denham and Akenside (meaning no less reverence), as "old" Chaucer. Warton ventured (wisely) on "immortal." Addison spoke of the "Merry Bard"; Spenser delighted in his "merry tales" and Cowper in his "merry page." Tennyson called him "the first warbler"; Wordsworth, the "time-honoured." Fenton chose "sprightly" and Lowell "vernal." Byron (being Byron) dismissed him as "obscene and contemptible." Coleridge bubbled over with what he called his "manly cheerfulness," Drayton said briefly, "noble Chaucer."

20. "Brave Prick-Song."

"Prick-song" is the music sung from notes written or *pricked* on the paper. It is the descant or melody warbled above the simple theme or plain-song which was sung from memory, and so formed its burden or undersong.

"The Jolly Cuckoos"

On a day when Jenkin
Did walk abroad to heare
 The birds rejoyce,
 With pleasant voyce;
In spring time of the yeare;
 Proudly and loudly
Her heard a bird then sing,
 Cuckoe, Cuckoe.
The cuckoe never lins [stays],
But still doth cry so merily,
And Cuckoe, cuckoe sings. . . ."

[1643]

In April, the koocoo can sing her song by rote,
In June—of tune—she cannot sing a note;
At first, *koo-coo, koo-coo,* sing still can she do,
At last, *kooke, kooke, kooke;* six *kookes* to one *koo.*

[1587]

21. "CUCKOO, JUG, JUG, PU WE, TO WITTA WOO!"

Four birds, I suppose, have part in this: cuckoo, nightingale (*yoog, yoog*), green-finch (?) and owl.

I rose anon, and thought I wouldė gone
Into the woods, to hear the birdis sing,
When that the misty vapour was agone,
And cleare and fairė was the morrowing;
The dew, also, like silver in shining,
Upon the leaves, as any baumė sweet.

. . . .

And in I went to hear the birdis sing,
Which on the branches, both in plain and vale,
So loudly y-sang, that all the wood y-rang,
Like as it should shiver in pieces smale;
And as me thoughten that the nightingale
With so great might her voice began out-wrest,
Right as her heart for love would all to-brest.

JOHN LYDGATE

22. "THE JEALOUS TROUT."

Thou that desir'st to fish with line and hook,
Be it in pool, in river, or in brook,
To bless thy bait and make the fish to bite,
Lo, here's a means! if thou canst hit it right:
Take Gum of Life, fine beat, and laid in soak
In oil well drawn from that which kills the oak,
Fish where thou wilt, thou shalt have sport thy fill;
When twenty fail, thou shalt be sure to kill.

It's perfect and good,
If well understood;
Else not to be told
For silver or gold.

So advises Master Will. Lauson in the *Secrets of Angling,* which was published in 1653; the ingredients (or *ingrediments* as I used to say when I was a child) of his "gum of life" being *Cocculus Juliæ, Assafoetida,* Honey, and Wheat-flour. The "that which kills the oak," I suppose, is ivy. But it looks as if there may have been a wink in his eye—to welcome the green in his reader's.

Here, on the same theme, are a few lines from a poem by Mr. Robert Bridges:

> . . . Sometimes an angler comes, and drops his hook
> Within its hidden depths, and 'gainst a tree
> Leaning his rod, reads in some pleasant book.
> Forgetting soon his pride of fishery,
> And dreams, or falls asleep,
> While curious fishes peep
> About his nibbled bait, or scornfully
> Dart off and rise and leap. . . .

And these are by J. Wolcot:

> Why flyest thou away with fear?
> Trust me there's naught of danger near,
> I have no wicked hooke
> All covered with a snaring bait,
> Alas, to tempt thee to thy fate,
> And dragge thee from the brooke. . . .
>
> Enjoy thy stream, O harmless fish;
> And when an angler for his dish,
> Through gluttony's vile sin,
> Attempts, a wretch, to pull thee out,
> God give thee strength, O gentle trout,
> To pull the raskall in!

But to return to the "line": "For dyeing of your hairs," says Isaak Walton in *The Compleat Angler,* "do it thus: Take a pint of strong ale, half a pound of soot, and a little quantity of the juice of walnut-tree leaves, and an equal quantity of alum; put these together, into a pot, pan, or pipkin, and boil them half an hour; and having so done, let it cool; and being cold, put your hair into it, and there let it lie; it will turn your hair to be a kind of water or glass-colour or greenish; and the longer you let it lie, the deeper coloured it will be. You might be taught to make many other colours, but it is to little purpose; for doubtless the water-colour or glass-coloured hair is the most choice and the most useful for an angler, but let it not be too green."

But there is a way of fishing without fly, hook or hairs, called "tickling." About 1277 Thomas of the Moor was charged with taking fish in his Lord's pond. This was his defence:

"Sir, for God's sake do not take it ill of me if I tell the truth, how the other evening I went along the bank of the pond, and saw the fish playing in the water so lovely and bright, and for the great craving I had for a perch I lay down on the bank of the pond and with my hand only and quite simply took and carried away this perch, and I will tell thee the cause of my covetous desire, my companion, that is my wife had lain in bed a whole month . . . and never eaten or drunk anything she could relish, and for the craving to taste a perch she sent me to the bank of the pond to take one perch only."

"And Birds had drawn their Valentines." (line 4)

To-morrow is S. Valentine's day,
All in the morning betime,
And I a Maid at your Window
To be your Valentine!

For first thing in the early morning if you go out on St. Valentine's Day, which is the 14th day of February, you will meet, if you meet anybody, your soon-to-be-loved one. So too the birds. In my young days, folks sent the daintiest pictures to their sweethearts on this day. So, too, in Pepys's time:

"This morning came up to my wife's bedside—I being up dressing myself—little Will Mercer to be her Valentine; and brought her name writ upon blue paper in gold letters, done by himself, very pretty. . . ."

"JOAN STROKES A SILLABUB OR TWAIN."

If you would make a Lemon Sillabub (as advised by Mrs. Charlotte Mason, "a Professed Housekeeper, who from about 1740 had upwards of Thirty Years experience in Families of the First Fashion") take "a Pint of cream, a pint of white wine, the rind of two lemons grated, and the juice. Sugar to the taste. Let it stand some time; mill or whip it. Lay the froth on a sieve; put the remainder into glasses. Lay on the froth."

Or try this, the *Everlasting Sillabub,* from a cook book of 1790, by "the Principal Cook at the London Tavern," who gives four others also—the *Solid,* the *under the Cow,* the *Whipt* and the *Lemon.*

"Take half a pint of Rhenish wine, half a pint of sack, with the juice of two large Seville oranges, and put them into two pints and a half of thick cream. Grate in just the yellow rind of three lemons, and put in a pound of double-refined sugar well beaten and sifted. Mix all together, with a spoonful of orange-flower water, and with a whisk beat it well together for half an hour. Then, with a spoon, take off the froth, and lay in on a sieve to drain, and then fill your glasses."

Mr. Nahum must have had a fancy for Cookery Books; there were dozens of them in his tower room. Indeed, the next best thing to eating a good dish is to read how it is made; and somehow the old "cookbook" writers learned to write most appetising English. Here is another "May-Day"—from Pepys.

"*May 1st,* 1669. Up betimes. Called by my tailor, and there first put on a summer suit this year; but it was not my fine one of flowered tabby vest, and coloured camlet tunic, because it was too fine with the gold lace at the bands, that I was afraid to be seen in it; but put on the stuff suit I made the last year, which is now repaired; and so did go to the office in it, and sat all the morning, the day looking as if it would be foul. At noon home to dinner, and there find my wife extraordinary fine, with her flowered tabby gown that she made two years ago, now laced exceeding pretty; and, indeed, was fine all over; and mighty earnest to go, though the day was very lowering; and she would have me put on my fine suit, which I did. And so anon we went alone through the town with our new liveries of serge, and the horses' manes and tails tied with red ribbons, and the standards gilt with varnish, and all clean, and green reins, that people did mightily look upon us; and, the truth is, I did not see any coach more pretty, though more gay, than ours, all the day. . . . [And] here was W. Batelier and his sister in a borrowed coach by themselves, and I took them and we to the lodge; and at the door did give them a sillabub, and other things, cost me 12s., and pretty merry. And so back to the coaches, and there till the evening, and then home."

Here, from *Delightes for Ladies,* of 1608, is an ancient dainty that would eat uncommonly well with a sillabub:—*"To make a marchpane.*—Take two poundes of almonds being blanched, and dryed in a sieve over the fire, beate them in a stone mortar, and when they bee small mixe them with two pounde of sugar beeing finely beaten, adding two or three spooneful s of rose-water, and that will keep your almonds from oiling: when your paste is beaten fine, drive it thin with a rowling pin, and so lay it on a bottom of wafers, then raise up a little edge on the side, and so bake it, then yce it with rose-water and sugar, then put it in the oven again, and when you see your yce is risen up and drie, then take it out of the oven and garnish it with pretie conceipts, as birdes and beasts being cast out of standing moldes. Sticke long comfits upright in it, cast biskets and carrowaies in it, and so serve it; guild it before you serve it: you may also print of this *marchpane* paste in your molds for banqueting dishes. And of this paste our comfit makers at this day make their letters, knots, armes, escutcheons, beasts, birds, and other fancies." Also pygmy castles and suchlike, for dessert, which the guests would demolish with sugar-plums.

"Good thou, save mee a piece of Marchpane, and as thou lovest me, let the Porter let in Susan Grindstone and Nell. . . ."

Romeo and Juliet

It might be assumed that good dishes would long since have earned for themselves good names, but it is not so. Centuries ago Norfolk Dumplings, Gloucester Bag Puddings, Worcester Black Puddings and Devonshire White Pot Puddings were already famous, but I have never heard of their having positive Christian names. There are a few memorable examples in Mrs.

Glasse's famous cook-book—the book that does *not* prescribe for jugged hare with "First catch your hare," but does angrily asseverate, "I have heard of a [French] cook that used six pounds of butter to fry twelve eggs!"

But in general to browse over Mrs. Glasse's pages is more likely to make the mouth water than to kindle the fancy. Here and there she succeeds in doing both: *e. g.,* Frangas incopades, Fricandillas, Oxford John, Bombarded Veal, Hottentot pie, a Bride's pie, a Thatch-house pie. There is Salmagundy, too, and Cowslip pudding, Florendine of Oranges, or Skirret pie. And could anything sound more soothing for the sick-room tea-tray than Panado, Brown Caudle, Buttered Water, Artificial Asses Milk, and Sago Tea!

With Steeple Cream and Moon-shine, however, we begin to recover, and with Mouse-trap at one end of the table and Carolina Snowballs or Hedgehog-in-Flummery at the other, there should certainly be Floating Island in between. And if, on returning from such a feast, you should chance to be bitten by a mad dog, Mrs. Glasse will also see to *that*:

"Take of the herb called in Latin *lichen cinereus terrestris,* in English, ash-coloured ground liverwort, cleaned, dried, and powdered, half an ounce. Of black pepper, powdered, two drachms. Mix these well together, and divide the powder into four doses, one of which must be taken every morning fasting, for four mornings successively, in half a pint of cow's milk, warm. After these four doses are taken, the patient must go into the cold bath, or a cold spring or river every morning fasting for a month. He must be dipped all over, but not to stay in (with his head above water) longer than half a minute, if the water be very cold. . . .

23. "The Sun arising."

"What other fire could be a better image of the fire which is there, than the fire which is here? Or what other earth than this, of the earth which is there?" So said Plotinus, and "I know," said Blake, "that this world is a world of imagination and vision. I see everything I paint in this world, but everybody does not see alike. To the eye of a miser a guinea is far more beautiful than the sun, and a bag worn with the use of money has more beautiful proportions than a vine filled with grapes. The tree which moves some to tears of joy is in the eyes of others only a green thing which stands in the way. . . . Some scarce see Nature at all. But to the eyes of the man of imagination, Nature is Imagination itself. As a man is, so he sees. As the eye is formed, such are its powers. You certainly mistake, when you say that the visions of fancy are not to be found in this world. To me this world is all one continued vision.". . . Indeed, when Blake was a child, he saw on Peckham Rye a tree, full, not of birds, but of angels; and his poems show how marvellously clear were the eyes with which he looked at the things of Nature.

'In the year 1872, an old lady might have been seen driving across the Rye in her silvery carriage; and she came to where, under a flowering tree, sat a small boy—the locks of hair upon his head like sheaves of cowslips, his eyes like speedwells, and he in very bright clothes. And he was laughing up into the tree. She stopped her carriage and said to him almost as if she were more angry than happy, "What are you laughing at, child?" And he said, "At the sparrows, ma'am." "Mere sparrows!" says she, "but why?" "Because they were saying," says he, "here comes across the Rye a blind old horse, a blind old coachman, and a blind old woman." "But I am not blind," says she. "Nor are they not '*mere* sparrows'," said the child. And at that the old lady was looking out of her carriage at no child, but at a small bush, in bud, of gorse.'

24. "And thank Him then"

—as does Robert Herrick's child, in his "Grace":

> Here a little child I stand,
> Heaving up my either hand;
> Cold as Paddocks though they be,
> Here I lift them up to Thee,
> For a Benizon to fall
> On our meat, and on us all. Amen.

A paddock is a frog or a toad. To either small cold hand that child had four cold fingers and a thumb; and in old times, says Halliwell, our ancestors had names not only for each of the five fingers but for each of the five toes. The fingers were called thumb, toucher, longman, leche-man, little-man: leche-man being the ring-finger, because in that "there is a sinew very tender and small that reaches to the heart." In Essex they used to call them (and still may)—Tom Thumbkin, Bess Bumpkin, Long Linkin, Bill Wilkin, and Little Dick. In Scotland: Thumbkin, Lick-pot, Langman, Berrybarn and Pirlie Winkie. In (?) Lancashire and Cheshire, Tommy Thumbkin, Billy Winkie, Long Duster, Jacky Molebar and Little Perky.

And here are some more from Dr. Courtenay Dunn's *Natural History of the Child*—a book which is graced with as handsome a frontispiece as ever I've seen:

Thumb	- Tommy Tomkins	or Bill Milker.
Forefinger	- Billy Wilkins	" Tom Thumper.
Third finger	- Long Larum	" Long Lazy.
Fourth finger	- Betsy Bedlam	" Cherry Bumper.
Little finger	- Little Bob	" Tippity, Tippity-Town-end.

Toes:

Big toe	- Tom Barker	or Toe Tipe.
Toe ii -	- Long Rachel	" Penny Wipe.
Toe iii -	- Minnie Wilkin	" Tommy Tistle.
Toe iv -	- Milly Larkin	" Billy Whistle.
Little Toe	- Little Dick	" Tripping-go.

So (if you wish) you can secretly name not only your fingers, toes, rooms, chairs and tables, etc., but also the stars in their courses, the trees in your orchard, and have your own privy countersign for the flowers you like best. "Give a dog a bad name, and hang him," says the old proverb. Give anything a *good* name, and it is yours for ever. There is the tale of the unhappy gardener in the Isle of Rumm who without ill intention called a snapdragon a scrofulariaceous antirrhinum. At which there arose out of the hillside a Monster named Zobj that reasoned with him in the manner of monsters. Doubtless the gardener meant well; but when he heard that Voice counting his last moments, not in common English, but in what Wensleydale Knitters still remember of the Norse—Yahn, Jyahn, Tether,

Mether, Mumph, Hither, Lither, Auver, Dauver, Dic—well . . .

While we are on this subject here is a Face Rhyme:

Bo Peeper
Nose Dreeper
Chin Chopper
White Lopper
Red Rag
And Little Gap.

This is another:

Here sits the Lord Mayor:
Here sit his men;
Here sits the cockadoodle;
Here sits the hen;
Here sits the little chickens;
Here they run in;
Chinchopper, chinchopper, chinchopper, chin.

The next three are foot rhymes, very soothing at times to fractious babies. The first is common in London, etc.:

This little pig went to market;
This little pig stayed at home;
This little pig had roast beef;
This little pig had none;
This little pig cried *Wee-wee-wee-wee-wee!*
All the way home.

The second comes from the Isle of Wight:

This gurt pig zays, I wants meat;
T'other one zays, Where'll ye hay et?
This one zays, In gramfer's barn;
T'other one zays, Week! Week! I can't get over the dreshel.

And this is from Scoltand:

This ain biggit the baurn,
This ain stealit the corn,
This ain stood and saw,
This ain ran awa',
An' wee Pirlie Winkie paid for a'.

As for the "gurt pig,"

> The cock sat in the yew tree,
> The hen came chuckling by,
> "I wish you all good morning, *and*
> A good fat pig in the sty,
> A *good fat pig* in the sty."

And last; here is a Dance-babbie-on-knee (or This-is-the-way) rhyme; also from Scotland:

> The doggies gaed to the mill,
> This way and that way;
> They took a lick out o' *this* wife's poke
> And they took a lick out o' *that* wife's poke,
> And a loup in the lead, and a dip in the dam,
> And gaed walloping, walloping, walloping, HAME.

And no doubt came to the conclusion expressed in the sixth stanza of Robert Herrick's *Ternary of Littles, upon a Pipkin of Jelly sent to a Lady:*

> A little Saint best fits a little Shrine,
> A little Prop best fits a little Vine,
> As my small Cruse bests fits my little Wine.
>
> A little Seed best fits a little Soyle,
> A little Trade best fits a little Toyle,
> As my small Jarre bet fits my little Oyle.
>
> A little Bin best fits a little Bread,
> A little Garland fits a little Head,
> As my small stuffe best fits my little Shed.
>
> A little Hearth best fits a little Fire,
> A little Chappell fits a little Quire,
> As my small Bell best fits my little Spire.
>
> A little streame best fits a little Boat,
> A little lead best fits a little Float,
> As my small Pipe best fits my little note.

A little meat best fits a little bellie,
As sweetly, Lady, give me leave to tell ye,
This little Pipkin fits this little Jellie.

25. "I SING OF A MAIDEN."

The spelling of this lovely and ancient little carol has been modernized; but here are its last four lines as they appear in a MS. of the early fifteenth century:

Moder and maiden
Was never non but sche,
Well may swich a lady
Godės moder be.

26. "UPON MY LAP MY SOVEREIGN SITS."

The "animal" that Mary Wollstonecraft, the mother of Mary Shelley, is telling her husband about in the following letter is *her* "sovereign"; and how curiously (after the rest of the letter has been read) this word reveals her entire adoration of the little creature.

PARIS, *January 15th*, 1795.

. . . My animal is well; I have not yet taught her to eat, but nature is doing the business. I gave her a crust to assist the cutting of her teeth; and now she has two she makes good use of them to gnaw with. . . . You would laugh to see her; she is just like a little squirrel; she will guard a crust for two hours, and, after fixing her eyes on an object for some time, dart on it with an aim as sure as a bird of prey—nothing can equal her life and spirits. . . . Adieu. Do not forget to love us—and come soon to tell us that you do.

MARY.

29. "SLEEP STAYS NOT, THOUGH A MONARCH BIDS." (line 11)

Why rather, sleep, liest thou in smoky cribs,
Upon uneasy pallets stretching thee,
And hushed with buzzing night-flies to thy slumber,
Than in the perfumed chambers of the great,

Under the canopies of costly state,
And lulled with sound of sweetest melody?
O thou dull god, why liest thou with the vile
In loathsome beds, and leavest the kingly couch
A watch-case or a common 'larum-bell?
Wilt thou upon the high and giddy mast
Seal up the ship-boy's eyes, and rock his brains
In cradle of the rude imperious surge,
And in the visitation of the winds,
Who take the ruffian billows by the top,
Curling their monstrous heads, and hanging them
With deafening clamour in the slippery clouds,
That, with the hurly, death itself awakes?
Canst thou, O partial sleep, give thy repose
To the wet sea-boy in an hour so rude;
And in the calmest and most stillest night,
With all appliances and means to boot,
Deny it to a king? Then happy low, lie down!
Uneasy lies the head that wears a crown.

Henry IV. Part ii.

30. I Remember, I Remember.

On page 494 there is a reference to the tune or intonation in the reading of a poem—the rise and fall of the voice—which when too regularly repeated becomes a mere sing-song, and when carried to an extreme is what is sometimes called elocution. There are many ways of reading verse aloud—one of them being with little change of pitch, and resembling a spoken chaunt, or "intoning." This drowses the waking mind; and the words resemble an incantation.

But whatever the best method may be, all poetry, unless its charm is to be wasted, should be *heard,* with the inward ear at least, if not with the outer; and the intonation, like the rhythm, is part and parcel of its meaning. Unless it be in accord with the thought and the feeling intended, it falsifies the poem. This is curiously true even of single words—that once were double. Stress lightly and raise the voice a little on the second or third syllable in each of the following words, and a meaning that may hitherto have been half-hidden slips up like a cuckoo out of a clock:

gate*way,* lock*smith,* hîghway*man,* hard*bake,* draw*back,* skîn*flint,* dream*land,* cup*board,* sea*worthy,* shoe*horn.*

No. 30 is a poem by Thomas Hood who (though *Alf* was denied to Tennyson, and *Bob* to Browning, in spite of *Will* and *Kit* and *Ben* before them) was affectionately known as *Tom,* and the first line of this poem—one as long-endeared and familiar to thousands of Englishmen as are wall-flowers, Sweet William and Old Man—is a delicate case in point. Where in it precisely should the stress be, and where the lift and cadence of the voice?

In some poems even the metre at first sight may be doubtful. Take for example the first stanza of Drayton's sonorous and spirited *Agincourt:*

Fair stood the wind for France
When we our sails advance,
Nor now to prove our chance
  Longer will tarry;
But putting to the main
At Caux the mouth of Seine,
With all his martial train
  Landed King Harry.

There are at least four ways of stressing the six longer lines. (1) Fair *stood* the *wind* for *France;* (2) *Fair* stood the *wind* for France; (3) *Fair stood* the *wind* for *France;* (4) *Fair* stood the *wind* for *France.* (1) becomes a miserable sing-song. (2) mere capering. (3) is stern, solemn, resolute. And (4) admits, I think, of the greatest variety of rhythm and intonation. Perhaps the best way is to treat each stanza as if it were composed of two metrical units—lines 1-4 and 5-8—and then read these with as much and as little variation as will provide the fullest meaning:

They now to *fight* are *gone*
Ar-mour on *ar*mour *shone*
Drum now to *drum* did *groan*
  To hear—was *won*der;
That with the *cries,* they *make*
The *very earth* did *shake:*
Trumpet to *trum*pet *spake,*
  Thun—der to *thun*der.

But complete tomes have been written on this subject; and the authors of them rarely agree. They add to one's knowledge, but not much to one's delight in the reading of poetry, and still less, I imagine, to the writing of it. In general, if you read a poem quietly over, first, to your head, then to your heart; most technical difficulties vanish like morning mist.

"THOSE FLOWERS MADE OF LIGHT." (line 12)

Hold up a flower between eye and sun, or even candle-flame, and it seems little but its own waxen hue and colour. Moonlight is too pale; the petals remain opaque. In the moon's light, indeed, blueness is scarcely distinguishable from shadowiness; red darkens but yellow pales, and the fairest flowers of all wake in her beams—jasmine, convolvulus, evening-primrose—as if they not only shared her radiance but returned a glow-wormlike fuminess of their own.

Once, long before I came to Thrae, having plucked for my mother a few convolvulus flowers, I remember when I was just about to give them into her hand I discovered that the beautiful cups of delight had enwreathed themselves together, and had returned as it were to the bud, never to reopen. I was but a child, and this odd little disappointment was so extreme that I burst out crying.

32.

See page 494: and for proof of the curious obedience of words to any bidden rhythm it is interesting to compare this poem—which seems as if it had been spoken in ordinary talk and yet is of a singular beauty—with its neighbours. Mr. Frost's colt is called "a little Morgan," because he is of a famous breed of horses of that name which are the pride of the State of Vermont.

AUTUMN EVENING.

The shadows flickering, the daylight dying,
And I upon the old red sofa lying,
The great brown shadows leaping up the wall,
The sparrows twittering; and that is all.

I thought to send my soul to far-off lands,
Where fairies scamper on the windy sands,

Or where the autumn rain comes drumming down
On huddled roofs in an enchanted town.

But O my sleepy soul, it will not roam,
It is too happy and too warm at home:
With just the shadows leaping up the wall,
The sparrows twittering; and that is all.

FRANCES CORNFORD.

35.

Only a single copy of the old play, *Mundus et Infans,* from which this fragment is taken, is known to be in existence. It was printed by Wynkyn de Worde in 1522; and was written roundabout 1500.

The lines need a slow reading to get the run and lilt of them: and even at that they jog and creak like an old farm-cart. But the boy, Dalyaunce, if one take a little pains, will come gradually out of them as clear to the eye as if you had met him in the street to-day, on his way to "schole" for yet another "docking."

Clothes, houses, customs, food a little, thoughts a little, knowledge, too—all change as the years and centuries go by, but Dalyaunce under a thousand names lives on. It never occurred to me when I was young to think that the children in Rome talked Latin at their games, and that Solomon and Caesar, Prester John and the Grand Khan knew in their young days what it means to be homesick and none too easy to sit down. Yet there are knucklebones and dolls in London that the infant subjects of the Pharaohs played with, and at Stratford Grammar School, for all to see, is Shakespeare's school desk. As for Dalyaunce, "dockings" are not nowadays so harsh as once they were.

In proof of this, there is a passage from a book, telling of his own life as a small boy, written by Guibert de Nogent. He is speaking of his childhood, about the year when William the Conqueror landed at Hastings:

'So, after a few of the evening hours had been passed in that study, during which I had been beaten even beyond my deserts, I came and sat at my mother's knees. She, according to her wont, asked whether I had been beaten that day; and I, unwillingly to betray my master, denied it; whereupon, whether I would or no, she threw back my inner garment (such as men call shirt), and found my little ribs black with the strokes of the osier, and rising everywhere into weals. Then, grieving in her inmost bowels at this punishment so excessive for my tender years, troubled and boiling with anger, and with brimming eyes, she cried, "Never now shalt thou become a clerk, nor shalt thou be thus tortured again to learn thy letters!" Whereupon, gazing upon her with all the seriousness that I could call to my face, I replied, "Nay, even though I should die under the rod, I will not desist from learning my letters and becoming a clerk?"'

But there were more merciful schoolmasters than Guibert de Nogent's, even in days harsh as his; as this further extract from Mr. G. G. Coulton's enticing *Medieval Garner* shows:

'One day, when a certain Abbot, much reputed for his piety, spake with Anselm concerning divers points of Monastic Religion, and conversed among other things of the boys that were brought up in the cloister, he added: "What, pray, can we do with them? They are perverse and incorrigible; day and night we cease not to chastise them, yet they grow daily worse and worse."

Whereat Anselm marvelled, and said, "Ye cease not to beat them? And when they are grown to manhood, of what sort are they then?" "They are dull and brutish," said the other.

Then said Anselm, "With what good profit do ye expend your substance in nurturing human beings till they become brute beasts? . . . But I prithee tell me, for God's sake, wherefore ye are so set against them? Are they not human, sharing in the same nature as yourselves? Would ye wish to be so handled as ye handle them? Ye will say, 'Yes, if we were as they are.' So be it, then; yet is there no way but that of stripes and scourges for shaping them to good? Did ye ever see a goldsmith shape his gold or silver plate into a fair image by blows alone? I trow not. What then? That he may give the plate its proper shape, he will first press it gently and tap it with his tools; then again he will more softly raise it with discreet pressure from below, and caress it into shape. So ye also, if ye would see your boys adorned with fair manners, ye should not only beat them down with stripes, but also raise their spirits and support them with fatherly kindness and pity' . . ."

In 1530—about thirty years, that is, after *Mundus et Infans* was written—the Headmaster of Eton at the time, Richard Cox, wrote an account of the "order" of the school:

"They [the boys] assembled in school at six of the Clock in the morning; they say *Deus misereatur* with a Collect; at nine they say *De profundis* and go to breakfast. Within a quarter of an hour come again and tarry (until) eleven and then to dinner; at five to supper, before an Anthem and *De profundis* . . .

When they go home two and two in order, [there is] a monitor to see that they do so till they come at their house door.

Also privy monitors how many the Master will.

Prepositors in the field when they play, for fighting, rent clothes, blue eyes, or such like.

Prepositors for ill kept heads, unwashed faces, foul clothes and such other. . . .

When any do come new, the master doth inquire from whence he comes, what friends he hath, whether there be any plague. No man goeth out of the school, nor home to his friends, without the master's licence. If there be any dullard the master giveth his friends warning and putteth him away, that he slander not the school."

I have seen an old woodcut showing a boy in the middle ages being whipped in a kind of machine (something like a roasting-jack), and a schoolmaster standing by, nicely smiling, in a gown. When Coleridge was a bluecoat boy at Christ's Hospital with Charles Lamb, he had a headmaster of this kind: " 'Boy!' I remember Bowyer saying to me once when I was crying the first day after my return after the holidays,—'Boy! the school is your father! Boy! the school is your mother! Boy! the school is your brother! the school is your sister! the school is your first cousin, and your second cousin, and all the rest of your relations! Let's have no more crying.' . . .

"Mrs. Bowyer was no comforter, either. Val. Le Grice and I were once going to be flogged for some domestic misdeed, and Bowyer was thundering away at us, by way of prologue, when Mrs. B. looked in and said, 'Flog them soundly, sir, I beg!' This saved us. Bowyer was so nettled at the interruption that he growled out, 'Away, woman, away!' and we were let off."

Charles Lamb also remembered his school-days: "I was a hypochondriac lad; and the sight of a boy in fetters, upon the day of my first putting on the blue clothes, was not exactly fitted to assuage the natural terrors of initiation. I was of tender years, barely turned of seven; and had only read of such things in books, or seen them but in dreams. I was told he had *run away*. This was the punishment for the first offence. As a novice I was soon after taken to see the dungeons. These were little, square, Bedlam cells, where a boy could just lie at his length upon straw and a blanket—a mattress, I think, was afterwards substituted—with a peep of light, let in askance, from a prison-orifice at top, barely enough to read by. Here the poor boy was locked in by himself all day, without sight of any but the porter who brought him his bread and water—who *might not speak to him;* or of the beadle, who came twice a week to call him out to receive his periodical chastisement, which was almost welcome, because it separated him for a brief interval from solitude: and here he was shut up by himself of *nights,* out of the reach of any sound, to suffer whatever horrors the weak nerves, and superstition incident to his time of life, might subject him to. This was the penalty for the *second* offence. Wouldst thou like, reader, to see what became of him in the next degree?

"The culprit, who had been a third time an offender, and whose expulsion was at this time deemed irreversible, was brought forth, as at some solemn *auto da fé,* arrayed in uncouth and most appalling attire . . . a jacket resembling those which London lamplighters formerly delighted in, with a cap of the same. . . . In this disguisement he was brought into the hall where awaited him the whole number of his schoolfellows, whose joint lessons and sports he was thenceforth to share no more. . . . The scourging was, after the old Roman fashion, long and stately. The lictor accompanied the criminal quite round the hall. . . . After scourging, he was made over, in his *San Benito,* to his friends, if he had any (but commonly such poor runagates were friendless), or to his parish officer, who, to enhance the effect of the scene, had his station allotted to him on the outside of the hall gate." So the poor friendless wretch, having proved his misery in *Christ's Hospital* by three times endeavouring to escape from it, was at last flogged into the streets again for good and all.

In 1821, when Charles Lamb was 46 and Coleridge 49, a tale was published entitled "*Young Wilfred; or, the Punishment of*

Falsehood: a Tale of Truth and Caution for the Benefit of the Rising Generation, by W. F. Sullivan, A. M., Teacher of Elocution and Belles Lettres." In this we get a close view—and one probably pretty true to the facts—of a similar ceremony in "a private academy." The Headmaster (and we get a close view of this unsightly, ungrammatical "folio," also), before the assembled school, addresses the miserable culprit thus:

" 'Thou unparalleled, ungrateful hypocrite; thou prince of liars! —before I send you back to your unfortunate parents, as a disgrace to them and to human nature, I will endeavour, with God's blessing, to expel the evil spirit out of thy little body; for if ever mortal being was possessed with a devil thou art he. Hand those two letters round the school. You see here, young gentlemen, a little monster of deceit, fraud, falsehood, treachery and cunning. During the twenty-five years I have kept school, and the many hundred pupils who have passed through my hands, I have never met even the shadow of his resemblance. Who would have thought so small a duodecimo could have contained such a folio of atrocious lies? I am truly shocked; I feel for your unhappy parents, and your miserable mother who must curse the hour in which she brought you into the world. I foresee, with pain I say it, unless a miracle work a speedy reformation, you inevitably must come to an untimely end. As it is, it is my duty to make you remember this day as long as you live.'

"On this the serving-man entered with a new birch-broom, which the Doctor opened and gave a sprig to every boy in the school: the culprit was now fastened to a desk, and each young gentleman advanced in rotation and inflicted a stripe, till the number of 200 was unsparingly bestowed. When taken down his wounds were dressed, and he was confined in a dark room, and no longer admitted among the boys. . . . On his quitting the academy he was saluted with the groans and hisses of the whole school assembled; and had they not been strictly prohibited, they would have pelted him to the imminent danger of his life."

Coleridge tells of yet another schoolmaster, whose name, like Bowyer and birch, also began with a B.: "Busby was the father of the English public school system. He was headmaster of Westminster through the reign of Charles I., the Civil War, the Protectorate, the reign of Charles II., and the Revolution of 1688.

Under him Westminster became the first school in the kingdom. When Charles II. visited the school, Busby stalked before the King with his hat upon his head, whilst his most sacred majesty meekly followed him. In private Busby explained that his conduct was due to the fact that he could not allow, for discipline's sake, the boys to imagine there could be a greater man than himself alive." Quite rightly, of course.

There is, too, the story of the little Lion that went to school to the Bear. Being, though of royal blood, a good deal of a dunce, Master Lion bore many sound cuffings from Dr. Bruin on the road to learning, and found it hot and dusty. After such administrations, he would sometimes sit in the sun under a window, learning his task and brooding on a day when he would return to the school and revenge himself upon the Doctor for having treated him so sore. But Master Lion was all this time growing up, and so many were the cares of the State when he had left his books and become a Prince and Heir Apparent, that for a time he had no thought for his old school. Being, however, in the Royal Gardens one sunny morning, and seeing bees busy about their hive, he remembered an old saying on the sweetness of knowledge and wisdom, and this once more reminded him of his old Master. Bidding his servants sling upon a rod half a dozen of the hives, he set out to visit Dr. Bruin. The hives were taken into his study, and the bees, being unused to flitting within walls out of the sushine, angrily sang and droned about the head of the old schoolmaster as he sat at his desk. Their stings were of little account against his thick hide, but their molestation was a fret, and he presently cried aloud, "Would that the Prince had kept his gifts to himself!" The Prince, who was standing outside the door, listening and smiling to himself, thereupon cried out: "Ah! Dr. Bruin, when I was under your charge, you often heavily smit and cuffed me with those long-clawed paws of yours. Now I am older, and have learned how sweet and worthy is the knowledge they instilled. This too will be your experience. My bees may fret and buzz and sting a little now, but you will think of me more kindly when you shall be tasting their rich honey in the Winter that is soon upon us." And Dr. Bruin, peering out at the Prince from amid the cloud of the bees, when he heard him thus call Tit for Tat, couldn't help but laugh.

But to return to Coleridge once more—who, in the bad old days, so far as food goes, never "had a belly full" at Christ's Hospital, and whose appetite was only "damped, never satisfied,"—here is one of his earliest letters (to his elder brother George), which *may* have an (indirect) reference to Dr. Bowyer's birch:

Dear Brother,—You will excuse me for reminding you that, as our holidays commence next week, and I shall go out a good deal, a good pair of breeches will be no inconsiderable accession to my appearance. For though my present pair are excellent for the purpose of drawing mathematical figures on them, and though a walking thought, sonnet or epigram would appear in them in very *splendid* type, yet they art not altogether so well adapted for a female eye—not to mention that I should have the charge of vanity brought against me for wearing a looking-glass. I hope you have got rid of your cold—and I am

Your affectionate brother,

Samuel Taylor Coleridge

And now for a pinch of sugar and spice after all these snips and snails, this being a letter home from school from Marjorie Fleming who was in her eighth (and last) year when she wrote it:

"*October 12th,* 1811.

My Dear Mother,—You will think that I entirely forgot you, but I assure you that you are greatly mistaken. I think of you always and often sigh to think of the distance between us two loving creatures of nature. We have regular hours for all our occupations, first at 7 o'clock we go to the dancing and come home at 8, we then read our Bible and get our repeating and then play till ten then we get our music till 11 when we get our writing and accounts we sew from 12 till 1, after which I get my gramer and then work till five. At 7 we come and knit till 8 when we don't go to the dancing. This is an exact description. I must take a hasty farewell to her whom I love, reverence and doat on, and whom I hope thinks the same of

Marjorie Fleming

P.S.—An old pack of cards would be very exeptible."

And last, for companion pieces, here, first, is a letter (the original being in the Bodleian Library), written in Greek on papyrus in the second or third century A. D. from a small boy to his father:

"Theon to his father Theon, greeting. It was a fine thing of you not to take me with you to town. If you won't take me with you to Alexandria, I won't write you a letter or speak to you. . . . Mother said to Archelaus, 'He upsets me. Take him away.' . . . So send for me, I implore you. If you won't send, I won't eat, I won't drink; there now! Farewell."

About fifteen centuries after Theon's ultimatum was dispatched, a small girl, (and "dutiful daughter"), sent her mother a loving little epistle stitched in on a piece of canvas. It runs—the commas being mine:

DEAR MOTHER, MY DUTY REMEMBER UNTO THE,
AND MY DEAR LOVE UNTO MY SISTER. WHEN I
SAW MY FATHER LAST HIS LOVE WAS TO THE, BUT
I THOUGHT IT LONG BEFORE I SAW THE BUT I DID
MY INDEAVOUR TO RITE UNTO THE NO MORE BUT
THEY DUTYFULL DAFTER S F
FROM WANSTEAD 1693 THE
25 OF THE 5 MONTH.

But what exactly S. F. meant by the words between her first "but" and her third, I can't be certain.

Eighty-five years after this, and on May Day, one Debby wrote to another in the same fashion, but added a pretty wandering border of flowers for a frame:

Dear Debby
I love you sincerely
My heart retains a grateful sense
of your past kindness
When will the hours of our
Separation be at an end
Preserve in your bosom a Remembrance
of your Affectionate
Deborah Jane Berkin
Bristol.
May 1st. 1778.

But enough:

> **F** for Francis, **I** for Iancis, **N** for Nickley Boney,
> **I** for Ihon the Waterman, and **S** for Signey Coney.

40.

This too should go to the lilt of its verbal music, as then the accents would come clearly. I think, in the reading of it, there should be four stressed syllables to the first, second and fifth lines in each stanza: "Whâr hae ye bêen a' day, mŷ boy Tâmmy"; and "The wêe thing gie's her hând, and says, There, gâng and ask my Mâmmy." A line of verse like this resembles a piece of elastic; if you leave it very slack you will get no music out of it at all; stretch it a little too far, it snaps.

41. "Rosy Apple, Lemon, or Pear."

This little jingle and Nos. 15, 16, 68, 75, etc., are Singing Game Rhymes, of which scores have been collected from the mouths of children near and far from all over the kingdom, and are now to be found in print in Lady Gomme's two stout engrossing volumes entitled *Traditional Games*. In these more than seven hundred games are described, including Rakes and Roans, Rockety Row, Sally Go Round the Moon, Shuttle-feather, Spannims, Tods and Lambs, Whigmeleerie, Allicomgreenaie, Bob-Cherry, Oranges and Lemons, Cherry Pit, Thumble-bones, Lady on Yandor Hill, Hechefragy, and Snail Creep.

A good many of these games have singing rhymes to them. And the words of them vary in different places. For the children in each of twenty or more villages and towns may have their own particular version of the same rhyme. As for the original from which all such versions must once have come—*that* may be centuries old. Like the Nursery Rhymes, they were most of them in the world ages before our great-great-great-grand-dams were babies in their cradles. The noble game of Hop Scotch, for instance, Lady Gomme tells us, was in favour before the year 1, and in case its champions are fewer than they were, it may be as well to mention that there are two varieties: Great Marelle and Little Marelle (the Little only fit for infants). "You trace one long square with four divisions in it. A semicircle is drawn above the narrowest end, and in it a St. Andrew's cross. Where the lines intersect, make a little round, called the copper, and in the last triangle to the right, a key." The stone is called a quoit, and the rules are as various as they should be famous.

The most mysterious game-rhymes of all are said to refer to ancient tribal customs, rites and ceremonies—betrothals, harvest-homes, sowings, reapings, well-blessings, dirges, divinations, battles, hunting and exorcisings—before even London was else than a few hovels by its river's side. Rhymes such as these having been passed on from age to age and from one piping throat to another, have become worn and battered of course, and queerly changed in their words.

These from Mr. Nahum's book have their own differences too. He seems to have liked best those that make a picture, or sound racy, gay and sweet and so carry the fancy away. Any little fytte or jingle or jargon of words that manages *that* is like a charm or a talisman, and to make new ones is as hard as to spin silk out of straw, or to turn beech leaves into fairy money. When one thinks, too, of the myriad young voices that generation after generation have carolled these rhymes into the evening air, and now are still—well, it's a thought no less sorrowful for being strange, and no less strange for the fact that our own voices too will some day be as silent.

Summer's pleasures they are gone like to visions every one,
And the cloudy days of autumn and of winter cometh on.
I tried to call them back, but unbidden they are gone
Far away from heart and eye and for ever far away.
Dear heart, and can it be that such raptures meet decay?
I thought them all eternal when by Langley Bush I lay,
I thought them joys eternal when I used to shout and play
On its bank at "clink and brandy," "chock" and "taw" and
"ducking stone,"
Where silence sitteth now on the wild heath as her own
Like a ruin of the past all alone. . . .

JOHN CLARE

42. "IN PRAISE."

The loveliest and gayest song of praise and sweetness to a

"young thing" I have ever seen. It is taken from a poem entitled *The Garland of Laurell,* and the headlong, twice-laureate poet who wrote it was described to Henry VIII. by Erasmus as *Britannicarum Literarum Lumen et Decus*!

"Ieloffer"—gelofer, gelofre, gillofre, gelevor, gillyvor, gillofer, jerefloure, gerraflour—all these are ways of spelling Gillyflower, gelofre coming nearest to its original French; *giroflée*—meaning spiced like the clove. There were of old, I find, three kinds of gillyflowers: the clove, the stock and the wall. It was the first of these kinds that was meant in the earlier writers by the small clove carnation (or Coronation, because it was made into chaplets or garlands). Its Greek name was dianthus (the flower divine); and its twin-sister is the Pink, so called because its edges are pinked, that is, jagged, notched, scalloped. Country names for it are Sweet John, Pagiants, Blunket and Sops-in-Wine, for it spices what it floats in, and used to be candied for a sweetmeat. Blossoming in July, the Gillyflower suggests July-flower, and if Julia is one's sweetheart, it may also be a Julie-flower. So one name may carry many echoes. It has been truly described as a gimp and gallant flower, and, says Parkinson, who wrote *Paradisus Terrestris,* it was the chiefest of account in Tudor gardens. There was a garden in Westminster in his own time belonging to a Master Ralph Tuggie, famous all London over for the beauty and variety of its gilliflowers; *e. g.,* "Master Tuggie his Princesse," "Master Bradshaw his daintie Ladie," "The Red Hulo," "The Fair Maid of Kent," "Lustie Gallant," "The Speckled Tawny," and "Ruffling Robin."

By 1700 there were 360 kinds and four classes of clove gillyflower—the Flake, the Bizarre, the Piquette or picotte (*picotée* or pricketed), and the Painted Lady, the last now gone. Its ancestor, the dianthus, seems to have crossed the Channel with the Normans, for it flourishes on the battlements of Falaise, the Conqueror's birthplace, and crowns the walls of many a Norman Castle—Dover, Ludlow, Rochester, Deal—to this day.

43. "PYGSNYE,"

which means Piggie's eye, Tiny-eye or Twinkle-eye—a loveword in use long before Chaucer—just as we nowadays call a child or loved-one Goosikins, or Pussikins, or Lambkin Pie, or Bunch-of-

Roses, or Chickabiddy, or Come-kiss-me-quick, or (further north), wee bit lassikie, *i. e.,* wee, small, tiny *little* wee lass. *Minion,* too, means anything small, minikin, delicate dainty, darling. Look close for example, at the grown-green florets of a stalk of mignonette.

44. "A Worm's Light." (line 10)

Many years ago I had the curious pleasure of reading a little book—and one in small print too (Alice Meynell's lovely *Flower of the Mind*)—by *English* glowworm light. The worm was lifting its green beam in the grasses of a cliff by the sea, and shone the clearer the while because it was during an eclipse of the moon.

49. The Chimney Sweep.

"Reader," pleaded Charles Lamb, "if thou meetest one of these small gentry in thy early rambles, it is good to give him a penny. It is better to give him two-pence. Better still—a basin of saloop, of which the chief ingredient is Sassafras; for it is a composition surprisingly gratifying to the palate of a young chimney-sweeper."

Oh! sweep chimney, sweep!
You maidens shake off sleep
If you my cry can follow.
I climb the chimney top,
Without ladder, without rope;
Aye and there! aye and there! aye and there you shall hear my halloo!

Arise! maids, arise!
Unseal and rub your eyes,
Arise and do your duty.
I summon yet again
And do not me disdain,
That my call, that my call, that my calling's poor and sooty.

Behold! here I stand!
With brush and scrape in hand,
As a soldier that stands on his sentry.

I work for the better sort,
And well they pay me for't.
O I work, O I work, O I work for the best of the gentry.

Oh! sweep chimney, sweep!
The hours onward creep.
As the lark I am alert, I
Clear away, and take
The smut that others make.
O I clean, O I clean, O I clean what others dirty.

50. "But never cam' He."

. . . "O wha will shoe my bonny foot?
And wha will glove my hand?
And wha will lace my middle jimp,
Wi' a lang, lang linen band?

"O who will kame my yellow hair,
With a haw bayberry kame?
And wha will be my babe's father,
Till Gregory come hame?"

"Thy father, he will shoe thy foot,
Thy brother will glove thy hand,
Thy mother will bind thy middle jimp
Wi' a lang, lang linen band!

"Thy sister will kame thy yellow hair,
Wi' a haw bayberry kame;
The Almighty will be thy babe's father,
Till Gregory come hame."

Anon.

"There's nane o' my ain to care,
There's nane to mind me now,
There's nane o' my ain to comb my hair,
There's nane to sponge my mou'.

"There's nane o' my ain to care,
Strange han's sall straighten me,
Strangers sall fauld about my limbs
The claes o' my deid body."

WILLIAM OGILVIE

Rock well, my cradle,
And *bee-baa,* my son;
You shall have a new gown
When ye lord comes home.
Oh! still my child, Orange!
Still him with a bell;
I can't still him, ladie,
Till you come down yoursel'.

"Haw" is an old English word meaning (?) blue or braw, and bayberry is the all-spice tree, in the light of whose flames sat Alexander Selkirk in his solitude on Juan Fernandez, surrounded by his "hundreds" of cats. So this sad one's yellow hair had for comb an uncommonly charming thing. In another version the comb is of "new silver," and in a third it is a "red river kame," which, thinks Child, may be a corruption of red *ivory.* And then, too, there is

". . . fair Ligea's *golden* comb,
Wherewith she sits on diamond rocks
Sleeking her soft alluring locks."

51. "THE ORPHAN."

"The first sense of sorrow I ever knew," wrote Richard Steele, "was upon the death of my father, at which time I was not quite five years of age; but was rather amazed at what all the house meant than possessed with a real understanding why nobody was willing to play with me. I remember I went into the room where his body lay, and my mother sat weeping alone by it. I had my battledore in my hand, and fell a-beating the coffin, and calling, papa; for, I know not how, I had some slight idea that he was locked up there. My mother catched me in her arms, and transported beyond all patience of the silent grief she was before in, she almost smothered me in her embraces; and told me in a flood of tears, 'Papa could not hear me, and would play with me no more, for they were going to put him under ground, whence he could never come to us again.' "

I HAD A LITTLE BIRD.

"My second child, but eldest daughter, like M[argaret] is between two and three weeks less than two years old . . . About three weeks since . . . in the earlier half of May, some of our neighbours gave [her] a little bird. . . . The present was less splendid than it seemed. For the bird was wounded; though not in a way that made the wound apparent; and . . . as the evening wore away it drooped . . .

At length sunset arrived, which was the signal for M.'s departure to bed. She came therefore as usual to me, threw her arms round my neck and went through her prayers. . . . As she was moving off to bed, [she] whispered to me that I was to 'mend' the bird with 'yoddonum' . . . For her satisfaction, I placed a little diluted laudanum near to the bird; and she then departed to bed, though with uneasy looks reverting to her sick little pet.

Occupied with some point of study, it happened that I sat up through the whole night: and long before seven o'clock in the morning she had summoned Barbara [her nurse] to dress her, and soon I heard the impatient little foot descending the stairs to my study. As the morning was one of heavenly splendour, I proposed that we should improve the bird's chances by taking it out-of-doors into the little orchard at the foot of Fairfield—our loftiest Grasmere mountain. Thither moved at once Barbara, little M., myself, and the poor languishing bird.

By that time in May, in any far southern county, perhaps the birds would be ceasing to sing; but not so with us dilatory people in Westmoreland. Suddenly, as we all stood around the little perch on which the bird rested, one thrilling song, louder than the rest, arose from a neighbouring hedge. Immediately the bird's eye, previously dull, kindled into momentary fire: the bird rose on its perch, struggled for an instant, seemed to be expanding its wings, made one aspiring movement upwards, in doing so fell back, and in another moment was dead. . . ."

THOMAS DE QUINCEY

53.

The first and third stanzas of this poem were (and are) my particular favourites, and especially the second line in each. Such poems are like wayside pools, or little well-springs of water. It does not matter how many wayfarers come thither to quench their thirst, there is abundance for all.

The *craftsmanship* of the poem seems simplicity itself. But the closer we examine it the more clearly we see the intricate devices that are responsible for its triumph. To express truth, and to express one's heart, need extreme care and skill—though the intense wish to do so may supply them almost without effort.

Listen here to the lingering chime of the vowels: "Nor *Ouse* on his *bosom,*" "The poplars are *felled;* fare*well*"; to the echoings of *retreat, screen, heat, scene, sweet* of the third stanza. How delightful throughout is the ease to throat and ear, to mind and spirit, effected by the interweaving alliteration of the f's and v's—*felled, farewell, faint, field fled, afford, before, fugitive,* fading away at last in *turf, if, life, grove* and *even.* The z's too and the m's—*melody charmed me*—and finally the *dream* and *durable* in the last stanza.

Not that this particular poem is either profound, subtle, or elaborate. It is simple, homely, true and tender. But it could not have proved itself so (and particularly in this particular metre) if the words, which are its all, had been clumsily put together, ill-matched, and art-less.

"The Perishing Pleasures of Man." (line 18)

And for yet another look behind, I cannot leave out this close-packed little rhyme from William Allingham, who made one of the happiest of all anthologies, "Nightingale Valley":

Four ducks on a pond,
A grass-bank beyond,
A blue sky of spring,
White clouds on the wing;
What a little thing
To remember for years—
To remember with tears.

Or this lovely scrap from the Scots:

> O Alva hills is bonny,
> Dalycoutry hills is fair,
> But to think on the braes of Menstrie
> It maks my heart fu' sair.

57. THE DESERTED HOUSE.

> . . . Ill fares the land, to hastening ills a prey,
> Where wealth accumulates, and men decay;
> Princes and lords may flourish, or may fade;
> A breath can make them, as a breath has made;
> But a bold peasantry, their country's pride,
> When once destroyed, can never be supplied. . . .

Oliver Goldsmith, when he wrote these lines was thinking of Ireland. But what of England now?

60.

Edward Thomas, who wrote this poem, knew by heart most of the villages, streams, high roads, by-roads, hills, forests, woods and dales of the southern counties of England and came so to know them by the slowest but best of all methods—walking; and, when so inclined, sitting down by the wayside or leaning over a farm or field gate to gaze and muse and day-dream. Here is another poem of his, fresh and sweet with country flowers:

> If I should ever by chance grow rich
> I'll buy Codham, Cockridden, and Childerditch,
> Roses, Pyrgo, and Lapwater,
> And let them all to my elder daughter.
> The rent I shall ask of her will be only
> Each year's first violets, white and lonely,
> The first primroses and orchises—
> She must find them before I do, that is.
> But if she finds a blossom on furze—
> Without rent they shall all for ever be hers,
> Codham, Cockridden, and Childerditch,
> Roses, Pyrgo and Lapwater,—
> I shall give them all to my elder daughter.

Not, of course, to find a blossom on furze or gorse as soon as any sun is in the new year's sky, is the rare feat; and if in wanderings over the hills and far away you should chance on secret hidden-away Pyrgo or Childerditch, sweet with its fragrance, then enquire for the beautiful, happy young Lady of the Manor. As a matter of fact, the scent of the furze-blossoms is not exactly sweet, but nutlike and aromatic.

"The gorse is most fragment at noon, when the sun shines brightest and hottest. At such an hour when I approach a thicket of furze, the wind blowing from it, I am always tempted to cast myself down on the grass to lie for an hour drinking in the odour. The effect is to make me languid; to wish to lie till I sleep and live again in dreams in another world in a vast open-air cathedral where a great festival of ceremony is perpetually in progress, and acolytes, in scores and hundreds with beautiful bright faces, in flame yellow and orange surplices, are ever and ever coming toward me, swinging their censers until I am ready to swoon in that heavenly incense!" . . .

W. H. Hudson

"A Stoat." (stanza 5)

It is the gentle custom of gamekeepers to slaughter at sight so-called *vermin, i.e.,* "worms of earth"—the little preying beasts and birds of the woodlands—owls, hawks, crows, jays, stoats, weasels, and the like. They then nail up their carcases to a shed side, or to a barn door or on a field-gate, leaving them to rot in the wind for a warning to their mates. Foxes, otters, badgers are "hunted" to death. It is said they enjoy the fun.

61. "The Howes of the Silent Vanished Races"

are, I suppose, the mounds, barrows, tumuli or Fairies' Hills, some of them round, some of them long, some of them chambered, beneath which the ancient races of Britain, centuries before the coming of the Saxons and the Danes, buried their dead. So once slept the mummied Pharaohs beneath their prodigious Pyramids. Age hangs densely over these solitary mounds, as over the Dolmens and the Cromlechs—Stonehenge, the Whispering Knights—and the single gigantic Menhirs—the Tingle Stone, the Whittle Stone, the Bair-down-Man and the demoniac Hoar Stone.

These were ancient and unintelligible marvels even when the monk Ranulph Higden wrote his *Polychronicon* in 1352: The second wonder, he says, is at Stonehenge beside Salisbury. There great stones marvellously huge, be a-reared up on high, as it were gates, so that there seemeth gates to be set up upon other gates. Nevertheless it is not clearly known nor perceived how and to what end they be so a-reared up, and "so wonderlych yhonged." And yet, what are they but as falling apple-blossom compared with the age of the world and the antiquity of the Universe:

1st Gravedigger. Come my spade; there is no ancient Gentlemen but Gardiners, Ditchers and Grave-makers; they hold up *Adam's* profession.

2nd Gravedigger. Was he a Gentleman?

1st Gravedigger. He was the first that ever bore Armes.

62. The Twa Brothers

—and here is as romantic and tragic a tale of two friends:

O Bessie Bell and Mary Gray,
They war twa bonnie lasses;
They biggit a bower on yon Burn-brae,
And theekit it o'er wi' rashes.

They theekit it o'er wi' rashes green,
They theekit it o'er wi' heather;
But the pest cam' frae the burrows-town,
And slew them baith thegither.

They thought to lye in Methven kirkyard,
Amang their noble kin;
But they maun lye in Stronach haugh,
To biek forenent the sin.

O Bessie Bell and Mary Gray,
They war twa bonnie lasses;
They biggit a bower on yon Burn-brae,
And theekit it o'er wi' rashes.

Biggit and *theekit* means builded and thatched; and the twelfth line, to bask beneath the sun.

64.

A tragic tale is hidden, rather than told, in this old Scottish ballad. It resembles a half ruinous house in a desolate country, densely green with briar and bramble, echoing with wild voices —its memories gone. Mr. Nahum's picture for it was of a figure in a woman's bright clothes and scarlet hood, but with what looked to me like the head of his own skeleton deep within the hood. And on a stone nearby sat a little winged boy.

66. "HER HIGH-BORN KINSMAN."

. . . And there was a wind in the night as they fared onward, a wind in the mid-air, playing from out the clouds. And presently after, the twain descended into the valley, the one traveller's foot stumbling as he went, against the writhen roots that jutted from between the stones of the path they followed. And it seemed that the voice of one unseen cried, Lo! And the traveller looked up from out of the valley of his journey, and, behold, a wan moon gleamed between the ravelled clouds; and the face of his companion showed for that instant clear against the sky in the shadow of its cloak. And it was the face of a nobleman; renowned for his patience; courteous and cold; whose name is Death. . . .

"BUT OUR LOVE . . ."

A Gyges Ring they beare about them still,
To be, and not seen when and where they will.
They tread on clouds, and though they sometimes fall,
They fall like dew, but make no noise at all.
So silently they one to th'other come,
As colours steale into the Peare or Plum,
And Aire-like, leave no pression to be seen,
Where e're they met, or parting place has been.

ROBERT HERRICK

. . .Lord Thomas was buried without kirk-wa',
Fair Annet within the quiere;

And out o' the tane their grew a birk,
The other a bonny briere.

And ay they grew, and ay they threw,
As they wad faine be neare;
And by this ye may ken right weil,
They were twa luvers deare.

68. "LONDON BRIDGE."

This is yet another singing-game rhyme. When London was nothing but a cluster of beehive huts in the hill clearings of the great Forest of Middlesex above the marshes and the Thames, there can have been no bridge. There *may* have been a bridge, it seems, in A. D. 44, eighty-seven years after the death of Caesar; and for centuries there was certainly a ferry, Audery the Shipwright being one of its ferrymen, his oars the shape of shovels, and his boat like a young moon on her back.

The rhyme appears to refer to the wooden bridge built in 994 at Southwark, which was destroyed in 1008 by King Olaf, the Saint of Norway, to whose glory four London churches are dedicated. Olaf had become the ally of Ethelred (the Unready), and to defeat the Danes who had captured the city he first screened his fighting ships with frameworks of osier for the protection of his men, who then rowed them up to the Bridge against the tide. They wapped and bound huge ropes or hawsers round its timber piers, swept down with the slack with the tide, and so brought the bridge to ruin.

The first stone bridge, in building from 1196 to 1208, was partially destroyed by fire four years afterwards. A picture of the romantic re-built bridge of Elizabeth's time shows its chapel, its precipitous gabled houses, its haberdashers', goldsmiths', booksellers' and needle shops, its cut-waters or starlings and narrow arches, its gate-house with the spiked heads atop, its drawbridge and pillory, and that strange timber mansion, with not a nail in its wood, called Nonesuch, where perhaps lived the Lord Mayor—all this may be gloated over in any old seventeenth-century map of London. (John Visscher's of 1616 shows a windmill in the Strand!) So narrow were its nineteen arches, and so vehemently flowed the tides beneath them, that at ebb it was mortally dangerous for a novice to shoot them in a boat. But between Windsor and Gravesend it is said there were forty thousand watermen and wherrymen in Shakespeare's day, yelling "Eastward Ho!", or "Westward Ho!" for passengers. The Bridge was the glory of London; as the Thames it spanned was its main thoroughfare. Fire was its chief enemy; the Great Fire in 1616 and that in 1633, after which it long continued to be used, though dark, dismal and dangerous. The present monster of granite, over which the people of London stream to and fro throughout the day, like ants at the flighting, was built thirty yards west of the old one and began to span the river in 1832.

70. "This City."

So these bygone all-welcoming Londoners spent their time, England being in effect, says Fuller, "all a great *Cooke's-shop,* and no reason any should starve therein."

London, thou art of townes *A per se* [1]
Soveraign of cities, seemliest in sight,
Of high renoun, riches and royaltie;
Of lordis, barons, and many a goodly knyght;
Of most delectable lusty ladies bright;
Of famous prelatis, in habitis clericall;
Of merchauntis full of substance and of myght;
London, thou art the flow'r of Cities all. . . .

Above all ryvers thy Ryver hath renowne,
Whose beryll stremys, pleasant and preclare,
Under thy lusty wallys renneth down,
Where many a swanne does swymme with wyngis fare;
Where many a barge doth sail and row with are,
Where many a ship doth rest with toppe-royall.
O! towne of townes, patrone and not compare:
London, thou art the floure of Cities all. . . .

Strong be thy wallis that about thee standis;
Wise be the people that within thee dwellis;
Fresh is thy ryver with his lusty strandis;

[1] First and foremost.

Blith be thy chirches, wele sownyng be thy bellis;
Rich be thy merchauntis in substaunce that excellis;
Fair be their wives, right lovesom, white and small;
Clere be thy virgyns, lusty under kellis! [2]
London, thou art the flow'r of Cities all. . . .

WILLIAM DUNBAR

Earth has not anything to show more fair:
Dull would he be of soul who could pass by
A sight so touching in its majesty:
This City now doth, like a garment, wear
The beauty of the morning; silent, bare,
Ships, towers, domes, theatres, and temples lie
Open unto the fields, and to the sky;
All bright and glittering in the smokeless air
Never did sun more beautifully steep
In his first splendour, valley, rock, or hill;
Ne'er saw I, never felt, a calm so deep!
The river glided at his own sweet will:
Dear God! the very houses seem asleep;
And all that mighty heart is lying still!

WILLIAM WORDSWORTH

But London awakes, and even in the seventeenth century we find Abraham Cowley fretting at evils now endlessly multiplied.

Well then; I now do plainly see
This busy world and I shall ne'er agree;
The very honey of all earthly joy
Does of all meats the soonest cloy;
And they, methinks, deserve my pity,
Who for it can endure the stings,
The crowd, the buzz, the murmurings
Of this great hive, the city.

ABRAHAM COWLEY

[1] Cap-nets of silk or of gold.

71. "He opened House to All." (line 22)

The subject being good victuals, here is the "Bill of Fare at the Christening of Mr. Constable's Child, Rector of Cockley Cley, in Norfolk, January 2, 1682."

"A whole hog's head souc'd with carrots in the mouth, and pendants in the ears, with guilded oranges thick sett.

2 Ox[s] cheekes stewed with 6 marrow bones.

A leg of Veal larded with 6 pullets.

A leg of Mutton with 6 rabbits.

A chine of bief, chine of venison, chine of mutton, chine of veal, chine of pork, supported by 4 men.

A Venison Pasty.

A great minced pye, with 12 small ones about it.

A gelt fat turkey with 6 capons.

A bustard with 6 pluver.

A pheasant with 6 woodcock.

A great dish of tarts made all of sweetmeats.

A Westphalia hamm with 6 tongues.

A Jowle of Sturgeon.

A great charg[r] of all sorts of sweetmeats with wine, and all sorts of liquors answerable."

And here is another from that inexhaustible Tom Tiddler's ground, *Rustic Speech and Folklore* for the "funeral meats" of a farmer who died near Whitby in 1760: "Besides what was distributed to 1,000 poor people who had 6d. each in money, there was consumed

110 dozen penny loaves,
9 large hams,
8 legs of veal,
20 stone of beef,
16 stone of mutton,
15 stone of Cheshire cheese, and
30 ankers of ale."

But even such a feast as this is little more than a fast compared with that given by Philip, Duke of Burgundy, the father of

Charles the Bold, on the 8th of February, 1454. It is described in the Memoirs of Olivier de la Marche, and I am indebted to G. G. and M. M. Stuart for permission to quote from their translation.

"The hall was a large one, hung with tapestry representing the life of Hercules. It was entered by five doors at which stood Archers in black and grey robes. Within were several Knights and Esquires superintending the banquet; the former were garbed in damascus cloth and the latter in satin of the same colours." So multitudinous were the dishes that Olivier de la Marche was unable to relate them: "But this much I remember—each course consisted of 48 varieties of food, and the vessels holding the roast meats were chariots of gold and azure."

And here are five of the fifteen *entremets* which stood on three tables—one large, one middle-sized and the last small:

"A cunningly constructed cruciform church, with glass windows and a bell; inside were four choristers."

"A beautiful fountain of glass and lead . . . round it were apricot trees of glass with leaves and flowers marvellously natural; the whole was enclosed in a little meadow surrounded by rocks of sapphire and other rare stones; in the centre stood a small figure of St. Andrew, holding his cross before him; from one point thereof sprung a jet of water to the height of a foot, falling back onto the meadow where it disappeared so cunningly that none could guess what became of it."

"A jester on a bear, among rocky mountains covered with ice most cunningly."

There was also "a great ship at anchor, laden with merchandise and manned by sailors; methinks that in the largest vessel in the world there could not be greater variety of sails and ropes than on this one," while the longest table was ornamented with "a huge pie, in which there were twenty-eight living musicians, who played in turn on divers instruments."

While the noble company were eating and drinking they were entertained with various devices, one of which was as follows:

"By the door through which the other entremets had entered came a wonderfully large and beautiful white stag with golden antlers; its back covered with red silk, as well as I can remember. It was ridden by a fair boy twelve years of age, clad in a short crimson velvet robe, fine shoes and a black cap cut into many points. He held the stag's antlers with each hand, and, as soon as they were in the hall he began a song, in a loud, clear voice, to which the stag sang the tenor part, there being no other performers except him and the child. The name of the song they sang was 'Naught have I ever seen like this.'" And no wonder.

At the end of the feast Toison-d'Or, king of arms, brought in a living pheasant and the Duke of Burgundy rose from his chair and vowed a vow upon this "noble bird":

"I swear firstly to God my Creator and to the glorious Virgin Mary, and secondly to the Ladies and the Pheasant, that if it please that most victorious and most Christian Prince, my King, to join a crusade and risk his life for the defence of the Christian faith and to oppose the damnable enterprise of the Grand Turk and the infidels, and unless I am prevented by some real bodily impediment, I will serve in person and with my army in that crusade, as faithfully as, by God's Grace, I may. . . ."

But man is mortal, and limited always to the possible, except in his dreams. For which reason the Duke of Burgundy's four dozen dishes to a course is but a Town Mouse's crumb of Wedding Cake compared to Mac Conglinnes' Vision in No. 73, which is from the Gaelic of 1100–1200 A. D., as translated by Kuno Meyer. *Bragget,* line 33, appears to have been a concoction or decotion of ale, honey, sugar and spice.

As for table-manners, they are always changing (for better or worse), as a few words from a minute volume—entitled *The Rules of Civility or Certain Ways of Deportment Observed amongst all Persons of Quality upon several Occasions* [1685]—will show:

"'Tis not manners as soon as you are set at the Table to bawl out, '*I eat none of this, I eat none of that; I care for no Rabbit; I love nothing that tastes of Pepper, Nutmeg, Onyons, etc. . . .*' It is better therefore to restrain, or at least conceal those repugnancies as much as we can; and to take all that is offer'd: If our disgust be invincible, we may let it lie upon our Plate, eat something else, and when we see our opportunity, give that away that we did not like.

"If we be to eat out of the dish, we must have a care of putting in our Spoons before our Superiors . . . much less are we to pick out the best pieces though we be the last that help ourselves. . . . 'Tis uncivil to put your hand twice together into the Dish; much less are we to eat bit by bit out of the Dish with our Fork. . . . Having served yourself with your Spoon, you must remember to wipe it, and indeed as oft as you use it, for some are so nice they will not eat Potage or anything of that Nature in which you put your Spoon unwiped, after you have put it into your Mouth.

"How hungry soever you be, it is indecent to eat hastily or ravenously, as if you would choak yourself . . . You must not eat Porridge out of the Dish, but put it handsomely upon your Plate, and if it be too hot, you must not blow every Spoonful you eat, but have patience till it cools of itself. If you happen to burn your Mouth, you must endure it if possible, if not you must convey what you have in your Mouth privately upon your Plate, and give it away to the Footman; For though Civility obliges you to be neat, there is no necessity you should burn out your Guts." Which is coarse but convincing.

"'What hour is't, Lollio?'

'Towards belly hour, sir.'

'Dinner time? thou mean'st *twelve* o'clock.'

'Yes, sir, for every part has his hour; we wake at six, and look about us, that's eye-hour; at seven we should pray, that's knee-hour; at eight walk, that's leg-hour; at nine gather flowers, and pluck a rose, that's nose-hour; at ten we drink, that's mouth-hour; at eleven, lay about us for victuals, that's hand-hour; at twelve go to dinner, that's belly-hour.'" From *The Changeling.*

72. "And bring us in Good Ale"

really *good* ale, that is, before beer was made "so mortal small"; a hundred and thirty-three years before tea-leaves came from China (to be boiled and the decoction stored in a barrel), and a hundred and forty before the first coffee-house in London; and even, one might be tempted to add, before milk came from the cow, for as late as 1512 the two young sons of the fifth earl of Northumberland, Lord Percy, aged eleven (who afterwards loved

Anne Boleyn), and his younger brother, Maister Thomas Percy, were allowed for "braikfaste" even on "Fysch," or Fast Days: "Half a Loif of houshold Brede, a Manchet, a Dysch of Butter, a Pece of Saltfish, a Dysch of Sproits or iii White Herrynge," and a *Potell of Bere, i.e.* two quarts or eight mugfuls.

But once again *good* ale, like that which sustained Mother Redcap of Holloway:

"Old Mother Redcap, according to her tale,
Lived twenty and a hundred years by drinking this good ale;
It was her meat, it was her drink, and medicine beside,
And if she still had drank this ale, she never would have died."

73.

"I' sooth a Feast of Fats" (from the Irish of the twelfth century) like that dream of the rats in the *"Pied Piper of Hamelin"* as they scuttled to their doom in the ice-cold Weser. For a feast of *sweets* there is Porphyrio's in the "Eve of St. Agnes":

"And still she slept an azure-lidded sleep,
In blanchèd linen, smooth, and lavendered,
While he from forth the closet brought a heap
Of candied apple, quince, and plum, and gourd;
With jellies soother than the creamy curd,
And lucent syrops, tinct with cinnamon;
Manna and dates, in argosy transferred
From Fez; and spicèd dainties, every one,
From silken Samarcand to cedared Lebanon.

These delicates he heaped with glowing hand
On golden dishes and in baskets bright
Of wreathèd silver: sumptuous they stand
In the retirèd quiet of the night,
Filling the chilly room with perfume light. . . ."

For a banquet of enchantment there is Lamia's, and of magical fruits, poor Laura's in *Goblin Market*; Romeo too went feasting, with the Capulets—but only his eyes; so too Macbeth, but *his* eyes betrayed him. Bottom in his ass's ears asked only for a munch of your good dry oats, a handfull of pease, and a bottle of hay, then fell asleep before even Queen Titania could magick them up for him. As for the poor Babes, blackberries and dewberries were *their* last supper. These are but a few scores of banqueting delights in poetry—but to include them all would need such a larder as Jack peeped into when he sat supping in the Grant's kitchen.

74. "Pigeon holes, Stool-ball, Barley-break."

This fragment is a patchwork of the half-forgotten. "Pigeon holes" was a ball-game, played on the green, with wooden arches and little chambers as in a dovecot—a kind of open-air bagatelle. "Stool-ball" was popular with Nancies and Franceses on Shrove Tuesday. Barley-break was in Scotland a kind of "I spy," played in a stackyard, and in England a sort of "French and English," in three marked spaces or compartments, the middle one of which was called hell. And here—while we are on the subject of old and gallant pastimes—is a brief and early exposition of our noble and National Game of Cricket. It comes from a book with the title, "A Nosegay for the Trouble of Culling; or, Sports of Childhood":

"Cricket is a game universally played in England, not by boys only, for men of all ranks pique themselves on playing it with skill. In Mary-le-bone parish there is a celebrated cricket ground much frequented by noblemen and gentlemen.

"The wicket consists of two pieces of wood fixed upright and kept together by another piece which is laid across the top and is called a bail; if either of these pieces of wood be thrown down by the ball the person so hitting them becomes the winner.

"The ball used in this game is stuffed exceedingly hard. Many windows and valuable looking-glasses have been broken by playing cricket in a room."

It was in a cricket match in the summer of 1775, when no less than three "balls" had rolled in between a Mr. Small's two stumps without stirring the bail, that it was decided to add stump iii.

But (primitive) Cricket was being played in England at least as far back as the year in which Chaucer was born, for on the border of a manuscript of the *Romance of Alexander* that was written and illuminated about 1340 and is now in the Bodleian Library, there are the liveliest coloured pictures showing children playing games—games that were then no doubt already centuries old, and are yet—as each new billow of children breaks on the world's shore—as new as ever. Shown in action are two kinds of Cricket, Bowls, Stilts, Hot-cockles, Whip-tops, Dice, Balancing, Blind-man's Bluff and Chess.

In full swing, apart from these, are Nine-men's Morris or Moreles, small boys Cock-fighting, Tilting, Quintain (a boy mounted on a kind of wheeled wooden horse without a head being dragged along towards the quintain, and holding for lance a stout pole), Punch and Judy, performing horses, and a performing bear (with a chain attached to its collar that would hold in curb a dinosaur). Instruments of music are also shown in play—mandore, harp, viol, psaltery, bagpipes, hurdy-gurdy, shawm, organ and drums.

As for "tansy" (line 5), here is a recipe for it (to go with the sillabub, No. 22): "Take 15 eggs, and 6 of the whites; beat them very well; then put in some sugar, and a little sack; beat them again, and put about a pint or a little more of cream; then beat them again; then put in the juice of spinage or of primrose leaves to make it green. Then put in some more sugar, if it be not sweet enough; then beat it again a little, and so let it stand till you fry it, when the first course is in. Then fry it with a little sweet butter. It must be stirred and fryed very tender. When it is fryed enough, then put it in a dish, and strew some sugar upon it, and serve it in."

75. "Mary's gone a-milking."

And, according to Sir Thomas Overbury (who dipped his pen in nectar as well as ink), *"A Fair and Happy Milk-maid,"* is "a Country Wench, that is so far from making herself beautiful by art, that one look of hers is able to put all face-physic out of countenance. . . .

"She doth not, with lying long abed, spoil both her complexion and conditions, . . . she rises, therefore, with Chanticleer, her dame's cock, and at night makes the lamb her curfew. In milking a Cow, and straining the teats through her fingers, it seems that so sweet a milk-press makes the milk the whiter or sweeter; for never came almond glove or aromatic ointment on her palm to taint it. . . . Her breath is her own which scents all the year long of June, like a new made haycock. She makes her hand hard with labour, and her heart soft with pity: and when winter evenings fall early (sitting at her merry wheel), she sings a defiance to the giddy wheel of Fortune. She doth all things with so sweet a grace, it seems *ignorance* will not suffer her to do ill, being her mind is to do well. . . . She dares go alone and unfold sheep in the night, and fears no manner of ill, because she means none: yet to say truth, she is never alone, for she is still accompanied with old songs, honest thoughts, and prayers, but short ones. . . .

"Thus lives she, and all her care is she may die in the springtime, to have store of flowers stuck upon her winding-sheet."

76. "Cypresse black as ere was Crow."

Cypresse (according to a memorandum from one of Mr. Nahum's books) is the fine cobweblike stuff we now call crape. Peaking-stickes, or poking-sticks, were gophering irons for frilling out linen, flounces, etc., etc., and not, as one might guess, curling tongs (since a pointed beard, and the V of hair on the forehead, used to be called peaks). A quoife or coif is a lady's head-dress, such as is still worn by nuns; while as for "maskes for faces," fine ladies in Shakespeare's day customarily wore them (as old pictures show) when they went to see his plays. Masks were useful too in disguising the faces of his players, when—as was the custom in the London theatres up to 1629—boys took women's parts; and in the streets eyes gleamed out of the holes in them, worn *then* for keeping the skin fair, untanned, and unfreckled, as Julia says of herself in Shakespeare's *Two Gentlemen of Verona:*

> But since she did neglect her looking-glasse,
> And threw her Sun-expelling masque away,
> The ayre hath starved the roses in her cheekes
> And pinched the lily-tincture of her face. . . .

78. Fairing. (line 5)

In this—the earliest known letter of Shelley's—he too asks for a fairing—the kickshaws and gewgaws sold in the booths of a fair—and a toothsome one; though I haven't yet been able to discover what he meant by "hunting nuts":

Monday, July 18, 1803. (Horsham).

Dear Kate,

We have proposed a day at the pond next Wednesday; and if you will come to-morrow morning I would be much obliged to you; and if you could any how bring Tom over to stay all night, I would thank you. We are to have a cold dinner over at the pond, and come home to eat a bit of roast chicken and peas at about nine o'clock. Mama depends upon your bringing Tom over to-morrow, and if you don't we shall be very much disappointed.

Tell the bearer not to forget to bring me a fairing—which is some ginger-bread, sweetmeat, hunting-nuts, and a pocket book. Now I end.

I am *not*,
Your obedient servant,
P. B. Shelley

[Not only has my ignorance of hunting-nuts been now [1927] enlightened—what Shelley wanted being a long oval-shaped ginger-nut convenient for pocketing; not only has a recipe for making them been sent me by one kind informant, and the news that they are still to be bought at Nottingham Fair by another; but a third generously supplied me with positive specimens still almost hot from the oven.]

"Bonny brown hair."

And what could be more enchanting? But was it squirrel-brown, or chestnut, or hazelnut, or autumn-beech, or heather-brown, or walnut, or old hay colour, or undappled-fawn, or dark lichen, or velvet brown, or marigold or pansy or wallflower-brown—or yet another?—every one of which would look charming beneath the rim of a round blue-ribanded "little straw hat."

79. "My Dad and Mam they did agree."

"Fifty years and three
Together in love lived we;

Angry both at once none ever did us see.
This was the fashion
God taught us, and not fear:—
When one was in a passion
The other could forbear."

80. "WIDDECOMBE FAIR."

To an eye looking down, the steeple of Widdecombe Church rises in the midst of Dartmoor like a lovely needle of ivory; and hidden beneath the turf around it lie, waiting, the bones of Tom Pearse, Bill Brewer . . . Old Uncle Tom Cobley and all.

83. "THERE WERE THREE GIPSIES"

—and they were of England (Somerset), though to judge from this old ballad they may have padded it down from the Highlands:

There cam' Seven Egyptians on a day,
And wow, but they sang bonny!
And they sang sae sweet, and sae very complete,
Down cam' Earl Cassilis' lady.

She cam' tripping adown the stair,
And a' her maids before her;
As soon as they saw her weel-faur'd face
They cast the glamourie owre her;

They gave to her the nutmeg,
And they gave to her the ginger;
And she gave to them a far better thing,
The seven gold rings off her finger.

There was a small black cobbled-up book entitled *Glamourie* in a red leather case in Thrae, but, alas, it was in a writing I could not easily decipher. On the fly-leaf was scrawled "H.B.", and beneath it was the following:

See, with eyes shut.
Look seldom behind thee.

In secret of selfship
Free thee, not bind thee.
Mark but a flower:
'Tis of Eden. A fly
Shall sound thee a horn
Wooing Paradise nigh.
Think close. Unto love
Give thy heart's steed the rein;
So—course the world over:
Then Homeward again.

84. "WHATEVER THEY FIND THEY TAKE IT." (line 21)

There was a robber met a robber
On a rig of beans;
Says a robber to a robber,
"Can a robber tell a robber
What a robber means?"

And if not; why not? This inextricable and delectable scrap of jingle I owe to Mr. Ralph Hodgson. And the following version of an old game rhyme (with its rare "wood") first met my eye by the kindness of another friend, Mrs. Lyon:

"My mother said that I never should
Play with the gypsies in the wood,
The wood was dark; the grass was green;
In came Sally with a tambourine.

I went to the sea—no ship to get across;
I paid ten shillings for blind white horse;
I up on his back and was off in a crack,
Sally, tell my Mother I shall never come back."

86.

This lament for matchless Robin Hood, who should shine in a far better place than between "Beggars" and "Gilderoy," is the only rhyme about him in this collection. The fact is, try as I might, I could not make up my mind which to choose of the old greenwood ballads. But they are all to be found in Professor Child's collection. And if this neglect of the merry outlaw should induce anyone to read *English and Scottish Ballads,* it will have been to good purpose.

87. "GILDEROY."

A pretty song about a monstrously ugly scoundrel, though handsome of feature. Gilderoy was a highwayman, sparing for his prey neither man nor woman, and if there were "roses" on his shoes, they were blood-red. At last fifty armed avengers surrounded his house at night and set on. He killed eight of them before he was captured; which, if true, was bonnie fighting. Nevertheless, such a villain he was that he was hanged, without trial, on a gibbet thirty feet high, and the bones of him (despite the last stanza of the ballad) dangled in chains forty feet above Leith Walk in Edinburgh for fifty years afterwards.

Three things there be that prosper all apace,
And flourish while they are asunder far;
But on a day they meet all in a place,
And when they meet, they one another mar.

And they be these—the Wood, the Weed, the Wag;—
The Wood is that that makes the gallows-tree;
The Weed is that that strings the hangman's bag;
The Wag, my pretty knave, betokens *thee.*

Now mark, dear boy—while these assemble not,
Green springs the tree, hemp grows, the wag is wild;
But when they meet, it makes the timber rot,
It frets the halter, and it chokes the child.

SIR WALTER RALEIGH

TOLD HOW A CREW WAS CURSED.

My name is Captain Kidd,
Captain Kidd.
My name is Captain Kidd,
Captain Kidd.
My name is Captain Kidd,
And wickedly I did;

God's laws I did forbid,
As I sailed.

My topsails they did shake
As I sailed.
My topsails they did shake
As I sailed.
My topsails they did shake,
And the merchants they did quake,
For many did I take
As I sailed.

88. "And his name was Little Bingo."

In bounding health, it is said, a dog's nose and a woman's elbow are always cold. The reason for which is explained in a legend (referred to in Mrs. Wright's *Rustic Speech and Folk Lore*). It seems that in the midst of its forty days' riding on the Flood, the Ark one black night sprung a little leak. And Noah having forgotten to bring his carpenter's bag on board, was at his wits' end to plug the hole in its timbers. In the beam of his rushlight he looked and he looked and he looked; and still the water came rilling in and in. His dog, Shafet, was of course standing by, head on one side, carefully watching his master. And Noah, by good chance at last casting his eye in his direction, seized the faithful creature and, thrusting his nose into the leak, for a while stopped the flow. But Noah, a merciful man, and partial to animals, quickly perceived that in a few minutes poor Shafet would perish of suffocation, and as, by this time, his wife had descended into the fo'c'sle to see what he was about, he released his dog's nose, and, instead of it, stuffed in her charming elbow. Yet even that failed at last to plug the hole, so Ham was made to sit on it.

But not all dogs are "good dogs"—as Launce in *The Two Gentlemen of Verona* knew:

"*Launce:* 'Nay, 'twill bee this howre ere I have done weeping. All the kinde of the *Launces,* have this very fault: I have received my proportion, like the prodigious Sonne, and am going with Sir *Protheus* to the Imperialls Court: I thinke *Crab* my dog, be the sowrest natured dogge that lives: My Mother weeping: my Father wayling: my Sister crying: our Maid howling:

our Catte wringing her hands, and all our house in a great perplexitie, yet did not this cruel-hearted *Curre* shedde one teare: he is a stone, a very pibble stone, and has no more pitty in him then a dogge!"

And while dogges are about, here is a rhyme which if it be repeated twelve times a minute twelve times a day will keep the tongue supple and the wits clear:

> There was a man, and his name was Dob
> And he had a wife, and her name was Mob,
> And he had a dog, and he called it Cob,
> And she had a cat called Chitterabob.
>
> Cob, says Dob,
> Chitterabob, says Mob.
> Cob was Dob's dog.
> Chitterabob Mob's cat.

90. "Poor old Horse."

> Sweet wind that up the climbing road
> Fliest, where Summer, heated stands,
> There drags the patient horse his load,—
> O! bless him with thy flowing hands!
> Wing o'er his dumb, distressèd face
> And bathe his weeping brow with grace.
>
> His sobs are mingled with thy sighs,
> His taut lips meet eternal steel
> Relentless as the goading cries
> That scorn his plodding, grace appeal:
> His parched tongue lolls, and yet he laves
> Hourly his heart in Love's deep waves!
>
> O! bless him, breeze, and shed him tears;
> And when he mounts his last hill's crest
> Thou, cherished by the labouring fears
> Along his streaming mane, shalt rest
> When he shall scan, with naked eyes
> The rolling plains of Paradise.

M. M. Johnson

91. "Ay me, Alas."

Messalina's monkey was, one would fancy, of the kind called a marmoset, "blacke and greene." "Their agilitie and manner of doing is admirable, for that they seeme to have reason and discourse to go upon trees, wherein they seeme to imitate birds." There are so few of these far fair cousins of ours in poetry that I am adding a bevy of them from Sir John Maundeville's *Travels.*

" . . . From that City, (that is to say Cassay—the City of Heaven), men go by Water, solacing and disporting themselves, till they come to an Abbey of Monks—that is fast by—that be good religious men after their Faith and Law. In that Abbey is a great Garden and a fair, where be many Trees of diverse manner of Fruits. And in this Garden, is a little Hill, full of delectable Trees. In that Hill and in that Garden be many divers Beasts, as of Apes, Marmosets, Baboons, and many other divers Beasts. And every day, when the Monks of this Abbey have eaten, the Almoner has the remnants carried forth into the Garden, and he smiteth on the Garden Gate with a Clicket of Silver that he holdeth in his hand, and anon all the Beasts of the Hill and of divers places of the Garden, come out, a 3000 or a 4000 of them; they approach as if they were poor men come a-begging; and the Almoner's servants give them the remnants, in fair Vessels of Silver, clean over gilt. And when they have eaten, the Monk smiteth eftsoons on the Garden Gate with the Clicket; and then anon all the Beasts return again to their places that they came from. And they say that these Beasts be Souls of worthy men, that resemble in likeness the Beasts that be fair: and therefore they give them meat for the love of God."

"There is," says Fuller, "a sort of apes in India, caught by the natives thereof in this manner. They dress a little boy in his sight, undress him again—leaving the child's apparel behind them in the place, and then depart a competent distance. The Ape presently apparels himself in the same garments, till the child's cloathes become his Chains, putting off his Feet by putting on his Shoes, not able to run to any purpose, and so soon taken."

92. "O Happy Fly."

And here is another of these creatures—"a sleepy fly that rubs its hands," in Thomas Hardy's words—William Blake's:

Little Fly,
Thy summer's play
My thoughtless hand
Has brushed away.

Am not I
A fly like thee?
Or art not thou
A man like me?

For I dance,
And drink, and sing,
Till some blind hand
Shall brush my wing.

If thought is life
And strength and breath,
And the want
Of thought is death;

Then am I
A happy fly
If I live
Or if I die.

But the Happy Fly is nowadays gone so dismally out of favour that it would perhaps be prudent to draw attention from him to Lovelace's "Grasshopper":

O thou that swing'st upon the waving hair
Of some well-fillèd oaten beard,
Drunk every night with a delicious tear
Dropt thee from heaven, where thou were reared!

The joys of earth and air are thine entire,
That with thy feet and wings dost hop and fly;
And when thy poppy works, thou dost retire
To thy carved acorn-bed to lie.

Up with the day, the Sun thou welcom'st then,
Sport'st in the gilt plaits of his beams,
And all these merry days mak'st merry men,
Thyself, and melancholy streams.

93. "Lo, the Bright Air alive with Dragonflies."

There is an old dialect children's rhyme about these lightlike shimmering *stingless* insects:

Snakestanger, snakestanger, vlee aal about the brooks;
Sting aal the bad bwoys that vor the fish looks,
Bút let the góod bwoys ketch aál the vish they can,
And car'm away whóoam to vry 'em in a pan;
Bread and butter they shall yeat at zupper wi' their vish
While aal the littull bad bwoys shall only lick the dish.

But even littull bad bwoys want a light to light them to bed, and "there is a kind of little animal of the size of prawnes," says Champlain, "which fly by night, and make such light in the air that one would say that they were so many little candles. If a man had three or four of these little creatures, which are not larger than a filbert, he could read as well at night as with a wax light."

As indeed men used to in South America if we are to believe Du Bartas:

"New-Spain's *cucuio,* in his forehead brings
Two burning lamps, two underneath his wings:
Whose shining rayes serve oft, in darkest night,
Th' imbroderer's hand in royall works to light:
Th' ingenious turner, with a wakefull eye,
To polish fair his purest ivory:
The usurer to count his glistring treasures:
The learned scribe to limn his golden measures."

95. "The Sale of the Pet Lamb."

"The Pet Lamb," by William Wordsworth, is of a more delicate light and colour and music than this poem. But it is much better known. And there is a secret something in the words of Mary Howitt's that wins one's heart for the writer of it.

"A THOUSAND FLOCKS WERE IN THE HILLS."

" . . . And so . . . I walked upon the Downes, where a flock of sheep was; and the most pleasant and innocent sight that ever I saw in my life. We found a shepherd [and his dog] and his little boy reading . . . the Bible to him; so I made the boy read to me, which he did, with the forced tone that children usually do read, that was mighty pretty, and then I did give him something, and went to the father, and talked with him. . . . He did content himself mightily in my liking his boy's reading, and did bless God for him, the most like one of the old patriarchs that ever I saw in my life, and it brought those thoughts of the old age of the world in my mind for two or three days after. We took notice of his woollen knit stockings of two colours mixed, and of his shoes shod with iron, both at the toe and heels, and with great nails in the soles of his feet, which was mighty pretty; and, taking notice of them, 'Why,' says the poor man, 'the Downs, you see, are full of stones, and we are fain to shoe ourselves thus; and these,' says he, 'will make the stones fly till they ring before me.' "

SAMUEL PEPYS. (July 14, 1667.)

97.

". . . Poor Wat, far off upon a hill,
Stands on his hinder legs with listening ear,
To hearken if his foes pursue him still:
Anon their loud alarums he doth hear;
And now his grief may be comparèd well
To one sore sick that hears the passing-bell.

Then shalt thou see the dew-bedabbled wretch
Turn, and return, indenting with the way;
Each envious briar his weary legs doth scratch,
Each shadow makes him stop, each murmur stay:
For misery is trodden on by many,
And being low never reliev'd by any. . . ."

WILLIAM SHAKESPEARE. *Venus and Adonis*

"As he was speaking, Harry, casting his eyes on one side, said, 'See! see! there is the poor hare skulking along! I hope they will not be able to find her: and, if they ask me, I will never tell them which way she is gone.'

"Presently, up came the dogs, who had now lost all scent of their game, and a gentleman mounted upon a fine horse, who asked Harry if he had seen the hare? Harry made no answer; but, upon the gentleman's repeating the question in a louder tone of voice, he answered that he had. 'And which way is she gone?' said the gentleman.

" 'Sir, I don't choose to tell you,' answered Harry, after some hesitation.

" 'Not choose!' said the gentleman, leaping off his horse, 'but I'll make you choose in an instant': and coming up to Harry, who never moved from the place where he had been standing, began to lash him in a most unmerciful manner with his whip, continually repeating, 'Now, you little rascal, do you choose to tell me now?' To which Harry made no other answer than this: 'If I would not tell you before, I won't now, though you should kill me,'

"But this fortitude of Harry, and the tears of Tommy, who cried in the bitterest manner to see the distress of his friend, made no impression on this barbarian, who continued his brutality till . . . When they were gone, Tommy came up to Harry in the most affectionate manner, and asked him how he did?—'A little sore,' said Harry, 'but that does not signify. . . .' "

But see "The Story of Cyrus" in the *History of Sandford and Merton.*

98.

This is another translation by Kuno Meyer from the ancient Irish—only the bare bones, that is, of a poem that in its original tongue must have been many times more musical with internal rhyme and gentle echo and cadence; for the craft of Gaelic verse was an exceedingly delicate one.

I like it for the sake of its cat, its monk, and its age, but chiefly because it reminds me of my own far-away days at Thrae—brooding there as I used to in solitude and silence over Mr. Nahum's books.

As for "white Pangur" and his kind, "it is needlesse," says Topsell, "to spend any time about [Puss's] loving nature to man, how she flattereth by rubbing her skinne against ones legges, how she whurleth with her voyce, having as many tunes as turnes; for she hath one voice to beg and to complain, another to testifie her delight and pleasure, another among her own kind by flattring, by hissing, by spitting, insomuch as some have thought that they have a peculiar intelligible language among themselves." So also John de Trevisa, in 1387: "The catte is a beaste of uncertain heare (hair) and colour; for some catte is white, some rede, some blacke, some skewed (piebald) and speckled in the fete and in the face and in the eares. He is a beste in youth, swyfte, plyaunte, and mery, and lepeth and reseth (rusheth) on all thynge that is tofore him; and is led by a strawe and playeth therwith. He is a right hevy beast in aege, and ful slepy, and lyeth slily in wait for myce. And he maketh a ruthefull noyse and gastfull, whan one proffreth to fyghte with another, and he falleth on his owne fete whan he falleth out of hye places."

The writings of the ancient Egyptians show that, far from detesting to wet his paws, he would then *swim* in pursuit of fish. They painted a cat for the sound "miaou" in their hieroglyphics; gazed into his changing moonlike eyes and revered him; and embalmed him when dead.

Having borrowed him from Egypt, the Romans brought him to Britain (though we already had a wilding of our own, *Felis Catus*), with the ass, the goat, the rabbit, the peacock, not to speak of the cherry, the walnut, the crocus, the tulip, the leek, the cucumber, etc. The Monk's Pangur, then, came of a long lineage.

So valuable were cats in *Wales* in the eleventh century (two or three hundred years after Pangur), that their price was fixed by law: for a blind kitten a penny; for a kitten with its eyes open, twopence; for a cat of one mouse, fourpence, and so on. And to kill one of the Prince's granary cats meant payment of a fine of as much wheat as would cover up its body when suspended by its tail. In Scotland (where the true wild ancient Caledonian cat is now steadily increasing) there has long been a complete Clan of Cats—apart from the witches. As for the Cheshire Cat, he grins, I imagine, not because he has nine lives, is said to be melancholy, may look at a king, and has nothing to do with Catgut, Cat's cradle, and Cat-i'-the-pan, but because he has read in a dictionary that Dick Whittington sailed off to the Isle of Rats, not with a Cat, but with *acat* or *achat,* meaning goods for trading—Coals! Long may he grin! How but one country Gib or Tom may befriend the brightfaced heartease (so sturdy a little dear that it will bloom at burning noonday in a gravel path) Charles Darwin tells in his *"Origin of Species,"* p. 57.

"Grimalkin's" "loving nature" to creatures *other* than man and the heartsease is hinted at in this old Scots nursery rhyme:

There was a wee bit mousikie,
That lived in Gilberaty, O,
It couldna get a bite o' cheese,
For cheetie-poussie-cattie, O.

It said unto the cheesikie,
"Oh fain wad I be at ye, O,
If 't were na for the cruel paws
O' cheetie-poussie-cattie, O."

and his powers, when of the right colour (though there's much to be said for a calemanchos cat), in this:

Wherever the cat of the house is black,
Its lasses of lovers will have no lack.

99. "ON WHAT WINGS DARE HE ASPIRE."

The verb *dare* (I gather from Webster) was once used only in the past tense, the preterite; for "dare he" therefore in this poem we should now write *dared he.*

100.

Andrew Marvell has three rare charms—his poetry is wholly his own; it is as delightful as the sound of his name; and the face in his portrait is as enchanting as either.

101.

"Of all the birds that I do know" should of course instantly conjure up "Of all the girls that are so smart"; but "Sallie" is known to the whole world "by heart." The "Philip" of Nos. 101–2 is, I suppose, the hedge-sparrow or dunnock, that gentle and happy little cousin of the warblers—as light and lovely in voice as they are on the wing. As everyone knows, a bull-finch can be taught to whistle like a baker's boy, and will become so jealous of his mistress that he will hiss and ruff with rage at every stranger. Jackdaws and magpies, too, will become friends to a friend. But a lady whom I have the happiness to know has a nightingale that was hatched in captivity, and so has never shared either the delights or the dangers of the wild. So easy is he in her company, that he will perch on her pen-tip as she sits at table, and sing as if out of a garden in Damascus.

102. "He would chirp."

". . . As she (St. Douceline) sat at meat, if anyone brought her a flower, a bird, a fruit, or any other thing that gave her pleasure, then she fell straightway into an ecstasy, and was caught up to Him Who had made these fair creatures. . . . One day she heard a lonely sparrow sing, whereupon she said to her companions, 'How lovely is the song of that bird!' and in the twinkling of an eye she was in an ecstasy, drawn up to God by the bird's voice. . . ."

The above is from *A Medieval Garner,* and this, from a Note to *A Saint's Tragedy,* by Margaret L. Woods: When the blessed Elizabeth "had been ill twelve days and more, one of her maids sitting by her bed heard in her throat a very sweet sound, . . . and saying, 'Oh, my mistress, how sweetly thou didst sing!' she answered, 'I tell thee, I heard a little bird between me and the wall sing merrily; who with his sweet song so stirred me up that I could not but sing myself.'"

> I have wished a bird would fly away
> And not sing by my house all day;
>
> Have clapped my hands at him from the door
> When it seemed as if I could bear no more.
>
> The fault may partly have been in me,
> The bird was not to blame for his key.

And of course there must be something wrong
In wanting to silence any song.

ROBERT FROST

"LOVING REDBREASTS." (line 31)

My dear, do you know
How a long time ago,
Two poor little children,
Whose names I don't know,
Were stolen away
On a fine summer's day,
And left in a wood,
As I've heard people say.

And when it was night,
So sad was their plight,
The sun it went down,
And the moon gave no light!
They sobbed and they sighed,
And they bitterly cried,
And the poor little things,
They laid down and died.

And when they were dead,
The robins so red
Brought strawberry leaves,
And over them spread;
And all the day long,
They sang them this song,—
Poor babes in the wood!
Poor babes in the wood!
And don't you remember
The babes in the wood?

Wherefore (apart from other excellent reasons)—

The robin of the red breast
Ay, and the cutty wren—
If e'er ye take 'em out of nest,
Ye'll never thrive again.

The robin of the red breast,
Martin and swallow—
If e'er ye steal one egg of theirs,
Bad luck'll follow.

For sure, the robin and the wren
Are God Almighty's cock and hen.

105. "'TIS A NOTE OF ENCHANTMENT."

It was a note of enchantment such as this that haunted the memory of Edward Thomas when he was writing his poem called *The Unknown Bird.* I give only a few lines, but the rest of the beautiful thing may be found in his *Poems*:

Oftenest when I heard him I was alone,
Nor could I ever make another hear.
La-la-la! he called seeming far-off—
As if a cock crowed past the edge of the world,
As if the bird or I were in a dream. . . .

. . . O wild-raving winds! if you ever do roar
By the house and the elms from where I've a-come,
Breathe up at the window, or call at the door,
And tell you've a-found me a-thinking of home."

WILLIAM BARNES

107. "LIKE A LADY BRIGHT."

"They say," says mad Ophelia, "they say the owle was a Baker's daughter. Lord, we know what we are, but know not what we may be. God be at your Table." And thus runs the story:

Our Saviour being footsore, weary and hungry, went one darkening evening into a baker's shop and asked for bread. The oven being then hot and all prepared for the baking, the mistress of the shop cut off a good-sized piece of the risen dough to bake for Him. At this her fair, greedy daughter, who sate watching what was forward from a little window, upbraided her mother for this wasting of profit on such an outcast, and snatching the platter out of her hands, she chopped the piece of dough into half, and half, and half again. Nevertheless when this mean small lump was put into the oven, it presently began miraculously to rise and swell until it exceeded a full quartern of wheaten bread. In alarm at this strange sight the daughter—her round blue eyes largely eyeing the stranger in the dim light—turned on her mother, and cried out: "O Mother, Mother, *Heugh, heugh, heugh!*"

"As thou hast spoken," said our Saviour, "so be thou: child of the Night." Whereupon, the poor creature, feathered and in the likeness of an owl, fled forth in the dark towards the woodside.

109. "The White Owl."

When night is o'er the wood
  And moon-scared watch-dogs howl,
Comes forth in search of food
  The snowy mystic owl.
His soft, white, ghostly wings
  Beat noiselessly the air
Like some lost soul that hopelessly
  Is mute in its despair.

But now his hollow note
  Rings cheerless through the glade
And o'er the silent moat
  He flits from shade to shade.
He hovers, swoops and glides
  O'er meadows, moors and streams;
He seems to be some fantasy—
  A ghostly bird of dreams.

Why dost thou haunt the night?
  Why dost thou love the moon
When other birds delight
  To sing their joy at noon?
Art thou then crazed with love,
  Or is't for some fell crime
That thus thou flittest covertly
  At this unhallowed time?

F. J. Patmore

III. "HER SMALL SOUL." (line 23)

Smallest of all shrill souls among the English birds is the wren, but she has a remote relative that dwells in the dark, silent and enormous forests of South America, the Humming Bird, so swift and tiny a creature that it sucks a flower's nectar on the wing, its plumage being of a sheen lovelier than words can tell. There are two early descriptions of it; the first from Purchas's *Pilgrimes*, by Antonia Galvano of New Spain:

"There be certaine small birds named *vicmalim*, their bil is small and long. They live of the dew, and the juyce of flowers and roses. Their feathers bee small and of divers colours. They be greatly esteemed to worke gold with. They die or sleepe every yeere in the moneth of October, sitting upon a little bough in a warme and close place: they revive or wake againe in the moneth of April after that the flowers be sprung, and therefore they call them the revived birds—*Vicmalim*."

The second is Gonzalo Ferdinando de Oviedo's—his very name a string of gems:

". . . I have seene that one of these birds with her nest put into a paire of gold weights [scales] altogether, hath waide no more than a *tomini*, which are in poise 24 graines, with the feathers, without the which she would have waied somewhat less. And doubtlesse, when I consider the finenesse of the clawes and feete of these birds, I know not whereunto I may better liken them then to the little birds which the lymners of bookes are accustomed to paint on the margent of church bookes, and other bookes of divine service. Their feathers are of manie faire colours, as golden, yellow, and greene, beside other variable colours. Their beake is verie long for the proportion of their bodies, and as fine and subtile as a sowing needle. They are verie hardy [valiant], so that when they see a man clime the tree where they have their nests, they fly at his face, and strike him in the eyes, comming, going, and returning with such swiftnesse, that no man should lightly beleeve it that had not seene it. . . ."

Nor this of bats, either, as related by W. H. Hudson. He was walking at dusk one summer's evening in a sunken lane frequented by these hooked, cowled, mouselike creatures, which pestered him by repeatedly darting at the light check cap he was wearing. To fend them off he raised a light flexible cane he was carrying into the aire and twirled it as rapidly as possible in a circle above his head—an inverted cone of motion. But this was not the slightest obstacle to his sharp-eyed, exquisite-skinned persecutors. They flew through it!

112. "IT CAUGHT HIS IMAGE."

And Shelley:

> . . . I cannot tell my joy, when o'er a lake
> Upon a drooping bough with nightshade twined,
> I saw two azure halcyons clinging downward
> And thinning one bright bunch of amber berries,
> With quick long beaks, and in the deep there lay
> Those lovely forms imaged as in a sky. . . .

Anyone so happy as to be able to remember Mary Coleridge as a friend, will agree that to have seen her eyes is to have seen her own pool and Shelley's lake imaging such lovely flitting halcyons.

114 "KING PANDION HE IS DEAD."

A wild and dreadful legend is hidden here—of a King who wronged his Queen and her sister, daughters of Pandion, and how they avenged themselves upon him, sacrificing his son to their hatred. That Queen, goes this old tale, became a nightingale, her sister a swallow (crimson still dying the feathers of her throat), the evil king a hoopoe, and his firstborn was raised to life again a pheasant.

115. "A SPARHAWK PROUD"

—a little bird but of a noble family. Listen, at least, to Auceps, the Faulkner or Falconer, in *"The Compleat Angler."* ". . . And first, for the Element that I use to trade in, which is the Air . . . It stops not the high soaring of my noble generous *Falcon;* in it she ascends to such an height, as the dull eyes of beasts and fish are not able to reach to; their bodies are too gross for such high elevations. . . . But her mettle makes her careless of danger, for she then heeds nothing, but makes her nimble

Pinions cut the fluid air, and so makes her high way over the steepest mountains and deepest rivers, and in her glorious carere looks with contempt upon those high Steeples and magnificent Palaces which we adore and wonder at; from which height I can make her to descend by a word from my mouth (which she both knows and obeys), to accept of meat from my hand, to own me for her Master, to go home with me, and be willing the next day to afford me the like recreation. . . ."

In hawking (as in hunting) the novice had to learn the appropriate *terms* of his craft or art, and every company or flock or flight of birds had its special word, such as: A siege of herons, a spring of teals, a gaggle of geese, a badelynge (paddling) of ducks, a muster of peacocks, a bevy of quails, a congregation of plovers, a dule of turtle-doves, a walk of snipes, a fall of woodcocks, a building of rooks, a murmuration of starlings, an exaltation of larks, a watch of nightingales and a charm of goldfinches.

To every beast of the chase, too, was given a name for its footprints, tail, age, droppings, and "lodgement": to the hart its *harbour,* the hare its *form,* the boar its *couch,* the marten its *tree,* the otter its *watch,* the badger its *earth,* and the coney its *sit* or its *burrow.*

120. "Come Wary One."

. . . Tak any brid,[1] and put it in a cage,
And do al thyn entente and thy corage
To fostre it tendrely with mete and drinke,
Of allė deyntees that thou canst bethinke,
And keep it al-so clenly as thou may;
Al-though his cape of gold be never so gay,
Yet hath this brid, by twenty thousand fold,
Lever in a forest, that is rude and cold,
Gon etė wormės and swich wrecchednesse.
For ever this brid wol doon his bisinesse
To escape out of his cagė, if he may;
His libertee this brid desireth ay. . . .

Geoffrey Chaucer

[1] Bird.

When I was a child of eight or nine I had a passion for sparrows, and used often to set traps for them; but even if I succeeded in taking one alive, which was not always, I could never persuade it to live in a cage above a day or two. However much I pampered it, it drooped and died. Then, like a young crocodile, I occasionally shed tears. One fine morning, I remember, I visited a distant trap and, as usual, all but stopped breathing at discovering that it was "down." Very cautiously edging in my fingers towards the captive, I was startled out of my wits by a sudden prodigious skirring of wings, and lo and behold, I had caught—and lost—a starting. He fled away twenty yards or so, and perched on a hillock. I see him now, his feathers glistening in the sun, and his sharp head turned towards me, his eyes looking back at me, as of foe at foe. And that reminds me of the Griffons—the guardians of the mines of the one-eyed Arimaspians.

". . . From that land go men toward the land of Bacharie, where be full evil folk and full cruel. . . . In that country be many griffounes, more plentiful than in any other country. Some men say that they have the body upward as an eagle, and beneath as a lion; and truly they say sooth that they be of that shape. But a griffoun hath the body more great, and is more strong, than eight lions, of such lions as be on this side of the world; and larger and stronger than an hundred eagles, such as we have amongst us. For a griffoun there will bear flying to his nest a great horse, if he may find him handy, or two oxen yoked together, as they go at the plough. For he hath his talons so long and so broad and great upon his feet, as though they were hornes of great oxen, or of bugles (bullocks), or of kine; so that men make cups of them, to drink out of. And of their ribs, and the quills of their wings, men make bows full strong, to shoot with arrows and bowbolts. . . ."

So, too, Marco Polo on the Rukh, or Roc—the bird to whose leg Sinbad bound himself in order to escape out of the precipitous valley of diamonds:

"By people of the island—that is the island of Madagascar, where ivory abounds, ambergris, and red sandal-wood—it is reported that at a certain season of the year, a . . . bird, which they call a rukh, makes its appearance from the southern region. In form it is said to resemble the eagle, but it is incomparably greater in size; being so large and strong as to seize an elephant with its talons, and to lift it up into the air, from whence it lets it fall to the ground, in order that when dead it may prey upon the carcase. . . .

"The grand khan having heard this extraordinary relation, sent messengers to the island. . . . When they returned to the presence of his majesty, they brought with them (as I have heard) a feather of the rukh, positively affirmed to have measured ninety spans, and the quill part to have been two palms in circumference. This surprising exhibtion afforded his majesty extreme pleasure, and upon those by whom it was presented he bestowed valuable gifts."

But a griffoun is only a gigantic starling, so to speak; and it is a pity mine and I were enemies. "If a sparrow come before my window," wrote John Keats in one of his letters, "I take part in its existence, and pick about the gravel." Traps, gins, guns and birdlime are little help in this.

A Skylark wounded in the wing,
A Cherubim does cease to sing . . .

The wild Deer wandering here and there
Keeps the Human Soul from care . . .

The wanton Boy that kills the Fly
Shall feel the Spider's enmity . . .

Kill not the Moth nor Butterfly,
For the Last Judgment draweth nigh . . .

The Beggar's Dog and Widow's Cat,
Feed them, and thou wilt grow fat . . .

To see a World in a Grain of Sand,
And a Heaven in a Wild Flower,
Hold Infinity in the palm of your hand,
An eternity in an hour.

William Blake

. . . What is heaven? a globe of dew,
Filling in the morning new
Some eyed flower whose young leaves waken
On an unimagined world:
Constellated suns unshaken,
Orbits measureless, are furled
In that frail and fading sphere,
With ten millions gathered there,
To tremble, gleam, and disappear.

PERCY BYSSHE SHELLEY

The men who wrote these words, truly and solemnly meant them. They are not mere pretty flowers of the fancy, but the tough piercing roots of the tree of life that grew within their minds.

126. "COME UNTO THESE YELLOW SANDS."

This poem and many others (but not all) I copied out of Mr. Nahum's book in their original spelling. At first I found the reading of them tiring and troublesome. It was like looking at a dried-up flower or beetle. But there the things were; and after a good deal of trouble I not only began to read them more easily, but grew to like them thus for their own sake. First, because this was as they were actually written, before our English printers agreed to spell alike; and next, because the old words with their look of age became a pleasure to me in themselves. It was like watching the dried-up flower or beetle actually and as if by a magic of the mind coming to life. Besides, many of Shakespeare's shorter poems were already known to me. It touched them with newness to see them as they appeared (seven years after his death), in the pages of the famous folio volume of *Plays* that was printed in 1623 by Isaac Jaggard and Edward Blount.

Not only that; for it is curious too to see how in the old days English was constantly changing—its faded words falling like dead leaves from a tree, and new ones appearing. In a book which William Caxton printed as far back even as 1490, he says: "And certainly our language now used varieth far from that which was used and spoken when I was born. For we Englishmen be born under the domination of the moon, which is never steadfast but ever wavering, waxing one season and waneth and decreaseth another season."

Moreover, if the spelling of a word alters its effect on the eye, it must also affect the *mind* of the reader; and I must confess that "my lovynge deare," looks to me to tell of somebody more lovable even than "my loving dear." And what of shoogar-plummes, cleere greye eies, this murrkie fogghe, the moones en-ravysshyng?

"Even when," says Mr. Havelock Ellis, in *The Dance of Life,* "we leave out of consideration the great historical tradition of variety in this matter, it is doubtful . . . whether the advantages of encouraging everyone to spell like his fellows overbalance the advantages of encouraging everyone to spell unlike his fellows. When I was a teacher in the Australian Bush I derived far less enjoyment from the more or less 'correctly' spelt exercises of my pupils than from the occasional notes I received from their parents, who, never having been taught to spell, were able to spell in the grand manner. We are wilfully throwing away an endless source of delight. . . ."

A small niece of a friend of mine once wrote a little tale with the title, "A Bqlir Chesterdrores"—a peculiar chest-of-drawers. Now that surely is spelling in the grand manner.

And John Aubrey would have agreed: "A Gentlewoman," he says in his *Miscellanies,* [1696], dreamt that "a pultess of blew corants" would cure her sore throat; and it did so. "She was a pious woman, and affirmed it to be true." But would a mere *poultice of black currants* have had the same effect?

And surely a butcher's book looks a little more *sensitive* when its entries show like this:

	s.	d.
nec la - - - -	5	9
bf stk - - - -	3	6
kdy - - - - -	1	0
Sho Mtt - - - -	11	3
P. saus - - - -	2	8
bris - - - - -	3	7

128. "Shee carries Me above the Skie."

. . . This palace standeth in the air,
By necromancy placèd there,
That it no tempest needs to fear,
Which way soe'er it blow it;
And somewhat southward toward the noon,
Whence lies a way up to the moon,
And thence the Fairy can as soon
Pass to the earth below it.

The walls of spiders' legs are made
Well mortisèd and finely laid;
He was the master of his trade
It curiously that builded:
The windows of the eyes of cats,
And for the roof, instead of slats,
Is covered with the skins of bats,
With moonshine that are gilded. . . .

Michael Drayton

129. Who calls?

To *see* the "pretty elf": "Gette a square christall in lenth three inches. Lay the christall in the bloude of a white henne, 3 Wednesdaies and 3 Frydaies. Take it out, wash it with Holy Aq. Take 3 hazle sticks an yeare groth, pill [peel] them fair and white. Write the fayrie's name in bloud mix'd with inke. Write on eche stick. Then burie themm under some hill whereat fayries haunte the Wednesdaie before you call her. The Fridaie following, take them uppe and call her at eight or three or tenn of the clock . . . but be in clene life and turn thy face towards East. You may command thys fayrie to the utmost."

131.

. . . Such a soft floating witchery of sound
As twilight Elfins make, when they at eve
Voyage on gentle gales from Fairy-Land,
Where Melodies round honey-dropping flowers,

Footless and wild, like birds of Paradise,
Nor pause, nor perch, hovering on untamed wing! . . .

S. T. Coleridge

133. "For Fear of Little Men."

"Terrestrial devils," says Robert Burton, "are those Lares, Genii, Fauns, Satyrs, Wood-nymphs, Foliots, Fairies, Robin Goodfellows, Trulli, etc., which as they are most conversant with men, so they do them most harm. . . . These are they that dance on heaths and greens . . . and leave that green circle, which we commonly find in plain fields, which others hold to proceed from a meteor falling, or some accidental rankness of the ground, so nature sports herself; they are sometimes seen by old women and children. . . . Paracelsus reckons up many places in Germany, where they do usually walk in little coats, some two foot long. A bigger kind there is of them called with us hobgoblins, and Robin Goodfellows, that would in those superstitious times grind corn for a mess of milk, cut wood, or do any manner of drudgery work. . . . Dithmarus Bleskenius, in his description of Iceland, reports for a certainty, that almost in every family they have yet some such familiar spirits. . . . Another sort of these there are, which frequent forlorn houses. . . . They will make strange noises in the night, howl sometimes pitifully, and then laugh again, cause great flame and sudden lights, fling stones, rattle chains, shave men, open doors and shut them, fling down platters, stools, chests, sometimes appear in the likeness of hares, crows, black dogs, etc." . . .

135.

So too with Hazel Dorn, in the following poem by Mr. Bernard Sleigh, who has very kindly allowed me to print it for the first time.

They stole her from the well beside the wood.
Ten years ago as village gossips tell;
One Beltane-eve when trees were all a-bud
In copse and fell.

Ominous, vast, the moon rose full and red
Behind dim hills; no leaf stirred in the glen
That breathless eve, when she was pixy-led
Beyond our ken.

For she had worn no rowan in her hair,—
Nor set the cream-bowl by the kitchen door,—
Nor whispered low the pagan faery prayer
Of ancient lore;

But trod that daisied ring in hose and shoon,
To hear entranced, their elf-bells round her ring;
The wizard spells about her wail and croon
With gathering ring.

Swiftly her arms they bound in gossamer,
With elvish lures they held her soul in thrall;
With wizard sorceries enveloped her
Past cry or call.

A passing shepherd caught his breath to see
A golden mist of moving wings and lights
Swirl upwards past the red moon eerily
To starlit heights.

While far off carollings half drowned a cry,
Mournful, remote, of "Mother, Mother dear,"
Floating across the drifting haze,—a sigh
"Farewell, Farewell!"

In the small hours of Beltane or May Day, it was once the custom to light up great bonfires on the hills of the Highlands—a relic of sun-worship as old as the Druids. Mr. Gilbert Sheldon tells me, indeed, that as late as 1899 he saw the hills round Glengariff ablaze with them. They must be kindled with what is called need-fire. And need-fire is made by nine men twisting a wimble of wood in a balk of oak until the friction makes sparks fly. With these they ignite dry agaric, a fungus that grows on birch-trees (which have a highly inflammable bark), and soon the blaze is reddening the complete countryside under the night-sky. Need-fire in a window-nook or carried in a lantern is—like iron—an invincible defence against witches and witchcraft. Beltane cakes—to be eaten whilst squatting on the hills, or dancing and watching the fire—are made out of a caudle of eggs, butter, oatmeal and milk.

"No Rowan in her Hair."

So potent is the flower or berry or wood of the rowan or witch-wood or quicken or whicken-tree or mountain ash against the wiles of the elf-folk, that dairymaids use it for cream-stirrers and cowherds for a switch.

Rowan-tree and red thread
Gar the Witches tyne their speed.

136. "True Thomas."

There are four early copies in handwriting—two of them written about 1450—of a rhymed romance telling how Thomas in his youth, while dreaming day-dreams under the Eildon Tree, was met and greeted by the Queen of fair Elfland. The ballad on p. 124 has been passed on from mouth to mouth.

Up to our own grandmothers' day, at least, this Thomas Rhymour of Ercildoune—a village not far distant from where the Leader joins the Tweed—was famous as a Wise One and a Seer (a See-er—with the inward eye). He lived seven centuries ago, between 1210 and 1297. Years after he had returned from Elfland—as the ballad tells—while he sat feasting in his Castle, news was brought to him that a hart and a hind, having issued out of the forest, were to be seen stepping fair and softly down the stony street of the town, to the marvel of the people. At this, Thomas at once arose from among his guests; left the feast; made down to the street; followed after these strange summoners: and was seen no more.

"Ilka tett," line 7, means every twist or plait; a "fairlie," stanza 11, is a wonder, mystery, marvel; and the "coat" in the last stanza, being of "even cloth," was finer than the finest *napless* damask.

So, too, Young Tamlane, when a boy "just turned of nine," was carried off by the Elfin Queen:

Ae fatal morning I went out
Dreading nae injury,
And thinking lang fell soun asleep
Beneath an apple tree.

Then by it came the Elfin Queen
And laid her hand on me;
And from that time since ever I mind
I've been in her companie. . . .

He seems to have been an outlandish and unhuman creature—if this next rhyme tells of him truly (*gait,* meaning road; *pin* (?) knife *; *coft,* bought; *moss,* peat-bog; and *boonmost*—you can guess):

Tam o' the linn came up the gait,
Wi' twenty puddings on a plate,
And every pudding had a pin,
"We'll eat them a'," quo' Tam o' the linn.

Tam o' the linn had nae breeks to wear,
He coft him a sheep's-skin to make him a pair,
The fleshy side out, the woolly side in,
"It's fine summer cleeding," quo' Tam o' the linn.

Tam o' the linn he had three bairns,
They fell in the fire, in each others' arms;
"Oh," quo' the boonmost, "I've got a het skin";
"It's hetter below," quo' Tam o' the linn.

Tam o' the linn gaed to the moss,
To seek a stable to his horse;
The moss was open, and Tam fell in,
"I've stabled mysel'," quo' Tam o' the linn.

[* *Pin,* a friend tells me, here means, not a knife, but a peg or skewer. "I remember," he writes, "hearing my grandmother talk of the killing of the 'Mert'—the cow killed at Martinmas for the family larder—and the making of black puddings from the blood. Each pudding was fastened with a *pin* . . . and all were hung on a pole, called, I think, the perk, and suspended from the kitchen ceiling, where they gleamed brown-black in the lamplight."]

137. "I MADE A GARLAND FOR HER HEAD."

. . . Linen was her small camise,
White with ermine her pelisse,
  She had a silken gown.
Tiger lilies were her hose,
Flowers o' may her little shoes,
  Fitted tightly on.

For a girdle, tender leaves,
When the weather rained, grew green,
  Buttoned up with gold.
Cords of flowers swung above
Her wallet shapen all for love,
  And Love the giver bold.

On a mule she rode along,
And the mule was silver shod,
  Saddle gold inlaid;
On a crupper right behind
Three rose trees stood up in line
  For to give her shade.

She went riding through the mead;
All the knights who met her steed
  Bowed with courtly state.
"Lady fair, whence are you sped?"
"I am the boast of France," she said,
  "Of renowned estate.

"My father is the nightingale
Who sings within the bosky dale
  On the tallest tree.

The mermaiden my mother is,
She who sings her melodies
  In the deep salt sea."

"Lady, blessed was your birth,
Parentage of famous worth
  And renowned estate.
Would that God our Father dear
Gave you for to be my peer
  And my wedded mate."

From the French, of the twelfth century; and translated by Claude Colleer Abbot.

138. "SABRINA."

This song is from *Comus,* a masque written by Milton for the entertainment of the Earl of Bridgewater, lord lieutenant of Wales, at Ludlow Castle in 1634. That Castle's Hall is now open to the sky—"the lightning shines there; snow burdens the ivy." From a neighbouring room the two princes, Edward V. and his brother, went to their violent death in the Tower. Below the ruinous Castle flow together the Teme and the Corve, on their way to the Severn—of which "fair" Sabrina, the daughter of Estrildis, is the Nymph, she having been drowned in its waters by Guendolen, the jealous queen of Locrine the son of Brut. Estrildis herself, the daughter of King Humber, "so farre excelled in bewtie, that none was then lightly found unto her comparable, for her skin was so whyte that scarcely the fynest kind of Ivorie that might be found, nor the snowe lately fallen downe from the Elament, nor the Lylles did passe the same."

Milton's poems—*Lycidas,* for instance—are occasionally "difficult" not so much because they are deep as because they refer to some ancient myth or legend. In the lines I have omitted from No. 138 are many such references awaiting the reader—one to the following tale of Glaucus, for example:

There is a secret herb which, if nibbled by fish already gasping to death in our air, gives them the power and cunning to slip back through the grasses into their waters again. Of this herb Glaucus tasted, and instantly his eyes dazzled in desire to share their green transparent deeps. Whereupon the laughing divinities of the rivers gave him sea-green hair sleeking the stream, fins and a fish's tail, and feasted him merrily. His story is told by Keats in the third book of his *Endymion,* while Leucothea's, another reference, is to be found in the fifth of the *Odyssey*. As for the Sirens, here is the counsel Circe gave Ulysses, the while his seamen lay asleep the night after they had returned in safety from Pluto's dismal mansions:

"... And then observe: They sit amidst a mead,
And round about it runs a hedge or wall
Of dead men's bones, their withered skins and all
Hung all along upon it; and these men
Were such as they had fawned into their fen,

And then their skins hung on their hedge of bones.
Sail by them therefore, thy companions
Beforehand causing to stop every ear
With sweet soft wax, so close that none may hear
A note of all their charmings. . . ."

139.

These Songs are from the last act of *A Midsummer Night's Dream*—the Duke and his guests are retired, and now sleep far from Life's Play; and Puck and the fairies are abroad in his palace.

"I AM SENT WITH BROOME BEFORE."

When the cock begins to crow,
And the embers leave to glow,
And the owl cries, Tu-whit—Tu-whoo,
When crickets do sing
And mice roam about,
And midnight bells ring
To call the devout:
When the lazy lie sleeping
And think it no harm,
Their zeal is so cold
And their beds are so warm.

When the long—long lazy slut
Has not made the parlour clean,
No water on the hearth is put,
But all things in disorder seem;
Then we trip it round the room
And make like bees a drowsy hum.
Be she Betty, Nan, or Sue,
We make her of another hue
And pinch her black and blue.

But when the Puritans came in, the fairies (naturally) fled away. And Richard Corbet bewailed their exile:

"Farewell, rewards and fairies!"
Good housewives now may say,
For now foul sluts in dairies
Do fare as well as they.
And though they sweep their hearths no less
Than maids were wont to do,
Yet who of late, for cleanliness,
Finds sixpence in her shoe? . . .

At morning and at evening both
You merry were and glad;
So little care of sleep or sloth
These pretty ladies had;
When Tom came home from labour,
Or Ciss to milking rose,
Then merrily merrily went their tabour
And nimbly went their toes.

Witness those rings and roundelays
Of theirs, which yet remain,
Were footed in Queen Mary's days
On many a grassy plain;
But since of late, Elizabeth,
And later, James came in,
They never danced on any heath
As when the time hath been.

For times change, and with them changes the direction of man's imagination. He turns his questing thoughts now this way, now that; and though our learned dictionaries may maintain that fairy rings are but brighter circles in green grass formed by "certain fungi, especially *marasmius oreades*"—who knows?—

> He that sees blowing the wild wood tree,
> And peewits circling their watery glass,
> Dreams about Strangers that yet may be
>   Dark to our eyes, Alas!

After all, Geoffrey Chaucer, even in *his* distant day, lamented that England was forsaken of the Silent Folk. Whisper, and they will return—bringing with them Prince Oberon, who "is of heyght but of III fote, and crokyed shulderyd. . . . And yf ye speke to hym, ye are lost for ever."

140. "Awn. 'Who feasts tonight?'"

Another mere fragment—from p. 182 of Mr. C. M. Doughty's Play, entitled *The Cliffs.* For the supreme gifts bestowed on the world by this great traveller and poet, the reader must seek out not only this volume, but his *Arabia Deserta,* and his *Dawn in Britain.*

"All in their Watchet Cloaks." (line 15)

> "Nan Page (my daughter) and my little sonne,
> And three or foure more of their growth, wee'l dress
> Like Urchins, Ouphes, and Fairies, greene and white,
> With rounds of waxen Tapers on their heads,
> And rattles in their hands . . ."

The Merry Wives of Windsor

141. A Hunt's-up

In his book on English Poesy, Puttenham, who was born about 1520, says that a poet of the name of Gray won the esteem of Henry VIII. and the Duke of Somerset for "making certeine merry ballades, whereof one chiefly was, 'the hunte is up, the hunte is up.'" Henry VIII., moreover, was himself a versifier, and a musician. He "did not only sing his part *sure,* but also composed services for his Chappel of four, five, and six parts." Here is the first stanza of one of his poems:

> As the holly groweth green,
> And never changeth hue,
> So I am, ever hath been
> Unto my lady true. . . .

which, with other equally surprising in sentiment, may be found in full in that casket of antiquities, *Early English Lyrics.*

Queen Elizabeth inherited her father's pleasure in music and poetry. She played "excellently well" on the virginal—an oblong quill-plucked instrument with a keyboard, like a diminutive pianoforte or harpsicord, and of a tone "small, but extraordinarily clear and bright in quality." She also made verses:

> The doubt of future foes
> Exiles my present joy,
> And wit me warnes to shun such snares,
> As threaten mine annoy.
>
> For falsehood now doth flow,
> And subject faith doth ebbe,
> Which would not be if reason rul'd,
> Or wisdome wev'd the webbe.

—and one cannot regret their brevity.

143.

When John Peel, his hunting over, was carried at last to his grave, "the old huntsmen gathered round it in a solid ring, each holding his dog by the slip." And when the final *Ashes to ashes, dust to dust,* was pronounced, the whole company scattered "their sprigs of rosemary over the coffin, then raising their heads, gave a simultaneous *Yo-ho! Tally-ho!* the sound of which became heightened by the dogs joining their voices, as they rung the last cry over their 'earthed' companion."

148. "A Fulle Fayre Tyme."

What wonder May was welcome in medieval days—after the long winters and the black cold nights, when roads were all but impassable, and men, "despisinge schetes" and nightgear, went to their naked beds with nought but the stars or a dip for candle and maybe their own bones and a scatter of straw for warmth? Is not "Loud sing, Cuckoo!" our oldest song? Nevertheless, "ne'er cast a clout . . ." for though

> March will search ye;
> And April try;
> May will tell ye
> Whether ye'll live, or die.

149.

Only the sound remains
Of the old mill;
Gone is the wheel;
On the prone roof and walls the nettle reigns.

Water that toils no more
Dangles white locks
And, falling, mocks
The music of the mill-wheel's busy roar. . . .

Only the idle foam
Of water falling
Changelessly calling,
Where once men had a work-place and a home.

Edward Thomas

150. "The Ample Heaven."

The unthrifty sun shot vital gold,
A thousand pieces;
And heaven its azure did unfold
Chequered with snowy fleeces;
The air was all in spice,
And every bush

A garland wore; thus fed my eyes,
But all the earth lay hush.

Only a little fountain lent
Some use for ears,
And on the dumb shades language spent—
The music of her tears.

HENRY VAUGHAN

"THE TIME SO TRANQUIL IS AND STILL." (line 13)

Clear had the day been from the dawn,
All chequered was the sky,
Thin clouds, like scarves of cobweb lawn,
Veiled heaven's most glorious eye.

The wind had no more strength than this,
—That leisurely it blew—
To make one leaf the next to kiss
That closely by it grew.

The rills, that on the pebbles played,
Might now be heard at will;
This world the only music made,
Else everything was still. . . .

MICHAEL DRAYTON

153. "O FOR A BOOKE."

Nor—says John Bunyan:

Nor let them fall under Discouragement
Who at their Horn-book stick, and time hath spent
Upon (their) A, B, C while others do
Into their Primer, or their Psalter go.
Some boys with difficulty do begin
Who in the end, the Bays, and Lawrel win.

On the other hand:

Some Boys have Wit enough to sport and play,
Who at their Books are Block-heads day by day.

Some men are arch enough at any Vice,
But Dunces in the way to Paradice.

Blockhead one may be, and in some respects almost certainly *is,* but to add books to one's "sport and play" is to add an interest and delight whose wellspring will never fail. In this too we are incalculably better off than were our great-grandfathers when *they* were young. Ballads, chapbooks and broadsides, even for multitudes of those who could read, were once almost the only literature available. And as late as the early years of the nineteenth century the companion pieces that follow were the kind of reading their elders considered proper for children. The first comes from "The Half Holiday Task Book or Mirror of Mind":

"A Gentleman met a little Girl in the street selling water-cresses; and although he did not just then want any cresses he was so pleased with her neat, clean and modest appearance that he kindly gave her a penny; which of course greatly delighted her, so she went along full of gratitude crying 'Water-cresses! Water-cresses!' and she soon sold all her stock. Now when she went home, her mother thought she had been asking more for her cresses than she ought because she had so much money; but the little girl told the truth, for

'Tis a sin, to cheat one's mother,
As great as cheating any other."

The second has a less happy but not less edifying ending; its title being, "Of the Boy and his Mother."

"A Boy having stollen his School-fellows Horn-book at School, brought it to his Mother: By whom being not chastised, he played the Thief daily more and more. In process of time, he began to steal great things; at last being apprehended of the Magistrate, was led to execution: But his Mother following and crying out, he entreated the Serjeants that they would permit him to whisper in her Ear, who permitting him, the Mother hastening laid her Ear to her Son's Mouth, he bites off a piece of his Mother's Ear with his Teeth.

"When his Mother and the rest rated at him, not only as being a Thief but also ungracious towards his own Mother, he said, 'She is the cause of my undoing, for if she had punished me for stealing the Horn-book, I had not proceeded to greater things, nor been led to my Execution.' "

Maybe. Still, the action *was* ungracious, and a boy who could steal a horn-book which was not only a lesson book but only worth about a ha'penny, was hardly a promising lad. Nowadays that stolen horn-book would be worth its weight in gold—they are so rare: though many millions of them must have been sold and used between 1450 and the beginning of the nineteenth century. They were usually made of wood but sometimes of cardboard or leather or metal or ivory. There is still in existence a delicate little horn-book of filigree silver, which was used by Queen Elizabeth. In shape they resembled a small oblong hand-glass—with a hole through the handle. A piece of string was passed through the hole, and the horn-book was tied round its owner's waist.

> He was never free
> From his A-B-C,
> A doleful thing for a child to be!

Fixed and fitted to one side of it was an oblong strip of parchment, card, or paper, containing the Criss-cross-row (the alphabet with a cross before A), a few digraphs, *ab, ba,* and so on, "In the name of the Father . . .", and the Lord's Prayer. This strip was protected from grubby fingers by a piece of transparent horn. Hence the name. Apart from horn-books, the alphabet was also stamped out in gilded gingerbread; so having learned your alphabet, you digested it.

After the horn-book followed the battledore, and "slates" came in when battledores were going out; the reference to them, at any rate, in the following extract from a little paper-bound book entitled *Henry* of 1817 suggests a novelty:

"Henry was a little boy about five years old; and one day, whilst his mother was busy at work, he stood by her side, and amused himself with trying to write upon a pretty little slate, that had been given to him for being a good boy; it had a red leather frame, and at the top was a little hole through which a string was put, with a slate pencil tied to the end of it, for Henry to write with; and there was another bit of string put through the same hole, with a little piece of sponge tied to it, that

Henry might rub out those letters he made badly: and after he had written on his slate till he was tired, he left off, and stood still a little time, and then he said to his mother, 'Mother, I am just thinking that I wish I knew where all the things in the world come from, and what is the use of them': and his mother said, 'I believe there are very few people that know so much as that, my dear; but you may, by paying attention, learn the use of a great many . . .'"

There we must leave him—on the Royal Road to Learning. The one thing, however, the vast majority of these bygone tales suggest is that their authors considered children to be little better than half-witted. Any stuffing, they thought (provided it was indigestible) was good enough for goslings; and a glance at some of the children's books of to-day will prove that this hideous falsity is not yet extinct. If every writer of learning or imagination made it his happy privilege to write but one book for the young on his own beloved subject, and put his *whole mind* into it, just as Faraday wrote his *History of a Candle*—what joy there would be in store for the children yet unborn.

Little articles, like horn-books, rattles, mugs, intended for work-a-day human use, at first crude and simple in workmanship [see Robinson Crusoe's entries in his Diary for January of the third year of his becoming a castaway], are apt as time goes by, to become more and more delicate and curious. As long, that is, as they are made by hand (so that a man can put his pleasure as well as his labour into them) and are not turned out by the thousand from a machine, which may have beauty and unfailing skill, but is sense-less.

In any case they remain lively little reminders of their own day and fashion and are well worth a close examination when found—antiquated needle-cases, old keys (great and small), seals, thimbles, bobbins, bodkins, penknives, scissors, watch-keys, perfume bottles, shoe-buckles, snuffers, patch-boxes; even old kitchen utensils—candlesticks, gridirons, tinder boxes, roasting jacks, warming pans, skillets, chafing dishes. Indeed there was a large and exciting volume published a few years ago on the subject of *Pins and Pin-Cushions* alone. Whatever concerns one's childhood, too, becomes enriched and endeared in memory, and even the most trivial objects that have passed out of common use and have become old-fashioned or antiquated, seem to belong to the childhood of humanity itself. Who would not treasure a fragment of Noah's Ark, a lock of Absalom's hair, Prester John's thumb-ring, Scheherezade's night-lamp, a glove of Caesar's or one of King Alfred's burnt cakes?

But to come back to the reader in his shadie nooke:

Tales of my Nursery! shall that still loved spot,
That window corner, ever be forgot,
Where through the woodbine—when with upward ray
Gleamed the last shadow of departing day—
Still did I sit, and with unwearied eye,
Read while I wept, and scarcely paused to sigh!
In that gay drawer, with fairy fictions stored,
When some new tale was added to my hoard,
While o'er each page my eager glance was flung,
'Twas but to learn what female fate was sung;
If no sad maid the castle shut from light,
I heeded not the giant and the knight.
Sweet Cinderella, even before the ball,
How did I love thee—ashes, rags, and all!
What bliss I deemed it to have stood beside,
On every virgin when thy shoe was tried!
How longed to see thy shape the slipper suit!
But, dearer than the slipper, loved the foot.

"Or the Streete Cryes all about."

A friend whose judgment in such matters it would be mere vanity to question assures me that this rhyme "O for a Booke" is nothing but a "modern imposture," and its spelling all sham. So be it: and yet even at that there is a warm breath of Summer in it and a green and shady tree, while the street cries it refers to are at any rate as old as Babylon.

According to *London Lickpenny* the cries most audible in his time—the fifteenth century—were "Hot Pease!" "Hot fine Oatcakes!" "Whiting, maids, whitings!" "Hot codlings!" "Maribones! Maribones!" "Have you any Old Boots?" "Buy a Mat!"

—with a general hullabaloo of "What d'ye lack? What d'ye lack?" and an occasional bawling of "Clubs!" to summon the tag, rag and bobtail to a row.

Many of the old cries were in rhyme.

Screens:

> I have Screenes, if you desier
> To keepe your Butey from the fire.

Oranges:

> Fine Sevil oranges! Fine lemmons, fine!
> Round, sound, and tender, inside and rine.
> One pin's prick will their vertue show;
> Tell their liquour by their weight, as anyone may know.

Cherries:

> Round and sound,
> Two-pence a pound,
> Cherries, rare ripe cherries!

Cherries dangling on a stick:

> Cherries a ha'penny a stick:
> Come and pick! Come and pick!
> Cherries big as plums! Who comes, who comes?

There were three rhymed cries for Hot Cross Buns alone:

> One a penny, poker,
> Two a penny, tongs,
> Three a penny, fire-irons,
> Hot Cross Buns!

> One a penny, two a penny,
> Hot Cross Buns,
> Sugar 'em and butter 'em,
> And stick 'em in your muns [mouths].

One-a-penny, two-a-penny, hot-cross-buns!
If your daughters will not eat 'em, why, then, give 'em to your sons;
But you haven't any of these pretty little elves,
You can't do no better than to eat 'em up yourselves.

One-a-penny, two-a-penny, hot-cross-buns:
All hot, hot, hot, all hot.

Of singing cries, nowadays we may still hear in the sunny summer London streets the sweet and doleful strains of Won't you buy my sweet blooming lavender: Sixteen branches a penny! And in the dusk of November the muffin-man's bell. Besides these, we have Rag-a'-bone! Milk-o! Any scissors to grind? Clo' props! Water-creesses! and, as I remember years ago,

Young lambs to sell, white lambs to sell;
If I'd as much money as I could tell
I wouldn't be crying, Young lambs to sell!

154. "GREEN BROOM."

Who liveth so merry in all this land
As doth the poor widdow that selleth the sand?
And ever she singeth as I can guesse,
Will you buy any sand, any sand, mistress?

The broom-man maketh his living most sweet,
With carrying of brooms from street to street;
Who would desire a pleasanter thing,
Than all the day long to doe nothing but sing?

The chimney-sweeper all the long day,
He singeth and sweepeth the soote away;
Yet when he comes home, altho' he be weary,
With his sweet wife he maketh full merry. . . .

—which carries with it a faint, a very faint, rumour of William Blake.

155. "WITH HEY! WITH HOW! WITH HOY."

In *Rustic Speech and Folk Lore* Mrs. Wright gives the decoys with which the country people all over England beguile their beasts and poultry into "shippon, sty, or pen"; or holla them on their way, but much, I have found, depends on him who hollas!

For *Cows*: Coop! Cush, cush!—While the milkmaid calls—Hoaf! Hobe! Mull! Proo! Proochy! Prut!

For *Calves*: Moodie! Mog, mog, mog! Pui-ho! Sook, sook!

For *Sheep*: Co-hobe! Ovey!

For *Pigs*: Check-check! Cheat! Dack, dack! Giss! or Gissy! Lix! Ric-sic! Shug, shug, shug! Tantassa, tantassa pig, tow a row, a row! Tig, tig, tig!

For *Turkeys*: Cobbler! Peet, peet, peet! Pen! Pur, pur, pur!

For *Geese*: Fly-laig! Gag, gag, gag! Ob-ee! White-hoddy!

For *Ducks*: Bid, bid, bid! Diddle! Dill, dill! Wid! Wheetie!

For *Pigeons*: Pees! Pod!

And for *Rabbits*: Map!

On Winter mornings when the air is still
The Ploughman's cries come floating down the hill,
    Ge-e-e-e Up! Ge-e-e-e Whoa!
The selfsame sharp and throaty cries are they—
The teamsters used in Julius Caesar's day—
    Ge-e-e-e Up! Ge-e-e-e Whoa!

Nothing is changed, since tillage first began
The same brown earth has yielded food to man.

Nothing is changed—save ploughman, team and share:
A thousand furrows have been made just there;

And every time, with cautious sidelong looks,
Have followed, close behind, the hungry rooks.

And every time the team was kept in hand
By those two potent phrases of command—
    Ge-e-e-e Up! Ge-e-e-e Whoa!
Which every horse on earth can understand
From Christiana to Van Dieman's Land,
    Ge-e-e-e Up! Ge-e-e-e Whoa!

E. V. Lucas

"Yea, and I do vow unto thee," cried the voice out of the rock; "call unto them but in their own names and language, and the strong and delicate creatures of the countries of the mind will flock into the living field of thy vision, and above the waters will befall the secret singing of birds, and thou shalt be a pilgrim. Mark how intense a shadow dwells upon this stone! Therein too lurk marvels to be seen." The voice ceased, and

I heard nothing but the tapping of a fragment of dry lichen which in the draught of the hot air caused by the burning sunlight stirred between rock and sand. And I cried, "O unfortunate one, I thirst!"

156. "LAVENDER'S BLUE."

"A poor thing," as Audrey says, but homely and melodious and once *some*body's own: such a somebody as inscribed on the walls of Burford Church:

> ". . . Love made me Poet
> And this I writt,
> My harte did do yt
> And not my witt."

It must be confessed however [in 1928], that it was not Audrey who said in the play what she was made to say here, but Touchstone; and that he did not say: "A *poor* thing" but an *ill-favoured!*

> O Memory, thou strange deceiver!
> Who can trust her? How believe her?
> While she keeps in one same pack
> Dream and real upon her back.
> When I call her, want her most,
> She's gone wandering and is lost.
> She's capricious as the wind,
> Yet what sweets she leaves behind.
> Where—without her—I? for lo,
> When she's gone I too must go!

159. "THERE IS A GARDEN IN HER FACE."

Thomas Campion was "borne upon Ash Weddensday being the twelft day of February. An. Rg. Eliz. nono"—1567. He had one sister, Rose. He was educated at Peterhouse, Cambridge, and this was his yearly allowance of clothes: A gowne, a cap, a hat, ii dubletes, ii payres of hose, iiii payres of netherstockes, vi payre of shoes, ii shirts, and two bandes. He was allowed also one quire of paper every quarter; and half a pound of candles every fortnight from Michaelmas to Lady Day. He studied law, may for a time have fought as a soldier in France, and became a physician. He died on March 1, 1620, and was buried on the same day at St. Dunstan's in the West, Fleet Street, the entry in the register under that date being: "Thomas Campion, doctor of Phisicke, was buried."

I have taken these particulars from Mr. S. P. Vivian's edition of his poems, because it is pleasant to share even this of the little that is known of a man who was not only a fine and original poet and "a most curious metrist"—though for two centuries a forgotten one—but also because he was one of the chief song-writers in the great age of English Music. Like all good craftsmen, he endeavoured to do his work "well, surely, cleanly, workmanly, substantially, curiously, and sufficiently," as did the glaziers of King's College Chapel, which is distant but a kingfisher's flight over a strip of lovely water from his own serene Peterhouse. It seems a little curious that being himself a lover of music he should have at first detested rhyming in verse. But he lived none the less to write such delicate rhymed poems as this.

In the preface to his *Book of Ayres,* he says, "I have chiefely aymed to couple my Words and Notes *lovingly* together, which will be much for him to doe that hath not power over both."

161.

I see His blood upon the rose
And in the stars the glory of His eyes,
His body gleams amid eternal snows,
His tears fall from the skies.

I see His face in every flower;
The thunder and the singing of the birds
Are but His voice—and carven by His power
Rocks are His written words.

All pathways by His feet are worn,
His strong heart stirs the ever-beating sea,
His crown of thorns is twined with every thorn,
His cross is every tree.

JOSEPH PLUNKETT

163.—"THESE FLOWERS, AS IN THEIR CAUSES, SLEEP."

—while, also, flowers may themselves be the *causes* of poems, as, in a degree, a rain-bow'd dewdrop in a buttercup is of the buttercup's causing.

In May, when sea-winds pierced our solitudes,
I found the fresh Rhodora in the woods,
Spreading its leafless blooms in a damp nook,
To please the desert and the sluggish brook.
The purple petals, fallen in the pool,
Made the black water with their beauty gay;
Here might the red-bird come his plumes to cool,
And court the flower that cheapen's his array.
Rhodora! Let the sages ask thee why
This charm is fasted on the earth and sky . . .
Why thou wert there, O rival of the rose!
I never thought to ask, I never knew;
But, in my simple ignorance, suppose
The self-same Power that brought me there brought you. . . .

R. W. EMERSON

And here anemone and cyclamen—in an enchanting little poem of but the day before yesterday:

Long ago I went to Rome
As pilgrims go in Spring,
Journeying through the happy hills
Where nightingales sing,
And where the blue anemones
Drift among the pines
Until the woods creep down into
A wilderness of vines.

Now every year I go to Rome
As lovers go in dreams,
To pick the fragrant cyclamen,
To bathe in Sabine streams,
And come at nightfall to the city
Across the shadowy plain,

And hear through all the dusty streets
The waterfalls again.

MARGARET CECILIA FURSE

"THE PHOENIX BUILDS HER SPICY NEST." (line 18)

The Phoenix, in faith rather than by sight, is thus described by Pliny: "She is as big as an eagle, in colour yellow, and bright as gold, namely all about the neck, the rest of the bodie a deep red purple; the taile azure blue, intermingled with feathers among of rose carnation colour: and the head bravely adorned with a crest and pennache finely wrought, having a tuft and plume thereupon right faire and goodly to be seene."

Her life is but three hundred and nine years less in duration than that of the many-centuried patriarch Methuselah. When the lassitude of age begins to creep upon her, she wings across sea and land to the sole Arabian Tree. There she builds a nest of aromatic twigs, cassia and frankincense, and enkindling it with her own dying ardour she is consumed to ashes. And yet —while still they are of a heat beyond the tempering of the sun that shines down on them from the heavens, they magically stir, take form and re-awaken; and she arises to life renewed— in her gold, her rose carnation, her purple and azure blue.

THE PHOENIX.

O blest unfabled Incense-Tree,
That burns in glorious Araby,
With red scent chalicing the air
Till earth-life grow Elysian there!

Half buried to her flaming breast
In this bright tree, she makes her nest,
Hundred-sunned Phoenix! when she must
Crumble at length to hoary dust!

Her gorgeous death-bed! her rich pyre
Burnt up with aromatic fire!
Her urn, sight-high from spoiler men!
Her birthplace when self-born again!

The mountainless green wilds among,
Here ends she her unechoing song!
With amber trees and odorous sighs
Mourned by the desert where she dies! . . .

GEORGE DARLEY

164. "THE BOWER OF BLISS."

This and No. 348 are but the merest fragments of the *Faerie Queene*; but they reveal what an echoing mutable melody are its words. And were ever light and colour so living, natural and crystal clear? Reading this verse, hearing its sounds and sharing its vision in the imagination, you cannot think Thomas Nash was too fantastical when he wrote: "Poetry is the Honey of all Flowers, the Quintessence of all Sciences, the Marrow of Art and the very Phrase of Angels." Indeed, as Spenser's epitaph in Westminster Abbey says of him, he was the Prince of Poets of his time, and poet of poets he has always remained. John Keats, when he was a boy, used to sit in a little summer-house at Enfield with his schoolfellow, Cowden Clarke, drinking in this honeyed verse, and laying up store of purest English for his own brief life's matchless work. So, too, Abraham Cowley:

"How this love (for poetry) came to be produced in me so early is a hard question. I believe I can tell the particular little chance that filled my head first with such chimes of verse as have never since left ringing there. For I remember when I began to read, and to take some pleasure in it, there was wont to lie in my mother's parlour (I know not by what accident, for she herself never in her life read any book but of devotion), but there was wont to lie Spenser's works; this I happened to fall upon, and was infinitely delighted with the stories of the knights and giants and monsters and brave houses which I found everywhere there (though my understanding had little to do with all this); and by degrees with the tinkling of the rhyme and dance of the numbers, so that I think I had read him all over before I was twelve years old. . . ."

167. "THE BUSY WOODPECKER."

The birds of England have few country names by comparison with her wild flowers; and in this the green Woodpecker and the Long-tailed Tit are easily first. But no wonder. For the woodpecker—plumage, laughter, and "habits"—is a captivating creature; and to anybody who cares to watch a living nimble delightful thing at all, even a glimpse of a Long-tailed Tit is an event. To see *one,* indeed, is usually to see a complete family. You hear their small shrill calling, look up, and lo!—scattering from tree to tree they flit, with their loose, grey, ruffish feathers, small hooked beaks, and long slim tails, searching for caterpillars and tiny beetles, clinging to spray or twig wrong-side-up and upside-down, noisy, merry, alert. And then—all gone, vanished, fled! Into some other green garden—as momentary as a rainbow.

Among the green woodpecker's country names are Sprite, Hickway, Woodspite, Popinjay, Yaffle, Highhoe, Rindtabberer, Yaffingale, Green peck, Yuckel, Cutbill, Rain Pie, Nickerpecker, and Woodweele; while the long-tailed Tit, who is cousin to the Blue or Tom, Cole, Marsh, Great Ox-eyed, and Crested Tits, and known (to the ornithologist) as *Acredula Caudata,* of the family *Paridae,* is also called Millithrums, Hedgejug, Long-tailed Mufflin or Capon or Mag or Pie or Pod; Huck-muck, Mumruffin, Juffit, Poke-pudding, Bum barrel and Bottle-Tom.

Wild birds of course *derive* their names—varying from county to county—from their songs, colours, customs, nests and haunts. But it is curious how capricious the choice has been. For while some of the most familiar birds—robin, sparrow, thrush, nightingale, blackbird—have few names; others hardly less familiar have many, like the Sand-piper, who is known to his friends all over the country either as Watery pleeps, or Killie-leepsie, or Willywicket, or Dickie-di-dee, or Sandie, or Water junket, or Skittery deacon, or Bundie, or Steenie Pouter; or like the Barn Owl, who is also Church Owl, Roarer, Billy Wix, Pudge, Cherubim, Outlet and Povey. Yet the Kingfisher is merely the Dipper, though —to make up this—there is a pleasant little story about it in connection with Noah.

Then again, though the Wheat-ear's "haunts"—old ruins, graveyards, cairns—"has gotten it a bad name," there seems little to grumble at in Wittol, Chock, Clodhopper, Jobbler, and Coney chuck: the Goldfinch is also King Harry, Speckled Dick, Foolscoat, and Sweet William; the long-tailed Duck is Coal-and-Candle-light or Caloo; the small-songed clumsy-toed but dainty-coloured Chaffinch is Pinktwink, Shell-apple, Chaffy, and Charbob; while that remarkably officious, multitudinous, pugnacious and amusing bird the starling is nothing much more than Jacob or Gyp.

Sea birds commonly have as many names as royal princesses, and fishermen keep an eye on them, both for luck and the weather. But there is no more room—except for a legend that Nature when she had finished the Great Northern Diver discovered that she had left out its legs, and then in a pet flung any sort of a pair after it; while on the other hand it is said that when the song thrush reaches its teens it shed its old legs and grows new ones.

"A spirit interfused around,
A thrilling, silent life . . ."

"The afternoon sunshine flooded the wide plain, and as he walked through it he seemed to be walking through a kind of sea that was dancing with millions and millions of little golden sparks of light. The grasshoppers shrilled like birds; all the soft din that filled his ears came from insects; it was as if the world had been abandoned by everything else. Sometimes, where there was a flat stone or a bare patch of sandy soil, a lizard or a snake glittered in ecstatic trance. They never moved, even when he passed close by them. And Demophon suddenly knew that he and the snakes and the lizards and the grasshoppers and the butterflies and even the earth over which he walked, were one. And he knew at the same time that what united them was just this spirit which had guarded him by the pool. It was in this they all drew their breath and had their common life. It was the spirit of love—but hatred and fear were death. It was not a very clear thought doubtless; perhaps it was not even a thought at all; and yet it lit up his mind, and something else that was not his mind. His very body was lost in its happiness, so that he passed swiftly across the round ground, as he had seen birds sliding down the air on motionless wide wings.

"What was it—this something that was not his mind, that was even closer to him than his mind? It dwelt in him: it was the sadness which rose and mingled with the beauty that flowed in through his eyes from the summer fields, and through his ears from the wind and the sea: it was his longing for his lost playmate, his love for those spotted snakes, his friendship with this tiny flying beetle that had settled on his hand. It dwelt in him; but might it not be truer to say that it *was* Demophon? His home really was, then, in those far-off islands in the West; and he was not setting out on a journey, but going back, going home. A sudden mist gathered in his eyes, and he shook his head half angrily. How foolish he was getting, and how babyish! And looking up he saw that the dark, wooded slopes of Helikon were close at hand."

From *Demophon* by FORREST REID

168. "IF I WERE AS WISE AS THEY,
I WOULD STRAY APART AND BROOD. . . ."

'Twas at the season when the Earth upsprings
From slumber; as a spherèd angel's child,
Shadowing its eyes with green and golden wings,
  Stands up before its mother bright and mild,
Of whose soft voice the air expectant seems—
So stood before the sun, which shone and smiled
  To see it rise thus joyous from its dreams,
The fresh and radiant Earth. The hoary grove
Waxed green, and flowers burst forth like starry beams;
  The grass in the warm sun did start and move,
And many sea-buds burst under the waves serene.
How many a one, though none be near to love,
  Loves then the shade of his own soul, half seen
In any mirror—or the spring's young minions,
The wingèd leaves amid the copses green:
  How many a spirit then puts on the pinions
Of fancy, and outstrips the lagging blast,
And his own steps, and over wide dominions
  Sweeps in his dream-drawn chariot, far and fast,
More fleet than storms. . . .

P. B. SHELLY

170.

The poems of Robert Herrick and of Thomas Campion, though well known in their own day, remained for many years practically unread and forgotten. Thomas Traherne's (who died in 1674) had an even more curious fate, for they were discovered in manuscript and by chance on a bookstall so lately as 1896, and were first taken to be the work of Henry Vaughan. Here is a passage in prose from his *Centuries of Meditation*:

"The corn was orient and immortal wheat which never should be reaped nor was ever sown. I thought it had stood from everlasting to everlasting. The dust and stones of the street were as precious as gold; the gates were at first the end of the world. The green trees when I saw them first through one of the gates transported and ravished me; their sweetness and unusual beauty made my heart to leap, and almost mad with ecstasy, they were such strange and wonderful things. The men! oh, what venerable and reverend creatures did the aged seem! Immortal cherubims! And young men glittering and sparkling angels! and maids strange seraphic pieces of life and beauty! Boys and girls tumbling in the street were moving jewels: I knew not that they were born or should die. But all things abided eternally as they were in their proper places. Eternity was manifest in the light of the day, and something infinite behind everything appeared, which talked with my expectation and moved my desire. . . ."

172. "But silly we." (line 9)

This poem, I think, carries with it the thought that in study of that great book, that fair volume, called the World, there is no full stop, no limit, pause, conclusion. Like bees, with their nectar and honeycomb, man stores up his knowledge and experience in books. These and his houses outlast him; the things he makes; and here and there a famous or happy or tragic name is for a while remembered. Else, we are given our brief chequered busy lives—then vanish away, seeming but restless phantoms in Time's panoramic dream. So far at least as this world is concerned. And generations of men—as of the grasses and flowers—follow one upon another.

Oh, yes, my dear, you have a Mother,
And she, when young, was loved by another,
And in that mother's nursery
Played *her* mamma, like you and me.
When that mamma was tiny as you
She had a happy mother too:

On, on . . . Yes, presto! Puff! Pee-fee!—
And Grandam Eve and the apple-tree.
O, into distance, smalling, dimming,
Think of that endless row of women,
Like beads, like posts, like lamps, they seem—
Grey-green willows, and life a stream—
Laughing and sighing and lovely; and, Oh,
You to be next in that long row!

And yet, "But silly we" is true of most of us and of most of our time on earth. As Coventry Patmore says:

An idle Poet, here and there,
  Looks round him, but, for all the rest,
The world, unfathomably fair,
  Is duller than a witling's jest.
Love wakes men, once a life-time each;
  They lift their heavy lids, and look;
And, lo, what one sweet page can teach
  They read with joy, then shut the book:
And some give thanks, and some blaspheme,
  And most forget; but, either way,
That and the Child's unheeded dream
  Is all the light of all their day.

Or again, in the words of Sir John Davies—long since dead:

. . . I know my Soul hath power to know all things,
  Yet is she blind and ignorant in all:
  I know I am one of Nature's little kings,
  Yet to the least and vilest things am thrall.
  I know my life's a pain and but a span,
  I know my sense is mocked with everything;
  And, to conclude, I know myself a man
  Which is a proud and yet a wretched thing.

175. "For Soldiers"

from an old book entitled, "A Posie of Gilloflowers, eche differing from other in Colour and Odour, yet all sweete." There were memorable and sonorous names for collections of poems in the days of Humfrey Gifford (of whom nothing is known but that he made this Posie)—such as *Wits Commonwealth; The Banket of Sapience; The Paradise of Dainty Devices; A Gorgeous Gallery of Gallant Inventions; A Handfull of Pleasant Delights.*

"YE BUDS OF BRUTUS LAND"

—sons of those, that is, who, according to the ancient myth were descended from Brut or Brute, the Trojan, lineally descended from "the demy god Eneas, the sonne of Venus," daughter of Jupiter, the conqueror of Albion and the founder of London, from whose name comes *Britain* and *British.* He landed at Totnes (then in Cornwall) in B.C. in 1136, and was a Jack nonpareil in his dealings with giants; three of his victims being Geomagog, Hastripoldius and Rascalbundy.

"SOLDIERS ARE PREST" (stanza 1)

that is, seized by the King's men, the press-gangs, and carried away by force to fight in the wars.

"YOUR QUEEN."

"To the Most High, Mightie and Magnificent Empresse Renowmed for Pietie, Vertue, and all Gratious Government ELIZABETH by the Grace of God Queene of England Fraunce and Ireland and of Virginia." So runs Spenser's dedication of *The Faerie Queene,* while in *The Shepheardes Calender* for April are the lines:

See, where she sits upon the grassie greene,
(O seemely sight)
Yclad in Scarlot like a mayden Queene,
And Ermines white.
Upon her head a Cremosin coronet,
With Damaske roses and Daffadilles set:
Bayleaves betweene,
And Primroses greene
Embellish the sweete Violet.

At her christening, wrote Edward Hall in his *Chronicles,* she was "yclad," not in "scarlot," but in purple:

"The seventh day of September being Sunday, between three and four of the Clock at afternoon, the Queen was delivered of a fair Lady. The Mayor and his brethren, and forty of the chief of the citizens, were commanded to be at the Christening the Wednesday following, upon the which day the Mayor, sir Stephen Pecocke, in a gowne of Crimson Velvet, with his collar of S.S. and all the Aldermen in Scarlet, with collars and chains, and all the council of the city with them, took their barge after dinner, at one of the clock . . . and so rowed to Greenwich, where were many lords, knights, and gentlemen assembled. All the walls between the King's place and the Friers, were hanged with Arras, and all the way strawed with green Rushes: the Friers' Church was also hanged with Arras.

"The Font was of silver, and stood in the midst of the Church, three steps high, which was covered with a fine cloth, and divers gentlemen with aprons, and towels about their necks, gave attendance about it. That no filth should come into the Font, over it hung a square Canopy of crimson Satin, fringed with gold. About it was a rail covered with red silk. Between the choir and the body of the Church, was a close place with a pan of fire, to make the child ready in. When all these things were ordered, the child was brought to the hall, and then every man set forward: First the citizens two and two, then gentlemen, Esquires and Chaplains, next after them the Aldermen, and the Mayor alone; next the Mayor the king's council, the king's Chaplain in copes; then Barons, Bishops, Earls. Then came the Earl of Essex, bearing the covered basins gilt; after him the Marquis of Exeter with the taper of virgin wax; next him the Marquis Dorset, bearing the salt; and behind him the lady Mary of Norfolk, bearing the chrysom which was very rich of pearl and stone.

"The old Duchess of Norfolk bare the child in a Mantle of purple velvet with a long train furred with Ermine. The Duke of Norfolk, with his Marshal's rod went on the right hand of the said Duchess, and the Duke of Suffolk on the left hand, and before them went the officers of arms. The Countess of Kent bare the long train of the child's mantle, and between the Countess of Kent and the child went the Earl of Wiltshire on the right hand

and the Earl of Derby on the left hand, supporting the said train. In the midst over the said child was borne a Canopy. . . .

"The Godfather was the lord Archbishop of Canterbury: the Godmothers were the old Duchess of Norfolk, and the old Marchioness of Dorset, widows. And the child was named Elizabeth. . . . And then the trumpets blew. Then the child was brought up to the altar, and the Gospel said over it: and after that immediately the Archbishop of Canterbury confirmed it, the Marchioness of Exeter being Godmother. Then the Archbishop of Canterbury gave to the Princess a standing cup of gold, fretted with pearl: the Marchioness of Dorset gave three gilt bowls pounced with a cover: the Duchess of Norfolk gave to her a standing cup of gold: and the Marchioness of Exeter gave three standing bowls graven, all gilt with a cover.

"Then was brought in Wafers, Comfits, and Ypocras in such plenty that every man had as much as he would desire. Then they set forwards, the trumpets going before in the same order, toward the king's place as they did when they came thitherward, saving that the gifts that the Godfather and the Godmothers gave were borne before the child. . . . And all the one side as they went was full of staff torches to the number of five hundred, borne by the guard and other of the king's servants. . . . In this order they brought the princess to the Queen's chamber, and the Mayor and the Aldermen tarried there awhile.

"And at the last the Dukes of Norfolk and Suffolk came out from the King, thanking them heartily, and said the King commanded them to give them thanks in his name: and from thence they were had to the cellar to drink, and so went to their Barges. . . ."

No other English princess has ever kindled so many poets to her praises. There is a book (now in the Bodleian Library) which was written by her at the age of eleven for a New Year's gift to her step-mother, Queen Katherine Parr. The embroidered binding has "K-P" in the centre, and this is surrounded by a diamond-shaped design with four flowers of hearts-ease embroidered at the corners. If this work is Elizabeth's, there was reason for her choice of this particular flower. For Queen Katherine, soon after Henry's death in January 1547 (and she had been forced to marry him) returned to her old love, Sir

Thomas Seymour, and about April of the same year they were secretly married. He was brutally unkind to her three step-children, Edward, Elizabeth, and Mary, but she herself did her utmost to protect them. She died September 5th, 1548, aged only 36.

A few months before his marriage with her, Sir Thomas (now Lord Admiral) Seymour received the following letter from the Princess Elizabeth herself—then in her fourteenth year. Two years afterwards he was executed for treason.

February 27, 1547.

MY LORD ADMIRAL,

The letter you have written to me is the most obliging, and, at the same time, the most eloquent in the world. And as I do not feel myself competent to reply to so many courteous expressions, I shall content myself with unfolding to you, in few words, my real sentiments. I confess to you that your letter, all eloquent as it is, has very much surprised me; for, besides that neither my age nor my inclinations allows me to think of marriage, I never could have believed that any one would have spoken to me of nuptials at a time when I ought to think of nothing but sorrow for the death of my father. And to him I owe so much, that I must have two years at least to mourn for his loss. And how can I make up my mind to become a wife before I shall have enjoyed for some years my virgin state, and arrived at years of discretion. . . . Let your highness be well persuaded that though I decline the happiness of becoming your wife I shall never cease to interest myself in all that can crown your merit with glory, and shall ever feel the greatest pleasure in being your servant and good friend.

ELIZABETH.

With a slight twist of that kaleidoscope, the imagination, these few historical "facts" might even now be transmuted into an entrancing folk-tale. But where are the folk?

In "A Midsummer Night's Dream," Oberon tells Puck how he saw that "Faire Vestall" again in danger of Love's sharp arrows—and "The Imperiall Votresse passèd on In maiden meditation, fancy free." But Shakespeare, if positively invited to Court, it is said, "was in paine."

Not so Francis Bacon. "He gave marks very early of a pregnant and happy disposition, far above his years. . . . Queen Elizabeth took a particular delight in trying him with questions; and received so much satisfaction from the good sense of his answers that she was wont to call him, in mirth, her young Lord Keeper." While he was still a boy, she once asked him his age. "He answered . . . that he was just two years younger than her happy reign."

It was a ready, pretty, yet considered grace-note, and the small sharp light it throws upon his young mind and character pierces clean through his life and work—work as far outside of Shakespeare's imaginative orbit as *Twelfth Night, The Tempest,* and *Macbeth*—or merely "Full fathom five"—were beyond his own. "He was immeasurably a less wise man than Shakespeare, and not a wiser writer."

And so with many other early sayings and doings, for a child is the beginning of a man, precisely as a sapling is the beginning of an oak. Both change, not in kind, but in degree.

176. "The Battle-Hymn."

The writer of this magnificent Battle-Hymn died in 1910, at the age of ninety-one. If only the writer of our own "National Anthem," had realised how much and how often his fellow countrymen were to be fated to use his words, he would have perhaps have taken a little more trouble with them (as much, at any rate, as Shelley and Flecker took in *their* versions of it), and would have found a pleasanter rhyme than "over us" for "glorious," and than "voice" for "cause." If, on the other hand, he had read the following *Grace* which Ben Jonson made at the moment's call before James the First, he might perhaps have refrained from rhyming altogether, and so, by sheer modesty, would have missed being immortalized:

Our King and Queen the Lord God Blesse,
The Paltzgrave, and the Lady Besse.
And God blesse every living thing
That lives, and breathes, and loves the King.

God Bless the Counsell of Estate,
And Buckingham the fortunate.
God blesse them all, and keep them safe,
And God blesse me, and God blesse Raph.

"The king," says John Aubrey, "was mighty enquisitive to know who this Raph was. Ben told him 'twas the drawer at the *Swanne* taverne, by Charing-crosse, who drew him good Canarie. For this drollery his majestie gave Ben an hundred poundes. . . ."

177.

"To those," it is said, "who have resided a long time by the falls of Niagara, the lowest whisper is distinctly audible." Their hearing accustoms itself to that unending and enormous roar, and becomes more exquisite. This is untrue of those whose finer sense is lulled by the roar of war: they become deafened, and cannot hear the voice of the soldier "out in the sun-dried veldt alone"—of which mere human fractions of "units" every army is composed. And so war may poison and defile even when its intention and its cause are honour and faith. In this particular poem (No. 177), the soldier is one of those who fought in the Transvaal in the years 1899–1901.

180.

Rupert Brooke, Wilfred Owen, Edward Thomas, Julian Grenfell, Charles Sorley, Francis Ledwidge, Alan Seeger, Joyce Kilmer—these are the names of but a few of the men, none of them old, many of them in the heyday of their youth and promise, who besides proving themselves soldiers in the Great War had also proved themselves poets. Within his powers, every true poet lives in his country's service. These in that service died.

". . . Old stairs wind upwards to a long corridor, the distant ends of which are unseen. A few candles gutter in the draughts. The shadows leap. The place is so still that I can hear the antique timbers talking. But something is without which is not the noise of the wind. I listen, and hear it again, the darkness throbbing; the badly adjusted horizon of outer night thudding on the earth—the incessant guns of the great war.

"And I come, for this night at least, to my room. On the wall is a tiny silver Christ on a crucifix; and above that the portrait of a child, who fixes me in the surprise of innocence, questioning and loveable, the very look of warm April and timid but confiding light. I sleep with the knowledge of that over me, an assurance greater than that of all the guns of all the hosts. It is a promise. I may wake to the earth I used to know in the morning."

H. M. Tomlinson.

184.

The reader may speculate how it is that while room has been found here for this entrancing rhyme, none has been made for Macaulay's longer Lays, Browning's Cavalier Songs, and a host of poems equally gallant and spirited. Perhaps he will forgive their absence if he will consider what is said on page xxxiii, and if he will also remember that every chooser is bound to make his choice.

There is, too, the little fable of the Woodcutter's son. This fuzz-headed boy, called Dick or Dickon, while playing on an elder pipe the tune of "Over the Hills" one dappled sunshine morning in the woods, happening to squinny his eye sidelong as he blew, perceived a crooked and dwarf old man standing beside him where before was only a solitary bearded thistle. This old man, the twist of whose countenance showed him to be one with an ear for woodland music, invited the Woodcutter's son to descend with him into the orchards of the Gnomes—and to help himself. This he did, and marvellously he fared. On turning out his pockets that night—the next day being a Sunday—his Mother found (apart from the wondrous smouldering heap of fruits—amethyst, emerald, rubies and the topaz, which he had given her) two or three strange unpolished stones, and these also from the Old Man's orchards. And she climbed up with her candle, he being abed, and asked him why he had burdened himself with such worthless, common-looking things when he might have carried off their weight in diamonds big as dumplings. "Well, you see, mother," he drowsily replied, "I chose of the best and brightest till my eyes dazzled; and then there was a bird that called, Dick! Dick! Dick! Dick! and those pebbles were among her eggs."

185. "We be the King's Men."

The Song of Soldiers from Act I., Scene 1., Part i. of that mighty play, *The Dynasts.* "The time is a fine day in March, 1805. A highway crosses the ridge, which is near the sea, and the south coast is seen bounding the landscape below, the open Channel extending beyond."

185. One Buonaparty

"Full of eager expectation," wrote Amelia Opie in a letter from Paris to a friend in England [in 1802], "I stationed myself where I could command the white marble stairs of the palace—those steps once stained with the blood of the faithful Swiss Guards, and on which I now expected to behold the 'Pacificator,' as he was called by the people and his friends—the hero of Lodi. Just before the review was expected to begin, we saw several officers in gorgeous uniforms ascend the stairs, one of whom, whose helmet seemed entirely of gold, was, as I was told, Eugène de Beauharnais. A few minutes afterwards there was a rush of officers down the stairs, and amongst them I saw a short, pale man, with his hat in his hand . . . but, though my friend said in a whisper, *'C'est lui,'* I did not comprehend that I beheld Buonaparte, till I saw him stand alone at the gate.

"In another moment he was on his horse, and rode slowly past the window; while I . . . gazed on him intently; endeavouring to commit each expressive, sharply chiselled feature to memory; contrasting also . . . his small, simple hat, adorned with nothing but a little tri-coloured cockade, and bis blue coat, guiltless of gold embroidery, with the splendid head adornings and dresses of the officers who followed him. . . .

"At length the review ended; too soon for me. The Consul sprang from his horse—we threw open our door again, and, as he slowly reascended the stairs, we saw him very near us, and in full face again, while his bright, restless, expressive, and, as we fancied, dark blue eyes, beaming from under long black eyelashes, glowed over us with a scrutinising but complacent look. . . .

"I could not speak; I had worked myself up to all my former enthusiasm for Buonaparte; and my frame still shook with the excitement I had undergone. . . ."

As regards that "dark blue eye" "which one could no more look into than one can look into the sun," Amelia Opie was right in using the word "fançied," as there seems to be little doubt that Napoleon's eyes were a light blue grey—*"gris bleu."* But eyes vary in colour not only according to the light dwelling upon them, but also to the colour they happen to neighbour, blue especially echoing blue. When that blue is tinged with lilac the owner of the eyes is, in this respect at least, rarely endowed. It is the eye-lid, however, with its exquisitely fine lines, curves and contours, and the set of the eye beneath the brow that gives most of its meaning and expression to the glassy pupil. But not all, perhaps, for sailors' eyes not only have a hint of distance in them, like the sea-birds', but seem to have been sea-washed. Nor do landsmen's eyes always remain the same colour throughout life. Age can curiously change a bright brown or amber into a hue with a distinct suggestion of green in it; though wholly *green* eyes are even more uncommon than the green light in the sunset which Coleridge saw (and which we therefore now see often)—a feat which much amused some of his contemporaries.

In short you cannot look too much at eyes, from Shelley's in the Gallery of the Bodleian, to Coventry Patmore's in the National Portrait Gallery; from the tiny bright shrewd bit of glass stuck in a pig's head to the giraffe's dark deep lustrous crystal; in which strange, living mirror you may be able to detect the reflection of your own tinied image.

186. Budmouth Dears

—from *The Dynasts*, Act II., Scene I., Part iii.—the song sung in Camp on the Plain of Vittoria by Sergeant Young (of Sturminster Newton) of the Fifteenth (King's) Hussars on the eve of the longest day in the year 1813 and of Wellington's victory.

187. "Trafalgar"

—from *The Dynasts,* Act V., Scene VII., Part i. Boatmen and burghers with their pipes and mugs are sitting on settles round the fire in the taproom of the *Old Rooms* Inn at Weymouth. The body of Nelson on board his battered *Victory* has lately been brought to England to be buried in St. Paul's; and this is the Song the Second Boatman sings.

"Nelson's mother died in 1767, leaving eight, out of eleven children. . . . Three years afterwards, when Horatio was only twelve years of age, being at home during the Christmas holidays, he read in the county newspaper that his uncle [Maurice] was appointed to the *Raisonnable,* of 64 guns. 'Do, William,' said he to a brother who was a year and a half older than himself, 'write to my father, and tell him that I should like to go to sea with Uncle Maurice.' Mr. Nelson was then at Bath, whither he had gone for the recovery of his health: his circumstances were straitened, and he had no prospect of ever seeing them bettered: he knew that it was the wish of providing for himself by which Horatio was chiefly actuated, and did not oppose his resolution; he understood also the boy's character, and had always said, that in whatever station he might be placed, he would climb, if possible, to the very top of the tree. Accordingly Captain Suckling was written to.

" 'What,' said he in his answer, 'has poor Horatio done, who is so weak, that he, above all the rest, should be sent to rough it out at sea? But let him come, and the first time we go into action a cannon-ball may knock off his head, and provide for him at once. . . .' "

Robert Southey.

"We knew not what the day had done for us at Trafalgar"

"Once, amidst his sufferings, Nelson had expressed a wish that he were dead; but immediately the spirit subdued the pains of death, and he wished to live a little longer; doubtless that he might hear the completion of the victory which he had seen so gloriously begun. That consolation—that joy—that triumph was afforded him. He lived to know that the victory was decisive; and the last guns which were fired at the flying enemy were heard a minute or two before he expired."

The "Nothe," line 8, [No. 187], is the promontory that divides for Weymouth, where lived Nelson's Captain Hardy, its harbour or back-sea on the north, and the Portland Roads, its front-sea on the south; "Roads," meaning protected seas where ships may *ride* at anchor. On this tempestuous and fateful night, October 21, 1805, the breakers were sweeping clean across the spit of land called the Narrows. On the further side runs for a round ten miles that enormous wall of pebbles—Chesil Beach, whose stones the tides sort out so precisely, the least in size towards Lyme Regis, that a native can tell even in a thick mist where he has landed on the beach merely by measuring them with his eye. About ten miles up this water swim in Spring the swans of the Swannery of Abbotsbury with their cygnets, each mother-bird striving to decoy as many of her rivals' fledgelings into her train as she can. So deals a proud and powerful nation with the lesser kingdoms of the earth; though stepmothers are not always welcome.

About four years and a half before Trafalgar, on April 2nd, 1801, Nelson and Parker had won the Battle of the Baltic—as Thomas Campbell (who was then twenty-four), in his now-famous poem tells:

> . . . Like leviathans afloat
> Lay their bulwarks on the brine;
> While the sign of battle flew
> On the lofty British line:
> It was ten of April morn by the chime:
> As they drifted on their path,
> There was silence deep as death;
> And the boldest held his breath,
> For a time. . . .

So accustomed, indeed, are we mere landsmen to the exploits of the Navy on the High Seas that we easily forget it was once to our forefathers a novelty and a wonder—such a wonder as might be compared with the fabulous Castles in Spain or the Gardens of Babylon, as the old nameless poet of the following lines recounts:

Cease now the talke of wonders! nothing rare
Of floateing ilandes, castles in the aire!
Of wooden walls, graves walkeing, flieing steedes,
Or Trojan horse! The present truth exceeds
Those ancient fables; floating iles great store,
Sent from the British Ile, now guard her shore,
And castles strong without foundations stande
More safe on waters pavement then on lande. . . .

189. "The Sailors."

Here is one of them—come home to his sweetheart, and she (until stanza 6) not recognizing him:

As I walked out one night, it being dark all over,
The moon did show no light I could discover,
Down by a river side where ships were sailing,
A lonely maid I spied, weeping and bewailing.

I boldly stept up to her, and asked her what grieved her,
She made me this reply, "None could relieve her,
For my love is pressed, she cried, to cross the ocean,
My mind is like the Sea, always in motion."

He said, "My pretty fair maid, mark well my story,
For your true love and I fought for England's glory,
By one unlucky shot we both got parted,
And by the wounds he got, I'm broken hearted.

"He told me before he died his heart was broken,
He gave me this gold ring, take it for a token,—
'Take this unto my dear, there is no one fairer,
Tell her to be kind and love the bearer.' "

Soon as these words he spoke she ran distracted,
Not knowing what she did, nor how she acted,
She run ashore, her hair showing her anger,
"Young man, you've come too late, for I'll wed no stranger."

Soon as these words she spoke, her love grew stronger,
He flew into her arms, he could wait no longer,
They both sat down and sung, but she sung clearest,
Like a Nightingale in spring, "Welcome home, my dearest."

He sang, "God bless the wind that blew him over."
She sang, "God bless the ship that brought him over,"
They both sat down and sung, but she sung clearest,
Like a Nightingale in spring, Welcome home, my dearest.

To get any rhythm into this doggerel is like persuading a donkey to gallop. And yet how clearly one sees the dark night, the disguised sailor and his sweetheart talking together on the river strand, and the ships on its bosom in the gloom; while the wistful, deceitful tale he tells her is as old as Romance. Once get cantering, too; how pleasing is the motion!

"Token of all brave Captains"

The captain stood on the carronade: "First lieutenant," says he,
"Send all my merry men aft here, for they must list to me;
I haven't the gift of the gab, my sons—because I'm bred to the sea;
That ship there is a Frenchman, who means to fight with we.
For odds bobs, hammer and tongs, long as I've been to sea,
I've fought 'gainst every odds—but I've gained the victory!"

"That ship there is a Frenchman, and if we don't take she,
'Tis a thousand bullets to one, that she will capture we;
I haven't the gift of gab, my boys, so each man to his gun;
If she's not mine in half an hour, I'll flog each mother's son.
For odds bobs, hammer and tongs, long as I've been to sea,
I've fought 'gainst every odds—and I've gained the victory!"

We fought for twenty minutes, when the Frenchman had enough;
"I little thought," said he, "that your men were of such stuff;"
Our captain took the Frenchman's sword, a low bow made to he;

"I haven't the gift of the gab, monsieur, but polite I wish to be.
And odds bobs, hammer and tongs, long as I've been to sea,
I've fought 'gainst every odds—and I've gained the victory!"

Our captain sent for all of us: "My merry men," said he,
"I haven't the gift of the gab, my lads, but yet I thankful be:
You've done your duty handsomely, each man stood to his gun;
If you hadn't, you villains, sure as day, I'd have flogged each mother's son,
For odds bobs, hammer and tongs, as long as I'm at sea,
I'll fight 'gainst every odds—and I'll gain the victory!"

FREDERICK MARRYAT.

191. THE GREEN GRASS IS GROWING ABUNE THEIR GRAVE.

. . . O thou, whom chance leads to this nameless stone,
From that proud country which was once my own,
By those white cliffs I never more must see,
By that dear language which I spake like thee,
Forget all feuds, and shed one English tear
O'er English dust. A broken heart lies here.

LORD MACAULAY.

192. "DARK ROSALEEN."

From his childhood, which was spent in a little shop in Dublin, Mangan had a dark and troubled life. But always a passionate love for his country, Ireland—his Dark Rosaleen—burned on in his imagination as it is revealed in the wild and haunting music of this poem.

197.

There are so many words in this poem strange to an English ear that it seems better to explain them here rather than interrupt the actual reading of it too much. After all, the little that is not plain speaks in its music, and that is a very large part of what we call its "meaning." For the meaning of a poem is *all* the experience, thought, vision, insight, music, happiness that we can get out of it—it is all that it *does* to us.

Stanza (1) "loaning" is a green path in the fields, and "ilka" means every; "wede" means faded or vanished. (2) "bught" is a sheep-fold; "scorning" I suppose means cracking jokes at one another; "dowie" means sad and drooping; "daffing" and "gabbing" is larking and gossiping; a "leglin" is a milkpail. (3) "hairst" means harvest; "bandsters," sheaf-binders; "lyart" is faded with age; "runkled" wrinkled; "fleeching" is wheedling or coaxing or flirting. (4) "swankies" means the blithe lads of stanza 2; "bogle" means goblin or bogey—an evening game like "I spy," I should think. (5) "Dool and wae" means sorrow or grief and woe.

199.

Robert Hayman, a Merchant of Bristol at the age of twenty-five, was a nephew of Sir Walter Raleigh's. He became Governor of a Plantation called *The British Hope* in Newfoundland. In 1628 he settled in Guiana (of whose gilded and barbaric Amazonian princesses his uncle tells in Hakluyt's *Voyages*). He made his will in 1633, and nothing more was afterwards heard of him—at least by the people of Bristol.

Poetry shines out of his stumbling verses like the setting sun through a thicket of thorns. Their "Totnes" is an exceedingly old town, mainly consisting of that "long street" where, when a boy, he met "godly Drake." At its East-Gate is the Brutus-stone—for here Brut of Troy is said first to have trodden English soil, having landed from the Dart. Twenty miles distant to westward of the town lies on its rivers Plymouth—the Spaniards' wasps' nest—its Francis Drake now gazing out to sea from the Hoe. Twenty miles to the east on the coast is Hayes Barton, where Raleigh was born about 1552. And seven miles down the Dart is the village of Greenway, the home of his half-brother, Sir Humphrey Gilbert, the discoverer of Newfoundland, who was in that year a boy of about sixteen. Here amid-stream juts up the Anchor Rock upon which, runs the story, the discoverer of tobacco and of the potato used to sit and smoke his pipe. In 1587 Gilbert and Raleigh sailed together in search of the as yet Unfoundland but on that voyage in vain.

200. "For Hally now is dead."

Hally was Henry, Prince of Wales, the eldest son of James I.,

Queen Elizabeth's godson, and a beloved patron of the arts and poetry to whom Sir Walter Raleigh looked for happy favours. He was little of body and quick of spirit, and, like Alexander, delighted "to witch the World with noble horsemanship." He died when he was nineteen. In Windsor Castle may be seen a suit of armour made for this young prince when he was a boy—a suit which for grace and craftsmanship is said to be one of the most beautiful things of its kind in the world.

201. "Ease after warre."

Soldier, rest! thy warfare o'er,
  Sleep the sleep that knows not breaking;
Dream of battled fields no more,
  Days of danger, nights of waking.
In our isle's enchanted hall,
  Hands unseen thy couch are strewing,
Fairy strains of music fall,
  Every sense in slumber dewing.
Soldier, rest! thy warfare o'er,
Dream of fighting fields no more:
Sleep the sleep that knows not breaking—
Morn of toil, nor night of waking. . . .

Sir Walter Scott.

202. "Henry before Agincourt."

Here, again, the verse of this ancient fragment jolts, jars, and moves cumbrously as a cannon over rocky ground. But how wide and moving a picture it presents, and how noble is its utterance.

203. "Alexander the Great."

"The ambition and desire he (Alexander) had of honour," says Plutarch, "showed a greatness of mind and noble courage, passing his years. . . . For when he was asked one day (because he was swift of foot) whether he would assay to run for victory at the Olympian Games, 'I could be content' (said he), 'so I might run with Kings.'" When, too, "they brought him news that his Father had taken some famous city, or had won some great battle, he was nothing glad to hear it, but would say to his playfellows: 'Sirs, my Father will have all: I shall have nothing left me to conquer with you that shall be aught worth' . . ."

"Is it even so?" said my lady.
"Even so!" said my lord.

205. "And the Kings asleep."

. . . Not a stone-cast from the summit of the hill where the snow was now parched and thinned away, stood a cairn of boulders and thereon sate three Eagles whose eyes surveyed the kingdoms of the world, its seas, and Man's lost possessions. And the Eagle that was eastwards of the three, a little rimpled her wings and cried: "Where now? where now?" And the Eagle that shook upon her plumes the dazzle of the dying sun stretched out her corded neck and yelped: "Man! Man!" And the midmost Eagle stooped low her golden head and champed between her talons with her beak upon the boulder: "The Earth founders," she mewed. And a stillness lay over the hill as though of a myriad watching eyes.

As a huge stone is sometimes seen to lie
Couch'd on the bald top of an eminence;
Wonder to all who do the same espy,
By what means it could thither come, and whence;
So that it seems a thing endued with sense;
Like a sea-beast crawled forth, that on a shelf
Of rock or sand reposeth, there to sun itself. . . .

William Wordsworth.

207. "Dance sedately"

—and here are two old rhymes for the dancing to. One for a Morris Dance:

Skip it and trip it nimbly, nimbly,
  Tickle it, tickle it lustily;
Strike up the tabour for the wenches' favour,
  Tickle it, tickle it lustily.

Let us be seene in Hygate Freene,
To dance for the honour of Holloway.
Since we are come hither, let us spare for no leather
To dance for the honour of Holloway.

And this for a Flower Dance:

Where's my lovely parsley, say?
My violets, roses, where are they?
My parsley, roses, violets fair,
Where are my flowers? Tell me where?

And yet another for one's Lonesome Low:

The king's young dochter was sitting in her window,
Sewing at her silken seam;
She lookt out o' the bow-window,
And she saw the leaves growing green,
My luve;
And she saw the leaves growing green.

She stuck her needle into her sleeve,
Her seam down by her tae,
And she is awa' to the merrie greenwood,
To pu' the nit and the slae,
My luve;
To pu' the nit and the slae.

"Dochter" is, of course, daughter, "nit" is nut, and "slae" sloe.

208.

This, alas, by a sad mishap, is but one half of Miss Sitwell's enchanting dancing rhyme—here is the other:

The King of China's daughter,
She never would love me,
Though I hung my cap and bells upon
Her nutmeg tree.
For oranges and lemons,

The stars in bright blue air,
(I stole them long ago, my dear)
Were dangling there.
The Moon did give me silver pence,
The Sun did give me gold,
And both together softly blew
And made my porridge cold;
But the King of China's daughter
Pretended not to see
Where I hung my cap and bells upon
The nutmeg tree.

209.

Pause an instant on the fifth word in the third stanza and you can actually *hear* the birds laughing—yaffle, blackcap, bullfinch and jay, and the droning and the whistling and the whir-r-r.

210. FA LA LA.

Scattered through this volume are many songs, a few of them—both words and music—exceedingly ancient. Mr. Nahum had a cofferful of old hand-written music (square crotchets and quavers and handsome clefs); and many outlandish instruments were hung up in the dust and silence in one of his cupboards. I remember some small living thing set a string jangling when for the first time the door admitted me to a sight of their queer shapes and appearances. In an old book of 1548, *The Complaynt of Scotland,* there is a list of names, not only of folk-tales such as "The tayl of the wolfe of the varldes end"; and "The tayl of the giantes that eit quyk men," but of song and dances that had long been in common love and knowledge even in those days. Here are a few of the songs:

God You, Good Day, Wild Boy.
Broom, Broom on Hill.
Trolly lolly leman, dow.
All musing of Marvels, amiss have I gone.
O Mine Heart, hey, this is my Song.
Shall I go with You to Rumblelow Fair?
That Day, that Day, that Gentle Day.

Alas, that Samyn Sweet Face!
In ane Mirthful Morrow.

And here some of the dances:

All Christian Men's Dance.
Long Flat Foot of Garioch.
The Lamb's Wind.
Leaves Green.
The Bace of Voragon.
The Loch of Slene.
The Bee.
Shake a Trot, and
The Vod and the Val.

The tunes to these were played at that time on four kinds of bagpipe (including a drone bagpipe), a trump, a recorder, a "fiddell," and a "quhissil"—which is the pleasantest way of spelling *whistle* I have yet seen. The melodies and words of most of them are, apparently, now forgotten.

None the less folk-dancing has taken new life again and many of the old dances have not only been retrieved but are being danced *now* [1928] all over England, Scotland and Wales: among them

Bonnets so Blue.
None so Pretty.
Jenny Pluck Pears.
Rufty Tufty.
Trunkles.
Dargason.
Lull me Beyond Thee.
Halfe Hannikin.
Hey diddle dis!
Laudnum Bunches.
Swaggering Boney.
Bonny Green Garters, and
Lumps of Plum Pudding.

"Fa la la" (No. 210) is not of this kind—a folk-song—but one of hundreds of madrigals, "ayres" and ballets of which both the words and the music were written in England in the first twenty years or so of the seventeenth century. Apart from the psalm-singing which the Flemish weavers had brought over with them in the previous century, the English had always been musical by nature. But now that natural gift broke into full flower, and English music, such as William Byrd's, John Dowland's, John Wilby's, Philip Rossiter's, Thomas Weelkes' and many others'—became as famous in Europe as English poetry is to-day. It was the advent of foreign music and musicians to England—the Italian, and Handel and Mendelssohn—that put it for a while ungratefully out of mind. But why should one excellent thing oust another?

About the beginning of this century the madrigals (like the carols) were triumphantly rediscovered. They are being not only read but sung again; and Dr Fellowes has lately published a volume containing the words of hundreds of these lively, nimble and heart-entrancing rhymes—intended by their writers to carry with them a double charm—not only their own verbal melody, grace and beauty, but also their music's.

My own technical knowledge of music is scanty indeed, but this may be said: a madrigal is intended to be sung, unaccompanied with instruments, by voices only—three to five, six, or seven, it may be, and men's and women's or boys', coursing, echoing, interweaving, responding and rilling together like the countless runnels and wavelets of a brook over its stones, or a wood full of singing birds at evening. An ayre is different. It is for the voice—singing its melody to the accompaniment of lute, viol or virginal, as a nightingale may sing at dusk above the murmur of a softly-brawling brook. A ballet, the most ancient of all three, went hand in hand and foot to foot with a dance.

All I wish to make clear is that the printed words of such jingles as No. 210 and 212 can give only a fraction of the pleasure their makers intended, who in writing had always the singing voice and often the twangling string in mind. Their very age to my fancy gives them an enticing strangeness, grace, and freshness. For in their company the imagination returns to the days when first they rang out in the taverns and parlours and palaces and streets of a London that from every steeple and tower was within sight of green fields; a noble city of only three hundred thousand inhabitants (including children) wherein you might any day find William Shakespeare, Ben Jonson, Chapman and the rest talking together in its taverns, the *Mermaid* or the *Triple Tun,* while that ill-fortuned traveller and statesman, Sir Walter Raleigh, fallen upon evil days, sat mewed up in the Tower of London, engrossed in his *History of the World.*

As for the taverns, they were as numerous as their signs were enticing. An inquisitive observer in the reign of James I. left behind him a list he had himself scribbled down solely of those between Whitehall, Charing Cross and the Tower.

"On the way from Whitehall to Charing Cross we pass," says he, "the White Hart, the Red Lion, the Mairmade, [the] iij Tuns, [the] Salutation, the Graihound, the Bell, the Golden Lyon.

"In sight of Charing Cross: the Garter, the Crown, the Bear and Ragged Staffe, the Angel, the King Harry Head.

"Then from Charing Cross towards ye cittie: another White Hart, the Eagle and Child, the Helmet, the Swan, the Bell, King Harry Head, the Flower-de-luce, Angel, the Holy Lambe, the Bear and Harroe, the Plough, the Shippe, the Black Bell, another King Harry Head, the Bull Head, the Golden Bull, 'a sixpenny ordinary,' another Flower-de-luce, the Red Lyon, the Horns, the White Hors, the Prince's Arms, Bell Savadge's In, the S. John the Baptist, the Talbot, the Shipp of War, the S. Dunstan, the Hercules or the Owld Man Tavern, the Mitar, another iij. Tunnes Inn, and a iij. Tunnes Tavern, and a Graihound, another Mitar, another King Harry Head, [the] iij Tunnes and the iij. Cranes."

His "Mairmade" does not appear to have been *the* Mermaid (where Raleigh in his heyday presided at "those *Lyrick* Feasts") for that, according to *A Life of Shakespeare,* was in Bread Street, Cheapside, but he noted no less than three *Triple Tuns,* and all of them in the City.

Not only in the Taverns and Inns, too, but in every barber's shop lively music abounded, and a gentleman was scarcely a *gentleman* if he had no skill at all with voice, lute or viol. "My Lord [Sandwich]," Pepys confided to his Diary on June 5th, 1660, "called for the lieutenant's cittern, and with two candlesticks, with money in them for cymbals, we made barber's music, with which my Lord was well pleased." And while a stray customer quilled the cittern, the barber barbered: "How, sir, will you be trimmed? will you have your beard like a spade or a bodkin, a pent-hous on your upper lip, or an ally on your chin? a low curle on your head like a bull, or dangling lockes like a spaniell? your mustachoes sharpe at the ends, like shomaker's aules, or hanging down to your mouth like goates flakes? your love-lockes wreathed with a silken twist, or shaggie to fall on your shoulders?"

In these early days the Booksellers also hung out their signs. In 1582 there were above sixty of them in the neighbourhood of Old St. Paul's alone, including the *Bible,* the *Gun,* the *Parrot,* the *Brazen Serpent,* the *Green Dragon,* the *Golden Anchor,* the *Cradle* and the *Swan.*

Fewer then than they are now were the human beings who remain deaf to the magic both of words and music. "I know very well," wrote Sir William Temple, "that many, who pretend to be wise by the forms of being grave, are apt to despise both poetry and music as toys and trifles too light for the use or entertainment of serious men. But whoever find themselves wholly insensible to these charms, would I think do well to keep their own counsel, for . . . while this world lasts, I doubt not but the pleasure and request of these two entertainments will do so too; and happy those that content themselves with these, or any other so easy and so innocent; and do not trouble the world or other men, because they cannot be quite themselves, though nobody hurts them!

"When all is done, Human Life is, at the greatest and the best, but like a forward Child, that must be played with and humoured a little to keep it quiet till it falls asleep, and then the Care is over."

211. "The onely pretty ring time."

"Amo, amas,
I love a lass,
As cedar tall and slender;
Sweet cowslip's face

Is her nominative case,
And she's of the feminine gender.
Horum quorum,
Sunt divorum,
Harum, scarum, Divo;
Tag rag, merry derry, periwig and hatband,
Hic—hoc—hârum, genitivo."

JOHN O'KEEFE.

There was a mayde came out of Kent,
Deintie love, deintie love;
There was a mayde cam out of Kent,
Daungerous be:
There was a mayde cam out of Kent,
Fáyre, propre, small and gent,
As ever upon the grounde went,
For so should it be. . . .

"When you speake (Sweet)
I'ld have you do it ever. When you sing,
I'ld have you buy and sell so: so give Almes,
Pray so: and for the ord'ring your Affayres,
To sing them too. When you do dance, I wish you
Nothing but that: move still, still so:
And owne no other function. . . .
My prettiest Perdita."

The Winter's Tale.

As for Kent and the "deintie love" that came out of it—(and see also Note 220) an old saying runs: "There could be nothing better—neither in *Kent* nor Christendom." In other words, Kent "has the first cut, and all the loaf besides." How else?—when, as far back as the year 55 B. C. Caesar realized that it was the most civilized region of England and it has ever since been her "garden." Its sea-cliffs named her—Albion; its time is the World's. Yet another old wayside rhyme runs:

A knight of Cales, and a gentleman of Wales,
And a Laird of the north country—

A yeoman of Kent with his yearly rent
Could buy them out—all Three.

Health, Wealth, and Happiness! Still no doubt even the minor counties have their charms; and each, too, boasts its own scenery, tradition, accent and wares. An interesting old list of the last, *i.e.,* their "natural commodities"—is given by Thomas Fuller in his *Worthies* [1672]. Here is a selection:

Cumberland	Pearls, Black-lead and Copper.
Hampshire	Red Deer, Honey, Wax and Hogs.
Cambridgeshire	Eels, Hares, Saffron and Willows.
Cornwall	Diamonds, Ambergris, ("sweetest of gums"), Garlic ("most stinking of roots"), Pilchards, Slate and Tin.
Lincolnshire	Pikes, Wild-fowl, Feathers and Pippins.
Somerset	Lead, Cheese, Mastiffs, Woad ("a deep black tincture"—with which our British ancestors blued themselves), "and that *Lapis Calaminaris* which, added to copper, makes brass."
Surrey	Fuller's Earth, Walnuts and Box.
Warwickshire	Sheep, Ash and Coal.
Sussex	Iron, Wheatears, Carps and Talc.
Worcestershire	Lampreys, Perry and Salt.
Yorkshire	Geat [Jet], Alum, Lime and Horses.
Northamptonshire .	Saltpetre and Pigeons.
Nottinghamshire ...	Liquorice.
Staffordshire	Nails.
Wiltshire	Wool.

And last, but still first, beloved *Kent,* with her Morello Cherries, her Flaxe, Saint Foine, Madder and Trouts.

And though myn English be sympill to myn entent,
Hold me excusid, for I was borne in Kent.

The Wheatear (of Sussex), a bird not much larger than a nightingale, was (and may still be) a glutton's delicacy. I myself have seen poulterers' shops (in "Stupidity St.") festooned with skylarks as if with holly at Christmas. Apart from their singing and their beauty, none but a gourmandizer, surely, hungers after *little* birds (*e.g.,* wagtails!) Four wheatears on a glutton's dish is a horrid sight; four hungry men sitting round a table with a fat roast goose in the middle is less so. A sense of proportion seems to be the umpire—though possibly not in relation to sprats or white-bait. When we read in Gulliver's Travels that the Queen of the Brobdignagians, who was sixty-six feet in height and upwards of six tons in weight, was seen by Gulliver to "craunch the Wing of a Lark, Bones and all, between her Teeth, although it was nine times as large as that of a full grown Turkey; and put a bit of Bread in her Mouth as big as twelve penny loaves"—we are intent chiefly on seeing as plainly as we can her Majesty at her meal, and are not in the least shocked by that gigantic lark.

The Lamprey (of Worcestershire), is chiefly famous for having been the death of Henry I. It is to be captured at its best on the western sea-sands, at midnight of harvest full-moon. It is a mottled, slimy, eel-like fish . . . "being so full of holes," says Fuller, "that it would appear Nature intended it rather for an instrument of music than for man's food." The best manner of dressing it, he counsels, is to drown it in malmsey, then "close the mouth thereof with a nutmegg, the holes with so many cloves. . . . When it is rolled up round, put in thereto a filbard-nut, kernells stamped, crums of bread, oil, spices, etc."

"Such pretie things would soon be gon
If we should nôt so them remembre."

212.

There *might* be an instant's check or faltering at the eighth line, but make it "when the WINDS BLOW and the SEAS FLOW" —the great flood of air and water banking up as it were into the words as does the Atlantic in a gale at the Spring Equinox—and all's well.

213. "AND THE FLEAS THAT TEASE IN THE HIGH PYRENEES."

"The flee is a lyttell worme, and greveth men mooste; and scapeth and voideth peril with lepynge and not with runnynge, and wexeth slowe and fayleth in colde tyme, and in somer tyme it wexeth quiver and swyft; and spareth not kynges."

Great fleas have little fleas upon their back to bite 'em,
And little fleas have lesser fleas, and so *ad infinitum*.
The great fleas themselves in turn have greater fleas to go on,
While these again have greater still, and greater still, and so on.

Now, the marvel of the Cuckoo, says Pliny, is that if anyone on hearing her two Springtime notes for the first time in the year takes up the earth lying within the compass of his *right* footprint, it will prove a sovran remedy against fleas.

214. "I LOVED A LASS."

George Wither, says Aubrey, could make verses as fast as he could write them. So, too, could Shakespeare. "What he thought," said his editors, "he uttered with that easiness that we have scarse received from him a blot in his papers."

Still:—"So, So-a! fair and softly!" said the old Shropshire farmer to Job his plough-horse when he kicked up his heels as if to break into a gallop; "So, So-a! When thou'rt a steeplechaser, my dear, or born a high-blood Arab, there 'll be time enough for that. *Some goes their best slow.*"

THE FIVES DID FIT HER SHOE.

. . . Her feet beneath her petticoat
Like little mice stole in and out,
As if they feared the light;
But oh, she dances such a way!
No sun upon an Easter-day
Is half so fine a sight.

Her cheeks so rare a white was on,
No daisy makes comparison;
Who sees them is undone;
For streaks of red were mingled there,
Such as are on a Catharine pear,
The side that's next the sun.

Her lips were red; and one was thin
Compared to that was next her chin
(Some bee had stung it newly);
But, Dick, her eyes so guard her face,
I durst no more upon them gaze,
Than on the sun in Júly. . . .

Why Júly ceased to be so pronounced (and what the first Cæsar would have thought of it) I cannot say. Until then (with April) it was the prettiest month-name in the calendar, which, in most respects, is an anomalous litter of relics. *A Student's Pastime* gives the Anglo-Saxon names and the author's—W. W. Skeat's—translation of them. What is delightful in them is that they are homely and country, not alien, names, and as close to nature as its fur is to a mole. Both December and January were called after *Yule*. June and July were both called by a word meaning mild or warm. February was Mire-month; March, Fierce-month; April, Easter-month; August, Weed-month; September, Holy-month; and October was (?) Windy or "storm felling" month. November was the month of Sacrifice, and May was Three-milkings-month, because then the cows could be milked thrice daily.

"I STILL DID SCORN TO STINT HER
FROM SUGAR, SACK OR FIRE. . . ."

The subject being lasses, sack and sugar, here is an extract taken from a rare little book entitled *The Journal of a Young Lady of Virginia* which I owe to the kindness of a friend, Mrs. Arthur Kinsolving. The year is 1782—six years after the end of the War of Independence. The Mr. Washington mentioned is not the great general George but a kinsman; the "young lady" is writing to her friend, Polly; and what a gay, light-hearted, romantic, nutritious experience it all is:

"*October* 26. I have but one moment to tell you we are just going to set out for Bushfield. Mr. Turberville's Coach is waiting for us at the road.

"*October* 27. When we got here we found the House pretty

full. Nancy was here. I had to dress in a great hurry for dinner. We spent the evening very agreeably in chatting. Milly Washington is a thousand times prettyer than I though her at first, and very agreeable. About sunset, Nancy, Milly, and myself took a walk in the Garden (it is a most butifull place). We were mighty busy cutting thistles to try our sweethearts, when Mr. Washington caught us; and you can't conceive how he plagued us—chased us all over the Garden, and was quite impertinent.

"I must tell you of our frolic after we went in our room. We took it into our heads to want to eat; well, we had a large dish of bacon and beaf; after that, a bowl of Sago cream; and after that, an apple pye. While we were eating the apple pye in bed—God bless you! making a great noise—in came Mr. Washington, dressed in Hannah's short gown and peticoat, and sezed me and kissed me twenty times, in spite of all the resistance I could make; and then Cousin Molly. Hannah soon followed, dress'd in his Coat. They joined us in eating the apple pye, and then went out. After this we took it in our heads to want to eat oysters. We got up, put on our rappers, and went down in the Seller to get them: do you think Mr. Washington did not follow us and scear us just to death! We went up tho, and eat our oysters. We slept in the old Lady's room too, and she sat laughing fit to kill herself at us. She is a charming old lady—you would be delighted with her. I forgot to tell, Mr. Beal attended us here. I have been makeing Milly play on the fortipianer for me; she plays very well. I am more and more delighted with her. She has just returned from the Fredericksburg races, and has given me a full account of them.

"I have been filling out tea, and after that we took a walk to the river by Moonlight. The garden extends to the river. Nancy observed walking by moonlight, she thought, reminded us of our absent Friends. I joined her in thinking so, and my thoughts were at that instant with my Polly. We returned in the house, and I prevailed on Milly to entertain us an hour or two on the forti-pianer. We wanted very much to sleep in a room by ourselves to-night and try the *dum cake,* but could not persuade Nancy—she was afraid. . . . Adieu, my ever dear Polly. . . . Farewell."

216. "A shining night."

A Mole-Catcher am I, and that is my trade,
I potters about wi' my spunt and my spade,
On a moonshiny night, O 'tis my delight
A-catching o' moles.

The traps that I set for the mole in his run,
There's never a night, sirs, but I catches one
On a moonshiny night. . . .

Along of the lanes as by night time I go,
There's things, that I see, as the folks don't know
On a moonshiny night. . . .

There's frolic and lark in the field and the park,
For others than moles will be out in the dark
On a moonshiny night. . . .

There's many a sight and there's many a sound
What maketh me laugh as I'm making my round
On a moonshiny night. . . .

But nothing I says, for I'm mum as a bell,
You certainly know that no tales will I tell,
On a moonshiny night, O 'tis my delight
A-catching o' moles . . .

218. Up in the morning early.

One man shall mow my meadow,
Two men shall gather it together,
Two men, one man, and one more
Shall shear my lambs and ewes and rams
And gather my gold together.

Two men shall mow . . .

And so, in the next stanza, to *three,* then *four* and *ad inf.*

"And St. John's Bell rings for Matins."

June 24 is not only the birthday of St. John the Baptist, but also the year's Sun Day, for about this day, following through the night but a little way beneath the horizon, he rises at dawn furthest North of East in his annual journey (see p. xiv). As on May-day so on St. John's it was once the custom, all England over, to set huge bonfires blazing on the hilltops, around which the country people danced and sang. The dairy-maid who had the breath and was fleet enough of foot to ring around, between dusk and daybreak nine such merry bonfires before they were burnt out, assured her heart of a happy marriage within the year.

219. "O it's dabbling in the Dew makes the Milkmaids fair!"

The aïr to gi'e your cheäks a hue
O' rwosy red, so feaïr to view,
Is what do sheäke the grass-bleädes grae
At breäk o' dae, in mornén dew;
Vor vo'k that will be rathe abroade,
Will meet wi' health upon their road.

But biden up till dead o' night,
When han's o' clocks do stan' upright,
By candlelight, do soon consume
The feäce's bloom, an' turn it white.
An' moon-beäms cast vrom midnight skies
Do blunt the sparklen ov the eyes.

Vor health do weäke from nightly dreams
Below the mornen's eärly beams,
An' leäve the dead-aïr'd houses' eaves,
Vor quiv'ren leaves, an' bubblen streams,
A-glitt'ren brightly to the view,
Below a sky o' cloudless blue.

William Barnes

The words in this poem are spelt as they are spoken in Dorsetshire. "Rathe" means early; and "below" beneath. The stanzas echo and re-echo with half-hidden rhymes.

220. "Bonny Lassie."

. . . She ware a frock of frolicke greene,
Might well beseeme a mayden queene,
Which seemly was to see;
A hood to that so neat and fine,
In colour like the columbine,
Y-wrought full featously.

Her features all as fresh above,
As is the grasse that growes by Dove;
And lyth as lasse of Kent.
Her skin as soft as Lemster wooll,
As white as snow on Peakish Hull,
Or swanne that swims in Trent. . . .

223. "Music, when soft Voices die, vibrates in the Memory."

There is sweet music here that softer falls
Than petals from blown roses on the grass,
Or night-dews on still waters between walls
Of shadowy granite, in a gleaming pass;
Music that gentlier on the spirit lies,
Than tir'd eyelids upon tir'd eyes;
Music that brings sweet sleep down from the blissful skies.

Tennyson

225.

This "Country Rhime," with Nos. 121 and 434, is taken from *A Book for Boys and Girls,* written by John Bunyan. It came into the world on May 12th, 1686, two years before Bunyan died on Snow Hill in London; and two years after the publication of the Second Part of *The Pilgrim's Progress,* "wherein is set forth the manner of the setting out of Christian's Wife and Children, their dangerous journey, and safe arrival at the Desired Country."

When Bunyan was young—though he afterwards repented of it—he exulted in ringing the bells with the ringers in the steeple of the village church of Elstow, where he was born, and where his grandfather, Thomas Bonyon, was "a common baker of human bread."

All these "Homely rhimes" are followed in this particular *Book for Boys and Girls* by "comparisons"; as here: first the bells; then a lesson about them. They are parables. But in Mr. Nahum's copying, many of the lessons were omitted; perhaps because he preferred to think out his own. Not that the poetry that is intended to teach, to praise virtue, and to instil wisdom in the heart and mind of its readers is any the less poetry for this reason. Nevertheless, *every* beautiful thing in this world—the hyssop in the wall and the cedar of Lebanon, Solomon in all his glory and the ring on his finger, carries with it joy and wonder of the life that is ours, and gratitude to the Maker of all. And poets who, when writing, are too intent upon teaching, are apt to forfeit their rarest poetry.

It is hard to believe that Bunyan was accused of having stolen his great book. But so it was; and in "An Advertisement to the Reader" he sturdily refutes the charge—laughs at it:

Some say the *Pilgrim's Progress* is not mine,
Insinuating as if I would shine
In name and fame by the worth of another,
Like some made rich by robbing of their Brother. . . .
  It came from mine own heart, so to my head,
And thence into my fingers trickled [trickle-èd] . . .
  Manner and matter too was all mine own,
Nor was it unto any mortal known,
'Till I had done it. Nor did any then
By books, by wits, by tongues, or hand, or pen,
Add five words to it, or wrote half a line
Thereof: the whole, and every whit is mine. . . .
Witness my name, if anagram'd to thee,
The letters make, *Nu hony in a B.*

JOHN BUNYAN.

226. "AS IF THE TOWER IN ALL ITS STONES AWOKE"

In foreign countries, says Fuller, England was once called the "ringing Island," being famous for having "greater, more, and more tuneable bells than any one country in Christendom, Italy itself not excepted." "The Art of Ringing, moreover, requires a Thoughtful and Ingenious Headpiece." inasmuch as a *maximus* (or peal of twelve bells) "will afford more changes than there have been hours since the Creation."

But long before bells were pealed or volleyed they were dinged or sounded singly, and for different purposes, and it was not only customary to give them names, but to inscribe their names in their metal. The bells that once sounded over the Lincolnshire fens from the Benedictine Abbey of Croyland, for example, were named Pega, Bega, Tatwin, Turketyl, Bettelin, Bartholomew and Guthlac; while in the thirteenth century the bells at Osney were named Auclaire, Doucement, Austin, Marie, Gabriel and John. The oldest known dated bell is that which hangs in St. Chad's Church, Claughton: it is inscribed *Anno Dni MCC No. VI* (A.D. 1296).

The most famous bells now heard in England are Great or Mighty Tom of Oxford, Great Peter of York, Old Gabriel of Lewes, Old Kate of St. Mark's Lincoln, Bell Harry and St. Dunstan of Canterbury, Black Tom of Dewsbury, Great Peter of Gloucester, and Great Peter and Grandison of Exeter; and the tolling of Tom of Lincoln is said to turn the milk sour for miles around. Great Paul, however, though of no great age, is England's prince of bells, his girth being such that he is beaten, not rung. His note is E Flat; his weight exceeds that of over two hundred grown men, and cut into his side are the words *"Vae mihi si non evangelisavero!"*—"Woe, woe, unto me if I proclaim not the Gospel!"

Like Great Paul, the earliest bells bear inscriptions in Latin, *e.g., "Maria Mater Dei est nomen meum: Sum Rosa pulsata mundi Maria vocata: Tu Petre pulsatus perversos mitiga flatus,"* —"Do thou, O Peter, with thy kneeling, assuage the angry storms," the last words referring to the belief that the ringing of bells has the effect described in the second couplet of this "old monkish rhyme."

"Men's death I tell
By doleful knell.

Lightning and thunder
I break asunder.

On Sabbath all
To church I call.

The sleepy head
I raise from bed.

The winds so fierce
I doe disperse.

Man's cruel rage
I doe asswage.

Alas, an incalculable number of ancient bells were melted down at the Reformation and in Puritan days, or had their angel heads and lettering ruthlessly defaced.

Later inscriptions are in English, the earliest of these being often doggerel, but good doggerel; the later—of the Georges and afterwards—still doggerel, but bad. Here are a few examples:

Be not over busie. (Early sixteenth century)

Jesus be our speed. (1595)

Gev God the Glory (1606)

Come when I call
To serve God all. (1633)

When you die
Aloud I cry (1687)

I ring to sermon with lusty boom,
That all may come *and none stay at* home (1657)

To speak a parting soul is given to me:
Be trimmed thy lamp as if I tolled for thee.

All men that hear my mournful sound
Repent before you lye in ground. (1602)

My roaring sounde doth warning geve
That men can not heare always lyve

Jesu, for Thy modir's sake,
Save all the souls that me gart make.
Amen.

231.

Now gaze the stags upon the glassy brooks,
Then slowly through their leafy walks retire,
The huntsman from his close-shut casement looks,
And heaps new wood upon his blazing fire;
The lowing kine, from out the flow'ry meads,
Now pale and frozen, under shelter stand,
The ox within his stall contented feeds,
And plough and wain are idle on the land;
The hind within the house his labour plies,
The dreaming hound upon the hearth is laid,
The flapping sea-gull from the coastward flies,
And robin now can perch on axe and spade:
This, this is Autumn, when the freezing sky,
And mournful air proclaim the Winter nigh.

Lord Thurlow

232.

Dorothy was William Wordsworth's only sister and his friend Coleridge's close friend. What she squandered on these two poets—her self, her talk, her imagination, her love—only they could tell. "She gave me eyes, she gave me ears," once wrote her brother; she shared his visionary happiness. With Coleridge she used to walk and talk so nearly and dearly that again and again in her *Journal* she uses all but the very words—that "thin gray cloud," the line on Spring, or on the one red leaf, for instance—which are so magically his own in *Christabel* (No. 345).

233. "To Autumn."

I read this—perhaps the loveliest of John Keats's odes, many times before I realised that the whole of it is addressed to the musing apparition or phantasm of Autumn whom in its second stanza he describes as if she were in image there before him. This, perhaps, was partly because the poem is usually printed with a full stop after "clammy cells," and partly because of my own stupidity.

Even those who care most for poetry may differ in their choice and appreciation of it. To Alice Meynell the *Ode to the Nightingale* seemed to be the "most imaginative," the *Grecian Urn* the finest ("for never was fancy more exquisite"), *To Autumn* "not in so high a rank but lovely and perfect." The *Psyche* and *Melancholy* she loved least, and yet what an unforgettable last two lines has the *Melancholy's* last stanza!

I saw old Autumn in the misty morn
Stand shadowless like Silence, listening
To silence, for no lonely bird would sing
Into his hollow ear from woods forlorn,
Nor lowly hedge nor solitary thorn;
Shaking his languid locks all dewy bright
With tangled gossamer that fell by night,
Pearling his coronet of golden corn. . . .

The squirrel gloats on his accomplished hoard,
The ants have brimmed their garners with ripe grain,
And honey bees have stored
The sweets of Summer in their luscious cells;
The swallows all have winged across the main;
But here the Autumn melancholy dwells,
And sighs her tearful spells
Amongst the sunless shadows of the plain.

THOMAS HOOD.

237.

This is Touchstone the Fool's last song in *As You Like It*: and if they could continue so to sing, it is a thousand pities (professional) fools have gone out of fashion. Their wit, though raw at times, might keep things sweeter. Moreover, Touchstone was of ancient lineage, as it proved by this letter written by King John (and quoted in *Readings in English Social History.*)

"To William Piculf, and Geoffry, his son.

John, by the grace of God, etc. Know ye, that we have given, and by the present charter have confirmed to William Piculf, our fool, Fonte-Ossanne with all its appurtenances, to have and to hold for himself, and his heirs, on condition of doing henceforward annually for ourselves the service of fool, as long as he shall live; and after his decease, his heirs shall hold the same land from us, by the service of one pair of gilded spurs, to be rendered to us annually.

Wherefore, we will and positively command that the foresaid Piculf and his heirs shall have and hold for ever, fairly and in peace, freely and in quiet, the foresaid land, with all its appurtenances, by virtue of the aforesaid service."

"A Foolish Thing."

I thee advise
If thou be wise
To keep thy wit
Thought it be small:
'Tis rare to get,
And far to fet,
'Twas ever yet
Dear'st ware of all.

George Turberville

"Far to fetch" it certainly is; but here is a little counsel to this end from the old Irish *Instructions of King Cormac* (of the ninth century). Of Carbery I know no more, but doubtless there is much to hear:

"O Cormac, grandson of Conn," said Carbery, "what is the worst for the body of man?"

"Not hard to tell," said Cormac. "Sitting too long, lying too long, long standing, lifting heavy things, exerting oneself beyond one's strength, running too much, leaping too much, frequent falls, sleeping with one's leg over the bed-rail, gazing at glowing embers, wax, biestings [very new milk], new ale, bull-flesh, curdles, dry food, bog-water, rising too early, cold, sun, hunger, drinking too much, eating too much, sleeping too much, sinning too much, grief, running up a height, shouting against the wind, drying oneself by a fire, summer-dew, winter-dew, beating ashes, swimming on a full stomach, sleeping on one's back, foolish romping." . . .

"O Cormac, grandson of Conn," said Carbery, "I desire to know how I shall behave among the wise and the foolish, among friends and strangers, among the old and the young, among the innocent and the wicked."

"Not hard to tell," said Cormac.

"Be not too wise, nor too foolish,
Be not too conceited, nor diffident,
Be not too haughty, nor too humble,
Be not too talkative, nor too silent,
Be not too hard, nor too feeble.
If you be too wise, men will expect too much of you;
If you be too foolish, you will be deceived;
If you be too conceited, you will be thought vexatious;
If you be too humble, you will be without honour;
If you be too talkative, you will not be heeded;
If you be too silent, you will not be regarded;
If you be too hard, you will be broken;
If you be too feeble, you will be crushed."

"Our Play is Done"

—after which, in Elizabeth's day, "the characters (one or more) were wont to kneel down upon the stage and to offer a solemn prayer for the sovereign, or other patron":

"My tongue is wearie; when my Legs are too, I will bid you good night; and so kneele down before you: But (indeed) to pray for the Queene." *Henry IV.*

238. The thistle now is older, His head is white as snow.

. . . There was a day, ere yet the autumn closed,
When, ere her wintry wars, the earth reposed,
When from the yellow weed the feathery crown,
Light as the curling smoke, fell slowly down;
When the winged insect settled in our sight,
And waited wind to recommence her flight;
When the wide river was a silver sheet,
And on the ocean slept th' unanchor'd fleet;

When from our garden, as we look'd above,
There was no cloud, and nothing seem'd to move. . . .

GEORGE CRABBE

242. "THE SEA-BLOOMS AND THE OOZY WOODS." (Stanza 3)

In the ever mutable loveliness of air, sky and particularly of water Shelley found endless delight and bewitchment. In reference to the third stanza of this transfiguring ode he wrote: "The vegetation at the bottom of the sea, of rivers, and of lakes, sympathizes with that of the land in the change of the seasons, and is consequently influenced by the winds which announce it." And, in a letter to his friend Thomas Love Peacock, describing the beauty of this Bay of Baiæ, he tells him, "The sea was so translucent that you could see the caverns clothed with the glaucous sea-moss and the leaves and branches of those delicate weeds that pave the bottom of the water."

This is the Sea. In these uneven walls
A wave lies prisoned. Far and far away
Outward to ocean, as the slow tide falls,
Her sisters, through the capes that hold the bay,
Dancing in lovely liberty recede.
But lovely in captivity she lies,
Filled with soft colours, where the waving weed
Moves gently, and discloses to our eyes

Blurred shining veins of rock, and lucent shells
Under the light-shot water, and here repose
Small quiet fish, and dimly-glowing bells
Of sleeping sea-anemones that close
Their tender fronds and will not now awake
Till on these rocks the waves returning break.

EDWARD SHANKS

245. "PASSED JOY."

I know that all beneath the moon decays,
And what by mortals in this world is brought
In Time's great periods shall return to nought;
That fairest states have fatal nights and days;

I know how all the Muse's heavenly lays,
With toil of spright which is so dearly bought,
As idle sounds, of few or none are sought;
And that nought lighter is than airy praise.

I know frail beauty's like the purple flower,
To which one morn oft birth and death affords;
That love a jarring is of minds' accords,
Where sense and will invassall reason's power.

Know what I list, this all can not me move,
But that—O me! I both must write and love!

WILLIAM DRUMMOND

246. "NO CRANE TALKS." (line 16)

"I hear the crane, if I mistake not, cry
Who in the clouds forming the forkèd Y,
By the brave orders practized under her,
Instructeth souldiers in the art of war.
For when her troops of wandring cranes forsake
Frost-firmèd Strymon, and (in autumn) take
Truce with the northern dwarfs, to seek adventure
In southern climates for a milder winter;
A-front each band a forward captain flies,
Whose pointed bills cuts passage through the skies,
Two skilful sergeants keep the ranks aright,
And with their voyce hasten their tardy flight;

And when the honey of care-charming sleep
Sweetly begins through all their veines to creep
One keeps the watch, and ever carefull-most,
Walks many a round about the sleeping hoast,
Still holding in his claw a stony clod,
Whose fall my wake him if he hap to nod.
Another doth as much, a third, a fourth,
Untill, by turns the night be turnèd forth."

So also, according to travellers, talk, argue as if in conference together, camp, sleep, and keep watch the wandering tribes of the gaudy-dyed Baboons.

247.

The North wind doth blow,
And we shall have snow,
And what will Cock Robin do then, poor thing?

He'll sit in a barn
And keep himself warm,
And hide his head under his wing, poor thing!

249.

If this poem is read heedfully, pausingly, without haste, the very words themselves will seem like snowflakes, floating into the mind; and then, the beauty and the wonder.

251.

Here again, as in music, there are "rests" in the second, fourth and fifth lines of each stanza. And is there any magic to compare with the solemn unearthly radiance of the world when it is masked with snow; then the very sparkling of the mind is like hoar-frost on the bark of a tree.

253. "The Wild Woods."

Allan Cunningham's in Scotland, and these—Mr. Robert Frost's—in Vermont, U. S. A.:

Whose Woods these are I think I know,
His house is in the village though
He will not see my stopping here
To watch his woods fill up with snow.

My little horse must think it queer,
To stop without a farmhouse near
Between the woods and frozen lake
The darkest evening of the year.

He gives his harness bells a shake
To ask if there is some mistake,
The only other sounds the sweep
Of easy wind and downy flake.

The woods are lovely dark and deep;
But I have promises to keep
And miles to go before I sleep:
And miles to go before I sleep.

255.

There may be a few small verbal puzzles in this fifteenth-century carol—otherwise as clear, sharp and shining as a winter moon.

Kechoun is kitchen, and Stephen (who waited on the King at bed and board) stepped out of it into the hall, "boar's head on hand." *Kyst,* means cast; *eylet,* aileth; *wod,* mad; and *brede* (?) to have wild fancies. *"By two and all by one"* means like one man.

In later times a clay or earthenware box made all of a piece, with a slit in it, was carried by apprentices through the streets on the Feast of St. Stephen, for money. Hence this day is now called "Boxing Day."

In the Isle of Man, however, the Christmas Box was called the Wren Box, and for this reason: There dwelt of old a Lorelei, siren or sea-elf, in the emerald-green creeks and caves of a solitary precipitous island. She was as lovely as she was cruel, and her shrill sweet voice rose amid the roaring and soughing of the waves in her steep rocky habitation as shines a poisonous flower in a dark forest. Thus she would at daybreak enchant to their doom sailors following their craft on the sea. Leaning to listen to this music creeping by them on the waters, they would draw in to her haunts. Of their bones were coral made; while she lived on; sang on. She was hunted down at last in her sea-grottoes by those who, like Ulysses, had sealed their ears against her incantations. Brought finally to bay, her beauty and bright hair suddenly dwindled and dimmed, and she escaped in the shape of—Jenny Wren. Alas, for Jenny Wren! condemned ever after for the woes of this siren to be pursued with sticks and stones by young loons, cullions and Jerry Sneaks, on every St. Stephen's Day. As goes the rhyme:

"Oh, where are you going?" says Milder to Melder;
"Oh, where are you going?" says the younger to the elder.
"Oh, I cannot tell," says Festel to Fose;
  "We're going to the woods," says John the Red Nose.

"Oh, what will you do there?" says Milder to Melder;
"Oh, what will you do there?" says the younger to the elder.
"Oh, I do not know," says Festel to Fose;
  "To shoot the cutty wren," says John the Red Nose.

"How will you get him?" etc., etc.

These gentry have different names in different parts, *e.g.*, Robin the Bobbin, Richard the Robin, and Jackey the Land; Fozie Mozie, Johnnie Rednosie, and Foslin 'Ene; and a sinister company they look, especially "Milder"!

In Ireland a totally different story was trumped up to excuse this dismal amusement: A party of Protestants, says John Aubrey, would have been surprised in sleep by the Popish Irish were it not for several wrens that "wakened them by dancing and pecking on the drums as the enemy were approaching. For this reason the wild Irish mortally hate these birds, to this day, calling them the Devil's servants, and killing them wherever they catch them; they teach their children to thrust them full of thorns; you will sometimes on holidays see a whole parish running like mad from hedge to hedge a-wren-hunting"—the wren!—the neatest, nattiest, nimblest bird in all these islands, with more sheer joy of life to the square inch as his shrill "shattering" voice declares—than most humans seem to have to the square acre.

257.

Lullay, lullay, thou lytil child,
Sleep and be well still;
The King of bliss thy father is,
As it was his will.

The other night I saw a sight,
 A mayd a cradle keep:
"Lullay," she sung, and said among,
 "Lie still, my child, and sleep."

"How should I sleep? I may not for weep,
 So sore am I begone:
Sleep I would; I may not for cold,
 And clothes have I none.

"For Adam's guilt mankind is spilt
 And that me rueth sore;
For Adam and Eve here shall I live
 Thirty winter and more."

258. "WELCOME TWELFTH DAY!"

and here is a rhyme (entitled Jolagiafir) for a memory-game that used once to be played on Twelfth Night after the bean and pea or silver-penny had been discovered in the Twelfth Cake, and the Wassail Bowl had gone round with the Mince Pies:

On the first day of Christmas, my true love sent to me
A partridge in a pear-tree.

On the second day of Christmas, my true love sent to me
Two turtle doves and a partridge in a pear-tree.

On the third day of Christmas, my true love sent to me
Three French hens, two turtle doves and
A partridge in a pear-tree.

And so on to—

On the twelfth day of Christmas, my true love sent to me
Twelve lords a-leaping, eleven ladies dancing,
Ten pipers piping, nine drummers drumming,
Eight maids a-milking, seven swans a-swimming,
Six geese a-laying, five gold rings,
Four colly birds, three French hens,

Two turtle doves, and
A partridge in a pear-tree.

Here's a "Twelve"; from Scotland:

What will be our twelve, boys?
What will be our twelve, boys?
Twelve's the Twelve Apostles;
Eleven's maidens in a dance;
Ten's the Ten Commandments;
Nine's the Muses o' Parnassus;
Eight's the table rangers;
Seven's the stars of heaven;
Six the echoing waters;
Five's the hymnlers o' my bower;
Four's the gospel-makers;
Three's the three thrivers;
Twa's the lily and the rose,
That shine baith red and green, boys.
My only ane, she walks alane,
And evermair has dune, boys.

An English version of this begins:

"I'll sing you one, O!
Green grow the rushes, O!
One and one is all alone
And evermore shall be, O!"

For eleven, it has "the eleven that went up to heaven"; for nine, "the bright shiners(?); for eight, "the bold rangers"; for five, "the symbol at your door" (the magic pentacle); for three, "the rivals" and for two, "the lilly-white boys, clothèd all in green, O!"

And this is the rudiments of yet another, which was sent me by a lady who tells me she remembers it from her childhood, and remarks that the refrain seems "very nonsensical"—like an ancient inscription on a stone which has been eroded by decay and rain and frost, and enringed by lichen:

I have three presents from over the sea!
Perry merry dixie Domine!
The first was a book which no man could read:
Petrum patrum paradise temple.
Perry merry dixie Domine!
The second was a blanket without a thread:
Perry merry dixie Domine!
The third was a cherry without a stone
Petrum patrum, etc.

Welcome all, and make good cheer!

An old lady, (Mrs. Samuel Chandler), of Warwickshire, aged 88, was presented on Christmas Eve, 1844, with a little diary—and much else besides—by her son Richard. She used it, not to record the present, but the past; and the following extract is its first entry. It appears in *The Folk Lore Journal*:

"Beginning with Christmas Eve in the year 1759 (my third year) I perfectly remember on that day being carried by Thomas, an old Man-servant, to my Grandmother's—living in the Village of Wootton Wawen, a mile and half from the Park, my Birthplace. Now as Pride is one of our earliest enemys, I date it to his agency that I certainly recollect on that eventful Day that I was wrap'd round by a scarlet broadcloth Cloak of my Mother's, bordered with white Fur.

"The object of my visit on that particular day was to see the Yule Block drawn into the house by a Horse, as a foundation for the Fire on Christmas Day, and according to the superstition of those times for the twelve days following, as the said Block was not to be entirely reduc'd to ashes till that time had passed by. On this subject being named in after years my good Father said [that] as they were of opinion that such an absurd practice would not be of long continuance, they sent me to see it to give me a chance at that early age of remembering that I had witness'd such a foolish ceremony; and the impression was so firmly stamp'd that even now in my 88th year it appears as visible to my mind's Eye as tho' it had been the transaction upon Christmas Eve now six weeks since.

"But the close of the day's tale remains still to be told. When I had been carried round the Kitchen several times, and told much more than I could then understand, my good Grandmother took me into her little Parlour and set me on her knees by a good fire, and without doubt gave me something very nice to eat, but this I do not retain, as my object seemed to be gratified by their strange sights; but I well remember old Thomas having orders to tap the Christmas Barrel of old Stingo, and bringing up a very large glass to shew the beauty of its appearance, and to drink to the health of good old Mistress and little Miss Sally [herself].

"Whilst this ceremony was performing, Carol Singers were heard at the Door. On its being opened, two tall Women entered, bearing between them a large Wassal Bowl, finely dress'd on the outside with Holly, Misseltoe, Ribbons, Laurustinus, and what other flowers could be had at that season. But what most delighted me was a pretty silver Cup, with a handle on each side slung in the middle withinside, and movd about as it was carried round. They sang a long Carol, with a chorus after each verse, repeating the word *Mirth,* etc., which I could not understand, and I well remember I was sadly puzzled to know the meaning, and ask'd my poor brother when I return'd home, who immediately sang the whole of it to me, explaining this great difficulty, and asking me why I did not enquire of Grandma or old Thomas. . . ."

259.

It looks as if this carol—of Henry VI.'s reign—was once a singing game: On the one side in the blaze of the Yule Log the Holly men with gilded and garlanded pole; and on the other Ivy with her maidens; each side taunting the other, and maybe tugging for prisoners. "Ivy-girls," too, used to be burned by companies of boys, and Holly-boys by girls—all yawping and jodelling at the sport.

"Poppynguy" may perhaps be the jay, but it would be pleasanter company for the lark, if here it means the green woodpecker. He drills out his holes in the small hours of the morning, his slender barb-tipped tongue busy with what stirs within. He drums for his lady-love and *yaffles* or laughs out, glassy and clear in the sunny green tops of the woods.

260. "When Isicles hang by the Wall."

. . . The winter falls, the frozen rut
Is bound with silver bars;
The snowdrift heaps against the hut,
And night is pierced with stars.

Coventry Patmore

There is a peculiar magic (which may perhaps be less apparent to the Greenlanders) in icicles. Nor are its effects unknown to the four-footed. In certain remote regions of Siberia there is said to be a singular little animal called the Ice-wolf. He has prick-ears, is a fierce feeder, and wears a winter coat so wondrous close and dense that three or four of our English moles' skins laid one over another would yet fall short of its match. But he seldom attains to a ripe age, and for this reason. As soon as he is freed from his dam's snow-burrow, he hastens off to the dwellings of the men of those parts, snuffing their fried seal-steaks and blubber, being a most incorrigible thief and very wary. And such is his craft that he mocks at gins, traps and pitfalls. But he has a habit which may prove his undoing. It is in this wise: The heat of these hovels is apt to melt a little of the snow upon them, its water trickling and coursing softly down till long, keen icicles are formed, upon which, whether hungry or fed, taking up his station in a plumb line beneath them, he will squat and gloat for an hour together, by reason of his pleasure in their clear glasslike colours. Hearing his breathing or faint snuffing, any human who wakes within will of a sudden violently shake the wall between. This dislodges the pendent icicles, and the squatting Ice-wolf is pierced to his death as with a sword.

Winter indeed makes crystal even of ink and has the power of enchanting every imagination; particularly Coleridge's:

Therefore all seasons shall be sweet to thee,
Whether the summer clothe the general earth
With greenness, or the redbreast sit and sing
Betwixt the tufts of snow on the bare branch
Of mossy apple-tree, while the night thatch
Smokes in the sun-thaw; whether the eave-drops fall

Heard only in the trances of the blast,
Or if the secret ministry of frost
Shall hang them up in silent icicles,
Quietly shining to the quiet Moon. . . .

"AND DICKE THE SHEPHEARDE."

The foddering boy along the crumping snows
With straw-band-belted legs and folded arm
Hastens, and on the blast that keenly blows
Oft turns for breath, and beats his fingers warm,
And shakes the lodging snows from off his clothes,
Buttoning his doublet closer from the storm
And slouching his brown beaver o'er his nose—
Then faces it agen, and seeks the stack
Within its circling fence where hungry lows
Expecting cattle, making many a track
About the snow, impatient for the sound
When in huge forkfulls trailing at his back
He litters the sweet hay about the ground
And brawls to call the staring cattle round.

JOHN CLARE.

261. "BLOW, BLOW THOU WINTER WIND."

The wind blows cold, the weather's raw,
The beggars now do skulk in straw,
Whilst those whose means are somewhat higher,
Do warm their noses by a fire.
Sack, *Hippocras,* now, and burnt brandy
Are drinks as warm and good as can be,
But if thy purse won't reach so high,
With ale and beer that want supply.

(1696.)

"To make *Hypocras* the best way.—Take 5 ounces of *aqua vitæ,* 2 ounces of pepper, and 2 of ginger, of cloves and grains of paradice each 2 ounces, ambergrease three grains, and of musk two grains, infuse them 24 hours in a glass bottle on pretty warm embers and when your occasion requires to use it, put a pound of sugar into a quart of wine or cyder; dissolve it well, and then drop 3 or 4 drops of the infusion, and they will make it taste richly."

264. "Woe weeps out Her Division when She sings."

This means, I think, that she adds her own grieved cadences to the melody, as may one, among many voices, singing in harmony.

265. "Is like a Bubble."

This rainbow "bubble"—like Shelley's dome of "many-coloured glass" in his *Adonais*—seems, before our very eyes, to be hovering in the empty blue heavens, until it smalls into a bead of gold, and vanishes. It brings to memory—though I am uncertain of the first line—an epitaph in the church at Zennor, a village clustered above the Atlantic on the dreamlike coast of Cornwall. The epitaph has been cut in fine lettering into its slate slab, and at each corner of the slab Cherubs' heads representing the winds of the world puff out their round and solemn cheeks:

Sorrow, and sin, false hope, and trouble—
These the Four Winds that hourly vex this Bubble:
His breath a Vapour, and his life a Span;
'Tis Glorious Misery to be born a Man.

266. "O, Sweet Content."

There is a jewel which no Indian mines
Can buy, no chymic art can counterfeit;
It makes men rich in greatest poverty;
Makes water wine, turns wooden cups to gold,
The homely whistle to sweet music's strain:
Seldom it comes, to few from heaven sent,
That much in little, all in naught—Content.

"Art Thou poor . . . Art Thou rich."

He that spendeth much;
And getteth nought;
He that oweth much,
And hath nought;

He that looketh in his purse
  And findeth nought,—
He may be sorry,
  And say nought.
He that may and will not,
He then that would shall not.
He that would not and cannot
May repent and sigh not.

He that sweareth
  Till no man trust him;
He that lieth
  Till no man believe him;
He that borroweth
  Till no man will lend him;
Let him go where
  No man knoweth him.

He that hath a good master,
  And cannot keep him;
He that hath a good servant,
  And is not content with him;
He that hath such conditions,
  That no man loveth him;
May well know other,
  But few men will know him.

HUGH RHODES [1550]

And, to make trebly sure:
Three false sisters: "Perhaps," "May be," "I dare say."
Three timid brothers: "Hush!" "Stop!" "Listen!"
Three deeps: Well! *well!* WELL!
A useful pair: *Almost* and *Very nigh*
  Saved many a lie.

Also and finally: "Be aisy, and if you can't be aisy, be as aisy as you can."

269. "LORD RAMESES OF EGYPT SIGHED."

The most ancient poem I know of consists of such a sigh. It comes from an Egyptian tomb, was composed about 5000 years ago, and might have been written by some serene and melancholy soul at his sick-room window yesterday afternoon. For, after all, these men whose mummies are now a mere wonder to the curious, once lived, as Raleigh says, "in the same newness of time which we call 'old time.' "

"Death is before me to-day
Like the recovery of a sick man,
Like going forth into a garden after sickness.

"Death is before me to-day
Like the odour of myrrh,
Like sitting under the sail on a windy day. . . .

"Death is before me to-day
Like the course of the freshet,
Like the return of a man from the war-galley to his house. . . .

"Death is before me to-day
As a man longs to see his house
When he had spent years in captivity."

He is so keenly (if not contentedly) aware and alive that every simile of tribute to death that he uses refers to some intensely happy experience in his own remembrance.

272. "THESE STRONG AND FAIR. . . ."

And here is another poem by William Barnes which I have ventured to spell not as it appears in its original dialect, but in the usual way:

If souls should only shine as bright
In heaven as in earthly light,
And nothing better were the case,
How comely still, in shape and face,

Would many reach that happy place,—
The hopeful souls that in their prime,
Have seemed a-taken before their time—
  The young that died in beauty.

But when one's limbs have lost their strength
A-toiling through a lifetime's length,
And over cheeks a-growing old
The slowly-wasting years have rolled
The deepening wrinkles' hollow fold;
When life is ripe, then death do call
For less of thought, than when it fall
  On young folks in their beauty. . . .

But still the dead shall more than keep
The beauty of their early sleep;
Where comely looks shall never wear
Uncomely, under toil and care,
The fair, at death be always fair,
Still fair to living, thought and love,
And fairer still to God above,
  Then when they died in beauty.

273.

I remember actually coming upon this poem (in Mr. Nahum's second book), and how I suddenly turned my head and looked up at the dark-socketed skull in its alcove in the turret room; it had no alarm for me then, though I can recall cold moments of dread or confusion, when I was a boy, at the thought of death. Then—or was it some time after?—I turned the page, and found the following poem by Thomas Campion, and, in Mr. Nahum's writing, this scrawl at the foot of it: "Yes, but the vision first."

The man of life upright,
  Whose guiltless heart is free
From all dishonest deeds,
  Or thought of vanity;

The man whose silent days
  In harmless joys are spent,
Whom hopes cannot delude
  Nor sorrow discontent:

That man needs neither towers
  Nor armour for defence,
Nor secret vaults to fly
  From thunder's violence:

He only can behold
  With unaffrighted eyes
The horrors of the deep
  And terrors of the skies.

Thus scorning all the cares
  That fate or fortune brings,
He makes the heaven his book,
  His wisdom heavenly things;

Good thoughts his only friends,
  His wealth a well-spent age,
The earth his sober inn
  And quiet pilgrimage.

". . . Yet suffer us, O Lord, not to repine, whether in the morning, at noon, or at midnight, that is to say, in our cradle, in our youth, or old age, we go to take our long sleep; but let us make this reckoning of our years, that if we can live no longer, *that* is unto us our old age; for he that liveth so long as thou appointest him (though he die in the pride of his beauty) dieth an old man. . . ."

274. "ADIEU! FAREWELL EARTH'S BLISS."

This solemn dirge was written in "time of pestilence,"—such a visitation as Daniel Defoe tells of in his "Journal of the Plague Year." So too this nameless writer [of 1625]—in a fragment of verse that is scarcely better than doggerel, though "Who yesterday sate singing" and "morning Mattens" and line 7 touch it with a *poetic* actuality Defoe seldom achieved:

This was that yeere of wonder, when this Land,
Was Ploughed up into Graves, and graves did stand
From morne, till next morne, gaping still for more.
The Bells (like our lowde sinnes) ne'er giving ore.
Then, life look't pale, and sicklier then the Moone,
Whole Households, well i'th morne, lying dead at Noone.
Then sicknesse was of her owne face affrayde,
And frighting all, yet was her self dismayde. . . .
Paules Organs (then) were passing-bells, to call
This day a Quirist to his Funerall
Who yesterday sate singing; Men did come
To morning Mattens, yet ere they got home,
Had Tokens sent them that they should no more
Hear Anthems there; They were to goe before
Him, to whose name, those Anthems were all sung,
To instruments, which were by Angels strung.

The Elizabethan poets brooded endlessly on the mystery of death. A music haunts their words like that of muffled bells, as in John Fletcher's poem:

. . . Come hither, you that hope, and you that cry,
Leave off complaining!
Youth, strength, and beauty, that shall never die,
Are here remaining.
Come hither, fools, and blush you stay so long
From being blessed,
And mad men, worse than you, that suffer wrong,
Yet seek no rest! . . .

And in William Davenant's:

Wake, all the dead! What ho! what ho!
How soundly they sleep whose pillows lie low!
They mind not poor lovers, who walk above
On the decks of the world in storms of love.

No whisper now nor glance shall pass
Through wickets or through panes of glass,
For our windows and doors are shut and barred.
Lie close in the church, and in the churchyard!
In every grave make room, make room!
The world's at an end, and we come, we come! . . .

275. "I WHO LOVED WITH ALL MY LIFE LOVE WITH ALL MY DEATH."

Not full twelve years twice-told, a weary breath
I have exchangèd for a wishèd death.
My course was short, the longer is my rest,
God takes them soonest whom he loveth best;
For he that's born to-day dies to-morrow,
Loseth some days of mirth, but months of sorrow.

There is an epitaph that instantly calls these words to mind in the steep-sloping graveyard at Manorbier whose ruinous castle towers above the turf of its narrow ocean inlet, as if it were keeping a long tryst with the church tower on the neighbouring height:

Weep not for her ye friends that's dear,
Weep for your sins, for death is near—
You see by her, she [was] cut down soon:
Her morning Sun went down at noon.

Not much better than doggerel; and yet it is not easy to forget such things—chancing on the weathered stone in the long grasses in the summer sunshine—birds, bees, and butterflies one's only company and the distant lully of the sea.

And then there are these two unforgettable fragments, the one from the Scots of John Wedderburn (1542), and the other of a century before, its authorship unknown:

WHO'S AT MY WINDOW?

Who's at my window, who, who?
Go from my window, go, go!
Who calleth there so like a stranger?
Go from my window—go!

Lord, I am here, a wretched mortal
That for Thy mercy does cry and call—
Unto Thee, my Lord Celestial,
See who is at my window, who.

THE CALL.

. . . Come home again, come home again;
Mine own sweet heart, come home again!
You are gone astray
Out of your way,
Therefore, sweet heart, come home again!

277. "HARK! NOW EVERYTHING IS STILL."

Death stands above me, whispering low
I know not what into my ear;
Of his strange language all I know
Is, there is not a word of fear.

WALTER SAVAGE LANDOR

" 'TIS NOW FULL TIDE 'TWEEN NIGHT AND DAY."
(line 17)

Leave me, O Love, which reachest but to dust;
And thou, my mind, aspire to higher things;
Grow rich in that which never taketh rust;
Whatever fades, but fading pleasure brings.

Draw in thy beams, and humble all thy might
To that sweet yoke where lasting freedoms be;
Which breaks the clouds, and opens forth the light,
That doth both shine and give us sight to see.

O, take fast hold! let that light be thy guide
In this small course which birth draws out to death—
And think how evil becometh him to slide,
Who seeketh heaven, and comes of heavenly breath.

Then farewell, world; thy uttermost I see:
Eternal Love, maintain thy life in me.

SIR PHILIP SIDNEY

278.

Of the *Lyke-wake Dirge* is known neither the age nor the author. The body from which the "saule" or spirit within fled away lies in its shroud, and the dirge tells of that spirit's journey. Its word "sleet," says Mr. Sidgwick, means either salt, for it was the custom to place in a wooden platter beside the dead, earth and salt for emblems, the one of corruption, the other of the immortal; or, as some suppose, "sleet" should be *fleet,* meaning embers or water or house-room. "Whinnies" means gorse. To explain the full meaning of Bridge of Dread would need many pages.

279.

Next this poem in Mr. Nahum's book was "Lead, Kindly Light," and there was a strange picture for it hanging in the round tower—the picture of a becalmed ship, clumsy of rig and low in the water which was smooth and green as glass. In the midst of the ship there was piled high what might be taken for a vast heap of oranges, their fair reddish colour blazing in the rays of the sun that was about to plunge out of the greenish sky below the line of the west. But what even more particularly attracted my eye at the time was that ship's figurehead—a curious head and shoulders, as if with wings, and of a kind of far beauty or wonder beyond me to describe.

281. "FEAR NO MORE."

Philaster. Fie, fie,
So young and so dissembling! fear'st thou not death?
Can boys contemn that?

Bellario. O, what boy is he
Can be content to live to be a man,
That sees the best of men thus passionate,
Thus without reason?

Philaster. O, but thou dost not know what 'tis to die.

Bellario. Yes, I do know, my Lord!
'Tis less than to be born; a lasting sleep,
A quiet resting from all jealousy;
A thing we all pursue; I know besides
It is but giving over of a game
That must be lost.

From *Philaster:* FRANCIS BEAUMONT and JOHN FLETCHER

284. "ALL THE FLOWERS."

". . . But those which perfume the air most delightfully, not passed by as the rest, but being trodden upon and crushed, are three—that is, burnet, wild thyme, and watermints. Therefore you are to set whole alleys of them, to have the pleasure when you walk or tread."

An Essay on Gardens, FRANCIS BACON

Bring, too, some branches forth of Daphne's hair,
And gladdest myrtle for the posts to wear,
With spikenard weaved and marjorams between
And starred with yellow-golds and meadows-queen.

The very names indeed of the aromatic herbs seem to "perfume the air"—bergamot, lavender, meadowsweet, costmary, southernwood, woodruff, balm, germander. And flowers even though dead remain sweet in their dust, as every bowl of potpourri will tell. To have "a repository of odours" always with them, when streets were foul and pestilence was a peril, gentle-people would in old times carry fresh nosegays or pomanders. The pomanders were of many kinds; an orange stuffed with cloves, etc., for the hand; or—for pocket or chatelaine—some little curiously-devised receptacle of silver containing tiny phials of precious essences—possibly no bigger than a plum. Or they might be compounded of rare ingredients: "Your only way to make a good pomander is this. Take an ounce of the purest garden mould, cleansed and steeped seven days in change of motherless rose water. Then take the best labdanum, benjoin, both storaxes, ambergris, civet, and musk. Incorporate them together, and work them into what form you please. This, if your breath be not too valiant, will make you smell as sweet as any lady's dog."

285

Francis Beaumont who wrote this memorable "Meditation" was himself to lie in Westminster Abbey not many years afterwards. The "once" in the eighteenth line means *once for all*; but I am a little uncertain of the meaning of "bones of birth" in the thirteenth.

Nearly a hundred years before him, Stephen Hawes had shared his thought:

> O Mortal folk, you may behold and see
> How I lie here, sometime a mighty knight.
> The end of joy and all prosperity
> Is death at last, thorough his course and might:
> For though the day be never so long,
> At last the bell ringeth to evensong.

And this is an epitaph of the second century:

"Fair indeed is the secret from the Blessed Ones—that for mortals Death is not alone no evil, but a good."

And this of the sixteenth:

IGO : TO SLE AND WEE
EPE : BEFO SHAL WAKE
RE : YOU TOGEATHER

The following lines, too, are said to have been found between the pages of Sir Walter Raleigh's Bible in the Gate House at Westminster, having been written by him, it is surmised, during the night of October 28, 1618, and a few hours before he was beheaded:

> Even such is Time, that takes in trust
> Our youth, our joys, our all we have,
> And pays us but with earth and dust;

Who, in the dark and silent grave,
When we have wandered all our ways,
Shuts up the story of our days.

But from this earth, this grave, this dust,
My God shall raise me up, I trust.

Having put off his gown and doublet he turned his eyes to the headsman with his axe. "I pr'ythee let me see it," he said, "lest thou sayest that I am afraid of it. It is sharp medicine, but it is a sound cure for all diseases"; and when he was instructed how he should kneel, he added, "If the heart be right it is no matter which way the head lies."

Sir Thomas More had taken the same journey as Raleigh, but eighty-three years before him. On Monday, July 5th, 1535, the night before he was beheaded, he wrote ("with a cole") this letter of farewell to his daughter Margaret Roper. He had seen her for the last time when she openly met and kissed him in the midst of his enemies and of the throngs on Tower Wharf, as he came from Judgment:

"Oure Lorde Blesse you, good daughter, & youre good husbande, & youre lyttle boye, & all yours, & all my children, & all my Godde chyldren and all oure frendes. . . . I comber you good *Margaret* much, but I would be sory, if it should be any lenger than tomorrow. For it is saint *Thomas* even, & the utas of saint *Peter:* & therefore tomorrow long I to go to God: it were a day verye mete & convenient for me. I never liked your maner toward me better, than whan you kissed me laste: for I love when doughterly love, and deere charitye, hath no laysure to loke to worldlye courtesy. Farewell my dere chylde, & praye for me, & I shall for you & all youre frendes, that we maye merilye mete in heaven. . . ."

286. "Sidney, O Sidney is dead."

"Sir Philip Sydney, Knight," says John Aubrey, "was the most accomplished courtier of his time. He was not only of an excellent witt, but extremely beautiful; he much resembled his sister. He was a person of great courage. Among others Mr. Edmund Spenser made his addresse to him, and brought his *Faery Queen.*

Sir Philip was busy at his study, and his servant delivered Mr. Spenser's booke to his master, who layd it by, thinking it might be such kind of stuffe as he was frequently troubled with. When Sir Philip perused it, he was so exceedingly delighted with it, that he was extremely sorry he was gonne, and where to send for him he knew not. After much enquiry he learned his lodgeing, and sent for him, and mightily caressed him. . . . From this time there was a great friendship between them, to his dying day. . . . His body was putt in a leaden coffin (which after the firing of Paule's, I myself sawe), and with wonderful greate state was carried to St. Paule's church, when he was buried in our Ladie's Chapell. There solempnized this funerall all the nobility and great officers of Court."

Here is part of a letter written to him, by his father, Sir Henry Sidney, in 1566, when Philip was a boy at Shrewsbury School:

SON PHILIP. . . . Above all things, tell no untruth. No, not in trifles. The custom of it is nought: and let it not satisfy you that, for a time, the hearers take it for a truth; yet after it will be known as it is, to your shame. For there cannot be a greater reproach to a gentleman, than to be accounted a liar. . . . Remember, my son! the noble blood you are descended of by your mother's side: and think that only by virtuous life and good action you may be an ornament to that illustrious family; otherwise, through vice and sloth, you may be counted *labes generis,* "a spot of your kin," one of the greatest curses that can happen to man.

This next fragment is from a letter written on October 18, 1580, by Sir Philip Sidney himself to his younger brother Robert (then seventeen). This Robert six years afterwards fought with him at Zutphen. He grew up a gallant gentleman, was created Earl of Leicester, and in his leisure wrote words to fit the music of John Dowland—afterwards lutenist to Charles I.

MY DEAR BROTHER,

For the money you have received, assure yourself (for it is true), there is nothing I spend so pleaseth me; as that which is for you. If ever I have ability, you shall find it so: if not, yet shall not any brother living be better beloved than you, of me. . . . Look to your diet, sweet Robin! and hold your heart in courage and virtue. Truly, great part of my comfort is in you! . . . Be careful of yourself, and I shall never have cares. . . . I write this to you as one, that for myself have given over the delight in the world; but wish to you as much, if not more, than to myself. . . . God bless you, sweet Boy! and accomplish the joyful hope I conceive of you. . . . Lord how I have babbled! Once again, farewell, dearest Brother!

Your most loving and careful brother,

PHILIP SIDNEY

And here in a few words is a fleeting glimpse of this renowned man as he appeared amidst the splendour and magnificence of the Tournament during the Anjou Fêtes in London, in 1581, five years before his death:

"Then proceeded Master Philip Sidney, in very sumptuous manner with armour part blue and the rest gilt and engraven. . . . He had four pages that rode on his four spare horses" (richly caparisoned in gold and pearls and feathers of silver) "who had cassock hats and Venetian hose all of cloth of silver laid with gold lace and hats of the same with gold bands and white feathers: and each one a pair of white buskins." . . . There followed him in as rich and splendid array his gentlemen, yeomen, and trumpeters.

Was never eie, did see that face,
Was never eare, did heare that tong,
Was never minde, did minde his grace,
That ever thought the travell long;
But eies, and eares, and ev'ry thought,
Were with his sweete perfections caught.

EDMUND SPENSER

287. "HIS PICTURE IN A SHEET."

Of John Donne's Book of Poems there was nothing in Mr. Nahum's first volume, much in the others. But what I then read of them I little understood. It is a poetry that awaits the mind as the body grows older, and when we have ourselves learned the experience of life with which it is concerned. Not that the simplest poetry will then lose anything of its grace and truth and beauty—far rather it shines the more clearly, since age needs it the more.

"*His Picture in a sheet*" refers to a drawing (prefixed to Donne's *Poems*) of his stone effigy in St. Paul's Cathedral, where a few days before his death he preached his last valedictory, or farewell, sermon.

288. "Do Thou the same."

So too Walter Savage Landor:

. . . Quieter is his breath, his breast more cold
 Than daisies in the mould,
Where children spell, athwart the churchyard gate,
 His name, and life's brief date.
Pray for him, gentle souls, whoe'er you be,
 And, O, pray too for me!

289. "Lamps in Sepulchres."

One morning, as I was sitting by the fire, a great cloud came over me, and a temptation beset me, and I sate still. And it was said [in me], All things come by nature; and the Elements and Stars came over me, so that I was in a moment quite clouded with it; but, inasmuch as I sate still and said nothing, the people of the house perceived nothing.

And as I sate still under it and let it alone, a living hope rose in me, and a true voice arose in me which cried: There is a living God who made all things. And immediately the cloud and temptation vanished away, and the life rose over it all, and my heart was glad, and I praised the living God.

From George Fox's *Journal*.

290. "A pretty Bud."

"To die young," in William Drummond's words, "is to do that soon, and in some fewer Days, which once thou must do; it is but the giving over of a Game, that after never so many Hazards must be lost."

Here is the last stanza of an epitaph written by Edmund Waller in memory of the "only son of the Lord Andover," who also died young. He lies in the chancel of the serene and ancient parish Church of Ewelme, and nearby, lovely and undefaced, are the tombs of Geoffrey Chaucer's son and daughter.

. . . Like Buds appearing ere the Frosts are past,
To become Man he made such fatal hast,
And to Perfection labour'd so to climb,
Preventing[1] slow Experience and Time,
That 'tis no wonder Death our Hopes beguil'd;
He's seldom Old, that will not be a Child.

Nor can he ever be said to be "old" who remains in some degree childlike in mind and nature. Even in the depths of winter there are well-springs that never cease to flow. And so it was with Waller himself. Like Herrick he lived to be over eighty, and during the last years of his life wrote one—and that perhaps the best—of the few poems by which he is remembered. This is its last stanza:

. . . The soul's dark cottage, battered and decayed,
Lets in new light through chinks that Time has made
Stronger, by weakness, wiser men become
As they draw near to their eternal home.
Leaving the old, both worlds at once they view
That stand upon the threshold of the new.

And in those who have not become old but who are soon to die the radiance of this new light is sometimes seen to shine. As if by a secret forewarning they have made haste to live in mind and spirit far beyond their years—Keats, Emily Brontë, Katherine Mansfield.

291. "A-left asleep."

May! Be thou never graced with birds that sing,
Nor Flora's pride!
In thee all flowers and roses spring—
Mine, only died.

In obitum MS. X° Maij. 1614, William Browne

[1] Hastening on before.

293. "Sunk Lyonesse."

There is a legend—recorded in an ancient monastic chronicle—that in the days of Arthur there stretched between Land's End and the Scillies a country of castles, of fair towns, and landscapes, named Lyonesse. When the tumult of the last great Arthurian battle was over, there befell a cataclysm of nature, and in a night of tempest this whole region was engulfed beneath the seas.

What truth is in this legend no certain history relates. But when the vast Atlantic breakers begin to lull after storm, to lie listening in the watches of the night is to hear, it would seem, deep-sunken belfries of bells sounding in the waters, and siren-like lamentations. I have myself heard this, and fancy though it may be, if the ear is once beguiled into its deceit, the bells clash and chime on and on in the imagination, mingled with the enormous lully of the surges, until at last, one falls asleep.

The "basin of boxwood" refers to a custom in the North of England of preparing sprays of box before a funeral. The mourners carried these little emblems to the graveside, and at the last dropped them down upon the coffin for a remembrance to the one who was gone.

299. "Sings no sad Songs for Me"

—and here is another such happy and tender word of farewell—but from one unknown:

> When from the world I should be ta'en,
> And from earth's necessary pain,
> Then let no blacks be worn for me,
> Not in a ring, my dear, by thee.
> But this bright diamond, let it be
> Worn in remembrance of me.
> And when it sparkles in your eye,
> Think 'tis my shadow passeth by.

302. "Readen ov a Head-Stwone."

This poem, again, is spelt as the words would be pronounced by the people of Dorsetshire, the county in which William Barnes was born and lived nearly all his long life. This way of speech is slower than in common English, and the words, especially those with the two dots, or diæresis, over them, should be lingered over a little in pronouncing them.

Londoners are apt to be scornfully amused at country speech —in their ignorance that much of it is older and most of it far more beautiful than their own clipped and nasal manner of pronouncing their words. There are two extremes of this Cockney talk—though even that is constantly changing, and Sam Weller might be taken for a foreigner if he returned to his old haunts to-day. The downright, full-throated coster-monger in the abundance of his heart opens his mouth as wide as possible, and so broadens his vowels, converting "tape" into *taip,* "type" into *toip,* "go on" into *gurn,* and "out" into *aht;* while the too, too genteel, practised in "prunes and prisms," narrow theirs, and for "coin" say *co-in,* for "type" say *tape,* and for "tape" say *tepe.* They may, on occasion, say "Listen to darlingest little Carlo; he is *snawing* in his sleep," having been warned against saying "Meh! the snow is thoring!"

For contrast (and for its own sake), I am adding (from Halliwell's *Dictionary*) a scrap of Derbyshire dialect in which a farm-hand, Thomas Lide, tells his master what he could *do* if only it were waiting to be done.

"Tummus," says the Farmer, "why dunner yo mend meh shoom?"

"Becoz, mester," replies Tummas, " 'tis zo cood, I conner work the tachin [waxed thread] at aw. I've brockn it ten times I'm shur to de [day]—it freezes so hard. Why, Hester hung out a smockdrock to dry, an in three minits it wor frozzen as stiff as a proker, an I conner afford to keep a good fire; I wish I cud. I'd soon mend yore shoon, an uthers tow. I'd soon yarn [earn] sum munney, I warrant ye. Conner [cannot] yo find sum work for m', mester, these hard times? I'll doo onnythink to addle [make] a penny. I con thresh—I con split wood—I con make spars—I con thack [thatch]—I con skower a dike, an I can trench tow [too], but it freezes so hard. I con winner [winnow] —I con fother [litter] or milk, if there be need on't. I wondner mind drivin plow or onnythink."

But half an hour with the great *Dialect Dictionary* will prove how inexhaustibly rich the English language once was and still is in words made, used, and loved by those who were unlearned in books, but had keen and lively eyes in their heads, quick to see the delight and livingness of a thing, and the wits to give it a name fitting it as close as a skin.

302. "THE VERSE WER SHORT BUT VERY GOOD."

This is not true of most inscriptions upon tombstones. Like poetry itself they are a test of the age in which they were written. The quiet and noble words on Spenser's tomb in Westminster Abbey are of 1598:

Here lyes (expecting the Second Comminge of our Saviour *Christ Jesus*) the body of Edmond Spencer the Prince of Poets in his tyme whose divine Spirrit needs noe other witnesse than the works which he left behind him.

He was born in London in the
Yeare 1553 and Died
in the yeare
1598.

"Michaell Draiton" is near by—"his bust in alablaster" above his tomb. "A memorable Poet of this age who Exchanged his Lawrell for a Crowne of Glorye A.D. 1631." And this his epitaph "made by Mr. Francis Quarles, who was a great friend . . . and a very good man":

Doe pious marble let thy Readers knowe
What they and what their children owe
To DRAITON'S Name whose sacred dust
Wee recommend unto thy TRUST.
Protect his Mem'ry and Preserve his Storye,
Remaine a lasting Monument of his Glorye.
And when thy Ruines shall disclame
To be the Treas'rer of his NAME,
His Name, that canot fade, shall be
An everlasting MONUMENT to thee.

Not far distant lies Margaret Cavendish, Duchess of Newcastle. She was, we read, "the youngest sister to the Lord

Lucas of Colchester, a noble familie, for all the Brothers were valiant and all the Sisters virtuous. This Dutches was a wise wittie and learned Lady, which her many books do well testify, she was a most virtuous and a Loving and careful wife, and was with her Lord all the time of his banishment and miseries, and when he came home never parted with him in his solitary confinement."

This inscription is of 1674.

In 1740, a belated and "preposterous" monument was erected to Shakespeare, in whose inscription an attempt to amend the lines taken from *The Tempest* ruined their poetry and their sense!

Later still [1771]—in a windy effort to hit off two poets on one slab—we have:

> No more the *Graecian* Muse unrival'd reagns
> To *Britain* let the Nations homage pay:
> She felt a Homer's fire in Milton's strains,
> A Pindar's rapture in the lyre of Gray.

If, then, even epitaphs in clear and simple prose are rare, how much rarer must be epitaphs with poetry in them. It is, therefore, an unusual and haunting experience to chance on an epitaph in church aisle or yard that calls as if with a human voice out of the silent past. The three that follow I owe to the kindness of a friend, Mrs. Graham Wallis:

The first is from the Galilee Chapel, Durham, where in the sixteenth century John Brinley was organist. It is dated October 13, A.D. 1576:

> Jno Brinlyes body here doth ly
> Who praysèd GOD with hand and voice:
> By musickes Heavenlie harmonie
> Dull myndes he made in God rejoice:
> His soul into the heavens is lyft
> To prayse him still that gave the gyft.

The next is from Chaldon Church, Surrey:

GOOD REDAR, WARNE ALL MEN AND WOMEN WHIL THEY BE HERE TO BE EVER GOOD TO THE POORE AND NEDY!

THE POORE EVER IN THIS WORLD SHALL YE HAVE:
GOD GRAUNTE US SUMWAT IN STORE FOR TO SAVE.
THE CRY OF THE POORE IS EXTREME AND VERY SORE:
GOD GRAUNTE US TO BE GOOD EVER MORE.
IN THIS WORLDE WE RUN OUR RASE:
GOD GRAUNTE US TO BE WITH CHRIST IN TYME AND SPACE

This—of June 1668 in Burford—is a memorial of three generations of one family named Bartholomew—mercers:

Lo, Huddled up together lye
Gray age, greene youth, white Infantcy;
If death doth Natures laws dispence
And Reconciles all difference
Tis fit one Flesh, one House, should have
One Tombe, one Epitaph, one Grave;
And they that lived and loved either
Should dye and Lye and sleep together.

Go reader—whether go or stay—
Thou canst not hence be long away.

And this, of April 2nd, 1777, is from the Churchyard of Strathfieldsaye:

Asleep beneath this humble Stone
Lies honest, harmless, simple John;
Who free from Guilt & Care & Strife,
Here closed his inoffensive Life;
He practised all the good he knew,
And did no harm. His only Sin
Was that he loved a drop of Gin;
And when his favourites was not near
Contented took his horn of Beer,
Tho' weak his head, to make amendes
Heav'n gave him Health, Content & Friends;
This little Village Nursed and Bred him
And Good Lord Rivers cloathed and fed him,
T'was there he Lived, Caressed by all,

The favourite of the Servant's Hall;
With them he eat his daily Bread;
They loved him Living, mourn him Dead,
And now have kindly Joined to Raise
This little Tombstone to his praise.
Nor should the learned and the wise
Such humble merit e'en despise;
Who knows but John may find a place
Where wit must never show its face?
Farewell John: [and] Grant Heaven that we
Harmless may live, and die, like thee.

It seemed no offence in earlier days than our own to refer to "a drop of Gin" on a tomb-stone, or, like the grave-diggers in *Hamlet,* to keep up one's spirits with a jest or two on a dismal occasion. I came, for example, quite by accident, on John Archer's epitaph in Selby Abbey:

Near to this Stone lies Archer (John)
  Late Saxon (I aver)
Who, without tears, thirty-four years,
  Did carcases inter.

But, Death at last, for his work's past,
  Unto him thus did say:
"Leave off thy trade, be not afraid,
  But forthwith come away."

Without reply or asking why,
  The summons he obey'd,
In Seventeen hundred and sixty-eight
  Resigned his life and spade.

And (owing to the good fellowship of the man who cut his stone) every stranger who reads his epitaph bids him a warm farewell and carries off a pinch of courage in his poke.

In the Church at Iver, Buckinghamshire, I found:

Beneath this place lies interned the body of Venturus

> Mandey, Bricklayer, son of Michael Mandey, Bricklayer, and grandson to Venturus Mandey, of this parish, Bricklayer, who had the honour of being Bricklayer to the Honble. Society of Lincolns Inn from the year of Our Lord 1667 to the day of his death. . . . He also translated into English DIRECTORIUM GENERALE URANOMETRICUM and TRIGONOMETRICA PLANA ET SPHERICA, LINEARIS ET LOGARITHMICA. . . .

There proper pride in an ancient Craft rings out like a cock-crow, dull though the words may be. Nor was Venturus Mandey the only Bricklayer connected with Lincoln's Inn who turned to letters, for "when a little child," rare Ben Jonson "lived in Harts-horn-lane near Charing Cross where his Mother married a Bricklayer for her second Husband." On leaving Westminster School he was admitted into St. John's College, Cambridge, but was there only a few weeks owing to lack of money, and was "fain to return to the trade of his father-in-law. And let not them blush that have, but those that have not, a lawful calling. He help'd in the building of the new structure of Lincolns-Inn, when having a Trowell in his hand, he had a book in his pocket."

Just as Charlotte Brontë remembered seeing her sister Emily standing at the table in the tiny kitchen of the parsonage at Haworth, kneading dough, and with a copy of Plato propped up against a pudding-basin.

303. "CARE IS HEAVY."

Dear God, though Thy all-powerful hand
Should so direct my earthly fate
That I may seem unfortunate
To them who do not understand
That all things follow Thy decree,
Staunchly I'll bear what e'er's Thy will—
Praying Thee but to grant me still
That none shall come to harm through me;
For, God, although Thou knowest all,
I am too young to comprehend
The windings to my journey's end;

I fear upon the road to fall
In the worst sin of all that be
And thrust my brother in the sea.

CONAL O'RIORDAN

304. "MOTHER, NEVER MOURN."

"It was my own mother (wrote Thomas Cantimpratanus about 1260) who told me the story which I am about to relate. My grandmother had a firstborn son of most excellent promise, comely beyond the wont of children, at whose death she mourned . . . with a grief that could not be consoled, until one day, as she went by the way, she saw in her vision a band of youths moving onwards, as it seemed to her, with exceeding great joy; and she, remembering her son and weeping that she saw him not in this joyful band, suddenly beheld him trailing weary footsteps after the rest. Then with a grievous cry the mother asked: 'How comes it, my son, that thou goest alone, lagging thus behind the rest?' Then he opened the side of his cloak and showed her a heavy water-pot, saying: 'Behold, dear mother, the tears which thou hast vainly shed for me, through the weight whereof I must needs linger behind the rest.' "

But not all mourners are, in their dreams, so rebuked or so comforted. St. Augustine, a loving son, pined in vain:

"If the dead could come in dreams," he wrote, "my pious mother would no night fail to visit me. Far be the thought that she should, by a happier life, have been made so cruel that, when aught vexes my heart, she should not even console in a dream the son whom she loved with an only love."

307. "LIKE STARS UPON SOME GLOOMY GROVE."

. . . Stars are of mighty use; The night
Is dark, and long;
The Rode foul, and where one goes right
Six may go wrong.
One twinkling ray
Shot o'er some cloud,
May clear much way
And guide a croud.

Gods Saints are shining lights: who stays
Here long must passe
O'er dark hills, swift streams, and steep ways
As smooth as glasse;
But these all night
Like Candles, shed
Their beams, and light
Us into Bed. . . .

HENRY VAUGHAN

310. TOM O' BEDLAM.

This poem has been at hide-and-seek with the world for many years past. Mr. Frank Sidgwick, having long played Seek, at last found it hidden away in the British Museum in a manuscript, No. 24665, inscribed "Giles Earle—his book, 1615." In this MS. the poem consists of eight stanzas of ten lines each, with a chorus of five lines. The version on page 291 is of twenty-five lines only, and has been taken from Alice Meynell's beautiful anthology *The Flower of the Mind.* They differ, says Mr. Sidgwick, from their original not only in their order, but, here and there, in their words. The "Moon" (l. 1), for example, is in the MS. *morn;* "lovely" (l. 2) is *lonely,* and "marrow" is *morrow;* "rounded" (l. 10) is *wounded;* "heart" (l. 16) is *host;* and "with" (l. 21) is *by.* It is a nice exercise of taste and judgment to choose between them and to find good reasons for one's choice. When and by whom "Tom o' Bedlam" was written is as yet undiscovered. It remains for the present a shining jewel in the crown of the most modest of all men of genius, known only as *Anon.*

314. "WHAT'S IN THERE."

This far-carrying rhyme belongs to the ancient and famous game of Dump. "He who speaks first in it," says Dr. Gregor, "or laughs first, or lets his teeth be seen, gets nine nips, nine nobs, nine double douncornes, an' a gueed blow on the back o' the head."

Faht and *fahr* are the pleasing Aberdonian way of saying *what* and *where.*

So may the omission of a few commas effect a wonder in the imagination. To the imagination indeed there is nothing absurd in, "I saw the sun at twelve o'clock at night"—for in the "little nowhere of the mind" it is possible to see both burning sun and black night *together*. Once in a dream I myself was enchanted by three moons in the sky, shining in their silver above waters as wide as those of Milton's curfew. Even the most commonplace objects (in waking life) will take to themselves a strangeness and beauty never seen or "marked" before, if (like Marcus Aurelius in the presence of his loaf of bread) we give them a few moments' rapt, intense attention. The object, the eye, the memory, the insight, the spirit within: these are the Five in Council.

Here is another old nursery "nonsense" rhyme that conjures up almost as lively and dreamlike pictures in the mind:

> There was a man of double deed
> Who sowed his garden full of seed;
> And when the seed began to grow,
> 'Twas like a garden full of snow;
> And when the snow began to fall,
> Like birds it was upon the wall;
> And when the birds began to fly,
> 'Twas like a shipwreck in the sky;
> And when the sky began to crack,
> 'Twas like a stick upon my back;
> And when my back began to smart,
> 'Twas like a pen-knife in my heart;
> And when my heart began to bleed,
> Then I was dead—and dead indeed.

319. "It had become a glimmering Girl."

"The Tuatha De Danaan—the divine Children of Danu which forgotten centuries ago invaded Ireland—can take all shapes, and those that are in the waters take often the shape of fish. A woman of Burren, in Galway, says, 'There are more of them in the sea than on the land . . . ,' and another Galway woman says, 'Surely those things are in the sea as well as on land. My father was out fishing one night off Tyrone. And something came beside the boat that had eyes shining like candles. And then a wave came in, and a storm rose all in a minute, and whatever was in the wave, the weight of it had like to sink the boat. And then they saw that it was a woman in the sea that had the shining eyes. So my father went to the priest, and he bid him always to take a drop of holy water and a pinch of salt out in the boat with him, and nothing could harm him.' "

W. B. YEATS

321. "ONE WITHOUT."

Was it the sound of a footfall I heard
On the cold flag stone?
Or the cry of a wandering far night bird,
On the sea-winds blown?
Was that a human shape that stood?
In the shadow below,
Or but the mist of the moonlit wood
As it hovered low?
Was it the voice of a child that called
From the hill side steep?
Or, oh, but the wind as it softly lulled
The world to sleep?

ELIZABETH RAMAL

325. "BROOME, BROOME ON HILL."

The story is of how a bright lady comes to keep her tryst with a knight-at-arms in the golden broom of Hive Hill. She finds him under a charm, an enchantment, asleep; and having left her ring on his finger for proof of her coming, she steals away. Presently after he awakes—her presence gone. To leave a quiet and happy room vacant at night is sometimes to have this experience, as it were, *reversed*. There comes a feeling that one's-self being gone, far gentler visitants may enter and share its solitude—while its earthly tenant sleeps overhead, and one by one the stars sink to their setting.

326. "The Changeling."

When larks gin sing
Away we fling,
And babes new-born steal as we go;
An elf instead
We leave in bed,
And wind out, laughing, Ho, ho, ho!

329. "Mariana."

It is difficult to read this poem slowly and intently enough if one is to experience to the *full* the living things and sights and sounds that by its words are charmed into the mind—the hushed solitude, the desolation. Tennyson (like Coleridge) had senses of a fineness rare even in a poet, and few artists have spent themselves so unwearyingly in the effort to record the "harvest" of those senses in words. It is said that the tone and timbre of a fine fiddle is improved by the music of the master who plays upon it—that a Paganini or a Kreisler may charm into the throbbing wood some ghostly life and feeling of his own. However fantastic this may be, it is truth itself of language; and a writer like Tennyson, master artist that he was, leaves a personal impress on the language he uses that cannot be deleted. English is a marvellous fiddle, echoing almost in every sentence one says or writes with many tongues and a thousand individual craftsmen, doers, and thinkers, utterly dissimilar one from another, while the words of which it was made were rooted in the soil of the people, and were brought to ripeness by the dews and rains and suns of their northern heavens. Take even, of all there is in *Mariana,* but the "peering mouse" in the sixth stanza—his sharp nose sniffing the air beneath the small wooden arch of his dark-glimmering mousery, where gnaw and shriek and gambol his fellows behind the mouldering wainscot. Or stay for a moment looking down on the "marish mosses" in the fourth stanza—of a hue as lively as a fairy's mantle in sunlight—greening the waters of the blackened sluice. So piece by piece the words of the poem build up in the imagination this solitary house with its forsaken Mariana, whom Tennyson himself had seen in the day-dream conferred on him by another poet, in *Measure for Measure:*

Isabella. Can this be so? did *Angelo* so leave her?

Duke. Left her in her teares, and dried not one of them with his comfort: swallowed his vowes whole, pretending in her discoveries of dishonour: in few, bestowed on her her owne lamentation, which she yet weares for his sake: and he, a marble to her teares, is washed with them, but relents not.

Isabella. What a merit were it in death to take this poore maid from the world. . . .

332. "Yes Tor."

Turn your back on Okehampton and break away due South into the wilds of Dartmoor, and there, "summering" together "beneath the empty skies," lie titanic Yes Tor and High Willes, rearing their bare vast shapes into the air.

333. "To heare the Mandrake grone." (stanza 2)

Of the dangerous plant Mandrake ("its root in something the shape and appearance of a man") is concocted Mandragora, one of the "drowsy syrups." "The leaves and fruit be also dangerous, for they cause deadly sleep, and peevish drowsiness." The fruit is "of the bigness of a reasonable pippin, and as yellow as gold when it is thoroughly ripe: fair without, ashes within." It is said that the mandrake's screams, when it is dragged out of the ground, will send the hearer mad. So anyone in need of it is advised first to seal his ears, then to tie the plant to a dog's tail and hike him on to haul it out of its haunt! "Avicenna the Arabian physician asserts that a Jew at Metz had a mandragore with a human head, and the legs and body of a cock, which lived five weeks, and was fed on lavender and earthworms, and, when dead, was preserved in spirits." Even up to the nineteenth century believers of witchcraft were wont to carry these monstrous little Erdmannikens in bosom or pocket for an amulet or charm.

The "Basilisk," old books maintain, is a fabulous beast whose icy glare petrifies with horror any human who meets her face to face. Approach her then with a mirror; and courage be your guide!

"HEMLOCK, HENBANE, ADDERS-TONGUE." (line 10)

Hemlock is that tall, dim-spotted plant of a sad green colour, and of a scent "strong, heady and bad," which is "very cold and dangerous," especially when "digged in the dark."

Clammy henbane is woolly-leafed, with hollow dark-eyed flowers of a purple-veined dingy yellow. "It lusts to grow in rancid soil, To 'stil its deadly oil."

Moonwort is the meek-looking little flowering fern that has the power to break locks, and to make any horse that chances to tread upon it cast his shoes.

The livid-flowered, cherry-like fruited Dwale, Enoron, Banewort, Nightshade or Naughty-man's-cherry is the most "daungerous" plant in England. While leopard's bane—though it bears a bright-yellow daisy-like flower, and witches are said to fear sun-colour—is venomous to animals.

I am uncertain of adder's tongue, for the fern of this name cures sore eyes; and cuckoo-pint which is also so called, is "a remedy for poison and the plague"!

Of these six insidious plants only one is openly mentioned by Shakespeare, and they have comparatively few country names; unlike, for example, the purple orchis, "which has so many," says Nicholas Culpeper, "that they would fill a sheet of paper": Long-purples, Dead-men's fingers, Crake-feet, Giddy-gandy, Neat-legs, Geese-and-goslings, and Gander-gooses, being a few choice specimens.

The gardener mentioned on page 509 would have called it *Orchis latifolia Lagotis,* and the advantage of this name over that of Dead-men's-fingers or Giddy-gandy is that if by any chance you should be entertaining a pleasant company of botanists or horticulturalists to tea—say, a Frenchman, a Spaniard, a German, a Dutchman, a Russian, a Swiss, and a Swede—and you wished to mention this particular variety of orchis, the mere gentle murmuring of *Orchis latifolia Lagotis* would set every face shining, and brighten every eye.

The Vegetable World, that is, has been classified, and also indexed in (mostly low) Latin; and living men of Science, in this as in much else, use in common a dead language. This vast and valuable achievement—when one considers for how many centuries Man has shared the world with its flowers—took an unconscionably long time, for in a book on Botany, published in Germany in 1547, only two hundred and forty species of plants were included. In a successor to it, published eighty-six years afterwards, there were six thousand; and in a complete collection of to-day there would be about a quarter of a million.

It would be a pretty courtesy, when the learned converse with the vulgar, if they translated their Latin into intelligible English. When even a botanist names a flower he mentions only its kind or variety—and that only in reference to some, but by no means to all, of its characteristics. It is important, then, to keep on reminding oneself that every living thing is not merely something which belongs to a family, species, genus, but is unique—itself only, and no other.

At the risk of their being merely tedious, here are a few more country names of English wild-flowers—names always lively, often humorous and sometimes curiously beautiful—but in danger nowadays of dying of disuse. To discover *why* each of these flowers has been so named would be an enthralling but laborious adventure.

The *Cuckoo-pint* or *Lords-and-Ladies* is called also Aaron, Adam-and-Eve, Adder's Meat, Bloody-Man's-Finger, Bobbin-Joan, Bulls-and-Cows. Calf's-foot, Friar's-cowl, Lamb-in-a-pulpit, Lily Grass, Nightingales, and Wake-Robin.

The *Wild Mercury* is Goosefoot, All-good, Blithe, Flowery Docken, Good King Henry, and Wild Spinach.

The *Marsh-Marigold* is Boots, Golds, Goldins, May-blobs, Meadow Bout, Water Buttercup, and Yellow Gowan.

The *Foxglove* is Dead-Men's-Bells, Finger Flower, Flap-Dock and Lusmore.

Goose-Grass is Bur-weed, Harif, Haritch, Cleavers, Geckdor, Love-man and Mutton-chops.

The common *Toad-flax* is Butter-and-Eggs, Gall-wort, Buttered Haycocks and Dragon-bushes.

Bird's-foot Trefoil is Cat-in-the-Clover, Crow's foot, Eggs-and-Bacon, Fingers-and-Thumbs, Ground Honey-suckle and Lamb's Toe.

The *Campion* is Flower of Constantinople, Flower of Bristowe, Gardener's-Eye, Jerusalem Cross and None-such.

Bog-myrtle is Candle-berry, Sweet Gale, Golden Osier, Sweet Willow.

Cat-mint is Ale-hoof, Blue-Runner, Devil's Candlesticks, Gill-go-by-ground, Robin-run-in-the-hedge and Tun-hoof.

Wood-Sorrel is Alleluia, Cuckoo-bread, Gowk-meat, Stubwort, and Wood-Sower.

Solomon's-Seal is David's Harp, Fraxinell, Ladder-to-Heaven and Lily-of-the-Mountain.

So, too, *Verbascum Thapsus* (the Wooly-beard), one of the mulleins, has for folk-names, not only Duffle, Fluff-weed, Ag-leaf and Torches, but also Candle-wick, Hag's-taper, Jacob's-staff, Shepherd's-club, Beggar's-blanket, and Adam's-Flannel; while the *Wild Chervil* is not only three kinds of comb—Lady's, Shepherd's and Venus's, but at least eleven kinds of needle—Adam's, Beggar's, Shepherd's, Tailor's, Witches'; Clock, Crow, Crake, Pink, Puck and Poke.

Nowadays, our minds and their contents, like our clothes, seem to tend to be more and more alike; and most children are taught in school—what most children are taught in school. A lively and happy country girl, when I asked her the name of a star-clustering wild-flower flourishing everywhere on her farm-land, replied that she didn't know, and explained with a smile "At school, you know, I never cared for Nature study." The very phrase was like a knell. It was as if a child after politely listening to "How many miles to Babylon?" or "Ride-a-cock-horse," or "The Queen was in her parlour," had muttered, "I'm sorry, you know! but I can't abide that William Wordsworth."

But while for the most part the meaning and reference of the names of wildflowers shines out of their faces, this is not usually so with the names of our English villages. They *have* a "meaning" well worth the discovering, but meanwhle they are curious, romantic, echoing sounds merely to hear and utter. Take but a few from *"a Topographical Map* [Jan. 1, 1769] *of the County* of KENT . . . *in which are expressed all the Roads, Lanes, Churches, Towns, Villages, Noblemen and Gentlemen's Seats, Roman Roads, Hills, Rivers, Woods, Cottages, and everything Remarkable in the* COUNTY, *together with the Division of the Lathes and their Sub-divisions into Hundreds"*: Allhollows,

Mammonds, Drele, Welmm, Brodnyx, Sarr, Kemsyng, Buglus, Ripple, Molash, Lullingstone, Sutton Valance, Ewell, Bingh-ton, Monchalsea. Listen to the *Shoals,* etc. [all Kent]: Columbine, the Culvery, Spreves, Spanyard, Cold Blow, Oase Edge, Knowle, Spile, Pann, Knockjohn and Girdler.

Then again, quite apart from cities, towns, villages, hamlets, streets, and houses, the vast majority even of our English fields and meadows have long had their own individual and proper names. The following are a few specimens from the village of Hitcham, in Buckinghamshire, which I have borrowed from a pamphlet by the Rev. C. H. D. Grimes:

Great and Little Cogmarthon.
Upper and Lower Brissels.
Homer Corner.
Parliament Close.
Hogg Hill.
Lily Field.
and Walnut Tree Close.

And these (by the kindness of Mr. Henry Williamson) are from a patch of North Devonshire:

Berber.
Vineyard.
Cunnycott.
Lunie Park.
Monticroft.
Hatchetty.
Netherams.
Zetheridge.
Bewhayes.
Flints, and
Plain.

The village of Yarnton in Oxfordshire, Mr. Leonard Rice-Oxley tells me, is divided into three districts—the *Clays,* the *Sands,* and the *Runtlings,* which is like saying, "Yes, we have three children—*John, Mary,* and *Mahershalalhashbaz."* But of all names, perhaps those which grammarians have given to the various species of words themselves are the most unalluring; *adjective, adverb, preposition, conjunction,* for example. And how many young heads are more meaningful than a parrot's when they repeat such terms as *vocative, ablative, conjunctive, infinitive, optative,* or even *person, mood, tense* and *voice*?

335. "A THOUSAND DARLING IMPS." (stanza 19)

"Aeriel spirits," says Robert Burton, "are such as keep quarter most part in the air, cause many tempests, thunder, and lightnings, tear oaks, fire steeples, houses, strike men and beasts, make it rain stones, . . . wool, frogs, etc., counterfeit armies in the air, strange noises, swords, etc."

Nothing vexed Linnet Sara more than to be asked if there were any such darling imps or spectres or ghosts or blackamoors in Thrae. All such to her were nothing but idle fiddle-faddle. She believed little but in what she could touch or weigh or measure. She much preferred things to go on in a fashion she could be quite sure of, and had little patience with what may have happened to one person only (however gifted) until it could be made to happen to a good many more. But she was a wonderfully steady worker, keeping everything neat, orderly and ready for use as she toiled solemnly on. Still, there was much in Miss Taroone, excellent servant though Sara was, that remained and would probably always remain, a little beyond her faithful handmaid. When she was cleaning and tidying up Mr. Nahum's room I doubt if she ever so much as opened the covers of that cumbersome old book of his called *The Other Worlde*—unless to beat the dust out of it.

"Now them jars up there is *fax!"* she would say, her large ruminating face close to mine, as we peered together into the quiet of her still-room. And yet, I am not so sure. Now and then when Sara was talking to me, I seemed to surprise, half-hidden in her features, and looking out at me, as if from the heart-shaped opening of a shutter, quite another face—and one as young and lovely as any that ever smiled out of the words of a poem.

Reginald Scot, who wrote *The Discoverie of Witchcraft* (1584), had a very different kind of kitchen company:

". . . Our mothers maide," he says, of his childhood, "so terrified us with . . . bull beggers, spirits, witches, urchens, elves, hags, fairies, satyrs, pans, faunes, syrens, kit with the cansticke, tritons, centaurs, dwarfes, giants, imps, calcars [astrologers], conjurors, nymphes, changlings, Incubus, Robin goodfellowe, the spoorne [? a fiend], the mare, the man in the oke, the hellwaine [a night-sky wagon], the fierdrake [a dragon], the puckle [a spectre], Tom thombe, hob gobblin, Tom tumbler, boneles, and such other bugs, that we were afraid of our onw shadowes: in so much as some never feare the divill, but in a dark night. . . ."

There seems to be no mention here of the salamander—a creature at least as rarely seen by mortal eyes as the puckle, spoorne or firedrake.

"When I was about five years old," says Benvenuto Cellini, "my father happened to be in a basement-chamber of our house, where they had been washing, and where a good fire of oak logs are still burning; he had a viol in his hand and was playing and singing alone beside the fire. The weather was very cold. Happening to look into the fire, he espied in the middle of the most burning flames a little creature like a lizard, which was sporting in the core of the intensest coals. Becoming aware of what the thing was, he had my sister and me called, and pointing it out to us children, gave me a great box on the ears, which caused me to cry with all my might. Then he pacified me by saying, 'My dear little boy, I am not striking you for anything that you have done, but only to make you remember that the lizard you see in the fire is a salamander, a creature which has never been seen before by any of whom we have credible information.' So saying he gave me some pieces of money, and kissed me."

"BELL AND WHIP AND HORSE'S TAIL" (stanza 22)

—such in old days was the Witch's vile punishment if she escaped drowning or the stake: to be whipped, tied to a horse's tail, and rung through the crowded streets.

"Agramie," I suppose, is agrimony, which, if worn by the wary, will enable the wearer to detect witches. Their eyes too will betray them, for *there* you will find no tiny reflected image of yourself as you will in the eyes of the honest. And if you would be rid of their company, pluck a sprig of scarlet pimpernel, and repeat this charm:

Herbe pimpernell, I have thee found
Growing upon Christ Jesus' ground:
The same guift the Lord Jesus gave unto thee,
When he shed his blood on the tree,
Arise up, pimpernell, and goe with me.
And God blesse me,
And all that shall wear *thee*. AMEN.

"Say this fifteen dayes together, twice a day, morning earlye fasting, and in the evening full."

Indeed, at last, whatever the peril, a quiet heart and heaven's courage, are charm enough:

I say that we are wound
With mercy round and round
As if with air. . . .
GERALD MANLEY HOPKINS

But Charms have been used for many other purposes than fending off witches and their witch-craft.

"Last summer," says John Aubrey, "on the day of St. John the Baptist, 1694, I accidentally was walking in the pasture behind Montague House, it was 12 o'clock. I saw there about two or three and twenty young women, most of them well habited, on their knees very busy, as if they had been weeding. I could not presently learn what the matter was; at last a young man told me, that they were looking for a coal under the root of a plantain, to put under their head that night, and they should dream who would be their husbands: It was to be sought for that day and hour."

He gives another prescription—with the same blissful end in view:

"You must lie in another county, and knit the left garter about the right legged stocking (let the other garter and stocking alone) and as you rehearse the following verses, at every comma, knit a knot:

This knot I knot,
To know the thing, I know not yet,
That I may see,
The man that shall my husband be,
How he goes, and what he wears,
And what he does, all days, and years.

Accordingly in your dream you will see him: if a musician, with a lute or other instrument; if a scholar, with a book or papers.

"A gentlewoman that I knew, confessed in my hearing, that she used this method, and dreamt of her husband whom she had never seen. About two or three years after, as she was one Sunday at church (at our Lady's church in Sarum), up pops a young Oxonian in the pulpit: she cries out presently to her sister, this is the very face of the man that I saw in my dream.

"Another way is, to charm the moon thus: at the first appearance of the new moon after new year's day, go out in the evening, and stand over the spars of a gate or stile, looking on the moon and say,

All haile to thee moon, all haile to thee;
I prithe, good moon, declare to me,
This night, who my husband—my husband—must be.

You must presently after go to bed."

Or again:

Pluck the yarrow (*millefolium,* or Nose-bleed) growing on a young man's grave, repeating, as you do so, the words following:

Yarrow, sweet yarrow, the first I have found,
In the name of Christ Jesus, I pluck from the ground;

As Joseph loved sweet Mary, and took her for his dear,
So in a dream this night, I hope, my true love will appear.

And then go to sleep, with the yarrow under your pillow. In the morning you may awaken a little feverish. That being so, repeat:

Right cheek! Left cheek! Why do ye burn?
Cursed be she that doeth me harm!
If she be maid, let her be slayed;
If she be widow, long let her mourn;
But if my own true love—burn, cheek, *burn!*

But remember:

Those dressed in blue
Have lovers true;
In green and white,
Forsaken quite.

Or it may be apples rather than sweethearts that need the charming. That being so, it is the custom in Sussex to *worsle* (wassail) the orchard. The worslers, armed with a cow-horn, make a ring round the trees, then sing out at the top of their voices:

Stand fast root,
Bear well top,
Pray God send us
A howling crop.
Every twig
Apples big,
Every bough
Apples enow.
Hats full, caps full,
Full quarter sacks full,
Holla, boys, holla! *Huzzah!*

Or butter. If so, plunge or thump or grind away at the churn handle, keeping time with this incantation:

Come, butter, come,
Come, butter, come,
Peter stands at the gate,
Waiting for a buttered cake,
Come, butter, come!

If it fail, it is not because of its novelty for it is to be found in a book of 1655 with the tempting title, "A Candle in the Dark"; and its author, Thomas Ady, heard it from a witch whose grandmother had learnt it in the days of Queen Mary.

The following charms are all in rhyme but are for miscellaneous purposes. Against a snakebite:

Underneath this hazelin mote,
There's a braggoty worm with a speckled throat;
Nine double is he:
Now from nine double to eight double,
And from eight double to seven double,
And from seven double to six double,
And from six double to five double,
And from five double to four double,
And from four double to three double,
And from three double to two double,
And from two double to one double,
And from one double to no double,
No double hath *he!*

For before going to Court:

With a four-leaved clover, double-topp'd ash, and green-topp'd seave [rush],
You may go before the Queen's daughter without asking leave.

For a bad finger:

Our Saviour was of Virgin born;
His head was crowned with a crown of thorne;
It never cankered nor festered at all,
And I hope in Christ Jesus *this* never shaull.

For one's general (and permanent) health:

He that would live for aye,
He must eat *sage* in May.

For a burn or whitlow:

There came two Angels from the North,
One was Fire, and one was Frost.
Out *Fire!* in *Frost!*
In the name of the Father, the Son, and the Holy Ghost.

And for warts—which, like red hair and extremely stout gentlemen, seem to be far less common than they were some forty years ago:

"I had from my childhood," says Francis Bacon, "a wart on one of my fingers; afterwards, when I was about sixteen years old, being then at Paris, there grew upon both my hands a number of warts—at the least a hundred, in a month's space. The English Ambassador's lady, who was a woman far from superstition, told me one day she would help me away with my warts; whereupon she got a piece of lard with the skin on, and rubbed the warts all over with the fat side; and, amongst the rest, that wart which I had had from my childhood; then she nailed the piece of lard, with the fat towards the sun, upon a post of her chamber window, which was towards the south.

The success was, that within five weeks' space all the warts went quite away: and that wart which I had so long endured for company. But at the rest I did little marvel, because they came in a short time and might go away in a short time again: but the going away of that which had stayed so long doth yet stick with me. They say the like is done by the rubbing of warts with a green alder stick, and then burying the stick to rot in the muck."

He leaves the question at "They say"—with the comment that further enquiry might be useful.

But things *worn*—magic rings, or gems, or roots, or stones—as well as things said, may act as charms or amulets:

"The best witnesses have it upon record how Charlemain's

mistress enchanted him with a ring, which so long as she [being dead] had about her, he would not suffer her carcase to be carry'd out of his chamber; how a Bishop taking it out of her mouth, the Emperor grew to be as much bewitched with the Bishop; but he, being chyd with his excess of favour, threw it into a Pond, where the Emperor's chiefest pleasure was to walk to his dying day."

366. "The Water Kelpy" (stanza 8)

is a fiend that haunts northern rivers and desolate waters. It is a horse-shape, and the sound of its neighings is a boding of death to the traveller.

But—if wits are set to work—he can be made not only harmless, but useful:

"A man carting home his peats for winter fuel was in the habit of seeing a big black horse grazing on the banks of the Ugie, at Inverugie Castle, near Peterhead, each morning as he passed to the 'moss.' He told some of his neighbours. They suspected what the horse was, and advised the man to get a 'wraith-horse' bridle, approach the animal with all care and caution, and cast the bridle over his head. The man now knew the nature of the creature, and followed the advice. Kelpie was secured, and did good work in carrying stones to build the bridge over the Ugie at Inverugie. When his services were no longer needed he was set at liberty. As he left he said:

'Sehr back an sehr behns
Cairryt a' the Brig o' Innerugie's stehns.'

The old man, who handed down this story to his children, from one of whom I have now got it, used to say to any of them that complained of being tired after a hard day's work: 'Oh, aye, ye're like the kelpie that cairryt the stehns to big the brig o' Innerugie—*Sehr back and sehr behns.*'"

Then again, "a miller was annoyed by a kelpie entering his mill during the night and playing havoc among the grain and meal. One night he shut up in the mill his boar, for a miller generally kept a good many pigs and a breeding sow or two. As usual kelpie entered the mill. The boar stood on his defence, and fought the kelpie. Next night the creature appeared at the miller's window, and called to him:

" 'Is there a chattie i' the mill the nicht?' "

" 'Aye, there is a chattie i' the mill, and will be for ever mair,' was the answer.

Kelpie returned no more to the mill."

"Thus did the evil creatures often press me hard, but, as was meet, I served them well with my war-sword; they had no joyous fill by eating me, wicked destroyers, sitting round their feast nigh the bottom of the sea; but in the morning wounded by the sword, slain by the dagger, they lay up along the sea-strand, so that they could never more hinder sea-farers on their course in the deep channel.

Light came from the east, the bright beacon of the Lord; the waves were stilled, and I could descry the sea-headlands, those wind-swept walls."

Beowulf, translated by C. B. TINKER

341. "THE WANDERING SPECTRE."

". . . The usewall Method for a curious Person to get a transient Sight of this otherwise invisible Crew of Subterraneans, . . . is to put his left Foot under the Wizard's right Foot, and the Seer's Hand is put on the Inquirer's Head, who is to look over the Wizard's right Shoulder . . . then will he see a Multitude of Wights, like furious hardie Men, flocking to him haistily from all Quarters, as thick as Atoms in the Air. . . . Thes thorow Fear strick him breathless and speechless."

So says "Mr. Robert Kirk, Minister at Aberfoill," in his *Secret Commonwealth* of 1691.

One needs but to find the wizard, and all is plain sailing—except, perhaps, that that "right shoulder" is a little surprising. Is it not rather from over one's left shoulder that one expects to be warned of any such preternatural beings? But then what is this "right" and "left" of ours? I remember well, at any rate, when as a child I had to think hard before I could make sure which was which—and know not even now *how* I do it!

Of these invisible "wights" the womenkind "are said to Spin very fine, to Dy, to Tossue, and Embroyder, but whether only curious Cob-webs, impalpable Rainbows . . . I leave to conjecture."

343. "And Clootie's waur nor a Woman was."
(stanza 19)

A strip or patch of wild weedy uncropped ground (like the Sluggard's garden) that in England is called *No Man's Land,* the Scots country folk call *Clootie's Croft* (or Clootie's little field). They hand it over by name, as it were, to the Fiend, hoping that he may rest content with its harvest of nettle and bramble and burr, and not range elsewhere. It is an old belief that if, like Christian, the wayfarer meets Apollyon straddling across his path, he may have to withstand him not only with sword and staff, but with his wits. Just so, too, in old times, sovereign princes would test strangers with dark questions and riddles. In this ballad the Field disguised as a knight comes wooing at a Widow's door, in the next he is abroad on the high road. Jennifer and the wee boy kept up their hearts, their wits about them, their eyes open, and "had the last word"; which, says Mr. Sidgwick, is a mighty powerful charm against evil spirits—as against Witches are the herbs vervain, dill, basil, hyssop, periwinkle and rue. Iron, too; the sign of the Cross, and running water.

Here is another such encounter from Lady Grey's *The White Wallet*—packed with poems new and old. You can almost hear the voices of the two speakers standing together in the quiet and dust of the morning road:

Meet-on-the-Road.

"Now, pray, where are you going, child?" said Meet-on-the Road.
"To school, sir, to school, sir," said Child-as-It-Stood.

"What have you in your basket, child?" said Meet-on-the-Road
"My dinner, sir, my dinner, sir," said Child-as-It-Stood.

"What have you for your dinner, child?" said Meet-on-the Road.

"Some pudding, sir, some pudding, sir," said Child-as-It-Stood.

"Oh, then I pray, give me a share," said Meet-on-the-Road.
"I've little enough for myself, sir," said Child-as-It-Stood.

"What have you got that cloak on for?" said Meet-on-the-Road.
"To keep the wind and cold from me," said Child-as-It-Stood.

"I wish the wind would blow through you," said Meet-on-the-Road.
"Oh, what a wish! Oh, what a wish!" said Child-as-It-Stood.

"Pray what are those bells ringing for?" said Meet-on-the-Road.
"To ring bad spirits home again," said Child-as-It-Stood.

"Oh, then, I must be going, child!" said Meet-on-the-Road.
"So fare you well, so fare you well," said Child-as-It-Stood.

And here, for titbits and *bonnes bouches*—and just in case—are Eight Ancient Riddles from *Popular Rhymes,* and a ninth which was sent in a letter by Lewis Carroll to the small friend he had in mind when he wrote *Alice in Wonderland.*

i

The fiddler and his wife,
The piper and his mother,
Ate three half-cakes, three whole cakes,
And three quarters of another.

ii

A house full, a yard full,
And ye can't catch a bowl full.

iii.

As I was going o'er London Bridge,
I heard something crack;
Not a man in all England
Can mend that!

iv.

I had a little sister,
They called her Pretty Peep;
She wades in the waters,
Deep, deep, deep!
She climbs up the mountains,
High, high, high;
My poor little sister,
She has but one eye.

v

As I was going o'er yon moor of moss,
I met a man on a gray horse;
He whipp'd and he wail'd,
I ask'd him what he ail'd;
He said he was going to his father's funeral,
Who died seven years before he was born!

vi.

As I looked out o' my chamber window,
I heard something fall;
I sent my maid to pick it up,
But she couldn't pick it all.

vii.

Black within, and red without,
Four corners round about.

viii.

Come a riddle, come a riddle,
Come a rot-tot-tot,
A wee, wee man, in a reid, reid coat,
A stauve in his hand an' a bane in his throat,
Come a riddle, come a riddle,
Come a rot-tot-tot.

ix.

Dreaming of apples on a wall,
And dreaming often, dear,
I dreamed that, if I counted all,
How many would appear?

Answers

I. 1¾ cakes each; since, if Mr. Piper marries, his wife will be Mr. and Mrs. Fiddler's dear daughter-in-law. ii. Smoke; iii. Ice; iv. A Star; v. The poor soul in the coffin was by trade a dyer; vi. Snuff; vii. A Chimney (in Days of Yore); viii. A cherry; ix. Ten.

344. "The Fause Knicht."

Such visitants, it would appear, have marvellous power even over faces or shapes in stone:

He's tied his steed to the kirk-stile,
Syne wrang-gaites round the kirk gaed he;
When the Mer-Man entered the kirk-door,
Away the sma' images turned their e'e. . . .

Wrang-gaites must mean widdershins, right to left, West to East, the opposite to *deiseal* (deshal)—left to right, sunwise.

Here is another such visitor—one who considerately intrudes not all at once but little by little:

The Strange Visitor.

A wife was sitting at her reel ae night;
And aye she sat, and aye she reeled, and aye she wished for company.

In came a pair o' braid braid soles, and sat down at the fire-side;
And aye she sat, and aye she reeled, and aye she wished for company.

In came a pair o' sma legs, and sat down on the braid braid soles;
And aye she sat, and aye she reeled, and aye she wished for company.

In came a pair o' muckle muckle knees, and sat down on the sma' sma' legs;
And aye she sat, and aye she reeled, and aye she wished for company.

In came a pair o' sma' sma' thees, and sat down on the muckle muckle knees;
And aye she sat, and aye she reeled, and aye she wished for company.

In came a pair o' muckle muckle hips, and sat down on the sma' sma' thees;
And aye she sat, and aye she reeled, and aye she wished for company.

In came a sma' sma' waist, and sat down on the muckle muckle hips;
And aye she sat, and aye she reeled, and aye she wished for company.

In came a pair o' braid braid shouthers, and sat down on the sma' sma' waist;
And aye she sat, and aye she reeled, and aye she wished for company.

In came a pair o' sma' sma' arms, and sat down on the braid braid shouthers;
And aye she sat, and aye she reeled, and aye she wished for company.

In came a pair o' muckle muckle hands, and sat down on the sma' sma' arms;
And aye she sat, and aye she reeled, and aye she wished for company.

In came a sma' sma' neck, and sat down on the braid braid shouthers;
And aye she sat, and aye she reeled, and aye she wished for company.

In came a great big head, and sat down on the sma' sma' neck;
And aye she sat, and aye she reeled, and aye she wished for company.

"What way hae ye sic braid braid feet?" quo' the wife."
"Muckle ganging, muckle ganging."
"What way hae ye sic sma' sma' legs?"
"*Aih-h-h!*—late—and *wee-e-e* moul."
"What way hae ye sic muckle muckle knees?"
"Muckle praying, muckle praying."
"What way hae ye sic sma' sma' thees?"
"*Aih-h-h!*—late—and *wee-e-e* moul."
"What way hae ye sic big big hips?"
"Muckle sitting, muckle sitting."
"What way hae ye sic a sma' sma' waist?"
"*Aih-h-h!*—late—and *wee-e-e* moul."
"What way hae sic braid braid shouthers?"
"Wi' carrying broom, we' carrying broom."
"What way hae ye sic sma' sma' arms?"
"*Aih-h-h!*—late—and *wee-e-e* moul."
"What way hae ye sic muckle muckle hands?"
"Threshing wi' an iron flail, threshing wi' an iron flail."
"What way hae ye sic a sma' sma' neck?'
"*Aih-h-h!*—late—and *wee-e-e* moul."
"What way hae sic a muckle muckle head?"
"Muckle wit, muckle wit."
"What do you come for?"
"For YOU!"

But sometimes it is the monster who's at home:

The cat sits at the mill door spinnin', spinnin'.
Up comes a wee moose rinnin', rinnin'.
"What are ye doin' there my lady, my lady?"
"Spinnin' a sark for my son," quo' Batty, quo' Batty.
"I'll tell a story, my lady, my lady,"
"We'll hae the mair company," quo' Batty, quo' Batty.
"There was once a wee woman, my lady, my lady."
"She tuk the less room," quo' Batty, quo' Batty.
"She was sweepin' her hoose one day, my lady, my lady,"
"She had it the cleaner," quo' Batty, quo' Batty.
"She found a penny, my lady, my lady."
"She had the mair money," quo' Batty, quo' Batty.
"She went to the market, my lady, my lady,"
"She didna stay at hame," quo' Batty, quo' Batty.
"She bocht a wee bit o' beef, my lady, my lady."
"She had the mair flesh meat," quo' Batty, quo' Batty.
"She cam' home my lady, my lady."
"She didna stay awa'," quo' Batty, quo' Batty.
"She put her beef on the coals to roast, my lady, my lady."
"She didna eat it raw," quo' Batty, quo' Batty.
"She put it on the window to cool, my lady, my lady."
"She didna scaud her lips," quo' Batty, quo' Batty.
"Up comes a wee moose an' ate it all up, my lady, my lady."
"Ay, and that's the way I'll eat *you* up too," quo' Batty, quo' Batty,

Quo' *Batty,* quo' BATTY,
Quo' BATTY.

345. "CHRISTABEL."

I have included only these few stanzas of this familiar magical poem because a book is but one book, and to print everything as lovely or almost as lovely would need many.

In reading it as Coleridge explained, all that is necessary to ensure lilt and cadence is to remember that every line, however few or many its words or syllables, has four stresses or accents, and that these fall in accord with its "meaning" as one reads it with clear eyes, attentive ear, and with all one's understanding. In his tale of Genevieve there is yet another false and lovely Fiend:

. . . But when I told the cruel scorn
That crazed that bold and lovely Knight,
And that he crossed the mountain-woods,
Nor rested day or night;

That sometimes from the savage den,
And sometimes from the darksome shade,
And sometimes starting up at once
In green and sunny glade,—

There came and looked him in the face
An angel beautiful and bright;
And that he knew it was a Fiend,
This miserable Knight . . .

"A TOOTHLESS MASTIFF BITCH."

This description of one *with* teeth—a dog seldom seen now—is taken from a German book on husbandry, translated by Barnabe Googe, and is quoted in *Animal Lore:*

"First the mastie that keepeth the house: for this purpose you must provide you such a one, as hath a large and a mightie body, a great and a shrill voyce, that both with his barking he may discover, and with his sight dismay the theefe, yea, being not seene, with the horror of his voice put him to flight; his stature must neither be long nor short, but well set, his head great, his eyes sharpe, and fiery, . . . his countenance like a lion, his brest great and shaghayrd, his shoulders broad, his legges bigge, his tayle short, his feet very great; his disposition must neither be too gentle, nor too curst, that he neither fawne upon a theefe, nor flee (fly) upon his friends; very waking, no gadder abroad, not lavish of his mouth, barking without cause. Neither maketh it any matter though he be not swift: for he is but to fight at home, and to give warning of the enemie."

347. "ONCE A FAIR AND STATELY PALACE."

The radiant, despoiled and spectral palace of this poem is indeed far away—the nether side of dream and night. Its monstrous word, *Porphyrogene,* means a prince, a child-Royal, one born in the Queen's chamber of an Eastern palace, walled with rare porphyry.

350. "SWEET WHISPERS ARE HEARD BY THE TRAVELLER."

(stanza 6)

On a poet's lips I slept
Dreaming like a love-adept
In the sound his breathing kept;
Nor seek nor finds he mortal blisses,
But feeds on the aërial kisses
Of shapes that haunt thought's wilderness.
He will watch from dawn to gloom
The lake-reflected sun illume
The yellow bees in the ivy-bloom,
Nor heed nor see, what things they be;
But from these create he can
Forms more real than living man,
Nurslings of immortality! . . .

PERCY BYSSHE SHELLEY

352. "MY A DILDIN."

This, and Nos. 353, 355 and 356 are four Singing-Game Rhymes, worn down into almost nonsensical jingle by multitudinous tongues in long long usage. (See No. 41, page 36).

And—since in my humble opinion it is not easy to get too much of this kind of good thing—here is another:

Bobby Shafto's gone to sea,
With silver buckles at his knee;
When he'll come home he'll marry me,
Pretty Bobby Shafto!

Bobby Shafto's fat and fair,
Combing down his yellow hair;
He's my love for evermair,
Pretty Bobby Shafto!

When first my brave Johnnie lad
Came to this town,
He had a blue bonnet
That wanted the crown;
But now he has gotten
A hat and a feather,—
Hey, brave Johnnie lad,
Cock up your beaver!

ROBERT BURNS

King Edelbrode cam owre the sea,
Fa la lilly.
All for to marry a gay ladye,
Fa la lilly.

Her lilly hands, sae white and sma',
Fa la lilly.
Wi' golden rings were buskit braw,
Fa la lilly. . . .

And here is a Bride of Elizabeth's day whom I chanced on in that packed and inexhaustible book, *Shakespeare's England.* When "buskit braw," she must have been as lovely to see as a hawthorn in May or a wax candle in a silver shrine:

"The bride being attired in a gown of sheeps russet, and a kirtle of fine worsted, her head attired with a billiment of gold, and her hair as yellow as gold hanging down behind her, which was curiously combed and pleated, according to the manner in those days: she was led to church between two sweet boys, with bride-laces and rosemary tied about their silken sleeves. . . . Then was there a fair bride-cup of silver and gilt carried before her wherein was a goodly branch of rosemary, gilded very fair, hung about with silken ribands of all colours: next was there a noise of musicians, that played all the way before her: after her came all the chiefest maidens of the country, some bearing great bride-cakes, and some garlands of wheat, finely gilded, and so she passed to the Church."

As for the silken ribands they may have been of Drakes colour or Ladies blush or Gozelinge colour or Marigold or Isabel or Peas porridge tawny or Popingay blew or Lutsy gallant, but they were certainly not Judas colour, Devil in the hedge, or Dead Spaniard.

355. "AND FEED HER WI' NEW MILK AND BREAD."

The Yellow-haired Laddie sat down on yon brae,
Cries—Milk the ewes, Lassie! let nane o' them gae!
And ay she milked, and ay she sang—
The Yellow-haired Laddie shall be by gudeman!
And ay she milked, and ay she sang—
The Yellow-haired Laddie shall be my gudeman! . . .

ALLAN RAMSAY

Apart from singing rhymes such as those actually used in the course of a game, there are the mere counting-out rhymes, for deciding on who is to be "he" and so on. Some of them have been reduced to little more than gibberish, whatever they may once have been.

First, the rhyme we used when I was young:

Eena, deena, deina, duss,
Catala, weena, weina, wuss,
Spit, spot, must be done,
Twiddlum, twaddlum, twenty-one!

The next—with some of its "sense" evidently gone astray—has fifty-four thumps in all:

Hinty, minty, cuty, corn,
Apple seed, and apple thorn,
Wire, briar, limber lock,
Three geese in a flock.
One flew east, and one flew west,
One flew over the cuckoo's nest.
Up on yonder hill.
That is where my father dwells;
He has jewels, he has rings,
He has many pretty things.
He has a hammer with two nails,

He has a cat with twenty tails.
Strike Jack, lick Tom!
Blow the bellows, old man!

This French set has six thumps to the line:

Un, deux, trois, j'irai dans les bois,
Quatre, cinq, six, chercher des cerises,
Sept, huit, neuf, dans mon panier neuf;
Dix, onze, douze, elles serout toutes rouges;
Treize, quatorze, quinze, pour mon petit Prince;
Seize, dix-sept, dix-huit, je les apporterai tout-de-suite.
Dix-neuf, vingt, pour qu'elles prennent leurs bains.

This German has eight in its first two lines, four in the rest—total, thirty-two:

Eine kleine weisse Bohne, wollte gern nach Engelland,
Engelland war zugeschlossen, und der Schlüssel war zerbrochen.
Bauer, bind den Pudel an,
Dass er mich nicht beissen kann.
Beisst er mich, so kost es dich
Tausend Thaler sicherlich.

The next is a haunting Scots example, with hints in it of some meddling to make it sense:

Eenity, feenity, fickety feg,
El, del, Dolmen eg;
Irky, birky, story, rock,
An, tan, toosh, Jock.

So, too, with this ancient one from Cornwall:

Ena, mena, bora mi;
Kisca, lara, mora di;
Eggs, butter, cheese, bread;
Stick, stock, stone dead.

The next is an ancient counting-out, or rather scoring rhyme, used in the very ancient game of Duck-and-Drake—played, of course, by so flinging across a sheet of water a flat stone or shell as to make it kiss the surface as many times as possible before it sink:

A Duck and a Drake,
And a half-penny cake,
And a penny to pay the old baker;
A hop and a scotch is another notch,
Slitherum, slatherum, take her!

The next one is American (but see Note No. 24), a method of scoring (from one to twenty) that was current up to the fifties of the last century:

Een,	Een-dix,
Teen,	Teen-dix,
Tether,	Tether-dix,
Fether,	Fether-dix,
Fitz,	Bompey,
Sahter,	Een-bompey,
Lather,	Teen-bompey,
Gother,	Tether-bombey,
Dather,	Fether-bompey,
Dix.	Giget.

And this gibberish (for groups of thirty) is from New York City:

A knife and a razor,
Spells Nebuchadnezzar,
A knife and a fork,
Spells Nebuchadnork.
A new pair of slippers,
And an old pair of shoes,
Spells Nebuchadnezzar,
The king of the Jews.

Old Dan Tucker
Came home to supper,
And ate the hind leg of a frog;

He peeped o'er the steeple,
Saw many fine people,
And looked at the mouth of a dog!

But there are dozens of similar rhymes in at least seventeen languages—all to be found in *Counting-out Rhymes,* by H. C. Bolton.

357. Quoth John to Joan.

This old song, which was set to music in the reign of Henry VIII., comes (like Dallyaunce of No. 35), out of a Morality Play, *Lusty Juventus,* the author of which is said to have been one R. Wever.

Oh, say, my Joan, will not that do?

...The little maid replied, some say a little sighed,
"But what shall we have for to eat, eat, eat?
Will the love that you're so rich in make a fire in the kitchen,
Or the little god of love turn the spit, spit, spit?"

358. Milk-white Fingers, Cherry Nose.

This is the only poem I have ever seen in which the midmost feature of a pretty face is compared to a cherry. And yet every frosty morning throughout the ages must have given many a dainty nose that fair bright coral colour.

There is indeed the widest of gaps between seeing a thing and noticing it; between merely noticing and realizing it, mind and heart; between realizing it and vividly conveying that realization. The unknown writer of 358 had a remarkably quick and ardent eye.

In *Notes on Noses,* a little brown book of a hundred and fifty-three pages published in 1859, the eloquent author (who omits his portrait) distinguishes six classes of "simple noses": the *Roman,* undulating, rugose and coarse, but powerful; the *Greek,* straight, tasteful and astute; the *Cogitative,* wide-nostrilled and meditative; the *Hawk,* worldly and shrewd; the *Snub,* feeble, insolent and foxy; and last, the *Celestial,* or "the snub turned up" —and for much the better. These, as he says, are the *simple* noses.

They may be found combined and re-combined in a complex specimen to such a degree that it is difficult to say where each begins and ends.

But the nose in our poem is a feminine nose; and of feminine noses the Roman "mars beauty"; the Greek (though Mrs. Barbauld and Mrs. Hemans, not to mention Hannah More, possessed specimens) is by no means, it seems, a sure sign of poetic gifts; while the Cogitative and the Hawk are rare in feminine faces—for "it is the duty of men to relieve women from the cares of commercial life." There remain, then, only the all-enticing coral-tipped *Celestial* and—but enough.

359. "Or the Bees their careful King."

In old times the "Governor" of a Bee Hive was sometimes referred to as the King and sometimes as the Queen. The choice depended in part on which kind of monarch was on the throne. A curious bee-story of the middle ages is related by Mr. Tickner Edwardes in his book on the Honey Bee.

A certain simple woman, on finding that her bees were storing little honey for her and were perishing of "the murraine," stole one of the holy wafers from the priest, and for miraculous remedy concealed it in one of her hives. "Whereupon the Murraine ceased and the Honie abounded. The Woman, therefore lifting up the hive at the due time to take out the Honie, saw there (most strange to be seene) a Chappell built by the Bees, with an altar to it, the wals adorned by marvellous skill of architecture, with windowes conveniently set in their places: also a doore and a steeple with bells. And the Host being laid upon the altar, the Bees making a sweet noise, flew around it." Apart from "the singing masons building roofs of gold," the gluttonous drones, the sentries, wax-makers, bread-kneaders, nurses in the hive, there are the Queen's Ladies-in-waiting: "For difference from the rest they beare for their crest a tuft or tossell, in some coloured yellow, in some murrey, in manner of a plume; whereof some turne downward like an Ostrich-feather, others stand upright like a Hern-top." But for truths even stranger than fantasy regarding bees and their kind, read Henri Fabre, M. Maeterlinck and Mr. Edwardes.

. . . There he arriving, round about doth flie,
From bed to bed from one to other border,
And takes survey, with curious busie eye,
Of every flowre and herbe there set in order:
Now this, now that he tasteth tenderly,
Yet none of them he rudely doth disorder;
Ne with his feete their silken leaves deface;
But pastures on the pleasures of each place.

And evermore, with most varietie,
And change of sweetnesse, (for all change is sweete)
He casts his glutton sense to satisfie,
Now sucking of the sap of herbe most meete,
Or of the dew which yet on them does lie,
Now in the same bathing his tender feete:
And then he pearcheth on some braunch thereby,
To weather him, and his moist wings to dry. . . .

EDMUND SPENSER

360. "AND HERE, AND HERE."

As Flora slept and I lay waking,
I smiled to see a bird's mistaking,
For from a bough it down did skip
And for a cherry pecked her lip. . . .

362. "MY HEART IS GLADDER THAN ALL THESE."

How many times do I love thee, dear?
Tell me how many thoughts there be
In the atmosphere
Of the new fall'n year,
Whose white and sable hours appear
The latest flake of eternity:
So many times do I love thee, dear!

How many times do I love again?
Tell me how many beads there are
In a silver chain
Of evening rain

Unravelled from the tumbling main,
And threading the eye of a yellow star:
So many times do I love again!

THOMAS LOVELL BEDDOES

363.

The word screen (line 4) means, I think, "Hide and shelter those smiles away that in their beauty seem to burn in the air": for all beauty resembles radiance in its influence on the mind. And this recalls to memory Southwell's poem, *The Burning Babe,* No. 256.

364. "A SONNET OF THE MOON."

The more closely one examines a fine *sonnet*—its way of rhyming, ascent, progress, poise, balance and cadences, the ease and exactitude with which what is said in it fills its mould or form—the more modestly one should hesitate before attempting to write or at least publish another. This particular sonnet (like No. 361), is of the English or Shakespearian kind, and is so lovely a thing that only a close attention would notice the carelessness of its rhymes. No. 342 is an example of the Petrarchan form of sonnet which our sixteenth-century poets borrowed from Italy. Comparison of them shows that, as with the old Chinese ginger jars, so in poetry: not only is the syrup delightful, but even the pot may be interesting.

Coleridge wrote few sonnets, and this is his explanation of the length one must be: "It is confined to fourteen lines, because as some particular number is necessary, and that particular number must be a small one, it may as well be fourteen as any other number. When no reason can be adduced against a thing, Custom is a sufficient reason for it."

The first sentence is no more and no less true also of a centipede's legs, a cat's claws or a paper of pins. But the second startles one's mind into instant attention, as one's body is when it collides with a stranger's in the street. There is a wide wisdom in it. How many natural, human and delightful things there are in this world, indeed, for which Custom is a sufficient reason: children, for instance, daisies in the grass, skylarks in the clouds, dreams in sleep, rhymes, gay clothes, friendship, laughter.

"The Pale Queen."

There is the apparition of a lovely face in the Moon—proud and mute—to be discovered by careful eyes usually on the extreme right of the disc, her own eyes gazing towards the left.

> O lady Moon, your horns point to the East;
> Shine, be increased!
> O Lady Moon, your horns point to the West;
> Wane, be at rest!

Christina Rossetti

368. "It was in and about the Martinmas time."

This old Scottish song was a favourite of Oliver Goldsmith's in his childhood. "The music of the finest singer," he said, "is dissonance to what I felt when our old dairy-maid sung me into tears with *Johnny Armstrong's Last Good-night,* or *The Cruelty of Barbara Allen.*"

As with the Scottish ballads so with this last poem—it is the brevity and bareness with which the story is told and is *not* told that sets it apart. Without one express word to prove it so, it is clear that Sir John had always loved the proud Barbara even if he had spoken lightly of her, and (as it seems to me) that she, without realizing it, had always loved him, though she refuses the word that would have saved his life.

"She heard the dead-bell ringing."

The jows of the Passing-bell in the 7th stanza are known as tolls or knocks or tellers in different parts of England, and the method of ringing differs according to the number of bells in the belfry. In general the tenor bell has been used—a bell often called Gabriel because it was wont to be rung morning and evening for the Angelus, summoning all who heard it to kneel and repeat the Angel Gabriel's Salutation in the first chapter of St. Luke's Gospel. The most usual custom has been to sound thrice three tolls for a man, and thrice two for a woman—hence, it has been suggested, the old saying, "Nine *tellers mark* a man" (rather than "Nine *tailors make* a man").

In Leverton, Lincolnshire, twelve tolls were once (and may still be) sounded for a man, nine for a woman, seven for a boy under sixteen, and six for a girl under eighteen.

In the belfry of Marsham, Norfolk, the following was the rule:

KNOCKS FOR THE DEAD.

iii for girl	vii for Matron
iv for Boy	viii for Bachelor
vi for Spinster	ix for Husband

But Church bells were rung for many other purposes, and though their *lin-lan-lone* is to some hearts a melancholy cadence to hear even in the serenity of a summer evening, it is not "surly" and "sullen." There was a ringing on St. Thomas's Day—called "Mumpsing"; and an all-night ringing on the Eve of All Saints. There was the Pancake Bell, the Gleaning Bell, the Harvest Bell and the Oven Bell, and a sudden jangling—the whole peal being rung out, or backwards, or confusedly and "out of tune and harsh"—for a warning of fire. But for further and fuller information see *English Bells and Bell-Lore,* by J. North, and many another book on this subject.

371. "I NEVER HAD BUT ONE TRUE LOVE, IN COLD GRAVE SHE WAS LAIN."

Yet another tragic and sorrowful poem is the story of the beautiful Princess Uillanita: She cared only for flowers white and colourless as dew in the first light of day. And one still evening, when she was in search of what she could not find, she came to a valley wherein a forest gloomed above a deep but placid river. Within the forest, refreshed by the mists of the river, grew none but flowers blue and dark and purple, and such was the young Princess's hatred of them that she covered her eyes with her hands, fled on, and so lost her way.

In the middle of the night and long after she had wept herself to sleep, the wailing of a bird pierced into her dreams, and she awoke to see one solitary star of the colourless radiance of Vega shining in a space of sky betwixt the branches above her head. Its thin ray silvered down—spearlike in its straightness—and of a beam easily sufficing to irradiate a tiny clustering flower which stood half-hidden in the moss at her hand's side, and was drenching the air with its fragrance. It was a flower utterly strange to her, whiter than hoarfrost, fairer than foam.

The enravished Princess gazed spellbound. "Why," whispered she to herself, in the quiet of the dark; "if I had not hated the sad-coloured flowers of this sombre forest, and so lost my way, if I had not been moved in my sleep to awaken, I never should have seen this crystal thing—that is lovelier than I deemed Paradise itself could bring to bloom." And she kissed the thin-spun petals, and fell again happily asleep.

372. "A Lament."

Only two stanzas out of six, and these, maybe, a little difficult in the old Scots:

Depart, depart, depart!
Alas! I must depart
From her that has my heart
  With heart full sore;
Against my will indeed
And can find no remede—
I wait the pains of death—
  Can do no more. . . .

Adieu mine own sweet thing,
My joy and comforting,
My mirth and solacing
  Of earthly gloir:
Farewell, my lady bright,
And my remembrance right,
Farewell, and have good night—
  I say no more.

373. Maidens, willow branches bear.

Thou art to all lost love the best,
  The onely true plant found,
Wherewith young men and maids distrest,
  And left of love, are crown'd.

When once the Lovers Rose is dead,
Or laid aside forlorne;
Then Willow-garlands, 'bout the head,
Bedew'd with teares, are worne. . . .

And underneath thy cooling shade,
(When weary of the light)
The love-spent Youth, and love-sick Maid,
Come to weep out the night.

ROBERT HERRICK

380. TO HELEN.

Who "the wayworn wanderer" is, I am uncertain; but apart from its rare music, how long a journey awaits the imagination in this poem, and how closely inwoven is its imagery. Yet it is said to have been written when Poe was still a boy.

381. "THERE IS A LADY."

Mr. Nahum's picture for this poem was of a little winged boy at evening, his quiver of arrows on his back, his bow the perch of a nightingale, and himself lying fast asleep under a hawthorn bush in full flower—a narrow green sun-dappled river near-by, rosy clouds and birds in the air, and strange snow-peaked hills afar.

"I DID BUT SEE HER."

There be none of Beauty's daughters
With a magic like thee;
And like music on the waters
Is thy sweet voice to me:
When, as if its sound were causing
The charmed ocean's pausing,
The waves lie still and gleaming,
And the lull'd winds seem dreaming. . . .

LORD BYRON

"TILL I DIE."

. . . Only our love hath no decay;
This no to-morrow hath, nor yesterday;

Running it never runs from us away,
But truly keeps his first, last, everlasting day.

JOHN DONNE

383. "IT IS NOT SO."

Silly boy 'tis ful Moon yet, thy night as day shines clearely.
Had thy youth but wit to feare, thou couldst not love so dearely.
Shortly wilt thou mourne when all thy pleasures are bereavèd;
Little knows he how to love that never was deceivèd. . . .

Yet be just and constant still! Love may beget a wonder,
Not unlike a Summer's frost, or Winter's fatall thunder.
He that holds his Sweetheart true, unto his day of dying,
Lives, of all that ever breathed, most worthy the envýing.

THOMAS CAMPION

385.

In this poem, as in all Christina Rossetti's work, there is a rhythm and poise, a serpentining of music, so delicate that on clumsy lips it will vanish as rapidly as the bloom from a plum. Indeed, each stanza is like a branch (with its twigs) of a wild damson-tree, its wavering line broken and beautiful with bud, flower and leaf. As fresh an air, and as clear a light, stirs and dwells in the poem as on the tree itself in April.

387.

This is from Part II., Act II., Scene i. of "Zapolya." Glycine sings unseen in a cavern—her voice comforting her lover wandering forlorn by night "in a savage wood."

389. I'LL OVERTAKE THEE.

I'll weave my love a garland,
He shall be dressed so fine,
I'll set it round with roses,
With lilies, pinks, and thyme;
And I'll present it to my love
When he comes back from sea:
For I love my love, and I love my love
Because my love loves me.

I wish I were an arrow
That sped ito the air,
To seek him as a sparrow,
And if he be not there
Then quickly I'd become a fish
To search the raging sea:
For I love my love, and I love my love
Because my love loves me.

I would I were a reaper,
I'd seek him in the corn;
I would I were a keeper,
I'd hunt him with my horn;
I'd blow a blast, when found at last,
Beneath the greenwood tree:
For I love my love, and I love my love,
Because my love loves me.

And again:

For I'll cut my green coat a foot above my knee,
And I'll clip my yellow locks an inch below mine ee.
Hey, nonny, nonny, nonny.

I'll buy me a white cut, forth for to ride,
And I'll go seek him through the world that is so wide.
Hey, nonny, nonny, nonny.

But others stay at home:

Queen Mary, Queen Mary, my age is sixteen,
My father's a farmer on yonder green.
He's plenty of money to dress me, an' a',
An' there's *nae* bonnie laddie will tak' me awa'!

This morning I rose and I looked in the glass;
Says I to myself: "What a handsome young lass!"
I tossed up my head and I gave a "Ha! ha!
There's nae bonnie laddie will tak' *me* awa!"

Further south than where this lively rhyme comes from, the "will" (l. 4 and 8) would be *shall.* The standard test is that of the unfortunate Scotsman who fell into the Thames (near Blackfriars) and each time his head appeared above the mirky flood cried piteously, "I wull *droon! Nae*body shall save me!" And the Londoners looking down from above, being respecters of persons, didn't even try.

391. "Chimborazo, Cotopaxi."

In medieval days it seems that a traveller here and there, happily supposing the world to be a floating island of undiscoverable dimensions hung in the wilds of space, and not knowing that it was merely a rotating and "oblate spheroid," would journey clear round it and so return to his amazement to the place from which he started. Here is such an experience from Sir John Mandeville—in our spelling: "It was told that a certain worthy man departed some time from our Country for to go search the World. . . . He passed India and the Isles beyond it, where are more than 5000 Isles, and so long and for so many seasons he went by Sea and Land, and so environed the World, that he came at last to an Isle whereon he heard spoken his own language —a calling of oxen in the Plough—such Words in fact as men were wont to speak to Beasts in his own country. Whereof he greatly marvelled, knowing not how that might be." For there —as if it were a picture in a dream—*there* was the chimney of his own house smoking up into the clear morning air! And what did he do? Maybe he stared; he sighed; he grew pale; he shuddered: and—turned back.

392. "Hallo my fancy."

For the first sight of this poem I must gratefully thank my friend Mr. Ivor Gurney. The poem was written by William Cleland while he was still at St. Andrews. All else I know of him is that he was born about 1661, and fell at Dunkeld in 1689. There is nothing in English to my knowledge that resembles it. *Erra Pater* (stanza 4) was the name given to a busy astrologer and almanac-concocter, William Lilly, of the time. King Phalaris's monstrous bull was of brass: he perished in it.

By "the tapers" (stanza 2) is meant, I fancy, those phosphoric fires that gather on the yard-arms of ships at sea when the air is electric with tempest. Sir Humphrey Gilbert's sailors were fearful at sight of this apparition, and of a hideous monster, too—which, to calm and cheer them, he said was *Bonum omen*—that had appeared swimming in the waves beside their frigate, the *Squirrel,* a little before she and her riding lights disappeared for ever. He himself had remained serene, had spent some time in reading, had called merrily over the water to his companion cockle-shell, "We are as near Heaven by sea as by land. And then—

". . . Men which all their life time had occupied the Sea, never was more outragious Seas. We had also upon our main yard, an apparition of a little fire by night, which seamen doe call Castor and Pollux. But we had onely one, which they take an evill signe of more tempest. . . . The same Monday night, about twelve of the clocke . . . suddenly her lights were out . . . and withall our watch cryed, *the Generall was cast away,* which was too true. For in that moment, the Frigat was devoured and swallowed up of the Sea. . . ."

Ariel. I boarded the king's ship; now on the beak,
Now in the waist, the deck, in every cabin,
I flam'd amazement: sometimes I'd divide
And burn in many places; on the topmast,
The yards, and boresprit, would I flame distinctly,
Then meet, and join. . . .

The Tempest.

As for Cupid (stanza 5), he is said to be the slyest archer that ever loosed arrow—and a dangerous child to entertain:

Cupid abroade was 'lated in the night,
His wings were wet with ranging in the raine;
Harbour he sought, to mee hee took his flight,
To dry his plumes I heard the boy complaine.
I opte the doore and graunted his desire,
I rose my selfe, and made the wagge a fire. . . .

or—as yet another poem goes on to tell—to take as a scholar:

> I dreamt by me I saw fair Venus stand,
> Holding young Cupid in her lovely hand,
> And said, kind Shepherd, I a scholar bring
> My little son, to learn of you to sing. . . .

And last, the pelican (in stanza 7). She was supposed in old days to be "the lovingest bird that is," since at need she would pierce her breast with her bill to feed her young ones. The singing (stanza 7) of the dying swan I have never heard—except in Tennyson's words—packed with poetic observation:

> The plain was grassy, wild and bare,
> Wide, wild, and open to the air,
> Which had built up everywhere
> An under-roof of doleful gray.
>
> With an inner voice the river ran,
> Adown it floated a dying swan,
> And loudly did lament.
> It was the middle of the day.
> Ever the weary wind went on,
> And took the reed-tops as it went. . . .
> Some blue peaks in the distance rose,
> And white against the cold-white sky,
> Shone out their crowning snows.
>
> One willow over the river wept,
> And shook the wave as the wind did sigh;
> Above in the wind was the swallow,
> Chasing itself at its own wild will,
> And far thro' the marish green and still
> The tangled water-courses slept,
> Shot over with purple, and green, and yellow.

393. "COLUMBUS'S DOOM-BURDENED CARAVELS." (line 13)

". . . The next day, Thursday, October 11, 1492, was destined to be for ever memorable in the history of the world. . . .

The people on the *Santa Maria* saw some petrels and a green branch in the water; the *Pinta* saw a reed and two small sticks carved with iron, and one or two other pieces of reeds and grasses that had been grown on shore, as well as a small board. Most wonderful of all, the people of the *Nina* saw 'a little branch full of dog roses'; . . . The day drew to its close; and after nightfall, according to their custom, the crews of the ships repeated the *Salve Regina*. Afterwards the Admiral addressed the people and sailors of his ship, 'very merry and pleasant,' . . . The moon was in its third quarter, and did not rise until eleven o'clock. The first part of the night was dark, and there was only a faint starlight into which the anxious eyes of the look-out men peered from the forecastles of the three ships. At ten o'clock Columbus was walking on the poop of his vessel, when he suddenly saw a light right ahead. The light seemed to rise and fall as though it were a candle or a lantern held in some one's hand and waved up and down. The Admiral called Pedro Gutierrez to him and asked him whether he saw anything; and he also saw the light. Then he sent for Rodrigo Sanchez and asked him if he saw the light; but he did not. . . . Dawn came at last, flooding the sky with lemon and saffron and scarlet and orange, until at last the pure gold of the sun glittered on the water. And when it rose it showed the sea-weary mariners an island lying in the blue sea ahead of them: the island of Guanahani; San Salvador. . . ."

Christopher Columbus, FILSON YOUNG

The appearance of the petrels, and that saffron and scarlet in the sunrise must have made the sight of land the more welcome: and it was only a week or two after the autumnal equinox:

When descends on the Atlantic
The gigantic
Storm-wind of the equinox,
Landward in his wrath he scourges
The toiling surges,
Laden with seaweed from the rocks:

From Bermuda's reefs; from edges
Of sunken ledges,

In some far-off, bright Azore;
From Bahama, and the dashing,
Silver-flashing
Surges of San Salvador;

From the tumbling surf, that buries
The Orkneyan skerries,
Answering the hoarse Hebrides;
And from wrecks of ships, and drifting
Soars, uplifting
On the desolate, rainy seas. . . .

LONGFELLOW

395. "TO SEA, TO SEA."

. . . To the ocean now I fly,
And those happy climes that lie
Where day never shuts his eye.
Up in the broad fields of the sky;
There I suck the liquid air
All amidst the gardens fair
Of Hesperus, and his daughters three
That sing about the golden tree:
Along the crispèd shades and bowers
Revels the spruce and jocund Spring;
The Graces, and the rosy bosomed Hours,
Thither all their bounties bring;
There eternal Summer dwells,
And west winds, with musky wing,
About the cedared alleys fling
Nard and Cassia's balmy smells. . . .
But now my task is smoothly done,
I can fly, or I can run,
Quickly to the green earth's end,
Where the bowed welkin slow doth bend;
And from thence can soar as soon
To the corners of the moon. . . .

JOHN MILTON

Master.	Steersman, how stands the wind?
Steersman.	Full north-north-east
Master.	What course?
Steersman.	Full south-south-west.
Master.	No worse, and blow so fair,
	Then sink despair,
	Come solace to the mind!
	Ere night, we shall the haven find.

"CAVED TRITONS' AZURE DAY" (line 12)

—Dark-fated Clarence in *King Richard III.* dreamt of that "azure day":

. . . As we paced along
Upon the giddy footing of the Hatches,
Me thought that Glouster stumbled, and in falling
Strooke me (that thought to stay him) over-board,
Into the tumbling billowes of the maine.
O Lord, methought what paine it was to drowne,
What dreadfull noise of water in mine eares,
What sightes of ugly death within mine eyes. . . .
Methought I saw a thousand fearful wrackes:
A thousand men that Fishes gnawed upon:
Wedges of Gold, great Anchors, heapes of Pearle,
Inestimable Stones, unvalewed Jewels,
All scattered in the bottome of the Sea.
Some lay in dead-men's Sculles; and in the holes
Where eyes did once inhabit, there were crept,
(As 'twere in scorne of eyes) reflecting Gemmes,
That wooed the slimy bottome of the deepe,
And mocked the dead bones that lay scattered by. . . .

396. HUGE SEA MONSTERS.

"Its appearance is like that of a rough rock. [It seems] as if it extended beside the shore of the channel like [an immense] reedy island surrounded by sand-dunes. For this reason it happens that seafarers imagine they are gazing with their eyes on some island, and so they fasten their high-stemmed ships with anchor ropes to this false land; they make fast their sea-horses as if they were at the sea's brink, and up they climb on the island, bold of heart; [while their] vessels stand, fast by the shore, surrounded by the stream. And then the voyagers, weary in mind, and without thought of danger, encamp on the isle. They produce a flame, they kindle a vast fire. Full of joy are the heroes, late so sad of spirit; they are longing for repose. But when the creature, long skilled in guile, feels that the sailore are securely resting upon him, and are keeping their abode there, in enjoyment of the weather, suddenly into the salt wave, together with his prey, down dives the Ocean-dweller and seeks the abyss; and thus, by drowning them, imprisons the ships, with all their men, in the hall of death."

The Whale, tr. by SKEAT

"JEWELS MORE RICH THAN ORMUS SHOWS."

Mr. Nahum's picture to this was of a man clothed in rags. As though in a cloud of despair, he sits gnawing his nails upon a heap of what appears to be precious stones and lumps of gold. Around him stretch the sands of the seashore, and there is a little harbour with a decayed quay, its river-mouth silted up with ooze and flotsam, so that nothing but a row-boat could find entrance there. An immense sun burns in the sky; and, though a thread of fresh water flows near at hand, the man among the jewels seems to be tormented with thirst. . . .

Ormus, or Hormuz, on its narrow island of wild-coloured rocks, date-palms, parrots and many birds, was once the rich mart and treasure-house between Persia and India—spices, pearls, ivory, gold, precious stones, and, in particular, the diamond, being its merchandise. In 1507 the Portuguese Conqueror Alfonso Albuquerque stole it from its dark princes. In 1622 Shah Abbas the Great razed it to the ground. To-day it is but a waste, inhabited by a few fishermen and diggers, its only commodities—that once were gems—salt and sulphur; while still in the height of its Summer blows Julot, Harmatan, Il Sirocco, the Flame-Wind, so deadly in its breath that the troops of an army of 1600 horsemen and 6000 foot, says Marco Polo, marching to punish the city for neglecting to pay tribute to the King of Kîrman, and camping overnight without its walls, were baked next noon as dry as pumice, and not a voice among them to tell the tale, though their bodily shape and colour seemed to appear unchanged. To protect themselves against this Julot, the citizens of Ormus used to build huts of sheltering osier-work over the water, and in the heat of the morning would stand immersed in its coolness up to the chin.

"APPLES" (line 23)

—these are pineapples, the "price" of the next line meaning excellence. "Ambergris" (line 28), is a rare and costly stuff which, as its name tells, resembles grey amber. It has a wondrously sweet smell, was once used in cooking, and is disgorged by the whale that supplies the world with the comforting ointment of childhood called spermaceti.

In Shakespeare's day, Marvell's "remote Bermudas" were known as the "Isle of Divels"—because of the nocturnal yellings, cries and yelpings that were reported to haunt them. English sailors, wrecked and cast away on Great Bermuda in 1709, however, brought home in their boats of cedar-wood the news that this wild music was caused (at least in part) by descendants of the hogs that had been left there by the long-gone Spaniard, Juan Bermudez and his men. They told, too, that it was an island fair and commodious, of a gentle climate, and a sweet-smelling air; and Shakespeare almost certainly had its enchantments in mind when he wrote of Ariel, Caliban and Miranda. Was not Ariel in Prospero's more solitary days called up at midnight "to fetch dewe From the still-vext Bermoothes"?

To the Puritan voyagers of Andrew Marvell's poem the Islands were as welcome and angelic as the Hesperides. And no poet could better tell of them than he. For in Marvell's verse dwells a curious happiness, like sunshine on a pool of water-lilies. Yet he, too, like other dreamers, was a man of affairs, and of endless industry and zeal. He was thrice Member of Parliament for his birthplace, Kingston-on-Hull, and, with Milton, was one of Oliver Cromwell's Latin Secretaries. John Aubrey describes him as "of a middling stature, pretty strong sett, roundish face, cherry-cheek't, hazell eie, brown hair. He was in his conversation very modest, and of very few words. And though he loved wine, he would never drink heartilie in company, and was wont to say, that, *he would not play the good fellow in any man's company in whose hands he would not trust his life.* . . . He was drowned on January 23, 1674, crossing the Humber "in a barrow-boat; the same was sand-warpt," and he "lies interred under the pews in the south side of St. Giles' church-in-the-Fields, under the window wherein is painted in glass a red lyon." But as his epitaph says (rather pompously): "A tomb can neither contain his character nor is marble necessary to transmit it to posterity; it will be always legible in his inimitable writings." And there, under the same roof, St. Giles's, share his rest vehement George Chapman, the dramatist and translator of Homer; James Shirley, the poet of "The glories of our blood and state"; Sir Roger L'Estrange, who into the pithiest of English translated Æsop's Fables, and was a staunch Royalist; and Richard Pendrell, who "preserved . . . his sacred Majesty King Charles ii. after his escape from Worcester fight."

O, fly, my soul! What hangs upon
Thy drooping wings,
And weighs them down
With love of gaudy mortal things?
The Sun is now i' the east: each shade,
As he doth rise,
Is shorter made,
That earth may lessen to our eyes.

O, be not careless then and play
Until the star of peace
Hide all his beams in dark recess!
Poor pilgrims needs must lose their way,
When all the shadows do increase.

James Shirley

397. "That talkative bald-headed Seaman came."
(line 23)

". . . And now my name; which way shall lead to all
My miseries after, that their sounds may fall
Through your ears also, and shew (having fled
So much affliction) first, who rests his head
In your embraces, when, so far from home,

I knew not where t' obtain it resting room:
 I am Ulysses Laertiades,
The fear of all the world . . ."

The Odysseys, GEORGE CHAPMAN

398.

The prose "argument" to the "Ancient Mariner," which is almost as rare an experience to read as the Rime itself, has been omitted. But here is a fragment of it relating to the passage on pages 390–4: ". . . The Wedding-Guest feareth that a Spirit is talking to him; but the ancient Mariner assureth him of his bodily life, and proceedeth to relate his horrible penance. He despiseth the creatures of the calm, and envieth that *they* should live, and so many lie dead. But the curse liveth for him in the eye of the dead men. In his loneliness and fixedness he yearneth towards the journeying Moon, and the stars that still sojourn, yet still move onward; and every where the blue sky belongs to them, and is their appointed rest, and their native country and their own natural homes, which they enter unannounced, as lords that are certainly expected and yet there is a silent joy at their arrival.

"By the light of the Moon he beholdeth God's creatures of the great calm—their beauty and their happiness. He blesseth them in his heart. The spell begins to break. By grace of the holy Mother, the ancient Mariner is refreshed with rain. He heareth sounds and seeth strange sights and commotions in the sky and the element. The bodies of the ship's crew are inspired and inspirited, and the ship moves on; but not by the souls of the men, nor by dæmons of earth or middle air, but by a blessed troop of angelic spirits, sent down by the invocation of the guardian saint. . . ."

"Dæmons of earth or middle air" have been told of also by land travellers—by Friar Odoric, for example, in the account of his journey through Cathay during the years 1316–1330:

"Another great and terrible thing I saw. For, as I went through a certain valley which lieth by the River of Delights, I saw therein many dead corpses lying. And I heard also therein sundry kinds of music, but chiefly nakers, which were marvellously played upon. And so great was the noise thereof that very great fear came upon me. Now, this valley is seven or eight miles long; and if any unbeliever enter therein he quitteth it never again, but perisheth incontinently. Yet I hesitated not to go in that I might see once for all what the matter was. And when I had gone in I saw there, as I have said, such numbers of corpses as no one without seeing it could deem credible. And at one side of the valley, in the very rock, I beheld as it were the face of a man very great and terrible, so very terrible indeed that for my exceeding great fear my spirit semed to die in me. Wherefore I made the sign of the cross, and began continually to repeat VERBUM CARO FACTUM, but I dared not at all to come nigh that face, but kept at seven or eight paces from it. And so I came at length to the other end of the valley, and there I ascended a hill of sand and looked around me. But nothing could I descry, only I still heard those nakers to play which were played so marvellously. And when I got to the top of that hill I found there a great quantity of silver heaped up as it had been fishes' scales, and some of this I put into my bosom. But as I cared nought for it, and was at the same time in fear lest it should be a snare to hinder my escape, I cast it all down again to the ground. And so by God's grace I came forth scathless. Then all the Saracens, when they heard of this, showed me great worship, saying that I was a baptised and holy man. But those who had perished in that valley they said belonged to the devil."

As an Arab journeyeth
Through a sand of Ayaman,
Lean Thirst, lolling its cracked tongue,
Lagging by his side along;
And a rusty wingèd Death
Grating its low flight before,
Casting ribbèd shadows o'er
The blank desert, blank and tan:
He lifts by hap to'rd where the morning's roots are
His weary stare,—
Sees although they plashless mutes are,
Set in a silver air
Fountains of gelid shoots are,
Making the daylight fairest fair;

Sees the palm and tamarind
Tangle the tresses of a phantom wind;—
A sight like innocence when one has sinned
A green and maiden freshness smiling there,
While with unblinking glare
The tawny-hided desert crouches watching her. . . .

The Mirage, FRANCIS THOMPSON

Thou to me art such a spring
As the Arab seeks at eve,
Thirsty from the shining sands;
There to bathe his face and hands,
While the sun is taking leave,
And dewy sleep is a delicious thing.

Thou to me art such a dream
As he dreams upon the grass,
While the bubbling coolness near
Makes sweet music in his ear;
And the stars that slowly pass
In solitary grandeur o'er him gleam.

Thou to me art such a dawn
As the dawn whose ruddy kiss
Wakes him to his darling steed;
And again the desert speed,
And again the desert bliss,
Lightens thro' his veins, and he is gone!

GEORGE MEREDITH

"AT LENGTH DID CROSS AN ALBATROSS"

"I remember the first albatross I ever saw," says Herman Melville in a footnote to *Moby Dick.* "It was during a prolonged gale, in waters hard upon the Antarctic seas. From my forenoon watch below, I ascended to the overclouded deck; and there, dashed upon the main hatches, I saw a regal, feathery thing of unspotted whiteness, and with a hooked, Roman bill sublime. At intervals, it arched forth its vast archangel wings, as if to embrace some holy ark. Wonderous flutterings and throbbings shook it.

Though bodily unharmed, it uttered cries, as some king's ghost in supernatural distress. Through its inexpressible, strange eyes, methought I peeped to secrets which took hold of God. As Abraham before the angels, I bowed myself; the white thing was so white, its wings so wide, and in those for ever exiled waters, I had lost the miserable warping memories of traditions and of towns. Long I gazed at that prodigy of plumage. I cannot tell, can only hint, the things that darted through me then. . . . By no possibility could Coleridge's wild Rhyme have had aught to do with those mystical impressions which were mine, when I saw that bird upon our deck. For neither had I then read the Rhyme, nor knew the bird to be an albatross. Yet, in saying this, I do but indirectly burnish a little brighter the noble merit of the poem and the poet."

"In flight," says Froude, "the albatross wheels in circles round and round and for ever round the ship—now far behind, now sweeping past in a long, rapid curve, like a perfect skater on an untouched field of ice. There is no effort; watch as closely as you will, you rarely or never see a stroke of the mighty pinion."

The greater part of the extract from Herman Melville is cited in the Notes to *The Road to Xanadu* by Professor Lowes, a packed and vivid book devoted to the revelation of what Coleridge was doing, thinking and seeing, and most particularly what he was reading a little before he wrote the *Ancient Mariner* and *Kubla Khan* and how all this was transmuted by his genius into this supremely original poetry. Collected from books that Coleridge without question had read and pondered on, Professor Lowes shows you, as it were, a handful of rich leaf-mould, then bids you glance again at the flower of poetry—like that telling of the ship becalmed—which sprang out of it. The miracle takes place before your very eyes—and remains a miracle.

"THE MARINERS ALL 'GAN WORK THE ROPES." (page 393)

Of Sea Shanties or Chanties, capstan and halliard, to whose haunting strains the sea-men of the old sailing ships used to set about every job of work—"the long haul," "the sweat-up," "the hand-over-hand," "the stamp-and-go,"—there is only space for one example—"Storm Along," but it is one of the finest of all.

In old days the shanty-men sang the first and third lines, and the rest joined in the refrain.

Stormey's dead, that good old man—
To my ay, Stormalong!
Stormey he is dead and gone
Ay, ay, ay, Mister Stormalong!

Stormey's dead and gone to rest—
To my ay, Stormalong!
Of all the skippers he was best—
Ay, ay, ay, Mister Stormalong!

We dug his grave with a silver spade—
To my ay, Stormalong!
His shroud of softest silk was made—
Ay, ay, ay, Mister Stormalong!

I wish I was old Stormey's son—
To my ay, Stormalong!
I'd build a ship a thousand ton—
Ay, ay, ay, Mister Stormalong!

I'd load her deep with wine and rum—
To my ay, Stormalong!
And all my shellbacks should have some—
Ay, ay, ay, Mister Stormalong!

"Without the chanties," says Mr. Masefield, "you would never get the work done. 'A song is ten men on the rope.' In foul weather . . . it is as comforting as a pot of hot drink." He himself says of one of them: "Another strangely beautiful chanty is that known as *Hanging Johnny*. It has a melancholy tune that is one of the saddest things I have ever heard. I heard it for the first time off the Horn, in a snowstorm, when we were hoisting topsails after heavy weather. There was a heavy grey sea running and the decks were awash. The skies were sodden and oily, shutting in the sea about a quarter of a mile away. Some birds were flying about us, screaming.

They call me Hanging Johnny,
Away-i-oh;
They call me Hanging Johnny,
So hang, boys, hang!

I thought at the time that it was the whole scene set to music. I cannot repeat those words to their melancholy wavering music without seeing the line of yellow oilskins, the wet deck, the frozen ropes, and the great grey seas running up into the sky."

AND NOW 'TWAS LIKE ALL INSTRUMENTS,
NOW LIKE A LONELY FLUTE,
AND NOW IT IS AN ANGEL'S SONG. . . .

In Hampstead there is a Children's Orchestra, and a friend, Miss M. M. Johnson, has very kindly permitted me to print for the first time a poem which she has written on this theme:

THE CHILDREN'S ORCHESTRA.

Like archangels in infancy
They sit, and play on wry, sweet strings,
With sober shoulders quaintly drooped:
But who has shorn their tender wings?

Half-circle-wise, celestially
The sprightly violins are ranged:
Behind them sombre 'cellists ply
Harmonious bows,—but half estranged.

Anon and ever each uplifts
To One a clear, obedient eye,
Who, armed with shining baton, stands
Enthroned,—their awful Deity. . .

Their inexpressive brows, still eyes,
And carven lips no rapture paints,
But she, who holds their hearts, can read
The ecstasies of infant saints.

And when the royal word goes forth
"Let strings be tuned," then all contend
With tangled notes and discords wild
Of sudden zeal, the air to rend.

Like archangels in infancy
They sit, and play on wry, sweet strings:
I think my earth-dimmed sight, alone,
Has quenched their crowns and shorn their wings.

"HE TOLD OF WAVES."

So, too, does the Ship's Captain in yet another ore-laden poem of the marvellous, "The Sale of St. Thomas," telling how the saint in terror of the unknown would turn back from his mission, is rebuked by his Master, and sold by him for twenty pieces of silver to the Captain of a slant-sailed vessel bound for the barbarous Indies. Here is but a fragment of the poem:

" . . . *A Ship's Captain.* You are my man, my passenger?
Thomas.
I go to India with you.
Captain. Well, I hope so.
There's threatening in the weather. Have you a mind
To hug your belly to the slanted deck,
Like a louse on a whip-top, when the boat
Spins on an axle in the hissing gales?
Thomas. Fear not. 'Tis likely indeed that storms are now
Plotting against our voyage; ay, no doubt
The very bottom of the sea prepares
To stand up mountainous or reach a limb
Out of his night of water and huge shingles,
That he and the waves may break our keel. Fear not;
Like those who manage horses, I've a word
Will fasten up within their evil natures
The meanings of the winds and waves and reefs.
Captain. You have a talisman? I have one too;
I know not if the storms think much of it.
I may be shark's meat yet. And would your spell
Be daunting to a cuttle, think you now?

We had a bout with one on our way here;
It had green lidless eyes like lanterns, arms
As many as the branches of a tree,
But limber, and each one of them wise as a snake.
It laid hold of our bulworks, and with three
Long knowing arms, slimy, and of a flesh
So tough they'ld fool a hatchet, searcht the ship,
And stole out of the midst of us all a man;
Yes, and he the proudest man upon the seas
For the rare powerful talisman he'd got.
And would yours have done better?

Thomas. I am one
Not easily frightened. I'm for India. . . ."

LASCELLES ABERCROMBIE

. . . In what torne ship soever I embarke,
That ship shall be my embleme of thy Arke;
What sea soever swallow mee, that flood
Shall be to mee an embleme of thy blood;
Though thou with clouds of anger do disguise
Thy face; yet through that maske I know those eyes,
Which, though they turne away sometimes,
They never will despise. . .

JOHN DONNE

400. "PARROTS OF SHRILLY GREEN"

—this gaudy and longevous bird, that seems to contain all the wisdom of Solomon and more than the craft of Cleopatra in his eye, perched first upon England many centuries ago. Skelton speaks of him:

My name is parrot, a bird of Paradise . . .
With my becke bent, my little wanton eye,
My fethers fresh, as is the emrawde grene,
About my neck a circulet, lyke the ryche rubye,
My little legges, my fete both nete and cleane. . . .

And so, too, John Maplet, a "naturalist" who in 1567 wrote *A Greene Forest*:

"The Parret hath all hir whole bodie greene, saving that onely about his necke she hath a Coller or Chaine naturally wrought like to Sinople or Vermelon. Indie hath of this kinde such as will counterfaite redily a mans speach: what wordes they heare, those commonly they pronounce. There have bene found of these that have saluted Emperours. . . ."

But which Emperors, and when and to what end he does not relate. A parrot of price would be she that had thus held converse with "Ozymandias, king of kings."

402. "THE MARCH OF TIME." (line 2)

Say, is there aught that can convey
An image of its transient stay?
'Tis an hand's breadth; 'tis a tale;
'Tis a vessel under sail:
'Tis a courser's straining steed;
'Tis a shuttle in its speed;
'Tis an eagle in its way,
Darting down upon its prey;
'Tis an arrow in its flight,
Mocking the pursuing sight;
'Tis a vapour in the air;
'Tis a whirlwind rushing there;
'Tis a short-lived fading flower;
'Tis a rainbow on a shower;
'Tis a momentary ray
Smiling in a winter's day;
'Tis a torrent's rapid stream;
'Tis a shadow; 'tis a dream;
'Tis the closing watch of night,
Dying at approaching light;
'Tis a landscape vainly gay,
Painted upon crumbling clay;
'Tis a lamp that wastes its fires,
'Tis a smoke that quick expires;
'Tis a bubble, 'tis a sigh:
Be prepared—O Man! to die.

They are like strings of precious stones, rosaries, these Tudor laments, one image following another, and however sad in colour, all making beauty:

. . . As withereth the primrose by the river,
As fadeth summer's sun from gliding fountains,
As vanisheth the light-blown bubble ever,
As melteth snow upon the mossy mountains:
So melts, so vanisheth, so fades, so withers,
The rose, the shine, the bubble, and the snow,
Of praise, pomp, glory, joy, which short life gathers,
Fair praise, vain pomp, sweet glory, brittle joy.
The withered primrose by the mourning river,
The faded summer's sun from weeping fountains,
The light-blown bubble vanishèd for ever,
The molten snow upon the naked mountains,
Are emblems that the treasures we uplay,
Soon wither, vanish, fade, and melt away. . . .

403. "BUT IN GREEN RUINS, IN THE DESOLATE WALLS OF ANTIQUE PALACES."

Through torrid tracts, with fainting steps they go,
Where wild Altama murmurs to their woe.
Far different these from all that charmed before,
The various terrours of that horrid shore;
Those blazing suns, that dart a downward ray,
And fiercely shed intolerable day;
Those matted woods, where birds forget to sing,
But silent bats in drowsy clusters cling;
Those poisonous fields, with rank luxuriance crown'd,
Where the dark scorpion gathers death around;
Where, at each step, the stranger fears to wake
The rattling terrours of the vengeful snake;
Where, crouching tigers wait their hapless prey,
And savage men, more murderous still than they;
While oft in whirls the mad tornado flies.
Mingling the ravaged landscape with the skies.
Far different these . . .

OLVER GOLDSMITH

"The wild Hyena."

In old times it was believed that if a hungry hyaena or jaccatray—which cannot wry his neck "because his backbone stretches itself out to the head"—dreams, he dreams so vividly that he calls into his sleeping brain a vision of the beasts he covets for prey. And this vision is so lifelike that he howls out of his sleep in mockery of the beasts—and thus decoys them to his den! He is a nocturnal scavenger, haunting graveyards, and "when" says Lyly, he "speaketh lyke a man," he "deviseth most mischief."

404. "In Xanadu did Kubla Khan."

"Now, this lord (the Great Caan)," says Friar Odoric in his *Cathay,* "passeth the summer at a certain place which is called Sandu, situated towards the north, and the coolest habitation in the world. But in the winter season he abideth in Cambalech. And when he will ride from the one place to the other this is the order thereof. He hath four armies of horsemen, one of which goeth a day's march in front of him, one at each side, and one a day's march in rear, so that he goeth always as it were, in the middle of a cross. And marching thus, each army hath its route laid down for it day by day, and findeth at its halts all necessary provender. But his own immediate company hath its order of march thus. The king travelleth in a two-wheeled carriage, in which is formed a very goodly chamber, all of lign-aloes and gold, and covered over with great and fine skins, and set with many precious stones. And the carriage is drawn by four elephants, well broken in and harnessed, and also by four splendid horses, richly caparisoned. And alongside go four barons, who are called Cuthe, keeping watch and ward over the chariot that no hurt come to the king. Moreover, he carrieth with him in his chariot twelve gerfalcons; so that even as he sits therein upon his chair of state or other seat, if he sees any birds pass he lets fly his hawks at them. And none may dare to approach within a stone's throw of the carriage, unless those whose duty brings them there. And thus it is that the king travelleth."

"A sunless Sea."

Our English eyes, loving light, weary a little of the short cold days in our country, when the sun makes "winter arches." Gloomier still would be our state in the regions told of by Marco Polo in the following passage:

"Beyond the most distant part of the territory of the Tartars, . . . there is another region [thick set with dark impenetrable woods] which extends to the utmost bounds of the north, and is called the Region of Darkness, because during most part of the winter months the sun is invisible, and the atmosphere is obscured to the same degree as that in which we find it just about the dawn of day, when we may be said to see and not to see. The men of this country are well made and tall, but of a very pallid complexion. They are not united under the government of a king or prince, and they live without any established laws or usages, in the manner of the brute creation. Their intellects also are dull, and they have an air of stupidity. The Tartars often proceed on plundering expeditions against these people, to rob them of their cattle and goods. For this purpose they avail themselves of those months in which the darkness prevails, in order that their approach may be unobserved; but, being unable to ascertain the direction in which they should return homeward with their booty, they provide against the chance of going astray by riding mares that have young foals at the time, which latter they suffer to accompany the dams as far as the confines of their own territory, but leave them, under proper care, at the commencement of the gloomy region. When their works of darkness have been accomplished, and they are desirous of revisiting the region of light, they lay the bridles on the necks of their mares, and suffer them freely to take their own course. Guided by maternal instinct, they make their way directly to the spot where they had quitted their foals; and by these means the riders are enabled to regain in safety the places of their residence."

406. "One held a Shell unto his Shell-like Ear."
(line 6)

. . . Gather a shell from the strown beach
And listen at its lips: they sigh

> The same desire and mystery,
> The echo of the whole sea's speech.
> And all mankind is thus at heart
> Not anything but what thou art:
> And Earth, Sea, Man, are all in each.

DANTE GABRIEL ROSSETTI

407.

This is, to me, a singularly beautiful fragment of poetry, and its loveliest lines are its simplest—the eighth and the last. This power so to use even commonplace or over-worn words—*innocence, dark, dial*—that, like Cinderella, they are not only transformed as at touch of magic wand, but seem to shed light on all around them, is the sovran mark of a poet. Set in this unique order, obedient to this rhythm, they resemble the sounding of a decoy in a haunt of wild birds, stir far echoes in the mind, arousing an inner and secret self.

For another simple example take these few lines from a sonnet by Keats:

> Keen, fitful gusts are whispering here and there
> Among the bushes, half leafless and dry;
> The stars look very cold about the sky,
> And I have many miles on foot to fare. . . .
>
> Of fair-haired Milton's eloquent distress,
> And all his love for gentle Lycid' drowned;
> Of lovely Laura in her light green dress
> And faithful Petrarch gloriously crowned.

What are the decoys here? Surely—apart from the broken rhythm of the second line—that *very cold about,* that *fair-haired* and that *light green dress.* Yet they are phrases such as might be used in mere talk. But what life and reality they give; while the more "poetical" words, *fare* and *gloriously* and even *eloquent* are rather a hindrance than a help.

Not, of course, that the words of a poem *are* its poetry. They are this no more than the paint and canvas of Piero della Francesca's *Resurrection,* or the time-worn stone of one of the figures in the façade at Chartres, are their beauty and supreme meaning. Words are but a *means* of conveying poetry from one imagination to another. So may a smile make lovely a plain face; or sunbeams weave a rainbow in the air. Even words themselves may be needless; for two human spirits may hold close converse together (of which only the rarest poetry in words or music, paint or stone could *tell*) without one syllable of speech between them:

"St. Louis, King of France, went on pilgrimage to visit the holy places all over the world; and hearing the exceeding great fame of the sanctity of Brother Giles, who was one of the first companions of St. Francis, he proposed in his heart, and determined at all cost, to visit him personally; for which reason he came to Perugia, where the said Brother Giles lived at that time.

"And coming to the door of the Community house, as a poor unknown pilgrim, with but few companions, he asked with great instance for Brother Giles, not telling the porter who he was that asked. The porter therefore went to Brother Giles, and told him there was a pilgrim at the door asking for him: and God inspired him and revealed to him that it was the King of France: wherefore, immediately, with great fervour of spirit, he came out of his cell and ran to the door and without further questioning, and without even having seen each other before, with the greatest devotion, inclining themselves, they embraced, and kissed one another, with as much familiarity as though for a long while they had been together in intimate friendship: but with all this, neither one nor the other spoke. But they stood thus embracing each other, with this sign of the love of charity between them, in silence.

"And after they had stood thus a great space, without either speaking a word to the other, they departed from each other, and St. Louis went his way on his journey, and Brother Giles returned to his cell."

Little Flowers of St. Francis

"Like solemn apparitions lulled sublime to everlasting rest."

. . . In the caves of the deep—lost Youth! lost Youth!—
O'er and o'er, fleeting billows; fleeting billows!—
Rung to his restless everlasting sleep

By the heavy death-bells of the deep,
Under the slimy-drooping sea-green willows,
Poor Youth! lost Youth!
Laying his dolorous head, forsooth,
On Carian reefs uncouth—
Poor Youth!
On the wild sand's ever-shifting pillows! . . .

O could my Spirit wing
Hills over, where salt Ocean hath his fresh headspring
And snowy curls bedeck the Blue-haired King,
Up where sweet oral birds articulate sing
Within the desert ring—
Their mighty shadows o'er broad Earth the Lunar Mountains fling,
Where the Sun's chariot bathes in Ocean's fresh headspring—
O could my Spirit wing! . . .

GEORGE DARLEY

Full fathom five thy Father lies,
Of his bones are Corrall made:
Those are Pearles that were his eies,
Nothing of him that doth fade,
But doth suffer a Sea-change
Into something rich, and strange:
Sea-Nimphs hourly ring his knell—
Ding dong.
Harke now I heare them, *ding-dong bell.*

WLLIAM SHAKESPEARE

411. "THE GOLDEN VANITY."

This is a patchwork of stanzas from three versions of the old ballad. In one version the "Golden Vanity" is said to be the "Sweet Trinity," and to have been built by Sir Walter Raleigh in the Netherlands. According to another, the Cabin-boy, after threatening to sink the "Goulden Vanite" as he had "sunk the French gallee," is taken on board and the Captain and merchant adventurers proved "far better than their word." But if stanza 12 is any witness, this seems unlikely. Can one not actually *see* the cold faces mocking down upon the water?

To an eye and ear new to them, these old Scottish ballads may seem a little difficult and forbidding. But read on, and their enchantment has no match—the very strangeness of the words, their rare music, the colour and light and clearness and vehemence, and, besides these, a wildness and ancientness like that of a folk-tune which seems to carry with its burden as many lost memories as an old churchyard has gravestones. The stories they tell are world wide. How they first came into being (for of some of them there are as many as twenty to thirty different versions), how they have fared in their long journey in time, and even when and by whom they were made, are questions on which even scholars are not yet agreed.

"Kevels" in line 5 of "Brown Robyn," means *lots,* and recalls a far older story:

"Now the word of the Lord came unto Jonah the son of Amittai, saying, Arise, go to Nineveh, that great city, and cry against it; for their wickedness is come up before me. But Jonah rose up to flee unto Tarshish from the presence of the Lord, and went down to Joppa; and he found a ship going to Tarshish, so he paid the fare thereof, and went down into it, to go with them unto Tarshish from the presence of the Lord. But the Lord sent out a great wind into the sea, and there was a mighty tempest in the sea, so that the ship was like to be broken. Then the mariners were afraid, and cried every man unto his god, and cast forth the wares that were in the ship into the sea, to lighten it of them. But Jonah was gone down into the sides of the ship; and he lay, and was fast asleep. . . . And they said every one to his fellow, Come, and let us cast lots, that we may know for whose cause this evil is upon us. So they cast lots, and the lot fell upon Jonah. . . . Then said they unto him, What shall we do unto thee, that the sea may be calm unto us? for the sea wrought, and was tempestuous. And he said unto them, Take me up, and cast me forth into the sea; so shall the sea be calm upon you: for I know that for my sake this great tempest is upon you. . . . So they took up Jonah, and cast him forth into the sea; and the sea ceased from her raging."

415. "A SEAL MY FATHER WAS."

Notes of music for the enticement of seals, with other beautiful old Gaelic airs and poems and tales, collected by Mr. Martin Freeman, will be found in Journals 23-5 of the Folk-Song Society.

417.

The Dowie Dee
It rins its lane;
But every seven year,
It gets ane!

418. "SIR PATRICK SPENCE."

The longer version of the ballad into which the genius of Sir Walter Scott wove a few new stanzas is the better known. But his was perilous work. Indeed, the secret of the art of this naked and lovely poetry seems nowadays to be lost: the marvel is how much it tells by means of the little it says.

To show, by one slight example, how the words of the same old ballad may vary in different versions, here are five variants of one stanza of Sir Patrick's, the first being that chosen (and adapted) by Scott:

(*a*) They hadna sailed a league, a league,
A league but barely three,
When the lift grew dark and the wind blew loud
And gurly grew the sea.

(*b*) They had not saild upon the sea
A league but merely three
When ugly, ugly were the jaws [waves]
That rowd unto their knee.

(*c*) They hadna sailed a league on sea,
A league but barely ane,
Till anchors brak, and tap-masts lap:
There came a deadly storm.

(*d*) He hadna gane a step, a step,
A step but barely ane,
When a bout [bolt] flew out of our goodly ship,
And the salt sea it came in.

(*e*) "Come down, come down, my pretty boy,
I fear we here maun die;
For thro and thro my goodly ship
I see the green-waved sea."

"LATE, LATE YESTREEN." (stanza 7)

With money in his pocket and bewaring of glass, the Man of Superstitions bows low and seven times to the new moon. If he sees a dim cindrous light filling in the circle of which this crescent is the edge, he "looks out for squalls"—the new moon has "the auld moone in hir arme." That light is the earth-shine. The sun illumines the earth; the earth like a looking glass reflects his radiance upon the moon; and she thus melancholily returns it; whereas the silver blaze on her eastern edge is light direct: eyes looking upward *thence* into her black skies are lit with her prodigious mornings.

Precisely how much history is contained in *Sir Patrick Spence* is doubtful. Little more can be said than that in 1281 Margaret, daughter of Alexander III. of Scotland, was married to Eric, King of Norway, and that of the knights and nobles who accompanied her to Norway many were drowned on the voyage home. But just as in the *Plays* you may trace Shakespeare's footprints through the old tales and chronicles he read—*King Lear, Macbeth, Cymbeline*—so in many of the ballads you can watch as it were the maker stringing his spirited stanzas on a definite thread of history. Take, for example *Sir Andrew Barton.*

What follows is an extract from Edward Hall's *Chronicle*:

"In June [1511]the kyng beyng at Leicester, tidynges were brought to him, that Andrew Barton a Scottish man, and a pirate of the sea, feigning that the king of Scots, had war with the Portingals, did rob every nation, and so stopped the king's streams that no merchants almost could pass, and when he took the englishmen's goods, he said they were Portingal's goods, and thus he haunted and robbed at every haven's mouth. The king moved greatly with this crafty pirate, sent Sir Edward Howard, lord Admiral of England, and Lord Thomas Howard, son and heir to the earl of Surrey, in all the haste to the sea, which hastily made ready two ships, and without any more abode, took the sea, and by chance of weather were severed. The lord Howard lying in the Downs, perceived where Andrew was making towards Scotland, and so fast the said lord chased him, that he overtook him, and there was a sore battle: the englishmen were fierce, and the Scots defended them manfully, and ever Andrew blew his whistle to encourage his men, yet for all that, the lord Howard and his men, by clean strength entered the main deck; then the Englishmen entered on all sides, and the Scots fought sore on the hatches, but in conclusion, Andrew was taken, which was so sore wounded, that he died there: then all the remnant of the Scots' were taken, with their ship called the Lion.

"All this while, was the Lord Admiral in chase of the Barque of Scotland, called *Jenny Pirwyn,* which was wont to sail with the *Lion* in company, and . . . he laid him on board, and fiercely assailed him, and the Scots as hardy and well-stomached men them defended, but the lord Admiral so encouraged his men, that they entered the Barque and slew many, and took all the other.

"Thus were these two ships taken, and brought to Black Wall, the second day of August; and all the Scots were sent to the Bishop's place of York, and there remained at the king's charge, till other direction was taken for them."

So far the Chronicle: and now the ballad, or rather, the second half of it, the first having told how Henry sent out the English ships, how they chased out Sir Andrew Barton in the *Lion,* sunk his pinnace, shot down his fore-mast, and killed, one after the other, the men he sent up the main-mast in order to let "its beams down fall"—that is, (?) to cut away the wreckage of the fore-mast. They having failed, he goes himself:

. . . But when hee saw his sisters sonne slâine,
Lord! in his heart hee was not well:
"Goe ffeitch me downe my armour of proofe,
For I will to the topcastle my-selfe.

"Goe ffeitch me downe my armour of prooffe,
For itt is guilded with gold soe cleere;
God be with my brother, Iohn of Bartton!
Amongst the Portingalls hee did itt weare."

But when hee had his armour of prooffe,
And on his body hee had itt on,
Every man that looked att him
Sayd, Gunn nor arrow hee neede feare none.

"Come hither, Horsley!" sayes my lord Howard,
"And looke your shaft that itt goe right;
Shoot a good shoote in the time of need,
And ffor thy shooting thoust be made a knight."

"I'le doe my best," sayes Horslay then,
"Your Honor shall see before I goe;
If I should be hanged att your maine-mast,
I have in my shipp but arrowes tow."

But att Sir Andrew hee shott then;
Hee made sure to hitt his marke;
Under the spole [shoulder] of his right arme
Hee smote Sir Andrew quite throw the hart.

Yett from the tree hee wold not start,
But hee clinged to itt with might and maine;
Under the coller then of his iacke[coat of mail],
He stroke Sir Andrew thorrow the braine.

"Ffight on my men," sayes Sir Andrew Bartton,
"I am hurt, but I am not slaine;
I'le lay mee downe and bleed a-while,
And then I'le rise and ffight againe."

"Ffight on my men," sayes Sir Andrew Bartton,
"These English doggs they bite soe lowe;
Ffight on ffor Scotland and Saint Andrew
Till you heare my whistle blowe!"

But when the[y] cold not heare his whistle blow,
  Sayes Harry Hunt, I'le lay my head
You may bord yonder noble shipp, my lord,
  For I know Sir Andrew hee is dead.

With that they borded this noble shipp,
  Soe did they itt with might and maine;
The[y] ffound eighteen score Scotts alive,
  Besides the rest were maimed and slaine.

My lord Haward tooke a sword in his hand,
  And smote of[f]Sir Andrews head;
The Scotts stood by did weepe and mourne,
  But neuer a word durst speake or say.

He caused his body to be taken downe,
  And ouer the hatch-bord cast into the sea,
And about his middle three hundred crownes:
  "Wheresoeuer thou lands, itt will bury thee."

With his head they sayled into England again,
  With right good will and fforce and main,
And the day before Newyeeres even
  Into Thames mouth they came againe.

My lord Haward wrote to King Heneryes grace,
  With all the newes hee cold him bring:
"Such a Newyeeres gifft I haue brought to your Gr[ace]
  As neuer did subiect to any king.

"For merchandyes and manhood,
  The like is no[where] to be ffound;
The sight of these wold doe you good,
  Ffor you have not the like in your English ground."

But when hee heard tell that they were come,
  Full royally hee welcomed them home;
Sir Andrews shipp was the kings Newyeeres guifft;
  A braver shipp you never saw none.

Now hath our king Sir Andrews shipp,
  Besett with pearles and precyous stones;
Now hath England two shipps of warr,
  Two shipps of warr, before but one.

"Who holpe to this?" says King Henerye,
  "That I may reward him ffor his paine":
"Harry Hunt, and Peeter Simon,
  William Horseley, and I the same."

"Harry Hunt shall have his whistle and chaine,
  And all his jewells, whatsoever they bee,
And other riche giffts that I will not name,
  For his good service he hath done mee.

"Horslay, right thoust be a knight,
  Lands and livings thou shalt have store;
Howard shal be erle of Nottingham,
  And soe was never Howard before.

"Now, Peeter Simon, thou art old;
  I will maintaine thee and they sonne;
Thou shalt haue five hundred pound all in gold
  Ffor the good service that thou hast done."

Then King Henerye shiffted his roome;
  In came the Queene and ladyes bright;
Other arrands they had none
  But to see Sir Andrew Bartton, knight.

But when they see his deadly fface,
  His eyes were hollow in his head;
"I wold give a hundred poun," sais Kinge Henerye,
  "The man were alive as hee is dead!

"Yett ffor the manfull part hee hath playd,
  Both here and beyond the sea,
His men shall haue halfe a crowne a day
  To bring them to my brother, King Jamye."

This ballad, then, whether or not its vivid and clean-cut details are at first or second hand, is packed with history. Sir Thomas Howard—who led the vanguard at the Battle of Flodden—was the father of Henry, Earl of Surrey, the poet, (see No. 46), and the uncle of Anne Boleyn. He was the Great-grandfather, too, of the Lord Thomas Howard (first Earl of Suffolk), to whom Sir Richard Grenville was second in command. (See "The Last Fight of the *Revenge*".)

In the 8th stanza before the end are the lines:

"Now hath England two shipps of warr,
Two shipps of warr, before but one."

one of these being, of course, *The Lion,* Sir Andrew's ship and Howard's prize. The other was the *Great Harry,* which was built in 1504, and *the first ship in the English navy.* Before this date "when the Prince wanted a fleet he had no other expedient but hiring ships from the merchants." But what a rumour—like the sound of the great west wind on a pine-clad mountain-side—sweeps through the mind at sight of those few words in italics.

419. "Allison Gross."

I have changed two words of the original.

420. "Sir Hugh."

The monastic story behind this ballad is that while, on July 31, 1255, Sir Hugh was playing, he was kidnapped by a Jew named Copin and crucified, and that eighteen of the principal Jews in England were hanged in consequence. Whether there be any truth in this, or it be wholly false, the ballad builds up a pellucid picture in the imagination—the ancient town; the boys at their game; the narrow, gabled, cobbled streets; the evening gold on roof and wall; night, lamentation; and the clanging of the bells.

421. "Edward."

The spelling of this ballad usually begins "Why dois your brand sae dripp wie bluid," and so on. This spelling Professor

Child thought "affectedly antique." But since, as he says, mere antiquated "spelling will not make an old ballad, so it will not *un*make one." And "Edward" in any guise is "one of the noblest" of the popular ballads. Here it is, then, in our present spelling.

422. "I WILL SING."

The king in the third line is James the Sixth of Scotland and the First of England, with the big head, slobbering tongue, quilted clothes and rickety legs, who delighted to speculate and write on such subjects as Fate, witchcraft and tobacco-smoking. The "wanton laird of young Logie" is John Wemyss who plotted against him with the Earl of Bothwell in 1592. His bold, crafty and merry young wife, May Margaret, says Mr. Sidgwick, had one or other of these four delectable maiden names—Vinstar, Weiksterne, Twynstoun, or Twinslace. It is dubious which.

All ladies in the days of the ballad carried knives at their girdles; the one in stanza 8 was clearly a wedding gift. Doughty uses they sometimes put them to.

423. "FAIR ANNIE."

In the margins of Mr. Nahum's copy of this ballad, two exquisite damosels were painted in green, blue and amethyst on gold (as in a monk's work), and between their fingers hung a linen napkin seemingly broidered with pearls and in the midst of it a sleeping dove. Whatever he may have meant by this, I confess that at first reading I fell in love with both these ladies. My feelings for the "noble knight" who ransomed fair Annie, then wearied of her, were different. It was strange to find a noble knight so *hard* a gentleman, not so much because he wearied of her (since to weary of one so true, intelligent and tender was even more of a punishment than a misfortune) but more particularly, with regard to his craving for "gowd and gear." He reminds me of a similar piece of humanity described in three short stanzas which were found by Mr. Macmath written on the flyleaf of a little volume printed at Edinburgh about 1670, and which appear in Child's *Ballads*:

"He steps full statly on the street,
He hads the charters of him sell,
In to his cloathing he is complete,
In Craford's mure he bears the bell. . . .

"I wish I had died my own fair death,
In tender age, when I was young;
I would never [then] have broke my heart
For the love of any churl's son.

"Wo be to my parents all,
That lives so farr beyond the sea!
I might have lived a noble life,
And wedded in my own countrée."

425. "But think na' ye my Heart was sair?" (line 21)

Down in yon garden sweet and gay
Where bonnie grows the lily,
I heard a fair maid sighing say,
"My wish be wi' sweet Willie!"

"Willie's rare, and Willie's fair,
And Willie's wondrous bonny;
And Willie hecht to marry me
Gin e'er he married ony.

"O gentle wind, that bloweth south
From where my Love repaireth,
Convey a kiss frae his dear mouth
And tell me how he fareth!

"O tell sweet Willie to come doun
And hear the mavis singing,
And see the birds on ilka bush
And leaves around them hinging.

"The lav'rock there, wi' her white breast
And gentle throat sae narrow;
There's sport eneuch for gentlemen
On Leader haughs and Yarrow.

"O Leader haughs are wide and braid
And Yarrow haughs are bonny;
There Willie hecht to marry me
If e'er he married ony.

"But Willie's gone, whom I thought on,
And does not hear the weeping
Draws many a tear frae's true love's e'e,
When other maids are sleeping.

"Yestreen I made my bed fu' braid,
The night I'll mak' it narrow,
For a' the lee-lang winter night
I lie twined o' my marrow.

"O came ye by yon water-side?
Pu'd you the rose or lily?
Or came you by yon meadow green,
Or saw you my sweet Willie?"

She sought him up, she sought him down,
She sought him braid and narrow;
Syne, in the cleaving of a crag,
She found him drowned in Yarrow!

Hecht (line 7) means vowed; *haughs* are water-meadows; and to be twined o' one's marrow, is to be separated from one's loved one.

427. The Twa Sisters.

Here is another ballad—"The Water o' Wearie's Well"—of a similar pattern. But in this the bewitched young princess not only beguiles her betrayer into his own snare, but adds a merry word at parting:

There came a bird out o a bush,
  On water for to dine,[1]
An sighing sair, says the king's daughter,
  "O wae's this heart o mine!"

He's taen a harp into his hand,
  He's harped them all asleep,
Except it was the king's daughter,
  Who one wink couldna get.

He's luppen on his berry-brown steed,
  Taen 'er on behind himsell,
Then baith rede down to that water
  That they ca Wearie's Well.

Wide[2] in, wide in, my lady fair,
  No harm shall thee befall;
Oft times I've watered my steed
  Wi the water o Wearie's Well."

The first step that she steppèd in,
  She stepped to the knee;
And sighend says this lady fair,
  "This water's nae for me."

"Wide in, wide in, my lady fair,
  No harm shall thee befall;
Oft times I've waterèd my steed
  Wi the water o Wearie's Well."

The next step that she stepped in,
  She stepped to the middle;
"O," sighend says this lady fair,
  "I've wat my gowden girdle."

[1] sup. [2] wade.

"Wide in, wide in, my lady fair,
No harm shall thee befall;
Oft times I've watered my steed
Wi the water o Wearie's Well."

The next step that she steppèd in,
She stepped to the chin;
"O," sighend says this lady fair,
"They sud gar twa loves twin!" [1]

"Seven king's daughters I've drownd there,
In the water o Wearie's Well,
And I'll make you the eight o them,
And ring the common bell."

"Since I am standing here," she says,
"This dowie [2] death to die,
One kiss o your comely mouth
I'm sure was comfort me."

He louted him oer his saddle bow,
To kiss her cheek and chin;
She's taen him in her arms twa,
And thrown him headlong in.

"Since seven king's daughters ye've drowned there,
In the water o Wearie's Well,
I'll make you bridegroom to them a',
An ring the bell mysell."

And aye she warsled, and aye she swam,
And she swam to dry lan;
She thankèd God most cheerfully
The dangers she oercame.

428. "Sweet William and May Margaret."

Hermione. Come Sir, now I am for you againe:
Pray you sit by us, and tell's a Tale.

[1] alas, that death should take lover from loved one!
[2] grievous.

Mamillius (her small son). Merry, or sad, shal't bee?
Hermione. As merry as you will.
Mamillius. A sad Tale's best for Winter:
I have one of Sprights, and Goblins.
Hermione. Let's have that, good Sir.
Come-on, sit downe, come-on, and doe your best
To fright me with your Sprights: you're powrefull
at it.
Mamillius. There was a man. . . .
Hermione. Nay, come sit downe: then on.
Mamillius. Dwelt by a Churchyard:
I will tell it softly,
Yond Crickets shall not heare it.
Hermione. Come on then, and giv't me in mine eare. . . .

The Winter's Tale

429. "THAT BIRK GREW FAIR ENEUGH." (stanza 6)

A strange feature of these ballads is that many of the stories they tell, or the customs, beliefs, lore they refer to, may be found scattered up and down throughout the world. In Russia, for one small instance, the birk or birch tree is honoured in this fashion: A little before Whitsuntide, says Sir James Fraser in *The Golden Bough,* the young women, with dancing and feasting, cut down a living birch-tree, deck it with bright clothes or hang it with ribbons; then set it up as an honoured guest in one of the village houses. On Whit Sunday itself they fling it, finery and all, into a stream for a charm.

And now for England: "Thirty years ago," says Mrs. Wright, it was still customary in some west-Midland districts to decorate village churches on Whit Sunday with sprigs of birch stuck in holes bored in the tops of the pews. I can remember this being done by an old village clerk in Herefordshire, but when he was gathered to his fathers in the same profession, the custom died with him." How happy must he have been then—as for that one evening was the Wife of Usher's Well herself—when he lifted his eyes upon a silver birch brushing with its light, green tresses the very gates of Paradise.

433. "A SPANGLE HERE."

Dew sate on Julia's haire,
  And spangled too,
Like leaves that laden are
  With trembling dew:
Or glittered to my sight,
  As when the Beames
Have their reflected light,
  Daunc't by the Streames.

ROBERT HERRICK

If the daisies are not to shut their eyes until Julia shut hers, should they not most assuredly wait also until "dear love Isabella," shut *hers?* She was the bosom friend and aunt of Majorie Fleming, Sir Walter Scott's little friend, who was born in 1803, and who, having written her few tim-tam-tot little rhymes, died in 1811. And here is Isabel:

Here lies sweet Isabell in bed,
With a night-cap on her head;
Her skin is soft, her face is fair,
And she has very pretty hair;
She and I in bed lie nice,
And undisturbed by rats or mice;
She is disgusted with Mr. Worgan,
Though he plays upon the organ.
Her nails are neat, her teeth are white,
Her eyes are very, very bright;
In a conspicuous town she lives,
And to the poor her money gives;
Here ends sweet Isabella's story,
And may it be much to her glory.

434.

Bunyan's "Comparison" for this poem (almost as though he had *this* year of grace in mind) runs thus:

Our Gospel has had here a Summers day;
But in its Sun-shine we, like Fools, did play,
Or else fall out, and with each other wrangle,
And did instead of work not much but jangle.
And if our Sun seems angry, hides his face,
Shall it go down, shall Night possess this place?
Let not the voice of night-Birds us afflict,
And of our mis-spent Summer us convict.

435. "SWEET ROSE WHOSE HUE ANGRY AND BRAVE"

that is, *red and resplendent,* though nowadays it might seem affected to use these words in this sense. Like most things in the world, words seldom remain exactly the same—cither in sound or in sense. To Chaucer's ear, or even Shakespeare's, we should seem to be talking a curious dialect. A word comes into being, flourishes for a time, but may gradually fall out of common use, then out of literary use, and at last be clean forgotten. Another may remain in use, but steadily (though almost inperceptibly) change in meaning and effect. Take but this single stanza from Milton's *Hymn on the Morning of Christ's Nativity* (written when he was a boy of 21):

The Shepherds on the Lawn,
Or ere the point of dawn,
Sat simply chatting in a rustic row;
Full little thought they than,
That the mighty Pan
Was kindly come to live with them below;
Perhaps their loves, or else their sheep,
Was all that did their silly thoughts so busy keep.

Apart from "or ere" which means *before,* and "than," *then;* no fewer than five of the words in these eight lines have so changed in usage as to affect our minds in a way which Milton cannot have intended or foreseen. We should not nowadays use the word "lawn" if we meant a pasture; "chatting" has now for us a rather too indoorish effect to be appropriate for the talk of shepherds; *rustic,* because of town wags, or maybe of "rustic furniture" is slightly belittling; *kindly* now means amiable or genial; and *silly,* a word that originally meant blessed, fortunate, prosperous ["silly Suffolk"] and then (and here) simple and artless, now means only foolish or weak-witted.

To some tastes it seems a barbarous pastime thus to pick a poem to pieces. For the moment, it is true, the poem—like a clock in similar conditions—ceases to "go." But only for the moment. At need it will at once put itself together again; and, as W. W. Skeat says, "Why are we to be debarred from examining a poet's language because his words are sweet and his descriptions entrancing? That is only one more reason for weighing every word that he uses."

And Ruskin too: "You must get into the habit of looking intensely at words. . . . Never let a word escape you that looks suspicious. It is severe work; but you will find it, even at first interesting, and at last, endlessly amusing."

And this is not merely advice, but a countersign and a *Sesame.* A word, too, is a symbol of four kinds: (*a*) of the meaning that has been given to it pure and simple—the dictionary meaning. (*b*) It is a graphic pattern, in print or in handwriting. Compare, for example the difference in graphic effect between "grey" and *gray;* between "errours" and *errorrs.* The latter is more pregnant with mistakes, so to speak—and mistakes not of the "u" kind! (*c*) The sound of a word is yet another symbol, and a vital one. (*d*) The formation of that sound with the throat, tongue, vocal organs, is the fourth, and important, particularly in poetry. Say over:

> "O what can ail thee, knight at arms."

or

> "Nothing is here for tears, nothing to wail. . . .
> Nothing but well and fair,
> And what may quiet us in a death so noble."

or

> "What need a vermeil-tinctured lip for that,
> Love-darting eyes, or tresses like the Morn?"

The very way of uttering such things is a delight—and therefore affects the mind and spirit within, and every word is like a fragment of honeycomb, its many cells filled with various nectars.

437.

From "Songs of Innocence"; and this is from "Songs of Experience":

When the voices of children are heard on the green
And whisp'rings are in the dale.
The days of my youth rise fresh in my mind,
My face turns green and pale.
Then come home, my children, the sun is gone down,
And the dews of night arise;
Your spring and your day are wasted in play,
And your winter and night in disguise.

For to grow old and look back to one's childhood, though in much it is a happy thing, may also be a thing chequered with dread and regret. The old poets never wearied of bidding youth gather its roses, seize its fleeting moments. But not all roses are sweet in the keeping and "lilies that fester smell far worse than weeds."

440. "AFTERWARDS."

Every fine poem says much in little. It packs into the fewest possible words—by means of their sound, their sense, and their companionship—a wide or rare experience. So, in particular, with such a poem as this. It tells of a man thinking of the day when he shall have bidden goodbye to a world whose every living and lovely thing—Spring, hawk, evening, wintry skies—he has dearly loved. And if what he relates is to be seen (and felt) as clearly and truly as if it were before one's very eyes, it must be read with a peculiar intensity—all one's imagination alert to gather up the full virtue of the words, and to picture in the mind each fleeting and living object in turn.

To compare the great and fine things of one age (the work in ours, for example, of Thomas Hardy, Charles Doughty, W. H. Hudson, Alice Meynell, Robert Bridges) with the great and fine things of another is an exceedingly difficult task (and to pit poet against poet, or imagination against imagination, a rather stupid one). But that in Elizabeth's day England was indeed a "nest of singing birds" may be realised by the fact that when Shakespeare was finishing his last play, *The Tempest,* in the Spring, apparently, of 1611—when, that is, he himself was aged 47 (and she herself had been eight years dead), Sir Walter Raleigh was 59, George Chapman 52, Samuel Daniel 49, Michael Drayton 48, Thomas Campion 44, Thomas Dekker (?) 41, John Donne and Ben Jonson were 38, John Fletcher was 32, Francis Beaumont 27, William Drummond 26, John Ford 25, William Browne and Robert Herrick 20, Francis Quarles 19, George Herbert 18, Thomas Carew (?) 16, James Shirley 15. John Milton was 2 and John Webster was an infant. It was seven years before the birth of Richard Lovelace and of Abraham Cowley, ten before Marvell's, and eleven before Vaughan's. Edmund Spenser had been twelve years dead, Sir Philip Sidney twenty-five.

Two hundred and fifty years afterwards—in 1861—another great queen was on the throne, Victoria. It was the year in which the Prince Consort died, and Edward, Prince of Wales, came of age. And the English imagination had come into its own again: William Barnes and Cardinal Newman were then 60, Edward Fitzgerald and Tennyson were 52, Robert Browning 49, Charles Kingsley 42, Matthew Arnold 39, Coventry Patmore 38, William Allingham 37, Dante Gabriel Rossetti and George Meredith were 33, Christina Rossetti was 31, William Morris 27, Algernon Swinburne 24, Thomas Hardy was 21, Mr. Robert Bridges 17, Robert Louis Stevenson 11, and Francis Thompson was 2. Other great writers, in English, then alive were Carlyle, Thackeray, Dickens, Ruskin, Darwin and Huxley; Emerson, Hawthorne, Longfellow and Walt Whitman. This is a clumsy catalogue, but *so* the strange flame of genius fitfully burns in this world. And 1611 knew as little of 1861 as 1861 knew of 2111. (But would that 1923 [or 1928] could leave to the future one-tenth part of such a legacy as did 1611—the Authorized Version of the English Bible.)

But to return to Shakespeare. He was born in April 1564. About 1591 he wrote the first of his plays, *Love's Labour's Lost.* By 1611 he had finished the last of them; 34 in all as they appear in the first Folio, 37 as they now appear in the Canon. And apart from these, his Poems. There followed a strange silence. On the 25th of March, 1616, "in perfect health and memory (God be praised!)," he made his will. On St. George's Day,

1616, he died. To reflect for a moment on that brief lifetime, on that twenty years' work which is now a perennial fountain of happiness, light and wisdom to the whole world, is to marvel indeed. The life-giving secret of this supreme genius none can tell. We know not even what keeps our own small lamp alight. But Thomas Campbell recounts a parable: "It was predicted of a young man lately belonging to one of our universities, that he would certainly become a prodigy because he read sixteen hours a day. 'Ah, but,' said somebody, 'how many hours a day does he *think?*' It might have been added, 'How many hours does he feel?'" So of Shakespeare: What was *his* (and from his childhood) seeing, thinking, feeling, dreaming, working day? As said his old friends and fellow-players, John Heminge and Henry Condell in their Preface to the Folio: "Reade him . . . and againe and againe: And if then you do not like him, surely you are in some manifest danger. . . ."

441. "With such a Sky."

It is a beauteous Evening, calm and free,
The holy time is quiet as a Nun
Breathless with adoration; the broad sun
Is sinking down in its tranquility;
The gentleness of heaven broods o'er the Sea:
Listen! the mighty Being is awake,
And doth with his eternal motion make
A sound like thunder—everlastingly. . . .

William Wordsworth

442. "Shepherds all, and Maidens fair, Fold your Flocks."

The curfew tolls the knell of parting day,
The lowing herd wind slowly o'er the lea,
The ploughman homeward plods his weary way,
And leaves the world to darkness and to me.

Now fades the glimmering landscape on the sight,
And all the air a solemn stillness holds,
Save where the beetle wheels his droning flight,
And drowsy tinklings lull the distant folds: . . .

These lines and the stanzas that follow them in the *Elegy Wrote in a Country Churchyard* are as familiar as any in English. Here, "a figure on paper"—from a letter to a friend written by Thomas Gray, on November 19, 1764, is a description—not of evening after the setting of the sun—but of a sun-*rise* as vivid as if one's own naked eye had watched its "Levee":

"I must not close my letter without giving you one principal event of my history; which was, that (in the course of my late tour) I set out one morning before five o'clock, the moon shining through a dark and misty autumnal air, and got to the sea-coast time enough to be at the Sun's Levee. I saw the clouds and the dark vapours open gradually to right and left, rolling over one another in great smoky wreathes, and the tide (as it flowed gently in upon the sands) first whitening, then slightly tinged with gold and blue; and all at once a little line of unsufferable brightness that (before I can write these five words) was grown to half an orb, and now to a whole one, too glorious to be distinctly seen. It is very odd it makes no figure on paper; yet I shall remember it, as long as the sun, or at least as long as I endure. I wonder whether anybody ever saw it before? I hardly believe it."

So each day and every day the sun rises, indeed is rising always above *some* watchful eye's horizon, and we come so to expect its rising, and so to be assured of it, as though it were no less certain than that twice two are four. But, in fact, it is only just certain enough to prevent night from being a dreadful apprehension, and life from becoming a mere routine. As Coleridge says in his *Table Talk:*

"Suppose Adam watching the sun sinking under the western horizon for the first time; he is seized with gloom and terror, relieved by scarce a ray of hope that he shall ever see the glorious light again. The next evening, when it declines, his hopes are stronger, but still mixed with fear; and even at the end of a thousand years, all that a man can feel is a hope and an expectation so strong as to preclude anxiety."

. . . High among the lonely hills,
While I lay beside my sheep,
Rest came down and filled my soul,
From the everlasting deep.

Changeless march the stars above,
Changeless morn succeeds to even;
Still the everlasting hills
Changeless watch the changeless heaven. . . .

CHARLES KINGSLEY

443. "SWIFTLY WALK O'ER THE WESTERN WAVE."

So ran the first line of this poem by Shelley in the first edition of this book when it appeared. Whereupon a friend pointed out (more, I hope, in sorrow than in anger), that Shelley had written not "o'er" but "over"—at least, so the word appears in the Harvard MS. of the poem, though not in the edition of 1824. And this is not a trivial point.

"Swiftly walk o'er the western wave, Spirit of Night" brings into the mind a vast sea, the dusk of the heavens above darkening into night; and that sea is calm and without waves on its surface.

"Swiftly walk over," on the other hand, seems to conjure up into the imagination the very spectre of Night advancing over the wave-tossed darkness of the waters, as light and surely as the stormy petrel itself. And this is but a further proof that the rhythm of a poem is essential, not only to its sensuous, but to its imaginative and intellectual meaning.

444. "LIGHT THE LAMPS UP, LAMPLIGHTER."

In towns and cities nowadays wayfarers in the streets are so much accustomed to seeing at fall of dusk their "electric" lamps suddenly shine out, as if at the bidding of a sorcerer, that the feat is passed unnoticed. So with gas-lamps in my young days, though then, like Robert Louis Stevenson, most children watched the long-twinkling-poled lamplighter on his rounds, as if he might well be a wizard in disguise. Before gas there was oil, and before oil candles; and householders in cities were responsible for keeping this much at least of light burning in the moonless, narrow, dangerous and deserted streets—the horn-sided candle-lantern having been the invention of King Alfred himself.

Then Watchman and Bellman went their solitary rounds, calling the hours and weather, and knocking up those whose hanging lanterns burned dim or had gone out. The next three old rhymes refer to this practice:

> Maids in your smocks, look to your locks,
> Your fire and candle-light!
> For well 'tis known much mischief's done
> By both in dead of night;
> Your locks and fire do not neglect,
> And so you may good rest expect.

> Maidens to bed, and cover coal!
> Let the mouse out of her hole!
> Crickets in the chimney sing,
> While the little bell doth ring;
> If fast asleep, who can tell
> When the clapper hits the bell?

> A light here, maids! Hang out your light,
> And see your horns be clear and bright,
> That so your candle clear may shine,
> Continuing from six to nine;
> That honest men that walk along,
> May see to pass safe without wrong!

"On the Vigil of Saint John Baptist (says John Stow in his *Survey,* of 1603), and on Saint Peter and Paule the Apostles, every mans doore being shadowed with greene Birch, long Fennel, Saint Johns wort, Orpin, white Lillies, and such like, garnished upon with Garlands of beautiful flowers, had also Lampes of glasse, with oyle burning in them all the night, some hung out braunches of yron curiously wrought, contayning hundreds of Lampes light at once, which made a goodly shew, namely in new Fishstreet, Thames streete, etc. Then had ye besides the standing watches, all in bright harnes in every ward and streete of this Citie and Suburbs, a marching watch, that passed through the principal streets thereof, to wit, from the little Conduit by Paules gate, through west Cheape, by ye Stocks, through Cornhill, by Leaden hall to Aldgate, then backe downe Fenchurch streete, by Grasse church, aboute Grasse church Conduite, and up Grass church streete into Cornhill, and through it into west Chepe againe."

"THE CHILDREN ARE GOING TO BED."

Hush-a-ba, birdie, croon, croon,
Hush-a-ba, birdie, croon.
The Sheep are gane to the siller wood,
And the cows are gane to the broom, broom.

And it's braw milking the kye, kye,
It's braw milking the kye,
The birds are singing, the bells are ringing,
And the wild deer come galloping by, by.

And hush-a-ba, birdie, croon, croon,
Hush-a-ba birdie, croon.
The Gaits are gane to the mountain hie,
And they'll no be hame till noon, noon.

This for the littlest ones, the cradle-creatures. But for the rest:

Boys and Girls, come out to play,
The Moon doth shine as bright as day;
Come with a whoop, come with a call,
Come with a goodwill or don't come at all;
Lose your supper and lose your sleep—
So come to your playmates in the street.

Snout. Doth the Moone shine that night wee play our play?

Bottom. A Calendar, a Calendar, looke in the Almanack, finde out Moone-shine, finde out Moone-shine.

Quince. Yes, it doth shine that night.

Bottom. Why then may you leave a casement of the great chamber window (where we play) open, and the Moone may shine at the casement.

Quince. Ay, or else one must come in with a bush of thorns and a lanthorne, and say he comes to disfigure, or to present the person of Moone-shine. . . .

Lysander. Proceed, Moone.
Moone. All that I have to say, is to tell you, that the Lanthorne is the Moone; I, the man in the Moone; this thorne bush, my thorne bush; and this dog, my dog. . . .

A Midsummer Night's Dream

Mon, in the monë, stond ant streit,
On is bot-forke is burthen he bereth:
Hit is muche wonder that he na down slyt,
For doute leste he valle he shoddreth ant shereth:
When the frost fresheth muche chele he byd,
The thornës beth kene is hattren to-tereth;
Nis no wytht in the world that wot wen he syt,
Ne, bote hit bue the hegge, whet wedës he wereth.

And that, I gather, means that—

The Man in the Moon stands up there stark and still in her silver, carrying his thornbush on his pitchfork. It's a marvel he doesn't slide down; he's shuddering and shaking at the thought of it. When the frost sharpens, he'll be frozen to the marrow. The prickles stick out to tear his clothes; but nobody in the world has seen him sit down, or knows, apart from his thornbush, what he has on.

I see the Moon,
The Moon sees me:
God bless the sailors,
And bless me.

449. "THAT BUSY ARCHER." (line 4)

Though I am young and cannot tell
Either what Love or Death is well,
Yet I have heard they both bear darts
And both do aim at human hearts. . . .

BEN JONSON

"ARE BEAUTIES THERE AS PROUD AS HERE THEY BE." (line 11)

. . . The palace of her father the King, was on that side the Moon no mortal sees, and of such an enchantment was her cold beauty that on earth none resembles it. Yet all her folly and pride was but to win the idolatrous love of far-travelling Princes, or even of wanderers of common blood; for the sake of that love and admiration only. And many perished in those rock-bound deserts and parched and icy lunar wildernesses on account of this proud damsel; before a strange fate befell her. . . .

And this is a fragment (from a thirteenth century MS.), to be found in *A Medieval Garner:*

"What shall we say of the ladies when they come to feasts? Each marks well the other's head; they wear bosses like horned beasts, and if any have no horns, she is a laughing stock for the rest. Their arms go merrily when they come into the room; they display their kerchiefs of silk and cambric, set on their buttons of coral and amber, and cease not their babble so long as they are in the bower. . . . But however well their attire be fashioned, when the feast is come, it pleases them nought; so great is their envy now and so high grows their pride, that the bailiff's daughter counterfeits the lady."

But this was in the dark ages.

450. "SHE HATH NO AIR" (line 5)

—and that being so:

". . . . There will be no sounds on the moon. . . . Even a meteor shattering itself to a violent end against the surface of the moon would make no noise. Nor would it herald its coming by glowing into a 'shooting star,' as it would on entering the earth's atmosphere. There will be no floating dust, no scent, no twilight, no blue sky, no twinkling of the stars. The sky will be always black and the stars will be clearly visible by day as by night. The sun's wonderful corona, which no man on earth, even by seizing every opportunity during eclipses, can hope to see for more than two hours in all, in a long lifetime, will be visible all day. So will the great red flames of the sun. . . . There will be no life (since) for fourteen days there is continuous night, when the temperature must sink away down towards the absolute cold of space. This will be followed without an instant of twilight by full daylight. For another fourteen days the sun's rays will bear straight down, with no diffusion or absorption of their heat, or light, on the way. . . ."

This is a matter-of-fact fragment out of "The Outline of Science," edited by Professor J. Arthur Thompson; but it would not be easy to say exactly how in its magical *effect* on the mind it differs from poetry. Indeed, there can hardly be a quicker journey to the comprehension of scientific fact than by way of the imagination. Moonless mountainous Hesper, the Evening Star, is an even lovelier thing to watch shining in the fading rose and green of sunset when we realise that at her most radiant—a radiance that casts an earthly shadow even—it is but a slim crescent of the planet that we see, a planet, too, almost sister in magnitude to the earth, but whose briefer year is of an ardour that might be happiness to fiery sprite and salamander, but would be unendurable to watery creatures like ourselves. Nor could language be used more scientifically (concisely, pregnantly and exactly), than in the words *moving, priestlike, human, mask,* in the following sonnet by John Keats—a sonnet written in mortal illness and in immortal sorrowfulness:

Bright star, would I were stedfast as thou art—
  Not in lone splendour hung aloft the night
And watching, with eternal lids apart,
  Like nature's patient, sleepless Eremite,
The moving waters at their priestlike task
  Of pure ablution round earth's human shores,
Or gazing on the new soft-fallen mask
  Of snow upon the mountains and the moors—

No—yet still stedfast, still unchangeable,
  Pillowed upon my fair love's ripening breast,
To feel for ever its soft fall and swell,
  Awake for ever in a sweet unrest,
Still, still to hear her tender-taken breath,
And so live ever—or else swoon to death.

John Keats

455. "Right good is rest."

Come, Sleep, and with thy sweet deceiving
Lock me in delight awhile;
Let some pleasing dreams beguile
All my fancies: that from thence
I may feel an influence
All my powers of care bereaving!

Though but a shadow, but a sliding,
Let me know some little joy!
We that suffer long annoy
Are contented with a thought
Through an idle fancy wrought:
O let my joys have some abiding!

John Fletcher

457. Before Sleeping.

I have pieced this rhyme together from well-known versions and fragments. But the Angels:

Aftir these thingis I saigh [saw] foure *aungelis* stondinge on the foure corneris of the erthe, holdinge foure wyndis of the erthe that thei blewen not on the erthe, neither on the see, neithir on ony tree.

Wiclif, *Apocalips,* ch. 7.

"And I beheld, and I heard the voice of many angels round about the throne and the beasts and the elders: and the number of them was ten thousand times ten thousand, and thousands of thousands."

The Authorised Version (1611).

Of these Angels, having their fitting place among the hierarchies—Seraphim, Cherubim, Thrones; Dominations, Virtues, Powers; Principalities, Archangels, Angels—no names are given. But Michael and Gabriel are archangels named in the Bible; and in the Apocrypha and elsewhere, Raphael, Zadkiel, Uriel, Chamuel, Jophiel. These too; steadfast or fallen: Samael,

Semalion, Abdiel and gigantic Sandalphon, Rahab, Prince of the Sea; Ridia, Prince of the Rain; Yurkemi, Prince of the Hail; Af of Anger; Abaddona of Destruction; Lailah of Night. And the angelic sentinels of Eden (in *Paradise Lost*):

> Now had night measured with her shadowy cone
> Halfway up-hill this vast sublunar vault;
> And from their ivory port the Cherubim
> Forth issuing, at the accustomed hour, stood armed. . . .

Then speak together Gabriel, Uzziel, Ithuriel, Zephon. And last there is he whose trumpet will awaken the dead in the day of Resurrection—strangely-angelled Poe's shrill-tongued Israfel:

> In Heaven a spirit doth dwell
> Whose heart-strings are a lute;
> None sing so wildly well
> As the angel Israfel,
> And the giddy stars (so legends tell),
> Ceasing their hymns, attend the spell
> Of his voice, all mute. . . .
>
> Yes, Heaven is thine; but this
> Is a world of sweets and sours;
> Our flowers are merely—flowers,
> And the shadow of thy perfect bliss
> Is the sunshine of ours.
>
> If I could dwell
> Where Israfel
> Hath dwelt, and he were I,
> He might not sing so wildly well
> A mortal melody,
> While a bolder note than this might swell
> From my lyre within the sky.

"That there are distinct orders of Angels, assuredly I believe, but what they are I cannot tell. . . . They are creatures that have not so much of a body as flesh is, as froth is, as a vapour is, as a sigh is; and yet with a touch they shall moulder a rock into less atoms than the sand that it stands upon, and a millstone into smaller flour than it grinds. They are creatures made, and yet not a minute older than when they were first made, if they were made before all measures of time begun; nor, if they were made in the beginning of time, and be now six thousand years old, have they one wrinkle of age in their face, one sob of weariness in their lungs. They are *primogeniti Dei,* God's eldest sons. . . ."

JOHN DONNE

Manoah, too, saw an angel, and Moses, and Gideon, and Nebuchadnezzar:

" 'Be it known unto thee, O king, that we will not serve thy gods, nor worship the golden image which thou hast set up.'

"Then was Nebuchadnezzar full of fury, and the form of his visage was changed against Shadrach, Meshach, and Abednego: therefore he spake, and commanded that they should heat the furnace one seven times more than it was wont to be heated. And he commanded the most mighty men that were in his army to bind Shadrach, Meshach, and Abednego, and to cast them into the burning fiery furnace. Then these men were bound in their coats, their hosen, and their hats, and their other garments, and were cast into the midst of the burning fiery furnace. Therefore because the king's commandment was urgent, and the furnace exceeding hot, the flame of the fire, slew those men that took up Shadrach, Meshach, and Abednego. And these three men, Shadrach, Meshach, and Abednego, fell down bound into the midst of the burning fiery furnace.

"Then Nebuchadnezzar the king was astonied, and rose up in haste, and spake, and said unto his counsellors, 'Did not we cast three men bound into the midst of the fire?'

"They answered and said unto the king, 'True, O king.'

"He answered and said, 'Lo, I see four men loose, walking in the midst of the fire, and they have no hurt; and the form of the fourth is like the son of God.' "

Daniel iii. 18-25.

458. "SLEEP SECURE."

. . . The night is come, like to the day
Depart not Thou, great God, away.
Let not my sins, black as the night,

Eclipse the lustre of Thy light;
Keep still in my Horizon; for to me
The Sun makes not the day, but Thee.

Howere I rest, great God, let me
Awake again at last with Thee;
And thus assured, behold I lie
Securely, or to awake or die.
These are my drowsie days; in vain
I do now wake to sleep again:
O come that hour, when I shall never
Sleep again, but wake for ever.

SIR THOMAS BROWNE.

459.

This is the Song sung by his guardian Angel to a young sleeping prince who has been cheated of his inheritance. It was printed by Charles Lamb in his *English Dramatic Poets,* from a Tragedy entitled *The Conspiracy,* written by Henry Killigrew when he was seventeen.

460. THE EVE OF ST. MARK.

The relics of this Saint, who for his miracles was thought to be a sorcerer, and was murdered by a mob, were interred in Alexandria. Hundreds of years afterwards these relics were coveted by the Venetians by reason of the story that the Saint had once visited their city and had heard speak to him an angel: *Pax tibi, Marce. Hic requiescet corpus tuum.* At length two Venetian merchants, having persuaded the Alexandrians that the sacred bones lay in danger of the raiding Saracens, travelled back with them to their own city, where they were reinterred with solemn ceremony in St. Mark's. This church was in 976 burned to the ground, and the relics were lost. A century passed; a wondrously beautiful church had, Phoenix-like, arisen from the ashes of the old, and during the ceremony, held in the faith that it would be revealed where they lay hid, suddenly a light shone forth from one of the great piers, there was a sound of falling masonry, and, lo, the body of the Saint, with arm outstretched, as if at finger's touch he had revealed his secret resting-place.

"... DOVES OF SIAM, LIMA MICE,
AND LEGLESS BIRDS OF PARADISE." (p. 462)

Why of Siam, why of Lima, I have as yet been unable to discover. But, according to Topsell, mice are of these kinds: the short, small, fearful, peaceable, ridiculous, rustik, or country mouse, the urbane or citty mouse, the greedy, wary, unhappy, harmefull, black, obscene, little, whiner, biter, and earthly mouse. Mice, too, he says, are "sometimes blackish, sometimes white, sometimes yellow, sometimes broune and sometimes ashe colour. There are white mice amonge the people of Savoy, and Dolphin in France, called alaubroges, which the inhabitants of the country do beleev that they feede upon snow." Then, again, "the field mouse, the farie, with a long snout; and the sleeper—that is of a dun colour and will run on the edge of a sword and sleep on the point."

What Topsell meant by "whiner" I am uncertain, but it may be he refers to the mouse that sings. This is a habit quite distinct from the common squeaking, shrilling and shrieking. It resembles the slow low trill of a distant and sleepy canary, but sweeter and more domestic, and is as pleasant a thing to hear behind a wainscot, as it is to watch the creatures gambolling. Whatever mischief their ravagings may cause, may I never live under a roof wherein (Cat or no Cat) there isn't an inch of house-room (and an occasional crumb of cheese) for Mistress Mouse!

The fable that the Bird of Paradise is "legless" was set abroad by travellers who had seen in old days its exquisite dismembered carcase prepared for merchandise. It is hard to explain how Man, capable of imagining a bird "whose fixed abode is the region of the air," and that lives "solely on dew," can also slaughter it and tie it up in bundles for feminine finery. But, as Iago says, "if thou wilt needs damn thyself, do it a more delicate way than drowning. Make all the money thou canst. . . ."

"AT VENICE. . . ." (p. 464)

So Keats left—unfinished—this, one of the happiest of his poems. There are others in this volume: but not the *Eve of St.*

Agnes, or *Hyperion,* or the odes, *to a Nightingale, on a Grecian Urn,* or the strange *On Melancholy.* Nor are any of his Letters here—as full a revelation of the powers and understanding of that rare mind, as the poems are of his imagination.

466. "Low in the South the 'Cross'."

We peoples of the Northern hemisphere, from the Chinese and Chaldaeans until this last flitting hour, have the joy of so many brilliant and neighbouring stars in our night sky that for us it is now full of stories, and thronged with constellations of our own fantasy and naming. The Chair of Cassiopeia, for instance, is but a feigned passing picture. Nevertheless, what a delight it is to recognise it shining in the very midst of the firmament in the dusk of early June. For this reason the peoples of the Southern hemisphere, with their Crown and Net, their Phoenix and Peacock, hold dear the Southern Cross. It marks their very home.

And (for the last time) let me repeat what Miss Taroone once said to me: "Learn the common names of every thing you see, Simon; and especially of those that please you most to remember: then give them names also of your own making and choosing—if you can. Mr. Nahum has thousands upon thousands of words and names in his mind and yet he often fails to understand what I say to him. Nor does he always remember that though every snail is a snail and a Hoddydoddy, and every toad is a toad and a Joey, and every centipede is a centipede and a Maggie-monyfeet, each is just as much only its own self as you, Simon, are You." For, "be it ever so humble," a good name is a difficult thing to come by—a name that sounds well, sounds right, and whose meaning continues to fit it however far one chase it through its etymological origins. For apt sound alone only a flash of intuitive insight (especially in a child) can instantly suit word to sight; or maybe to hearing, (timbrel, trombone, bassoon); to touch (slimy, plush, velvet); to taste (syrop, caramel, myrrh, blancmange); to smell (bergamot, musk). These words, of course, happen to refer to these particular senses, but sounds that do *not* may be appropriate to them. Are not *crumpets, muffins, jumbles, parkin, candy, lollipops, comfits, humbugs, bulls'-eyes, brandy-snaps, ratafias, gob-stoppers* and *toffee*—are these not "good" names for goodies? But children's fashions change, and names with them.

It is a poor name anyhow that means well but cannot prove it. A family of brothers, for example, consisting of a Cyril, an Edwin, a Walter, an Oscar, a Philip, a Cuthbert, a Eustace, an Adolphus and an Ambrose does not radiantly bring to mind (as it should) a group of all the manly virtues—a lord, a conqueror, a ruler of hosts, a bonny fighter, a lover of horses, the All-splendid, the Foursquare, a noble hero, and the Ever-happy One.

But to return to the stars. By strange good fortune,—even apart from such honest homely terms as the Plough, the Pointers, the Guards, the Chair—the stars have been starrily named. These, for example: Merak, Megrez, Alcor, Alphacca, Alarneb, Dubhe, Markab, Murfrid, Almirzam, Alpheratz, Alphard, Zosma, Denebola, Fomalhaut. They are not only good names for stars, just as Kit Marlowe or Richard Lovelace or Geoffrey Chaucer is a good name for an English poet; or Tycho Brahe or Johannes Hevelius or Giovanni Donati is for an astronomer; or Vasco da Gama, Fernando Magellan or Francis Drake is for an adventurer; or Diego Rodriguez de Silva Velasquez is for a painter; but they mean as well as they sound. Nor can you ever be utterly alone, however dark the way, if you can see but one star shining and can hail it by name. To which divine end the following doggerel is intended:

If to the heavens thou lift thine eyes
When Winter rules o'er our northern skies,
And snow-cloud none the zenith mars,
At Yule-tide midnight these thy stars:

Low in the south see bleak-blazing Sirius.
O'er him hang Betelgeuse, Procyon wan.
Wild-eyed to west of him, Rigel and Bellatrix,
And rudd-red Aldebaran journeying on.
High in night's roof-tree beams twinkling Capella,
Vega and Deneb prowl low in the north,
Far to the east, rovers the Lion-heart, Regulus;
While the twin sons of Zeus toward the zenith gleam forth.

But when Midsummer Eve in man's sleep-drowsed hours,
Awaiteth the daybreak with dew-bright flowers,

Though three of these Night Lights aloft remain,
For nine thou may'st gaze, but wilt gaze in vain.
Yet comfort find, for, far-shining there,
See golden Arcturus, and cold Altaïr,
Crystalline Spica, and, strange to scan,
Blood-red Antares, foe to man.

Of these names, Regulus (the little Prince), Bellatrix (the She-Warrior), Capella (the little Goat), Arcturus (the Bearward) and Spica (the Wheatear), come from the Latin. Procyon (the Herald), Antares (the War-maker), and Sirius (the Fervent) are Greek. While Altair (the flying one), Deneb (the Hen's Tail), Rigel (Orion's Foot), prodigious Betelgeuse (his arm), Vega (the falling One), and Aldebaran (the Follower—of the Pleiads), are Arabian.

As for the precious stones, the mere recital of their names resembles an incantation, and may be of sovran use as a lullaby:

Ruby, amethyst, emerald, diamond,
Sapphire, sardonyx, fiery-eyed carbuncle,
  Jacynth, jasper, crystal a-sheen;
Topaz, turquoise, tourmaline, opal,
  Beryl, onyx and aquamarine:
Marvel, O mortal!—their hue, lustre, loveliness,
Pure as a flower when its petals unfurl—
Peach-red carnelian, apple-green chrysoprase,
  Amber and coral and orient pearl!

469. "Once a Dream did weave a Shade."

Full in the passage of the vale, above,
A sable, silent, solemn, forest stood,
Where nought but shadowy forms was seen to move,
As idless fancy'd in her dreaming mood;

And up the hills, on either side, a wood
Of blackening pines, ay waving to and fro,
Sent forth a sleepy horror thro' the blood;
And where this valley winded out, below,
The murmuring main was heard, and scarcely heard, to flow.

A pleasing land of drowsy-head it was,
Of Dreams that wave before the half-shut eye,
And of gay Castles in the clouds that pass,
For ever flushing round a summer sky. . . .

JAMES THOMSON

470. "AWAKE, AWAKE!"

"I thank God for my happy dreams," wrote Sir Thomas Browne in the *Religio Medici,* "as I do for my good rest. . . . And surely it is not a melancholy conceit [or fancy] to think we are all asleep in this World, and that the conceits of this life are as meer dreams to those of the next as the Phantasms of the night to the conceits of the day. There is an equal delusion in both, and the one doth but seem to be the embleme or picture of the other; we are somewhat more than ourselves in our sleeps, and the slumber of the body seems to be but the waking of the soul. . . ."

The Door of Death is made of gold,
That Mortal Eyes cannot behold;
But, when the Mortal Eyes are closed,
And cold and pale the Limbs reposed,
The Soul awakes; and, wondering sees
In her mild Hand the golden Keys:
The Grave is Heaven's golden Gate,
And rich and poor around it wait;
O Shepherdess of England's Fold,
Behold this Gate of Pearl and Gold! . . .

I give you the end of a golden string;
Only wind it into a ball,
It will lead you in at Heaven's gate,
Built in Jerusalem's wall.

WILLIAM BLAKE

"ABOVE THE LIGHT OF THE MORNING STAR."

The morning star, Phosphor, beaming in the first crystal light of daybreak, and heralding the sun, is of an unearthly serenity and beauty—pure and lustrous as a dew-drop on a thorn. But the light in Blake's *poem* never was on sea or land; only in his imagination; though now, by what is little short of a miracle, we share it with him.

Blake was born in 1757, and died (in 1827) when he was 70. His *Songs of Innocence* were published in 1789—songs which he hoped and intended "every child" might "*joy* to hear." Now from about 1750 to 1830 was the hey-day of the sampler; not, that is, the original "exampler," which was a delicate slip of embroidery giving stitch patterns for grown-ups, but the show-pieces on canvas or linen of a little girl (aged six or upwards) to prove her skill and diligence with the needle.

In size these samplers range from that of a large bandanna handkerchief to a few inches square. The earlier ones are oblong in shape; and a few are heart-shaped, oval or circular. The vast majority of them must have taken months (of tedious days and hours) to finish—tongue-tip out, and fingers sore with needle-pricks, though the eyes that watched the stitches (as many little mistakes prove) must often have filled up with day-dreams.

Few samplers are very beautiful in design, pattern and colour; and as with so much else, alas, the earlier are the best. But even the coarsest of old samplers has that tinge of the romantic which the mere passing of time never fails to confer on anything made by man, and gives in abundance to anything made by a child. So it may be in due season with the "decorative stitchery" of to-day! Over and over again in these mementos of young creatures who have long ago left the world we see around us, one finds an almost monotonous repetition of angular little Cupids and crowns and coronets; houses, birds, bees and butterflies; trees, ships, flowers and animals; since

> "There's nothing near at hand or farthest sought
> But with the needle may be shaped or wrought."

Alphabets large and small, and a row of digits usually appear above, and a name and a date below. How much is lost by the absence of the last two particulars only an interested observer can say!

Ten years or so after Keats set aside unfinished the "Eve of St. Mark" (No. 460) with its

"Parrot's cage and panelled square,
And the warm-angled winter screen,"

Charlotte and Emily Brontë stitched in the last stitch of *their* samplers. Anne's (the youngest sister) was a year later. Remarkably crude specimens they are, but could any reader of *Villette, Wuthering Heights,* or *The Tentants of Wildfell Hall,* even glance at such remembrances with a cold and unsympathetic eye?

But mention of samplers has appeared in these pages not merely for their own sake (though that is a happy one) but for the sake of their rhymes. And seven out of ten of them, at least, must be thus decorated. Far, however, from these rhymes being songs "of pleasant glee" or "happy cheer" they are "nearly always in a moral, minor or miserable key." The mothers and schoolmistresses of William Blake's day supposed that the best literary fare for young children was a sort of physic, sour with awful warnings; and all his life, for the world at large, Blake was like the sun in Winter, that cannot shed his light and warmth on the world because of the cold of the clouds in between. Surely, if little Tom Babington Macaulay had supped up with his bread and milk (or was it water-porridge and salt?) *The Chimney Sweeper, The Laughing Song, Night, Spring,* and *A Dream,* he couldn't, at the age of eight, have "made up" such dismal stuff as this:

Some men make Gods of red and blue
And rob their Sovereign of his due:
The good shall go to Heaven. The fell
Blasts of thy wrath can bear to hell.

Young or old, male or female, the authors of sampler rhymes—and very few of them appear to be traceable—seem to have thoroughly enjoyed thinking of Hell and brimstone, death and children, all in the same breath. Yet for the most part they thought of these inexhaustible themes so meanly and shallowly that when they wrote verses about them they often failed even to find decent rhymes. Elizabeth Hicks, for example, at the ripe age of ten, when she might have been reading—well, any good book that calls to the young heart and mind, was made—stitch by stitch—to rhyme not only *youth* with *truth,* and *lips* with *keeps,* but *trust* with *first,* and *speak* with *lake.* Fortunately false and feeble sentiments are usually shown up by their style alone; the grammar is frail, the workmanship feeble, and the words have a dull and lumpy effect.

The examples that follow have (with very kind permission) been taken from two volumes, richly illustrated, entitled respectively *Samplers* and *Samplers and Tapestry Embroideries,* and from some specimens in my own possession. I have usually, but not always, followed the original spelling, but seldom the punctuation. First shall come a few in a wholly minor, moral and miserable key:

No. 1 is *Against Lying.*

O 'Tis a Lovely Thing for Youth
To Walk betimes in wisdom's Way;
To fear a Lie, to speak the Truth,
That we may trust to all they say.

But Liars we can never trust,
Tho' they should speak the Thing that's true;
And he that does one Fault at first,
And lies to hide it, makes it two.

The Lord delights in them that speak
The Words of Truth, but ev'ry Liar
Must have his portion in the Lake
That burns with Brimstone and with Fire.

Then let me always watch my Lips,
Lest I be struck to Death and Hell,
Since God a Book of Reckoning keeps
For ev'ry Lye that Children tell.

ELIZABETH HICKS, 1780

But that Book may be of many volumes, and in *Father and Son* is a vivid and unforgettable account of the effect on a small boy of detecting his best beloved grown-up in a lie.

The next few rhymes—like the last—are all of them haunted by the horror of Death and of Time—the future that cannot be hindered or delayed; the present that is but a passing breath; the past that none can change, expunge or recall; and the nameless little "soul" of No. 5 who sat, needle in hand, considering these mysteries had just turned seven! They are reminders, too, first, that children in the past had far less chance of evading an early death; and next, that "The Cry of the Children" was written as late as 1844. Whether that little "worldling" Mary Brewitt's "she" [No. 6.] was a slip or an extremely unusual conception of the *Skulker* I cannot say.

2. Dear Child delay no time,
But with all speed amend
The longer thou dost live
The nearer to thy End.
Yesterday is gone
To-morrow is none of thine
Oh! [now this] day thy life
To vertuous acts incline.

SUSANNA INGRAM, 1700

3. Death at a Distance we but slightly fear.
He brings his Terrors as he draws more near.
Through Poverty, Pain, Slav'ry, we drudge on,
The worst of Beings better please than none;
No Price too dear to purchase Life and Breath,
The heaviest Burthen's easier borne than Death.

SUSANNA GELLETT, 1800

4. Swiftly, see, each Moment flies!
See and learn, be timely Wise!
Every moment shortens Day;
And every Pulse beats Time away;
Then seize the Minutes as they fly:
Know to Live, and learn to die.

ELIZABETH HEWITT, 1778

5. And now, my Soul, another year [the 6th]
Of thy short life is past;
I cannot long continue here,
And this may be my Last!

6. Worldling, beware betimes!
Death skulks behind thee!
And as She leaves thee
So will Judgment find thee.

MARY BREWITT, 1725

No. 7 (which is decked with a sprightly Lion and Unicorn above and two floating cherubs carrying what appear to be bagpipes below) is one stanza only (the last but one of six) on keeping the Sabbath, and is well worth a moment's reflection. The last stanza returns to hell.

7. . . . But O, ye thoughtless Sinners, know,
If in your maker's courts below
No sweetness to your souls is given,
'Twould be no Joy to be in Heaven. . . .

ELIZABETH CRESWELL, 1808
(aged 11)

No. 8 is unusual, not for the fleeting picture it gives of a horror-stricken little fugitive, but because it was the joint work of a brother and sister, Edward and Ruth Bachelor; in 1717.

8. O Thou to Whom Angels their Hymns address,
To whom all knees must bow, All Tongue confess;
I have offended God. Where shall I fly
To hide myself from his offended eye?

In No. 9 [probably of the seventeenth century] and in the last two lines of No. 10 there is a curious but vivid glint of imagination:

9. Youll mend your Life tomorrow Still you cry.
in what far Country does this morrow lie?

it Stays to long, tis fetch'd to far I fear:
Twill be both very old and Very dear.

10. Gay dainty flowers go swiftly to decay,
Poor wretched life's short portion flies away.
We eat: we drink: we sleep: but lo, anon
Old age steals on us, never thought upon.

MAY WAKELING, 1742
(aged 10)

And No. 11—so matter-of-fact and yet so imaginative with its meals and its reckoning—comes from the *Emblems* of a true poet, Francis Quarles:

11. Our life is nothing but a winters day,
Some only break their fast and so away,
Others stay dinner, and depart full fed,
The deeper age but sups and goes to bed.
Hee's most in debt, that lingers out the day,
Who dys betimes, has lesse and lesse to pay.

MARG'T BURNELL, 1720

Emblems, however, was published in 1635, years before English Poetry had turned to wit, artifice and commonsense. But as early as 1829, on a sampler worked at the age of 12 by Elizabeth Jane Gates, is the thought Blake himself had in mind when he wrote "The Little Black Boy." But while Blake's poem cannot but in some degree affect the heart and mind of its reader, the rhyme only argues with his intellect:

12. There's mercy in each ray of light, that mortal eye e'er saw,
There's mercy in each breath of air, that mortal lips can draw,
There's mercy both for bird, and beast, in God's indulgent plan,
There's mercy for each creeping thing—But man has none for man.

The next few rhymes are still morally inclined, but there is less of the minor and little of the downright miserable:

13. Look Well to that thou takest in Hand.
It's Better worth Than House or Land;
When Land is gone and Money is spent
Then learning is most Excelent.
Let [? glorious] vertue Be thy guide,
And it will keep the out of pride.

ELIZABETH CREASEY, 1686

Mary Green spelt better (or less persuasively) but must have been rejoiced to get to her last stanza:

14. How shall the young secure their hearts
And guard their lives from sin?
Thy word the choicest rules imparts
to keep the conscience clean. . . .

'Tis like the Sun a heavenly light
That guides us all the day
And thro' the dangers of the night
A Lamp to lead our way.

Apart from a charming wreath round her rhyme (No. 15) Sarah Tracey's industry (she was 11 in 1823) is displayed in an unusually large sampler with a remarkably handsome house and dovecote at the foot of it, in front of which a complete family of children (with their mother) are at play among the haycocks:

15. Industry taught in early days
Not only give the teachers praise
But give us pleasure when we view
The work that innocence can do. . . .

The Parents with exulting joy
Survey it as no childish toy
But as prelude to [? what] each day
A greater genius will display.

Go on, dear Child, learn to excell
Improve in work and reading well
For books and work do both contend
To make the Housewife and the friend.

Rhyme No. 16 is enclosed in a frame of gold and green in the middle of a particularly fine piece of needlework, in colour, proportion and skill. It was the work of "Cathrine Tweedall" (1775), John Ruskin's paternal grandmother. The sentiments it conveys might be the making of a successful pickpocket, of "an entirely honest merchant," or of such genius as inspired Ruskin himself! But it banishes a good many "wretches":

16. She who from Heaven expects to gain her end
Must by her own efforts her self befriend;
The wretch who ne'er exceeds a faint desire
Goes not half way to what she would acquire;
She that to virtues high rewards would rise
Must run ye race before she win ye prize.

Little Ann Maria Wiggins (and maybe with as "fond" a mother) was only seven when she steadily stitched in similar sentiments (No. 17), but the delight of her sampler (as of her own eyes too, I hope), is the sprightly and lively goldfinch eyeing a butterfly that is perched on a spray above the rhyme, while both are surrounded by a wreath of rose, convolvulus and hearts-ease, with a bunch of white and red currants and cherries at the outside corners.

17. All Youth set right at first with Ease go on
And each new Task is with new Pleasure done.
But if neglected till they grow in years
And each fond Mother her dear Darling spares,
Error becomes habitual and you'll find
Tis then hard Labour to reform the Mind.

So again with Elizabeth Goss (1793) in a large sampler containing sixteen assorted birds, four butterflies, and eight animals, with a red house, a prodigious yellow lion (shaped like a fortipianer), two Chinamen, a kind of pagoda and flowers galore. And her warning steals a little further into the heart because it is half hidden in metaphor:

18. Sweet green leaves the rose Adorn,
Yet beneath it lurks a thorn.
Fair and flow'ry is the brake,
Yet it hides the vengeful snake.
Artless deeds and simple dress,
Mark the Chosen shepherdess.

So again with Jessie Maria Taylor (1831) who was evidently needling in a day-dream when she put in her second "guide" instead of *guard,* and who had a hazy notion of the "dart."

19. May Virtue point out wisdom's way,
And ever Guide me when I stray;
And ever Guide my youthful heart
When vice and folly throws Adart.

More simple, and therefore nearer poetry, is the quatrain in Caroline Codling's sampler, a pretty and skilful piece of needlework (enriched with flower-baskets, vases, small birds and large peacocks), apart from its clumsy lettering. But what did "Amidre Sworld" mean for *her?*

20. Assist Me While I wander Here
Amidre Sworld of Cares
Incline My Heart to Pray With Love
And Then Accept My Prayers.

And in Mary Ann Enderwick's (1831), poetry itself smiles tenderly out of the frame. But she was a niece of Isaac Watts, and the author of "The Sluggard" wrote her rhyme:

21. Jesus permit thy gracious name to stand
As the first efforts of a youthful hand,
And as her fingers on the canvas move
Inspire her tender heart to seek thy love;

With thy dear children let her have a part,
And write thy name thyself upon her heart.

But not even Isaac Watts could write as piercingly as the author of the lines on E. Wilmhurst's sampler (1786)—as delicate in design as it is in workmanship;

22. The loss of Gold is much;
The loss of Time is more;
The loss of Christ is such
As no Man can Restore.

And there is true poetry, too, in these lines on a sampler (in the Greg collection in Manchester) though I know not whose:

23. Child in age, child in heart,
Thy magnificent array
Could not joy or pride impart;
Thou hadst treasure more than they:
More than courtiers kneeling low,
More than flattery's ready [? ease],
More than conquest o'er the foe,
More, even more, than these—
Treasures in which the mind hath part,
Joys that teach the soul to rise,
Hopes that can sustain the heart
When the body droops and dies.
Therefore Star thou art; not shaded
In the darkness of the tomb:
Royal Rose thou art, not faded,
But in paradise dost bloom.

Actual glimpses of these long-gone young needle-imps, stooping over their frames, can only be imaginary, of course; but there *is* such a glimpse, prim and arch, in Frances Gray's sampler (1819):

24. With cheerful mind we yield to Men,
The higher honours of the Pen,

The Needle's our great Care:
In this we chiefly wish to shine,
How far the art's already mine,
This Sampler will declare!

It is a little obscure in Tabitha Anon's:

25. Sweet it is to be a child
Tender merciful and mild
Ever ready to perform
Acts of kindness to a worm.

It grows clearer in Sarah Pelham's—who "in the six year of her age" stitched in

26. When i was Young
and in my Prime
here you may see
how I spent my time:

and in Ann Woolfray's (1736):

27. When this you see remember me
And keep me in your mind
And be not like the Weathercock
That turns at every wind.

and in Frances Johnson's (1797):

28. In reading this if any faults you see
Mend them yourself and find no fault in me:

But it positively scintillates in:

29. This is my Work so
You may see. what
care my mother as
took of me. ann bell.

while as far back as 1712 Elizabeth Clements heaved a sigh of relief which (one trusts) continued to re-echo in innumerable small bosoms for scores of years afterwards:

30. THIS I HAVE DONE I THANK MY GOD
WITHOUT THE CORRECTION OF THE ROD.

But of all the samplers I have actually seen, or brooded over in books, or envied in shop-windows, there are two that come closest. One of them is unusually small—less than five inches square. It is nameless and dateless; it is worked on the finest of linen with the finest of stitches and the happiest of flowers; and I have a fancy its verses may have been written by the nameless one herself who must just have left childhood behind her:

31. The peace of Heaven attend thy shade,
My early friend, my favourite maid!
When life was new, companions gay,
We hail'd the morning of our day.
Untimely gone, for ever fled,
The roses of the cheek so red!
The affections warm, the temper mild
The sweetness that in sorrow smil'd!

And last and dearest:

32. Elizabeth Walters is my name
in Wales is my nation
ystradveltœ is my dwelling
and Christ is my salvation
When i am dead and in my grave
and all my bones are rotten
[if] this you see
Remember me
when i am quit forgoten.

Her lovely and remote mountain village lies about eleven miles north of the Porth-yr-Ogof, through the gloom of which foam the roaring waters of the Fellte. It is "the last outpost of civilisation on the way to Brecon"—where Henry Vaughan lived and died. In that last outpost, either in 1701 or in 1791 (the figures are uncertain) this ten-year-old at last finished her long, narrow, coarse, but deftly panelled sampler. Did she ever grow up? Did she ever venture out into the Civilisation of Queen Anne or of George III.? Not for me: she stays 10—and unchanging.

473. "DOES THE ROAD WIND UP-HILL ALL THE WAY."

"Gentle herdsman, tell to me,
Of courtesy I thee pray,
Unto the town of Walsingham
Which is the right and ready way."

"Unto the town of Walsingham
The way is hard for to be gone;
And very crooked are those paths,
For you to find out all alone. . . ."

Tarry no longer: toward thine heritage
Haste on thy way, and be of right good cheer.
Go each day onward on thy pilgrimage;
Think how short time thou shalt abidė here.
They place is bigged [1] above the starres clere,
None earthly palays [2] wrought in so stately wise,
Come on, my friend, my brother most entere [3]
For thee I offered my blood in sacrifice.

JOHN LYDGATE

475.

Oh what a thing is man, how far from power,
From settled peace and rest!
He is some twenty sev'ral men, at least,
Each sev'ral hour.

476. EVE.

Shee was brighter of her blee, [4]
then was the bright sonn:

[1] Builded. [2] Palace. [3] In all and everything. [4] Hue.

Her rudd [1] redder than the rose,
that on the rise [2] hangeth:
Meekly smiling with her mouth,
and merry in her lookes.
Ever laughing for love,
as shee like would.
And as shee came by the bankes,
the boughes eche one
They louted [3] to that ladye,
and layd forth their branches;
Blossomes, and burgens
breathèd full sweete;
Flowers flourished in the frith,[4]
where shee forth stepped;
And the grasse, that was gray,
greened belive.[5]

477.

This poem for its full beauty must be read very slowly. Eve in long memory is musing within herself, hardly able to utter the words because of her grief and sorrow, and of the heavy sighs between them.

"DEATH IS THE FRUIT."

I am Eve, great Adam's wife,
'Tis I that outraged Jesus of old;
'Tis I that robbed my children of Heaven,
By rights 'tis I that should have gone upon the Cross. . . .

There would be no ice in any place,
There would be no glistening windy winter,
There would be no hell, there would be no sorrow,
There would be no fear, if it were not for me.

TR. KUNO MEYER

[1] Complexion. [2] Twig. [3] Made obeisance. [4] Woods.
[5] Instantly, at very sight of her.

"THE KIND HART'S TEARS WERE FALLING." (stanza 7)

To day my Lord of Amiens, and my selfe,
Did steale behinde him as he lay along
Under an oake, whose anticke roote peepes out
Upon the brooke that brawles along this wood.
To the which place a poore sequestred Stag
That from the Hunter's aime had tane a hurt,
Did come to languish; and indeed my Lord
The wretched annimall heaved forth such groanes
That their discharge did stretch his leatherne coat
Almost to bursting, and the big round teares
Coursed one another downe his innocent nose
In pitteous chase. . . .

As You Like It

479. "'OH, WHAT ARE YOU SEEKING. . . ?'"

"In Persia there is a city which is called Saba, from whence were the three magi who came to adore Christ in Bethlehem; and the three are buried in that city in a fair sepulchre, and they are all three entire with their beards and hair. One was called Baldasar, the second Gaspar, and the third Melchior.

"Marco inquired often in that city concerning the three magi, and nobody could tell him anything about them, except that [they] were buried there in ancient times. After three days' journey you come to a castle which is called Palasata, which means the castle of the fire-worshippers; and it is true that the inhabitants of that castle worship fire, and this is given as the reason.

"The men of that castle say, that anciently three kings of that country went to adore a certain king who was newly born, and carried with them three offerings, namely, gold, frankincense and myrrh; gold, that they might know if he were an earthly king; frankincense, that they might know if he were God; and myrrh, that they might know if he were a mortal man. When these magi were presented to Christ, the youngest of the three adored him first, and it appeared to him that Christ was of his stature and age. The midde one came next, and then the eldest, and to each he seemed to be of their own stature and age. Having compared their observations together, they agreed to go all to worship at once, and then he appeared to them all of his true age.

"When they went away, the infant gave them a closed box, which they carried with them for several days, and then becoming curious to see what he had given them, they opened the box and found in it a stone, which was intended for a sign that they should remain as firm as a stone in the faith they had received from him. When, however, they saw the stone, they marvelled, and thinking themselves deluded, they threw the stone into a certain pit, and instantly fire burst forth in the pit. When they saw this, they repented bitterly of what they had done, and taking some of the fire with them they carried it home. And having placed it in one of their churches, they keep it continually burning, and adore that fire as a god."

MARCO POLO

480. "LULLY, LULLAY."

This was found about 1855, copied out in an old MS.—the Commonplace-book of Richard Hill "servant with Mr. Wyngar, alderman of London" in 1493. The carol below is of the late fourteenth century, and these are the first two stanzas:

Jesus, sweete sonë deare!	Jesus, sweetė sonė deare!
On porful bed list thou here,	On wretched bed thou lyest here,
And that me greueth sore;	And that me grieveth sore;
For thi cradel is ase a bere,	For thy cradle is but a byre,
Oxe and assė beeth thi fere:	Only ox and ass are near,
Weepe ich mai tharfore.	Weep I must therefore.
Jesu, swetė, beo noth wroth,	Jesu, sweetė, be not wroth,
Thou ich nabbe clout ne cloth	Though I've neither clout nor cloth,
The on for to folde,	Thee in for to enfold—
The on to folde ne to wrappe	Thee to enfold unto thy rest

For ich nabbe clout ne lappe;	Though I've neither clout nor vest,
Bote ley thou thi fet to my pappe,	Lay thy feet within my breast
And wite the from the colde. . . .	And guard thee from the cold. . . .

483 "This is the Key."

And so—like the mediaeval traveller who had made a complete circuit of the world without knowing it—we have come back to the place which we started from.

"The Elephant," says Topsell, in his *Historie of Foure-footed Beastes,* "is delighted above measure with sweet savours, ointments, and smelling flowers, for which cause their Keeper will in the summer time lead them into the meadows of flowers, where they of themselves will by the quickness of their smelling, choose out and gather the sweetest flowers, and put them into a basket if their Keeper have any. . . .

"[Having sought] out water [wherewith] to wash themselves, [they will] of their own accord return back again to the basket of flowers, which, if they find not, they will bray and call for them. Afterward, being led into their stable, they will not eat meat until they take off their flowers and dress the brims of their manger therewith, and likewise strew their room or standing place, pleasing themselves with their meat, because of the savour of the flowers stuck about their cratch."

"A *cratch,"* says Robert Nares,—one of the most companionable of all writers on English words—"a cratch was a manger, particularly that in which our Saviour was laid. This opens to us the meaning of a childish game, corruptly called scratch-cradle, which consists in winding packthread double round the hands, into a . . . representation of a manger, which is taken off by the other player on his hands, so as to assume a new form, and thus alternately for several times, always changing the appearance. The art consists in making the right changes. But it clearly meant originally the *cratch-cradle;* the manger that held the Holy Infant as a cradle.

> 'If all things should be writ which erst was done
> By Jesus Christ (Gods everlasting sonne),
> From cratch to crosse, from cradle to his tombe,
> To hold the bookes, the world would not be roome' "

Now Mr. Nahum himself, it seems to me, might have written these four lines, and he would undoubtedly delight in Topsell's elephants and their pleasure in flowers. Was not that *Other Worlde* of his yet another "Basket of Flowers": the forth-showing in formal beauty—in this world's soil, and beneath ministering rain, sunshine and dew—of the imaginations of men? Even Miss Taroone could have uttered a secret word or two in the great ear of the Elephants at their cratch: and were there not in her garden at Thrae flowers beyond telling?

> First ere the morning breaks joy opens in the flowery bosoms,
> Joy even to tears. . . . First the Wild Thyme
> And Meadow-sweet downy and soft waving among the reeds
> Light springing on the air lead the sweet Dance: they wake
> The Honeysuckle sleeping on the Oak: the flaunting beauty
> Revels along upon the wind: the White-thorn, lovely May,
> Opens her many lovely eyes: listening the Rose still sleeps:
> None dare to wake her: soon she bursts her crimson curtained bed,
> And comes forth in the majesty of beauty: every Flower,
> The Pink, the Jessamine, the Wall-flower, the Carnation,
> The Jonquil, the mild Lilly opes her heavens: every Tree
> And Flower and Herb soon fill the air with an innumerable Dance.
> Wet all in order sweet and lovely. . . .

And so, Farewell.

AND SO
FAREWELL

ACKNOWLEDGMENTS

FOR the use of copyright poems in this volume I have to thank—and most gratefully I do so—the following authors and publishers:—Mr. Martin Armstrong (and Mr. Martin Secker); Mr. Lascelles Abercrombie (and Mr. John Lane); Mr. Edmund Blunden (and Mr. Cobden Sanderson); Mr. H. H. Bashford (Messrs. Harrap & Company and Messrs. Houghton, Mifflin & Company); Mrs. Bunston de Bary; Mr. Laurence Binyon (and Messrs. Elkin Matthews); Mr. Hilaire Belloc (and Messrs. Duckworth & Company); Mr. Robert Bridges (and Mr. John Murray); Mr. Gordon Bottomley; Mr. Padraic Colum (Messrs. Maunsell & Roberts Ltd., and Messrs. the Macmillan Company); Mr. William H. Davies (Mr. Jonathan Cape and Mr. Alfred A. Knopf); the executors of the late Lord de Tabley; Mr. C. M. Doughty; Mr. Edward L. Davison (and Messrs. G. Bell & Sons); Mr. Charles Dalmon (and Messrs. Methuen & Company); Mr. John Drinkwater (Messrs. Sidgwick & Jackson, and Messrs. Houghton, Mifflin & Company); Mr. Vivian Locke Ellis; Mr. Robert Frost (and Messrs. Harcourt, Brace & Company); Mr. John Freeman; Miss Eleanor Farjeon (Messrs. Selwyn & Blount, Messrs. J. M. Dent & Sons, and Messrs. E. P. Dutton & Company); Mrs. Furse (and Messrs. Constable & Company); Mr. Robert Graves; the Viscountess Grey; Mr. Edmund Gosse; Mr. Wilfrid Gibson (Messrs. Elkin Mathews, and Messrs. Macmillan & Company); Mr. Crosbie Garstin (and Messrs. Sidgwick & Jackson); Mr. Thomas Hardy (and Messrs. Macmillan & Company); Mr. Ralph Hodgson (and Messrs. Macmillan & Company); Miss Gwen John; Mr. Rudyard Kipling (Messrs. Macmillan & Company, and Messrs. Doubleday, Page & Company); Mr. Sidney Royse Lysaght (and Messrs. Macmillan & Company); Mr. Harold Monro; Mr. John Masefield; Mrs. Manning-Sanders (and Messrs. the Hogarth Press); Mr. T. Sturge Moore (and Mr. Grant Richards); Miss Charlotte Mew (Mr. Harold Monro and Messrs. the Macmillan Company); Miss Viola Meynell; Sir Henry Newbolt; Mr. Alfred Noyes (and Messrs. William Blackwood & Sons); Mr. Seumas O'Sullivan (Messrs. Maunsell & Roberts); Mr. Conal O'Riordan; Mr. F. J. Patmore; Miss Madeleine Caron Rock; Miss Lizette Woodworth Reese (and Mr. Thomas B. Mosher); Mr James Stephens (Messrs. Maunsell & Roberts and Messrs. the Macmillan Company); Mr. Siegfried Sassoon; Miss Edith Sitwell (and Mr. B. H. Blackwell); Mr. Edward Shanks (and Messrs. Collins, Sons & Company; Mr. J. C. Squire (and Messrs. Hodder & Stoughton); Mrs. Katharine Tynan Hinkson; Mr. Herbert Trench; Mr. Walter J. Turner (and Messrs. Sidgwick & Jackson); Miss Elinor Wylie (and Messrs. Harcourt, Brace & Company); Mr. Francis Brett Young (and Messrs. W. Collins, Sons & Company); Mr. W. B. Yeats (Messrs. T. Fisher Unwin and Messrs. the Macmillan Company).

It is, too, a happy privilege to have been permitted to include poems by Mrs. Webb, Mr. Eric Batterham, Mr. Gilbert Sheldon, Mr. Bernard Sleigh, Miss Elizabeth Ramal, and Mr. Colin Francis which have not hitherto appeared in any other published collection.

My most grateful thanks are due also to Mr. Edward Marsh (Messrs. Sidgwick & Jackson and Messrs. Dodd, Mead & Company) for two poems by Rupert Brooke; to Mr. Clement Shorter for six poems by Emily Brontë, and a poem by Dora Sigerson Shorter; to Sir Henry Newbolt for seven poems by Mary Coleridge; to Mr. Cobden Sanderson for three poems by John Clare; to Mr. John Murray and to the executors of Canon Dixon for two poems; to Mrs. Flecker (and Mr. Martin Secker) for two poems by James Elroy Flecker; to Lady Gomme for rhymes from "Traditional Games"; to the Viscountess Grey for poems from "The White Wallet"; to Miss Antonie Meyer (and Messrs. Constable & Company) for six translations by Kuno Meyer; to Mrs. Meynell and to Mr. Wilfrid Meynell (and Messrs. Burns & Oates) for three poems; to Mr. William Meredith and to Messrs. Constable & Company for two poems by George Meredith; to Mrs. Sharp for a poem by "Fiona Macleod" (William Sharp); to Miss Morris, Mr. S. C. Cockerill (and Messrs. Longmans, Green & Company) for two poems by William Morris; to Mrs. Owen for a poem by Wilfrid Owen; to Mrs. C. Patmore (and Messrs. G. Bell & Sons, Ltd.) for two poems by Coventry Patmore; to Messrs. Macmillan & Company for eight poems by Christina Rossetti; to Mr. Lloyd Osbourne (Messrs. Chatto & Windus and Messrs. Charles Scribner's Sons) for four poems by Robert Louis Stevenson; to Mr. William Heinemann for a poem by Algernon Charles Swinburne; to Miss E. Margaret Courtney Boyd for a poem by William Bell Scott; to Mrs. Thomas (and Messrs. Selwyn & Blount) for seven poems by Edward Thomas; to Mr. Wilfrid Meynell (and Messrs. Burns & Oates) for three poems by Francis Thompson; and to Messrs. P. J. and A. E. Dobell for quotations from the writings of Thomas Traherne.

For permission to use extracts in prose and verse, references to the sources of which have for the most part appeared in previous pages, I am much indebted to Dr. Blackman for his translation on page 589; to Mr. Basil Blackwell for my first acquaintance with Bunyan's "Book for Boys and Girls"; to Mrs. Child Sargent, and Mr. George Lyman Kittredge (and to Messrs. George G. Harrap & Company) for selection from "English and Scottish Popular Ballads"; to Mr. G. G. Coulton; to Dr. Courtenay Dunn (and to Messrs. Sampson Low, Marston & Company); to Messrs. J. M. Dent & Sons for a quotation from " A Hind in Richmond Park" by W. H. Hudson; to Mr. Tickner Edwardes (and Messrs. Methuen & Company); to Lady Gomme; to Messrs. Longmans, Green & Co. for a quotation from "The Diary of Master William

Silence"; to Miss Emma Phipson (and Messrs. Kegan, Paul, Trench, Trubner & Company); to Mr. H. M. Tomlinson; to Professor J. Arthur Thompson (and Messrs. George Newnes); to Mrs. Wright; to Mr. W. B. Yeats; to Mr. Filson Young; to the Clarendon Press, and to the Hakluyt Society.

For generous help, counsel and kindness in the preparation of this book, it is a happiness to express my gratitude to many friends—to Miss Naomi Royde Smith, Mr. Martin Freeman, Mr. J. W. Haines, Mr. Gilbert Sheldon, Mr. Frank Morley, Mr. Forrest Reid, and to Mr. James MacLehose; and, last, to my niece, Miss Lucy Rowley, to whom it owes more than words can say.

As regards material which appears for the first time in this new edition [1928], my sincere thanks are due to Mr. Claud Colleer Abbott for his translation of an old song from the French; to the Medici Society and to Mr. Leigh Aston for extracts from "Samplers"; to the Oxford University Press for a translation from the Greek; to Mrs. Frances Cornford (and to Mr. Harold Monro) for "Autumn Evening"; to Mr. Havelock Ellis for an extract from "The Dance of Life"; to Mr. Robert Frost (and to the *London Mercury* and the *Yale Review*) for "The Minor Bird"; to Messrs. Longmans, Green & Co. for extracts from "Samplers and Tapestry Embroidery"; to Miss M. M. Johnson for two poems, "The Horse," and "The Children's Orchestra"; to Mr. E. V. Lucas (and to Messrs. Methuen & Co. and the George H. Doran Co.) for "The Ploughman"; to Mr. John Masefield (and to Messrs. Methuen & Co. and Messrs. the Macmillan Company) for an extract from "A Sailor's Garland"; to Professor R. B. Morgan (and to the Cambridge University Press, Messrs. Chatto & Windus and the Selden Society) for extracts from "Readings in English Social History"; to Mr. William Ogilvie for "There's nane of my ain to care"; to Mrs. Joseph Plunkett for a poem by Mr. Joseph Plunkett; to Mr. Forrest Reid (and to Messrs. Constable & Co.) for an extract from "Demophon"; to Mr. Edward Shanks (and to Messrs. Collins & Co.) for "This is the sea"; to the Oxford University Press for an extract from W. W. Skeat's "A Student's Pastime"; to G. G. and D. M. Stuart for an extract from a translation from the French; to Miss Dorothy Wooldridge for three traditional poems included in her anthology, "The Poetry of Toil"; to my sister, Mrs. Roger Ingpen, for extracts from "Women as Letter Writers"; to Mrs. Bell, Mr. J. H. Clapham, Miss Molly Lyal, Mr. Sidney Smith, Mr. P. Taylor, and Mrs. Amy Wallis for valuable help and suggestions, and last, to my friend, Mr. Leonard Rice-Oxley, for his kindness in reading my proofs.

If by any inadvertence, copyright material has been included in these pages for the use of which permission has not been granted, or if I have failed to return thanks where thanks are due, I hope my sincere apologies will be accepted.

Many of the poets who gave their personal permission for the inclusion of poems in *Come Hither* when it was first compiled, are no longer living, and within reach of my gratitude. But in recognition of this particular and treasured kindness, and of incalculably more besides, I cannot forbear taking this opportunity of once more recording their names: Alice Meynell, Charlotte Mew, Mary Webb, Thomas Hardy, W. H. Hudson, Herbert Trench, Edmund Gosse, and Charles M. Doughty.

INDEX OF AUTHORS

[*Poems by writers whose names are unknown will be found marked with an asterisk in the Index of Poems. In the following Index the names of writers still living are similarly denoted. The numbers are page numbers—those in italic referring to the notes.*]

INDEX OF POEMS

[*An asterisk denotes that the name of the author of the poem is unknown.*]

NOTES

NOTES

NOTES

NOTES

INDEX OF NOTES

A NOTE
ON THE TYPE IN WHICH
THIS BOOK IS SET

The type in which this book has been set (on the Linotype) is based on the design of Caslon. It is generally conceded that William Caslon (1692–1766) brought the old-style letter to its highest perfection and while certain modifications have been introduced to meet changing printing conditions, the basic design of the Caslon letters has never been improved. The type selected for this book is a modern adaptation rather than an exact copy of the original Caslon.

SET UP, ELECTROTYPED, PRINTED
AND BOUND BY VAIL-BALLOU PRESS,
BINGHAMTON, N. Y.
PAPER MANUFACTURED BY
S. D. WARREN CO.,
BOSTON